D1471851

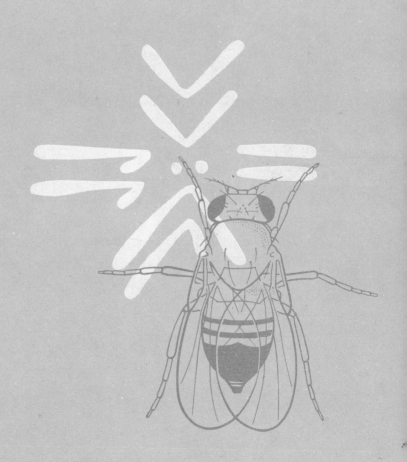

PRINCIPLES OF GENETICS

Edmund W. Sinnott, Consulting Editor

McGraw-Hill Publications in the Botanical Sciences

ARNOLD   *An Introduction to Paleobotany*

CURTIS AND CLARK   *An Introduction to Plant Physiology*

EAMES   *Morphology of Vascular Plants*

EAMES AND MacDANIELS   *An Introduction to Plant Anatomy*

GATES   *Field Manual of Plant Ecology*

HAUPT   *An Introduction to Botany*

HAUPT   *Laboratory Manual of Elementary Botany*

HAUPT   *Plant Morphology*

HILL   *Economic Botany*

HILL, OVERHOLTS, AND POPP   *Botany*

JOHANSEN   *Plant Microtechnique*

KRAMER   *Plant and Soil Water Relationships*

LILLY AND BARNETT   *Physiology of the Fungi*

MAHESHWARI   *An Introduction to the Embryology of the Angiosperms*

MILLER   *Plant Physiology*

POOL   *Flowers and Flowering Plants*

SHARP   *Fundamentals of Cytology*

SINNOTT, DUNN, AND DOBZHANSKY   *Principles of Genetics*

SINNOTT AND WILSON   *Botany: Principles and Problems*

SMITH   *Cryptogamic Botany*

　　Vol. I.   Algae and Fungi

　　Vol. II.   Bryophytes and Pteridophytes

SMITH   *The Fresh-water Algae of the United States*

SWINGLE   *Textbook of Systematic Botany*

WEAVER AND CLEMENTS   *Plant Ecology*

There are also the related series of McGraw-Hill Publications in the Zoological Sciences, of which E. J. Boell is Consulting Editor, and in the Agricultural Sciences, of which R. A. Brink is Consulting Editor.

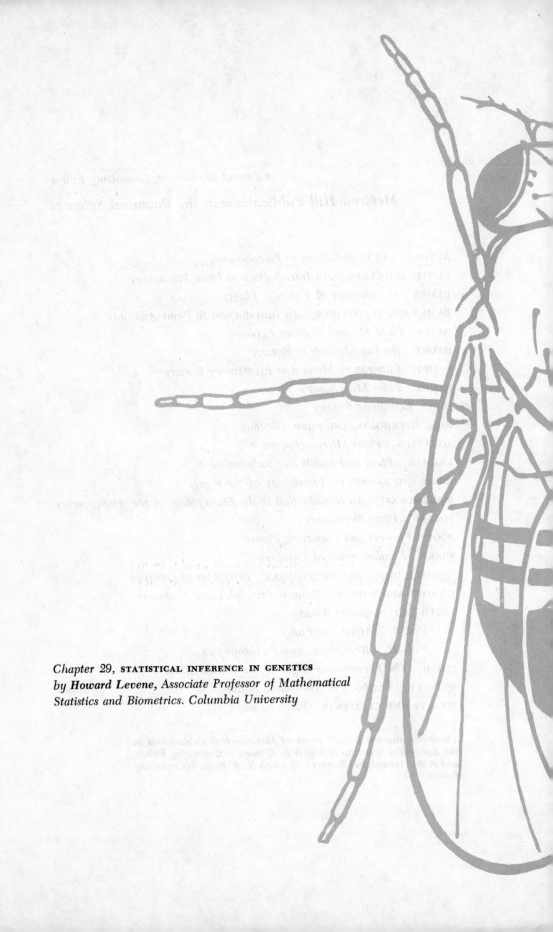

Chapter 29, STATISTICAL INFERENCE IN GENETICS
by Howard Levene, Associate Professor of Mathematical
Statistics and Biometrics. Columbia University

PRINCIPLES OF GENETICS

FIFTH EDITION

EDMUND W. SINNOTT

Sterling Professor of Botany, Emeritus, Yale University

L. C. DUNN

Professor of Zoology, Columbia University

THEODOSIUS DOBZHANSKY

Professor of Zoology, Columbia University

INTERNATIONAL STUDENT EDITION

McGRAW-HILL BOOK COMPANY, INC.
New York   Toronto   London
KŌGAKUSHA COMPANY, LTD.
Tokyo

This book is set in Times Roman

which was originally designed

by Stanley Morison for

The Times *of London.*

The headings and captions are

Caledonia Bold. The illustrations

were drawn by Robert J. Demarest

and Richard K. Enseki.

TOSHO INSATSU
PRINTING CO., LTD.
TOKYO, JAPAN

PREFACE

REVISIONS OF textbooks in a rapidly changing field are the more radical the longer the interval between revisions. The period since 1951 has witnessed some remarkable changes in several fields of genetics, and these have led to new viewpoints about certain central concepts, such as those concerning the gene. We have rewritten and rearranged the text of the fourth edition and have added material not hitherto included. It was our purpose to keep the primary emphasis on elementary principles but at the same time to make the student aware of the wide range of problems disclosed by recent research.

Many of the changes in viewpoint in the recent history of genetics have been due to the increasing use of microorganisms as experimental material. As a result, much new material on the lower fungi, bacteria, and viruses is distributed throughout the book; and we have included one entirely new chapter on varieties of sexual reproduction. This has been drawn largely from the discoveries, during the past few years, of sexuality in many species in which it had not been recognized before and of reproductive mecha-

nisms that lead to the same result as sexuality, namely, to permit new combinations of genes to arise.

A second major change is a new treatment of statistics as applied to genetics. Here the emphasis is on methods of thought and ways of reaching valid conclusions. Although this appears as the last chapter in the book, the methods set forth in it are required as soon as statistical problems are encountered. This means that the study of this chapter should begin as soon as the introductory materials in Chapters 1 and 2 have been studied.

Interest in and information concerning human heredity have also increased considerably. In general this has been dealt with in connection with the general principles of the transmission mechanism, of development, and of evolution. Wherever an example from man illustrates a general fact or theory, we have chosen such an example. One exception to this is the inclusion of a chapter on inheritance of simple traits in man. Separate treatment here is useful, since the methods of studying human traits perforce differ from those used with experimental animals and plants We have also added a new chapter on the use of twins as material for studying the relative effects of heredity and of environment.

The problems of the effects of the use and misuse of radiations from X rays and atomic energies on the heredity of human and other populations have, quite properly, claimed increasing attention. Although the understanding of these problems is not yet adequate for definitive treatment in a textbook, we have tried to present some of the fundamental facts that must serve as a basis for such discussions. Here belongs, first of all, the study of mutation, spontaneous and induced. No less important is understanding of the basic regularities of population genetics, particularly of the composition and dynamics of the genetic load of mutations carried in all sexually reproducing populations. These topics are often regarded as "too advanced" for a basic textbook, but we believe that they have an importance and timeliness which justify their consideration even in an elementary course in genetics.

In several of the later chapters of the book we have similarly gone beyond the usual range of a first course in genetics as traditionally conceived and have tried to show, with brief examples, the present boundaries of genetics as the study moves forward. Since the chapters are reasonably self-contained, individual ones from about Chapter 20 may be skipped at the discretion of the instructor.

This revision is also a new book as regards its illustrations, most of which have been made expressly for this edition by Mr. Robert Demarest, whose understanding collaboration we acknowledge with gratitude.

Certain mechanical features differ from those in previous editions. (1) We have given an annotated bibliography at the end of the book and have omitted citations to journal papers. The books chosen are those in which further information accompanied by literature citations can be found. An exception to this is the references accompanying the chapter on statistical inference, in which the student must be referred to special tables and statistical methods. (2) We have retained problems for solution by the student only in those chapters in which the material lends itself to quantitative treatment, that is to say, Chapters 3 through 19. In connection with answers to these problems, we should emphasize that where solutions can be stated in terms of exact ratios or probability, this should always be done, even when it is not specifically called for.

ACKNOWLEDGMENTS

We are indebted to many colleagues (as acknowledged in the legends) for permission to copy or borrow illustrative material. Our greatest debt is to Mr. Leigh Van Valen, who not only solved and collated the problems with the text but read the whole book in proof. A number of improvements have resulted from his thoughtful criticisms. We are grateful also to several colleagues who read and criticized certain individual chapters in manuscript: Prof. R. W. Siegel of U.C.L.A., who had also earlier made a critical appraisal of the fourth edition; Prof. F. J. Ryan of Columbia University; and Dr. Bruce Wallace of the Long Island Biological Laboratory.

We acknowledge with special gratitude the aid and patience in connection with the preparation of the manuscript of Natalie Sivertzev Dobzhansky, Louise Porter Dunn, and Glenda Sloane.

L. C. DUNN

T. DOBZHANSKY

CONTENTS

*Target Theory.   Induction of Chromosomal Aberrations.
Chromosome Breakage and Reunion.   Comparison of Spontaneous
and Induced Mutations.   Mutagenic Effects of Ultraviolet Rays.
Chemical Mutagens.   Directed Mutation.*

PRINCIPLES OF GENETICS

1 HEREDITY AND THE CONTINUITY OF LIFE

"THE WHOLE subject of inheritance is wonderful," wrote Charles Darwin in 1868. With his usual candor and honesty, Darwin admitted, however, that the biology of his day provided no solution for what continued for many years to be called the "riddle of heredity." Yet at the time Darwin made this remark, the essential steps that led to the solution of the riddle had already been taken by another great biologist, Gregor Mendel, whose work, published in 1866 in a provincial scientific journal in his native Austria, remained unknown to most biologists until 1900.

The facts of heredity are so familiar that they were long generally taken for granted. An old proverb has it that "like begets like." Human babies are always cast in the human mold and usually resemble in particular ways their parents and siblings. Puppies always grow to be dogs and usually have the body shape, size, color, and other characteristics of their breed. Yet understanding why this is so and how the equally obvious variety within the family, race, or species could arise and be maintained required more than the recognition of the fact. A scientific understanding of heredity could arise only out of knowledge of the basic facts of biology, particularly those concerned with reproduction and the means by which living matter perpetuates itself.

LIFE COMES ONLY FROM LIFE

Although heredity is a phenomenon familiar to everyone, it took a very long time and much deliberate study for even the essential facts to be grasped. It was not immediately obvious that a living individual always arises from another living individual of the same species and never from another species or from lifeless matter. In myths, human beings arose from animals, trees, or stones and men were turned into natural objects. Aristotle (384–322 B.C.), the greatest naturalist of antiquity, did not hesitate to accept the general belief of his time—that not only plants but even such complex animals as fleas, mosquitoes, and snails arise spontaneously from decaying matters.

Belief in spontaneous generation, shared even by eminent naturalists until the nineteenth century, died out in biology only after the deliberate work of a succession of careful experimenters such as Redi (1626–1698), Spallanzani (1729–1799), and others. These experimenters proved that when decaying matter was thoroughly guarded from contamination, it did not give rise to flies, protozoa, or bacteria, which arose only when eggs or spores had been introduced into the matter. But it remained for Louis Pasteur (1822–1895), one of the greatest experimentalists of all time, to convince the most skeptical that even among the most minute organisms then known, the spark of life could be kindled only by life itself.

What Spallanzani, Pasteur, and their followers proved was that heredity and living matter are coextensive. One always accompanies the other. In the world of microbes, at that time only recently revealed by the microscope, just as among higher forms, like begets like. This meant that all organisms, from bacteria to man, reproduce themselves by converting materials taken from the environment—food—into the living stuff of their own bodies. *Heredity, in the last analysis, is self-reproduction,* the common property of all life and the property that distinguishes living from nonliving matter.

VIRUSES, THE LIVING, AND THE NONLIVING

In the seventeenth century, Leeuwenhoek's discovery of microorganisms seemed to reopen the question of spontaneous generation, which had only a short time before been settled by Redi. Similarly, the discovery of viruses in 1892 by the Russian botanist Ivanovsky again put the question in a new form. Ivanovsky showed that the mosaic disease of the tobacco plant can be transmitted by self-reproducing and, hence, living bodies so small that they can pass through the pores of a filter through which bacteria cannot pass. We must reckon, then, with forms of life smaller than bacteria.

Soon it was realized that many diseases of plants and animals, including man, are caused by filterable viruses. Until the development of the electron microscope, these viruses were referred to as ultramicroscopic. Now they are known to constitute a group of organisms of various sizes and forms but all of them too small to be visible through ordinary light microscopes. In 1935 W. M. Stanley obtained from the sap of tobacco leaves affected with mosaic disease some needlelike crystals which, when dissolved in water and rubbed into healthy tobacco leaves, produced the mosaic disease. The crystals were shown to consist of nucleoprotein that could be broken down into protein and ribonucleic acid. Nucleoproteins are known to be the principal constituents of the chromosomes of higher organisms (cf. p. 11); all viruses so far examined consist of nucleoproteins, some (chiefly plant viruses) containing ribonucleic acids, others (including the bacterial viruses) containing desoxyribonucleic acid. Photographed through an electron microscope, tobacco mosaic virus appears in the form of rodlike particles about 300 mμ long. For comparison, it may be mentioned that the smallest microorganisms visible through ordinary microscopes (Rickettsiae) are about 450 mμ in diameter and that the rod-shaped hemoglobin molecule is about 15 mμ long and 3 mμ wide (Fig. 1.1).

Viruses may be called organisms, since they share with other living bodies the fundamental property of self-reproduction. Particles of living virus must be introduced to transmit a virus disease; but once a disease such as tobacco mosaic has been produced, one can extract from the diseased plant vastly greater quantities of the virus than were introduced. The virus has multiplied; it has reproduced itself, converting materials from its host into its own particu-

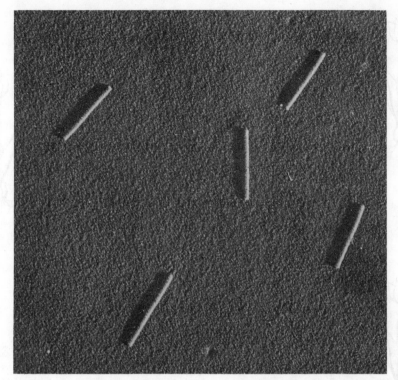

Fig. 1.1. Electron microscope photograph of five individual molecules of tobacco mosaic virus magnified 100,000 times. (*Courtesy of R. C. Williams, Virus Laboratory, University of California*)

lar form of nucleoprotein. This is what any organism does with its food when it grows and reproduces.

Naturally, viruses have their own peculiarities. All now known are parasites capable of reproducing themselves only in the living cells of a host animal, plant, or microorganism. They cannot be cultivated on artificial media, as many bacteria can. The tobacco mosaic virus, at any rate, seems to contain neither water nor enzyme systems to enable it to carry on its own metabolism. It is as though the virus somehow distorts the metabolic processes of a living host cell, forcing it to synthesize more virus materials. These peculiarities, together with the production of crystallike forms, are unusual in living organisms and have led some investigators to regard viruses as lying athwart the

line dividing the animate from the inanimate.

The very fact that such a doubt could arise is itself significant. We may be dealing here with life processes in their simplest form. The study of viruses can thus be expected to shed new light on the nature of life in general and on heredity in particular. Although it has been shown that in the simplest organisms known, life comes from life, and although no break in the continuity of life is yet evident, the question of spontaneous generation of living from lifeless matter is not closed. It may now take on other forms, as efforts to bridge the greatest remaining gap in organic evolution continue.

REPRODUCTION

Belief in the unbroken continuity of life on earth leads us to look upon every organism

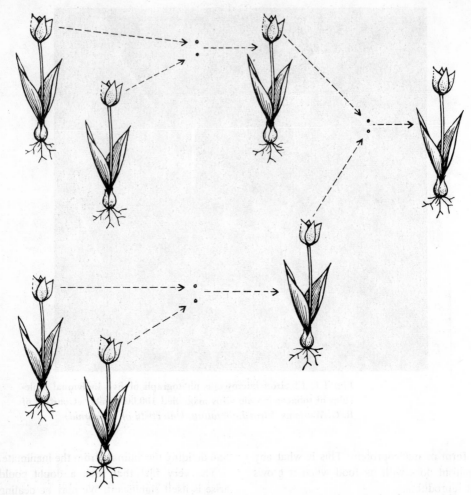

Fig. 1.2. The narrow hereditary bridge. Each plant receives from each parent only one minute sexual cell. The entire inheritance must pass over this narrow bridge between the generations.

now living as the latest member of a long and uninterrupted succession of living beings, extending back, generation before generation, to the dawn of life. The actual origin of life itself is lost in the mists of the remote past, but the pageant of the evolutionary history of living things, which unfolds in the fossil record of ancient times, indicates beyond reasonable doubt that the animals and plants of today are direct lineal descendants of earlier organisms.

Since individual living things grow old and die, the continuity of life must be maintained by the transmission of heredity to new individuals—to offspring. This process of reproduction occurs in different organisms in a bewildering variety of apparently quite distinct ways. In *asexual*, or *vegetative*, reproduction, the body of the parent is divided into two or more parts and each part grows into a new individual. With animals this method occurs chiefly among the simpler types, although some higher forms retain the ability to regenerate a whole body from a part. In some plants a small portion of the body, when removed and placed under fa-

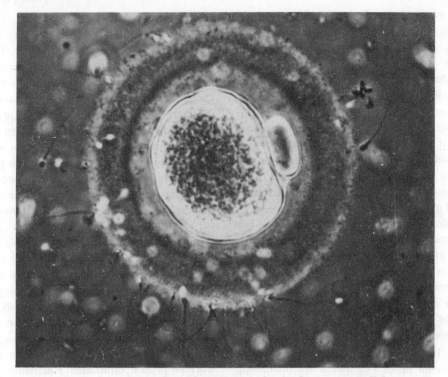

Fig. 1.3. A photomicrograph of a human egg cell being entered by spermatozoa, one of which is destined to unite with the egg nucleus. The first polar body has just been extruded. (*Courtesy of L. B. Shettles, College of Physicians and Surgeons, Columbia University*)

vorable conditions, may establish itself as a new individual. For example, potatoes are cultivated more easily from pieces of tubers than from seeds, and most fruit trees are propagated by cuttings or grafts.

Far commoner, both among plants and animals, is *sexual reproduction*. The essential feature of this type of reproduction is that the new individual arises through the union of two sex cells, or *gametes,* which form a single cell, or *zygote,* from which the new individual develops. In both sexual and asexual reproduction there exists, then, a physical, living link between the parents and the offspring. A part, however small, of the parent grows and develops to become the body of the offspring. Whatever is inherited must be contained in this part; hence the dis-

covery of the mechanism of sexual reproduction and particularly the identification of the gametes—the physical links between the generations—were important preparatory steps in the study of heredity (Fig. 1.2).

DISCOVERY OF EGG, SPERM, AND FERTILIZATION

In most organisms the reproductive cells are too small to be seen with the unaided eye; hence the invention of the microscope was necessary before sexual reproduction could be understood. The eggs of birds can be easily seen to be produced in the ovaries, but the tiny vesicles on the surface of the ovaries in mammals were not recognized as eggs until de Graaf in 1673 proved that they were. At about the same time, Malpighi in Italy and Swammerdam in Holland identified the much larger eggs of insects, while Leeuwenhoek and his student Hamm turned their newly developed microscope upon the seminal fluid and found it swarming with "animalcules," which we now call *sperms* or *spermatozoa* (Fig. 1.3). This started the school of animalculists, which maintained that it was the male element that transmitted heredity. An earlier school, the ovists, insisted that it was the egg that contained the hereditary material, whereas the seminal fluid gave only the stimulus to make the egg develop. We now know that the eggs and the spermatozoa, however dissimilar their sizes and appearances, contain similar parts, *nuclei*, which make them equally potent in the transmission of heredity. This idea apparently did not occur to anyone until the end of the nineteenth century.

Proof of what nowadays seems self-evident, that the new individual originates from the union of an egg and a spermatozoon, was obtained only gradually. Leeuwenhoek noted the association of the sperm with the egg in 1680; Spallanzani in 1785 obtained offspring from artificial insemination of dogs. He also filtered the seminal fluid of frogs and toads and proved that the presence of spermatozoa was indispensable for fertilization; the liquid in which the spermatozoa were suspended did not suffice. The culminating step was taken ninety years later when, in 1875, Oscar Hertwig observed in sea urchins that fertilization involves the union of the sperm nucleus with that of the egg.

SEXUAL REPRODUCTION IN PLANTS

Although it had been known since ancient times that female date trees would produce fruits only when their flowers had been dusted with pollen from male trees, this knowledge led to no generalized understanding until 1694, when Cammerarius showed that in corn no seeds are produced unless pollen is applied to the pistils.

Eighteenth-century biologists found it hard to believe that at least some plants, like animals, reproduce sexually. However, Linnaeus (1707–1778), the father of systematic biology, and Koelreuter (1733–1806) artificially crossed different varieties and species of plants and observed the hybrid offspring. When pollen of one species is placed on the stigma of another, the offspring, if any, usually combine the characteristics of both parents. Heredity is evidently transmitted in plants through the pollen as well as through the ovules, just as in animals it is transmitted both through the spermatozoa and through the eggs. Moreover, the hybrids obtained by using a species A as a female parent and a species B as a male parent are generally similar to those obtained by using B as a female and A as a male. This shows that, contrary to the opinions of the ovists and the animalculists, both sexes transmit the same heredity to the progeny. In this work on plant hybridization, Koelreuter and Gaertner (1772–1850) were predecessors of Gregor Mendel (1822–1884), who discovered the laws of heredity described in the following chapters.

PREFORMATION AND EPIGENESIS

The grand synthesis Newton (1642–1726) made of the physical science of the eighteenth century seemed to men of the Age of Enlightenment to explain all natural phenomena, including biology and sociology. Some of the audacious ideas formulated then still influence the thought of biologists, even though their inadequacy in their original form has long been recognized. The ideas of *preformation* and *epigenesis* belong in this category of enduring modes of thought.

An observer endowed with too lively an imagination and a faulty microscope claimed in 1694 that he could see inside the human spermatozoon a miniature figure of a man—a "homunculus." Swammerdam and, especially, the Swiss naturalist Bonnet (1720–1793) seized upon this spurious discovery, which to them seemed important; it seemed, in fact, to explain all heredity and even all creation. Man's body, they thought, is already *preformed* in the spermatozoon. It follows that the development of the fetus and of the child required only growth to turn this tiny homunculus into a full-sized man. The ovists squared their favorite notion that the egg is most important by supposing that the homunculus is located in the egg rather than in the spermatozoon. According to Bonnet's "encapsulation theory," a female contains all the "germs" of all her immediate and remote progeny, one generation within the other. Mother Eve had in her ovaries the germs of all men to come, stored like boxes within boxes. The philosopher Leibnitz added the finishing touch: God preformed everything on the day of creation; all that happens was predestined from the beginning.

Improved microscopes, however, showed the homunculus to be a figment of the imagination. C. F. Wolff (1733–1794) and, especially, K. E. von Baer (1792–1876) overthrew the doctrine of preformation in its crude original form and replaced it with the theory of epigenesis. According to this view, the process of development consists of more than growth. The sex cells are mere drops of structureless liquid containing nothing whatever resembling the body that is to develop from them. The developing body goes through a series of radical transformations during which organs are formed which were not present beforehand even in rudimentary form. Being a *vitalist,* Wolff believed that the organs arise owing to the action of a mysterious vital force. Von Baer corrected this exaggeration; he was the first actually to see the egg cell of a mammal (a dog) and the first to produce a detailed description, amazingly accurate, of the embryonic development of a chick. From the very beginning, at fertilization, the body possesses a highly developed structure, or organization. As the development proceeds, this organization undergoes an orderly series of changes, leading by stages to the formation of a fetus and then of an adult body.

The early ideas about preformation and epigenesis seem to us naive and crude today. But, as we shall see, these ideas are still alive in modified forms in modern biology.

BIOLOGICAL AND LEGAL INHERITANCE

The preformist way of thinking is implicit in the very language we use in speaking of heredity. In English and most other languages, the word "inheritance" means both the transmission of biological heredity from parents to offspring and the transmission of the property of a person to his heirs. Yet biological and legal inheritance are so profoundly different that nothing but confusion results from failure to distinguish them clearly. Indeed, the inheritance of a house, a farm, or a jewel means that certain physical objects change their owners without necessarily changing themselves in the process. Inheritance of an eye color or a singing voice is obviously something quite different. The only material objects that one inherits biologically from one's parents are the genes carried in the egg and sperm cells from which the body originates.

Biological heredity is realized through a dynamic process of organic development. The union of the sex cells at fertilization is followed by transformation of the fertilized egg into an embryo, a fetus, an infant, a child, an adolescent, an adult, a senescent, and finally a dead body. Now, the course of this development in every creature is more or less like that in its ancestors. This path is determined by heredity interacting with the environment (cf. p. 19). When the development follows a certain path, there are formed eyes of a certain color, a particular kind of singing voice, and other traits. Eye color is not handed down from parents to children; it arises epigenetically in the process of development. When, in this book, we discuss the inheritance of eye color in mice or men or flies, we shall be using this phrase as a shorthand expression to mean the processes of development that lead mice or men or flies to have bodies of a certain structure and to possess various organs, among them eyes of a certain color.

Biological heredity is sometimes defined as the transmission of similarities from parents to offspring. This is, of course, correct as far as it goes. However, a "similarity," say a similarity of eye colors, is not a material object that is packed in the gametes and thus "transmitted." A similarity or difference is what an observer perceives when he compares the development patterns of different organisms. Some persons are born blond and remain so; the hair of other persons darkens with age; still others have dark hair until it turns gray. Heredity determines not so much the "similarities" as the course of the processes of growth and development.

DARWIN'S HYPOTHESIS OF PANGENESIS

The distinction between biological and legal inheritance was not fully appreciated until recently and even now is not recognized in all quarters. Biologists of the nineteenth century, including Charles Darwin, noted simply the fact that whatever characteristics are observed in individuals of one generation are often met with also in individuals of the next generation. Since it was already known in Darwin's day that neither egg nor sperm contains anything like a homunculus, Darwin tried to visualize the operation of heredity by means of an interesting speculation. He fully realized that this speculation had no solid factual basis and so called it the "provisional hypothesis of pangenesis."

Darwin's conjecture was that each cell of the body produces its own rudiments or diminutive copies, called *gemmules,* which in animals are shed into the blood stream. The blood transports the gemmules into the testes and ovaries, where the gemmules of the different body parts are gathered together to form the gametes. When these give rise to a new organism, the different kinds of gemmules give rise to the same kinds of organs, tissues, and cells which produced them in the parents. Heredity, then, was supposed to be due to the transmission of gemmules, representing different organs, parts, and components of the body.

Note how definitely preformistic is the hypothesis of pangenesis. In effect, it assumes the existence in the gametes of a sort of invisible homunculus composed of gemmules as a mosaic picture is composed of stones. The hypothesis in its original form was invalidated by Galton (1822–1911) very soon after Darwin proposed it. Galton transfused blood between white and black rabbits, very reasonably expecting to produce a mixture of gemmules which would make the offspring of the transfused parents spotted or dappled. Nothing of the sort was observed. Nevertheless, variants of the hypothesis of pangenesis have been adopted by believers in the inheritance of so-called acquired characters, most recently by Lysenko and his followers in Russia.

INHERITANCE OF ACQUIRED CHARACTERS

Biologists and nonbiologists alike are familiar with two sets of facts about heredity. First, organisms are modified by environment. Sustained use or exercise of an organ such as a muscle or of a faculty such as skill in performing a certain kind of work generally strengthens and develops the organ or the ability. Disuse and lack of exercise weaken or reduce organs and faculties. Second, offspring tend to resemble their parents. It is tempting to connect these two sets of facts and to conclude that modifications induced in the parents by the environment (acquired characters) will be transmitted to and inherited by the offspring, in the absence of the environmental stimulus. The hypothesis that acquired characters may be inherited seemed so reasonable that it was accepted as true, without careful test or verification, by most biologists up to and including Darwin.

Lamarck, the French biologist (1744–1829) who was the father of the first theory of biological evolution, considered the inheritance of acquired characters to be the most important, if not the sole, mechanism of evolutionary change. The type of evolutionary thought in which this view is accepted is known as *Lamarckism*. According to Lamarck, variations are induced in organisms in response to urgent need and striving on the part of individuals and through use or disuse of organs. The modifications thus called into being he regarded as heritable. Indeed, to Lamarck, all variations were acquired, and all variations were heritable. Darwin accepted the inheritance of acquired characters as an important though subsidiary factor in evolution and considered natural selection to be the directing agent of the evolutionary process. To Darwin and the Lamarckians, the virtue of the hypothesis of pangenesis was precisely that it gave an ostensibly reasonable, though actually spurious, explanation of how such inheritance could take place.

WEISMANN, A FORERUNNER OF MODERN GENETICS

August Weismann (1834–1914) challenged the popular belief that acquired characters are inherited. He made controlled experiments to test the validity of the belief and developed the *germ plasm* theory, which represented a forward step in the understanding of heredity.

He regarded the reproductive tissues—the germ cells and the cells from which they arise—as the germ plasm, which he supposed to be separate and distinct from the other tissues of the body (*somatoplasm*). The proponents of pangenesis believed the reproductive cells to be compounded of representative particles secreted by the somatoplasm. Weismann showed that the exact opposite is true; the germ plasm perpetuates itself and incidentally engenders the formation of the rest of the body, the *soma*. Weismann's position was once epitomized in the aphorism of Samuel Butler: "The hen is the egg's way of making another egg." In modern language (which, of course, Weismann did not use), we should say that the genes reproduce themselves and that the rest of the body is a by-product of their self-reproduction. This makes it understandable why changes induced by the environment in the body, in the soma, are not transferred to the germ plasm, as they might be if pangenesis occurred. Acquired characters cannot, therefore, be inherited.

Weismann's famous experiments consisted in cutting off the tails of mice for a series of generations and observing that the progeny still had tails of normal length. To a modern biologist, this procedure seems exceedingly crude, but it is well to remember that such hereditary variations as hornlessness and taillessness in animals were widely believed to have arisen from the practice of dehorning or of docking the tail continued over many generations.

Although the conception of a distinct germ plasm is useful and helps in explaining many facts and planning experiments with higher animals, its applicability is limited. It does not apply at all in the lower animals, in which no distinction between soma and germ can be made, or in plants, in which many or all parts of the plant body may give rise to germ cells or to new individuals without the intervention of a sexual process. Even in higher animals it is possible that the gametes may arise from tissue not fundamentally different from that which produces other parts of the body and that the sex organs are not completely insulated from those forces that effect changes in the body tissues.

A more satisfactory statement of the distinction between the heredity, which is transmitted in the gametes, and the developing organism, which results from the action of heredity, had to wait for the formulation of the *genotype* and *phenotype* concepts by Johannsen in 1911 (see Chap. 2). Weismann, however, made important contributions for understanding heredity in his studies of the chromosomal mechanism of inheritance.

THE CELLULAR BASIS OF REPRODUCTION
The unbroken continuity of life depends, as we have seen, on the transmission of living

brief account of cell structure, cell multiplication by mitosis, and the meiotic divisions by which gametes are formed emphasizes only those main features that are essential for understanding the transmission mechanism of heredity. More complete and detailed accounts will be found in treatises on cytology.

Fig. 1.4. Diagram of a generalized cell.

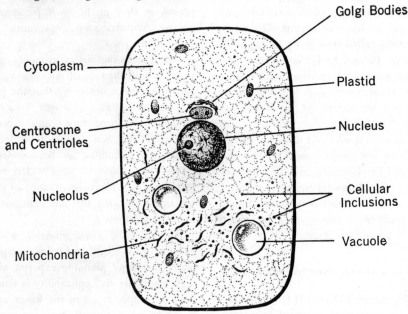

Cytoplasm
Centrosome and Centrioles
Nucleolus
Mitochondria
Golgi Bodies
Plastid
Nucleus
Cellular Inclusions
Vacuole

substance from parents to offspring. However, living substance is organized, in all forms above the parasitic viruses, into cells. The *cell theory*, as finally established by Schleiden and Schwann (1838) and Virchow (1855), states that all organisms are composed of one or more cells and that cells arise only from preexisting cells. Germ cells come from division of certain cells of the parent body and in turn produce by division the cells of the body of the offspring. Thus the human body starts from a single cell, but by the time of birth it consists of some 200 billion (2×10^{11}) or more cells.

Our knowledge of the structure and behavior of cells and their parts is the result of a hundred years of study. The following

THE CELL
Typically, the cell consists of a denser body, the *nucleus,* enclosed in its own membrane and surrounded by less dense semifluid colloidal *cytoplasm.* The cell is enclosed in a semipermeable membrane through which metabolic exchanges occur (Fig. 1.4). In plant cells, there is in addition a cell wall of cellulose or related substances.

In the cytoplasm there are, typically, a variety of structures concerned with the metabolic and synthetic activities of the cell. Two types of small bodies are always present and are probably essential constituents. The *mitochondria,* ranging in size from the smallest particles visible through a light microscope to several microns in length, are centers of enzyme activity in oxidative metabolism. The *microsomes* are submicroscopic particles recognizable by their enzymatic activities and their concentrations of ribonucleic acid, lipid, and protein. Various types of cells contain a variety of other kinds of submicroscopic particles.

In addition, animal cells contain Golgi bodies, the function of which is not precisely known, and centrosomes, which function in cell division. Most plant cells contain plastids of various kinds, the most prominent of which are the chloroplasts, in which the activities of photosynthesis are centered. Some of the structures in the cytoplasm are often quite different in different cells of the same individual as well as in cells of different organisms.

THE NUCLEUS

The nuclei of cells are of more constant appearance than their other features, at least in cells of the same species. The structures of greatest interest for genetics are the chromosomes. These contain two forms of nucleic acid, mostly desoxyribonucleic acids (DNA) and also some ribonucleic acid (RNA) combined with some basic proteins. DNA has a specific affinity for certain dyes, and methods are thus available for making

TABLE 1.1

The diploid (2n) numbers of chromosomes in some animal and plant species (*After Makino, Darlington, and other sources*)

Common and scientific names	Chromosomes	Common and scientific names	Chromosomes
Man, *Homo sapiens*	46(?), 48(?)	Yellow pine, *Pinus ponderosa*	24
Rhesus monkey, *Macaca mulatta*	48	Cabbage, *Brassica oleracea*	18
Horse, *Equus caballus*	66	Radish, *Raphanus sativus*	18
Pig, *Sus scrofa*	40	Cucumber, *Cucumis sativus*	14
Sheep, *Ovis aries*	54	Upland cotton, *Gossypium hirsutum*	52
Cattle, *Bos taurus*	60	Plum, *Prunus domestica*	48
Cat, *Felis maniculata*	38	Cherry, *Prunus cerasus*	32
Dog, *Canis familiaris*	78	Apple, *Malus sylvestris*	34 and 51
Rat, *Rattus norvegicus*	42	Pear, *Pyrus communis*	34, 51, and 68
Domestic mouse, *Mus musculus*	40	Garden pea, *Pisum sativum*	14
Guinea pig, *Cavia cobaya*	64	Sweet pea, *Lathyrus odoratus*	14
Rabbit, *Oryctolagus cuniculus*	44	Bean, *Phaseolus vulgaris*	22
Opossum, *Didelphys virginiana*	22	Scarlet oak, *Quercus coccinea*	24
Chicken, *Gallus domesticus*	77, 78	Orange, *Citrus sinensis*	18, 27, and 36
Turkey, *Meleagris gallopavo*	81, 82	Sunflower, *Helianthus annuus*	34
Pigeon, *Columba livia*	79, 80	Tobacco, *Nicotiana tabaccum*	48
Frog, *Rana esculenta*	26	Potato, *Solanum tuberosum*	48
Toad, *Bufo vulgaris*	22	Tomato, *Solanum lycopersicum*	24
Platyfish, *Platypoecilus maculatus*	48	Banana, *Musa paradisiaca*	22, 44, 55, 77, and 88
Goldfish, *Carassius auratus*	94	Garden onion, *Allium cepa*	16
Housefly, *Musca domestica*	12	Indian corn, *Zea mays*	20
Vinegar fly, *Drosophila melanogaster*	8	Barley, *Hordeum vulgare*	14
Mosquito, *Culex pipiens*	6	Summer wheat, *Triticum dicoccum*	28
Honey bee, *Apis mellifica*	32, 16	Bread wheat, *Triticum vulgare*	42
Shrimp, *Eupagurus ochotensis*	254	Rye, *Secale cereale*	14
Hydra, *Hydra vulgaris*	32	Rice, *Oryza sativa*	24

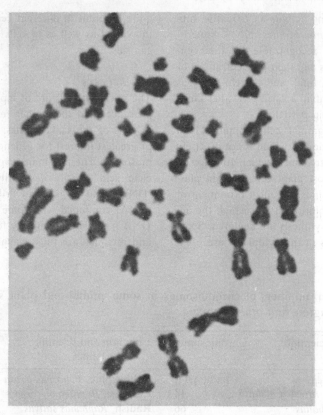

Fig. 1.5. The chromosome complement of man. Photograph of the 46 chromosomes from a cell in mitosis. (*From Tjio and Levan in Hereditas*)

the chromosomes clearly visible during division, when the various chromosomes separate, so that their individual peculiarities and numbers can be recognized. In most organisms that reproduce sexually, chromosomes regularly occur in pairs, of which one member has come from the mother and the other from the father. The number of pairs varies in somatic cells from 2 (in a race of *Ascaris megalocephala*, a parasitic worm, and in a species of the crustacean Cyclops) or 3 (in the plant genera Crepis and Drosophyllum and in some species of Drosophila flies), through almost continuous gradations in numbers up to 100 in the crayfish and even higher numbers in some ferns and protozoa (see Table 1.1). In man it was supposed until recently that the normal number

was 24 pairs, but critical studies of the best preparations of some somatic tissues now reveal only 23 pairs (Fig. 1.5).

In most higher organisms the gametes contain half as many chromosomes as the somatic cells; that is, one member of each pair enters each gamete in the process of chromosome reduction, or *meiosis*. In *Drosophila melanogaster,* for example, the normal somatic or zygotic number is 8 and the gametic number is 4; in corn the numbers are 20 and 10, respectively. Thus the zygotic, or *diploid,* number (characteristic of body cells of the species) is 2n; the gametic or *haploid* number is represented by n. The whole collection of chromosomes in a nucleus is referred to as the *chromosome complement* (Table 1.1).

Cells of some lower organisms, especially bacteria, were formerly thought not to have nuclei; recently, however, bodies resembling nuclei and chromosomes were revealed in some bacteria and yeasts (Fig. 1.6). Some viruses, including bacteriophages, show a distinct resemblance in chemical composition to chromosomal materials, since they consist chiefly of DNA or RNA nucleoproteins.

MITOSIS

Cell nuclei were first seen and named by Robert Brown in 1831, but their biological

otherwise it is a misnomer, since this stage of the life cycle of cells is probably the period of the most lively metabolic and synthetic activity in the nucleus.

When a cell is preparing to divide, the chromosomes become clearly visible as stainable threads that gradually shorten and thicken by means of coiling, or spiralization. This is the *prophase* stage. Next, the nuclear membrane disappears, and a spindle-shaped structure appears in which *spindle fibers,* denser than the surrounding cytoplasm, connect the chromosomes with the two poles of the spindle. In animals these

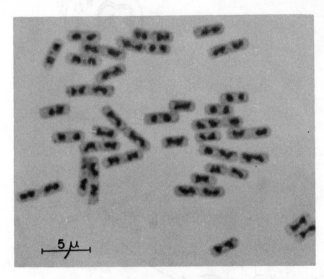

Fig. 1.6. Dividing nuclei in bacterial cells (*Bacillus cereus*). (*After Robinow*)

significance became apparent only when Strasburger (1875), Bütschli (1876), and others discovered that nuclei arise exclusively from other nuclei by means of a remarkable process of division which Fleming (1882) called *mitosis* (Fig. 1.7). Nuclei are, therefore, cell organs that cannot originate from cytoplasmic constituents.

During the period of *interkinesis,* which intervenes between successive nuclear and cell divisions, separate chromosomes are usually not distinguishable in the nucleus. Interkinesis has often been called the resting stage, but this refers only to the fact that the cell is not actively dividing at this time;

poles are marked by the *central bodies,* or *centrosomes,* which have already divided. The chromosomes now are arranged in a single plane, about midway between the two poles of the spindle, to form an *equatorial plate.* This stage of mitosis is known as the *metaphase;* chromosomes can be most easily seen and counted during this stage.

At some time during prophase or metaphase, each chromosome becomes visibly split along its length into two daughter chromosomes. There is no agreement among cytologists as to just when the actual duplication, which must involve the production of a duplicate of every constituent gene in the chromosome, takes place. Interkinesis is the most likely stage at which this synthetic activity may take place. However that may be, at the end of the metaphase the daughter halves of each chromosome begin to di-

verge from each other and eventually pass to the opposite poles of the mitotic spindle. This separation of the daughter chromosomes occurs at *anaphase*. The details of the anaphasic movements of chromosomes again

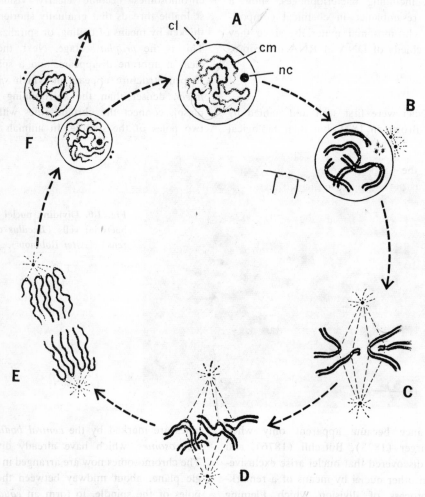

Fig. 1.7. Diagram of cell division by mitosis illustrated by a cell with two pairs of chromosomes. (*A*) Interphase, or "resting" nucleus; *cl*, centrioles; *cm*, centromere; *nc*, nucleolus. (*B*) Prophase. Each chromosome is visibly double, the duplicates still joined by the centromeres, which have not yet divided. (*C*) Metaphase. The double chromosomes are aligned at the equator between the poles of the spindle. (*D*) Anaphase. The centromeres have split and the chromosomes are beginning to move toward the poles. (*E*) Telophase. The chromosome halves have moved to the poles, one complete set (two pairs) going to each pole. (*F*) Daughter nuclei. Each chromosome set is included within a new nucleus, in each of which the conditions at (*A*) are restored.

differ in different organisms. In most cases, each chromosome contains at a fixed point in its body a minute structure called the *centromere,* which is primarily concerned with the anaphase movements of the chromosomes and which leads the way on the spindle toward the poles. In some insects, however, the centromeric activity is manifested at many points, or perhaps even along the entire length of the chromosome.

The anaphase merges into the *telophase,* during which the daughter chromosomes assembled at the poles of the spindle become included in a new nuclear membrane. The chromosomes gradually lengthen, uncoil, and become less darkly stainable. Meanwhile, the mitotic spindle disappears and, in plants, a new cell wall or cell membrane is formed in the equatorial plane between the two nuclei; in animals, the cell is divided into two daughter cells by a cleavage furrow. The cycle is completed by the advent of a new interkinesis.

FERTILIZATION, OR SYNGAMY

It is a very remarkable fact that the processes of cell division are, with minor variations, similar in all organisms, plants and animals, simple and highly complex. Even more remarkable is the fundamental similarity of sexual reproduction in the diverse organisms in which it occurs. This basic uniformity of sexual processes is hidden behind the façade of what appears to be great diversity; and, indeed, it took much insight and much work on the part of biologists to discover that the uniformity exists.

Consider that in many organisms the sexes are separate and reproduction occurs only when an egg produced by a female individual unites with a spermatozoon contributed by a male. Yet, many other organisms are *hermaphrodites,* and in them eggs and spermatozoa are produced in the same body. In many organisms the egg is millions of times greater in mass than the spermatozoon and very different from it in form and structure;

yet in some organisms the uniting gametes are very similar and even indistinguishable. In their details, the reproductive processes in plants are quite different from those in animals.

The essential and crucial event of sexual reproduction, regardless of its diverse appearances, is the occurrence of *fertilization,* which is the fusion of the nuclei of the gametes. This was perceived by O. Hertwig (1865) and Fol (1877), working with marine animals, and by Strasburger (1877, 1884) who studied both the higher plants and the simpler algae. The haploid nuclei of the gametes fuse to form a single *zygotic* nucleus.

NUCLEI AND CHROMOSOMES AS TRANSMITTERS OF HEREDITY

The discoverers and students of mitotic cell division were profoundly impressed by the orderly complexity of this process. The biological function of all the elaborate maneuvers that occur in the cell during mitosis is evidently a precise duplication and division of the contents of each chromosome of the mother nucleus between the nuclei of the daughter cells. Weismann (1892) and Roux (1905) concluded that it is the substance concerned with the transmission of heredity which requires so meticulously accurate a division and distribution. This led to the inference that the hereditary materials are borne in the cell nuclei and their chromosomes.

Similar opinions were expressed even earlier by Strasburger (1884) and O. Hertwig (1884) on the basis of their studies of fertilization. The argument was developed most clearly by Strasburger and Hertwig and by Boveri (1862–1915). The traits of a child, they maintained, are influenced by the maternal and the paternal heredities to about the same extent. The mother and the father, the female and the male gametes, are equally efficient in the transmission of heredity. Now, how can the female and male gametes, which in many organisms are very different in size and structure, transmit the same heredity to the same extent?

Unless one makes the improbable conjecture that similar hereditary endowments are carried in different structures in egg and sperm, the only solution is that both these types of cells must have some structures that are similar and that it is these similar structures that are the principal carriers of heredity, whereas the remaining portions of the cells are subsidiary in respect to heredity. The parts that are similar in female and male gametes of the same species are the nuclei and, especially, the chromosomes. These, accordingly, may be supposed to be the carriers of heredity.

QUESTIONS FOR DISCUSSION

1.1 In your opinion, what would constitute proof of spontaneous generation of life?

1.2 List the arguments for and against considering viruses as organisms.

1.3 What form of reproduction occurs in the growth of tissue cultures? How would you try to improve the growth or other qualities of such cultures?

1.4 What do you think accounts for the recent revival in the USSR of belief in the inheritance of acquired characters? In the hypothesis of pangenesis? (Cf. Huxley (1949) and Zirkle (1949).)

1.5 What advantages and disadvantages to human society would result from the inheritance of acquired characters?

1.6 How could you explain the possession by animals of highly developed instincts that the individual itself has had no opportunity of acquiring, assuming (a) that acquired characters are inherited and (b) that they are not?

1.7 What evidence would you require to demonstrate that docking the tails in puppies changes their heredity?

1.8 If members of a white-skinned race are exposed to bright sunlight, their skin is darkened, or "tanned." Races native to regions of bright sunlight—for example, Negroes in the tropics—are genetically dark-skinned. How would Lamarck explain the dark skin of such races? How would you?

1.9 If a character is found to be transmitted only by the mother, in what part of the gamete is it probably transmitted?

1.10 The hair color of an individual may be brown in youth, black in maturity, and white in old age. What color would you call his hair in a study of the inheritance of hair color?

1.11 What elements in the cytoplasm do you think may have a continuity independent of that of the nucleus?

1.12 In some invertebrates, the materials in the cytoplasm of the egg are distributed unequally to different blastomeres, which thereafter form different parts of the embryo. Does this constitute an argument for preformation?

1.13 Which do you think arose earlier in evolution, sexual reproduction with fertilization or parthenogenesis?

1.14 Other things being equal, would you expect greater variability among organisms reproducing asexually or among bisexual species?

CHAPTER 2

2 HEREDITY AND ENVIRONMENT

THE SINGLE GAMETIC nucleus contributed by the parent to each offspring is usually too small to be visible to the unaided eye. Yet this extremely narrow bridge is the only physical link between parents and offspring, and across it everything must pass which is *transmitted* from one generation to the next. Muller has estimated that all the spermatozoa from which the present population of the world arose (about two and a half billion individuals) would have no greater bulk than an ordinary aspirin tablet. The chromosomes, or the parts essential for heredity, of two and a half billion eggs would occupy about the same space. This minute amount of substance nevertheless determines, in cooperation with environmental factors, the kinds of human beings that inhabit the earth. Indeed, the nuclei of egg and sperm, these tiny packets of reproductive substance into which so much is packed and out of which so much emerges, are the most remarkable bits of living matter in existence.

Regardless of whether an organism reproduces sexually or asexually, the bit of the parental body that gives rise to the new individual undergoes growth. The body of an adult man has a mass about fifty billion times greater than that of the fertilized egg from which it developed. The source of the material at the expense of which this tremendous increase in mass must occur is evident—it is the food that the organism consumes. Every organism consists quite literally of transformed food. But similar nutrients can be used to build the bodies of diverse organisms—say a man, a dog, a cat, or a pig. The kind of body formed obviously depends not only on the food consumed but chiefly on the heredity of the organism that consumes it.

HEREDITY, GROWTH, AND ASSIMILATION

In order for growth to occur, materials must be taken from the environment and incorporated into the developing body. In green plants, these materials are water and mineral salts from the soil and carbon dioxide and oxygen from the air, plus the energy of sunlight. In living things other than green plants,

17

growth takes place by incorporation into the body of whatever organic and inorganic foods the organism requires. However, what is taken in becomes a constituent of a living body only through profound chemical transformations wrought by the body upon the substances in the food. Every organism assimilates its food in a definite way, so that the organism is always a more or less faithful copy of its parents and other ancestors. The parental organism reproduces itself in its offspring by organizing in its own peculiar way the materials taken from the environment. The essence of heredity is thus *self-reproduction* of the organism at the expense of the environment.

Self-reproduction is especially evident when individuals of one generation become the parents of the next, and a bit of the body of one individual gives rise to a new but similar body of another. However, the processes of metabolism, and hence of heredity, operate at all stages of life. This has been demonstrated especially clearly in physiological experiments in which animals or plants were given isotopes or radioactive tracer elements in their diets. In growing individuals as well as in adults, which no longer grow, the tracer atoms become assimilated and incorporated into amino acids, proteins, carbohydrates, and other body constituents. However, these body constituents are not retained indefinitely but after some time are broken down and replaced by newly synthesized ones, and the tracer atoms are shed with the excretion products (Schoenheimer, 1940). Thus the body is constantly rebuilt and renewed in the processes of metabolism. It is heredity that ensures that the composition of the body remains more or less constant or undergoes orderly change and development.

GENOTYPE AND PHENOTYPE

So long as an organism is alive, its heredity interacts with its environment; this interaction determines what an individual organism is like at a given moment and what it can develop into in the future. To facilitate clear thinking about this matter, the Danish geneticist Johannsen proposed in 1911 to distinguish the *genotype* of the organism from its *phenotype*. The genotype is the sum total of heredity, the genetic constitution that an organism receives from its parents. The phenotype is the appearance of the organism —the sum total of all its characteristics, such as color, form, size, behavior, chemical composition, and structure, both external and internal, gross and miscroscopic. The concepts of genotype and phenotype have replaced in modern biology the earlier notions of germ plasm and soma introduced by Weismann (see Chap. 1).

We recognize persons or individuals of any species of animal or plant by their phenotypes. The phenotype of an individual changes with time, as illustrated, for example, by a series of photographs of a person taken at different ages from infancy to senility. But we know also that more subtle physiological changes constantly occur in an individual, so that the phenotype is never exactly the same from one moment to the next.

The genotype of an individual can be determined by observing its effect on the phenotype and by studying the ancestry or the progeny of the individual. When two or more individuals develop in similar environments and come to possess different phenotypes, we can conclude that these individuals have different genotypes. Thus, among closely related persons, some may have brown eyes and others blue, apparently regardless of the environment. On the other hand, when individuals with similar genotypes develop in different environments, their phenotypes may be quite different. Suppose, for example, that one of a pair of identical twins contracts a serious infectious disease and the other escapes the infection; the former may become a cripple and the latter remain in good health. The difference is evidently environmental. However, when individuals developing in similar or in different environments have similar phenotypes, it does not necessarily follow that their genotypes are also similar. Thus, some persons with brown eyes carry in their genotypes a gene for blue eyes, whereas others do not, and these different genotypes cannot be distinguished by the eye color because of the phenomenon of dominance.

In contrast to the phenotype, which changes continuously, the genotype is relatively stable throughout the life of the individual. An aged person has genes similar to those he had in his youth, as a child, or as a fetus, but his phenotype is quite different from what it was earlier. As we shall see in Chapter 16, the constancy of the genotype does not mean that the genes are unchangeable. Rather, it means that the constituents of the genotype, the genes, usually reproduce themselves faithfully throughout life.

HEREDITY AND VARIATION

No two persons or individuals, even of the same sex, are ever exactly alike. The primary reason for this is that the environment of organisms is never the same in different places and at different times. No two plants growing side by side in a meadow receive precisely the same amounts of light, water, and minerals; no two animals receive quite the same food at the same stage of development. Two individuals with the same genotype may become different in phenotype when they come into contact with different conditions of food, temperature, light, humidity, and other external factors. Such differences among organisms of similar heredity are referred to as *environmental variations* or *modifications*.

The same soil and the same climate, however, furnish the environment in which an acorn gives rise to an oak and a maize seed develops into a corn plant. The same food makes a puppy grow into a dog and a kitten into a cat. These species have different geno-

types. The same is true of individuals of the same species, at least in species that reproduce by sexual generation. As we shall see in Chapter 18, no two persons, except for identical twins, are likely to have identical genotypes. This is *hereditary,* or *genotypic, variation;* it arises from variations in the elements responsible for heredity, the genes, which may undergo changes known as *mutations.* The changed form of a gene may thereafter be transmitted and enter into a variety of combinations with other changed or unchanged genes, producing genotypic variety (Chaps. 16 and 17).

The process of heredity, which makes like beget like, is therefore just as universal as is variation—the fact that the likeness never amounts to complete identity. The aim of the science of genetics was defined by Bateson in 1905 as "the elucidation of the phenomena of heredity and variation." The geneticist studies the causes both of the similarities and of the dissimilarities between the developmental patterns of different organisms.

DISTINGUISHING HEREDITY AND ENVIRONMENTAL VARIATIONS

People often ask the naive question, which is more important, heredity or environment? This question is meaningless. The phenotype of any organism is necessarily a result of the interaction of a genotype with an environment; both are absolutely necessary. Thus a person, with all his physical, physiological, and mental traits, is necessarily a product of growth and development brought about by a certain genotype in a certain succession of environments. The phenotype of a person at a given moment is determined, of course, not only by the environment that prevails at that particular moment but also by the whole succession of environments he has experienced during his lifetime. Every person is the product of his genotype and of his life experiences.

It is, however, possible and often neces-

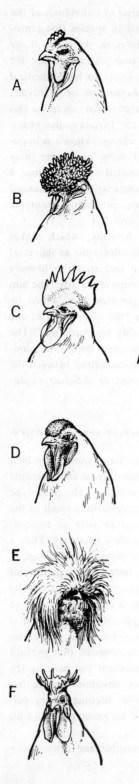

sary to discover the extent to which the observed differences between the phenotypes of different individuals are due to heredity and the extent to which they are environmentally induced.

Breeders of agricultural plants and animals are always on the lookout for genotypic variants which, when raised under farm conditions, give greater yields of grain, fiber, milk, meat, wool, or other products useful to man. Even slight genotypic improvements in yield are desirable, since they may be expected to recur again and again in the progeny of the improved variety. However, yields are influenced not only by

Fig. 2.1. Variation in the head appendages of male fowls. Each form is typical of a breed or variety. (A) Pea comb. (B) One type of walnut comb. (C) Types of single comb. (D) Rose comb. (E) Crest. (F) Y comb. (*After Robinson*)

genotype but also by environmental factors such as the quality of the soil, the amount of moisture, heat, and light, and the quality and quantity of the fertilizer or food supplied. It is evidently important to know whether a difference in yield observed between several samples of seed planted in experimental plots is predominantly genotypic or environmental. Out of this practical need, there has developed a whole branch of agricultural science which devises experimental procedures whereby the relative influence of genotypic and environmental factors can be ascertained. One of these procedures consists in making replicated plantings that reduce the environmental disturbances.

As stated above, phenotypic differences between individuals that have developed in sim-

Fig. 2.2. Extreme size variations in horses. The Clydesdale stallion Kuroki, weight 2,200 pounds, and a Shetland pony foal, weight 21 pounds. (*Courtesy of Iowa State College*)

Fig. 2.2. Extreme size variations in horses. The Clydesdale stallion Kuroki, weight 2,200 pounds, and a Shetland pony foal, weight 21 pounds. (*Courtesy of Iowa State College*)

ilar environments can be ascribed to differences in genotypes. Figures 2.1 and 2.2 represent some varieties of poultry and of horses. The differences between these varieties are mainly genotypic, since they appear in individuals raised under similar conditions.

CLONES, PURE LINES, AND INBRED LINES

Two conditions must be fulfilled in studies on the interactions of heredity and environment. First, the environment must be controlled; experimental animals or plants must be raised under similar conditions or under conditions that differ in known ways. Second, the genotype of the experimental organisms must be controlled; it is necessary to have a supply of individuals with similar genotypes, or with genotypes differing in known ways.

Strictly speaking, neither of these conditions can be fully satisfied in practice. The environment can be made reasonably, but never absolutely, uniform, by raising the experimental animals or plants in incubators or in constant-temperature rooms and in uni-

form soil and by treating them uniformly. Some environmental diversity unavoidably slips in. The most satisfactory control of the genotype is possible in organisms that reproduce asexually by simple fission or by buds, runners, stolons, etc. The progeny of a single individual obtained asexually is known as a *clone*. Members of a clone have the same genotype unless mutation (see Chap. 16) intervenes. For example, clones of bacteria can be obtained by isolating single bacterial cells and permitting them to grow and divide on suitable nutrient media. Some varieties of fruit trees (for example, many varieties of oranges) are clones propagated for many generations by grafting buds of a single original tree.

Some organisms that reproduce sexually are capable of self-fertilization, or selfing—that is, of producing progeny by fertilization of female gametes by male gametes of the same individual. Of course, self-fertilization is possible only in hermaphrodites, in which the same body carries organs of both sexes. This is, however, a common condition in many groups of plants and in some animals.

Most cultivated wheats, oats, barleys, beans, peas, tomatoes, etc., reproduce chiefly by self-fertilization. Selfing also occurs among animals, for example, in some fresh-water snails. The progeny of a single individual obtained by selfing is called a *pure line*. Members of a pure line do not necessarily have identical genotypes, but the genotypic uniformity among them is likely to be greater than in progeny obtained by cross-fertilization of different individuals.

In many organisms neither asexual reproduction nor selfing is possible, and consequently neither clones nor pure lines can be obtained. In such organisms, resort is had to inbreeding, that is, to mating of close relatives, such as brothers and sisters. After some generations of inbreeding, *inbred lines* are obtained in which the genotypic uniformity is greater than it was in the initial crossbred population. Inbred lines are important both in scientific experiments and in agricultural practice. One can measure the effects of environmental factors, such as amount and kind of fertilizer and type of soil in crop plants, by growing members of an inbred line under different conditions. In laboratory animals such as mice, rats, and guinea pigs, the existence of inbred lines is useful for the measurement of the effects of nutrition, sensitivity to disease, effects of drugs, etc.

EXPERIMENTS ON RACES OF PLANTS FROM DIFFERENT ENVIRONMENTS

Very instructive experiments on genotypic and environmental variations among plants have been made in California by Clausen, Keck, and Hiesey. It has been known for a long time that representatives of a plant species which grow in different habitats, especially at different elevations in mountains, may be very different in phenotype. For example, a species of cinquefoil, *Potentilla glandulosa*, which grows wild at about sea level on the coast of California (see the plant at the extreme left in the bottom row in Fig.

2.3), has a rather long stem and large leaves and takes some two hundred days to reach the flowering stage. At about four thousand to five thousand feet above sea level in the Sierra Nevada, a much taller and more slender form is found which requires only 50 to 60 days to reach the flowering stage in its native habitat (see the second plant from the left in the middle row in Fig. 2.3). Finally, at about ten thousand feet elevation, in the Alpine Zone of the Sierra Nevada, there grows a dwarf plant, which in its native habitat takes about fifty-five days to flower (see the first plant from the right in the top row in Fig. 2.3). The environments in the native habitats of these plants are very different indeed: at sea level, winters are so mild that the plants have little or no winter dormancy; at mid-elevation, winters are cold, but summers are warm; and in the Alpine Zone winters are long and severe, and summers very short and cool. To what extent, then, can the differences between the plants that are native in these habitats be ascribed to genotype and to environment?

To answer this question, the plants collected in several localities were each cut into three parts and the parts were replanted in three experimental gardens: at about sea level (Stanford), at 4,600 feet (Mather), and at 10,000 feet (Timberline). The division of the same plant ensures that each part will have the same genotype. The results of this experiment are shown in Figure 2.3. The vertical rows show the plants native to different habitats but grown together in the same experimental garden. The differences between the plants in the vertical rows are, accordingly, genotypic. The horizontal rows show how the same plant behaves in different environments; these differences are environmental.

NORM OF REACTION

The plants shown in the horizontal rows in Figure 2.3 are members of a clone, since they were obtained by dividing a single

Fig. 2.3. Three different races of *Potentilla glandulosa* grown in different environments. The differences among the plants in the same vertical column are genotypic and are due to adaptation of their ancestors to different altitudes. The differences among the plants in the same horizontal row represent responses of the same genotype to different environments. (*Courtesy of Clausen, Keck, and Hiesey*)

individual and replanting the parts in different places. It follows that these plants are genotypically identical or very similar. And yet it can be seen that these plants with uniform heredity look very different when grown in different environments. The same genotype reacts to different environments from the interplay between a given genotype and various environments in which this genotype may live constitute the *norm,* or *range, of reaction* of that genotype. It is evident that we never know the entire norm of reaction of any genotype. Indeed, to know it we would have to expose different individuals

Fig. 2.4. The effect of amount of light on flowering time in chrysanthemums of the variety Cordova. The plant at the left received no extra light. Each of the three plants at the right received one hour extra light at midnight from a 100-watt bulb; of these three, the plant at the left received light from September 25, the center plant from October 9, the right one from October 23. Extra light has delayed the flowering time. (*Courtesy U. S. Department of Agriculture*)

in different ways, so that the plants develop differently and acquire different phenotypes. The small size of the plant shown on the right in the middle row in Figure 2.3 is simply a different response of the same genotype which in another environment reacts to produce the tall and strong plant in the middle of the same row.

The diverse phenotypes that may arise with this genotype to all environments and to study the resulting phenotypes. This is impossible, because the number of environments is infinite. Thus, to know the entire norm of reaction, or the range of potentialities, of a human genotype, one would have to observe persons with this genotype leading all the lives possible to human beings.

Nevertheless, it is very important to know, particularly in man and in agricultural animals and plants, how a given genotype will respond to certain environments which actually exist or which can be created. One can measure the effects of factors such as amount and kind of fertilizer and type of soil on crop plants by growing these plants under different conditions. Plants grown in poor soil may be quite different in height, number of leaves, and yield of fruit and seed from plants grown in rich soil. Thus sweet

tern of black feet, ears, and tail and white body are transmitted faithfully to the descendants. If fur is plucked from the white parts and the animal is kept in a cold place while the fur is growing in again, the new fur comes in black rather than white. On the other hand, if fur is plucked from the black parts and the part is kept warm—by a bandage, for example—the new hair comes in white rather than black. It appears at first that the black-and-white pattern is itself inherited, but the experiment shows that what

Fig. 2.5. The effect of temperature on hair color in the Himalayan rabbit. The white hair on a small area of the back of this rabbit was pulled out and the animal was then put in a cold room. The hair that grew in under cold conditions was black. Hair in this region which grows under warm conditions is white. (*After Laura Kaufman*)

potatoes grown in soil rich in potassium are round and fleshy, but when this element is scarce they become long and spindling. In the same way, the precise ration fed to a steer, a cow, or a laying hen makes a great deal of difference in the number of pounds of beef, quarts of milk, or dozens of eggs produced. So powerful may be the effects of environment on characters of this sort that much attention is given in agricultural practice to manipulation of factors such as feed, fertilizers, water, temperature, time of planting, time of breeding, etc., in order that the most desirable phenotypes shall be evoked from a given norm of reaction (Fig. 2.4).

Some potentialities of a genotype in rare or artificial environments may be quite unsuspected until they are discovered more or less accidentally. Thus in rabbits there is a true-breeding variety known as Himalayan (Fig. 2.5) in which the pink eyes and the pat-

is really inherited is the ability of certain parts to form pigment or not to form it, depending on the particular temperature obtaining in that part at a specific time. More generally, any character is a result both of heredity and of environment. Any phenotype, healthy or pathological, arising under the influence of any environment found in nature or created artificially by man, is necessarily within the range of reaction of the genotype that produces it.

INDIVIDUAL ADAPTATION AND HOMEOSTASIS

A biologically highly significant fact is disclosed by studying the norms of reaction of plants and animals. Many of the reactions of the body to its environments are not haphazard but are *adaptive,* that is, such as to promote health, survival, and reproduction. This apparent "wisdom of the body" is usually observed when carriers of normal, healthy genotypes respond to environments in which representatives of their species normally live. When a genotype fails to respond adaptively to normal environments, this genotype is said to cause a hereditary disease.

Adaptive reactions are of many kinds. Physiological *homeostatic* reactions enable life processes to go on undisturbed despite environmental shocks that tend to upset them. In man, death results if the body temperature is allowed to rise or fall by more than a few degrees above or below normal. However, such dangerous variations do not usually occur, even though the body is exposed to high or to low external temperatures. In hot weather the skin is covered with sweat, the evaporation of which helps to cool it; the blood vessels in the skin become dilated and facilitate the dissipation of heat. In cool environments, the loss of heat through the skin is, on the contrary, minimized. Another example of physiological homeostasis is maintenance of constant osmotic pressure and of constant pH concentration in the blood. This is due to the marvelously precise functioning of the kidneys and to the presence in the blood of "buffering" substances that prevents it from becoming either too acid or too alkaline.

The development of an organism in different environments may follow different paths but such paths that the resulting phenotypes are fit to survive and to reproduce in the respective environments. This is called *developmental homeostasis,* or *canalization of development.* For example, in many insects the size of the adult body greatly depends on the amount of food available to the larvae. When food is scarce, the insect may still survive but develops into a dwarf compared to one grown on abundant food. In man and other animals, bone fractures heal in such ways that the resulting bones support the mechanical stresses to which they are exposed. When one of the kidneys is incapacitated by disease or removed by a surgical operation, the second kidney increases

in size to perform the function of both. Muscles that are extensively used grow larger and stronger; those that are seldom used become smaller and weaker. The organism that has suffered but recovered from certain infectious diseases becomes immune, temporarily or permanently, to new infection with the same disease.

Physiological homeostasis is not sharply distinct from developmental homeostasis, and situations intermediate between the two are common. A good example is the number of red blood corpuscles per unit volume of blood, which gradually increases in persons who come to live and work at higher elevations and diminishes when these persons return to lower elevations or to sea level (Table 2.1). Greater numbers of red corpuscles make the transport of oxygen to the body tissues more efficient; this is of importance when the oxygen pressures are low. It is obviously important in the acclimatization of men or of animals for living and working at high altitudes.

TABLE 2.1
The number of red blood corpuscles per cubic millimeter of blood in men living at different elevations above sea level (*After Houssay*)

Elevation (meters)	Erythrocytes (millions)
0	4.25
1300	5.2
2400	6.0
3100	6.6
3700	6.8
4100	7.5
4800	7.8
5600	8.3

ADAPTEDNESS AND GENOTYPIC VARIATION

It is important to realize that homeostasis and all other forms of adaptedness are conditioned by the genotype, but that the "wisdom of the body" is neither a necessary and inherent property of every development pattern, nor is it manifested in every environment. When exposed to sunlight or to ultraviolet light of certain wave lengths, most white persons react by developing a protective tan coloration. The tan prevents dangerous burns that result from too sudden or too prolonged exposure of unadapted skin. When the skin is protected from exposure to sun, the tan gradually disappears. However, people of races native to the tropical zones mostly have permanently dark skins regardless of sun exposure. Still other people, albinos, fail to develop the pigment even after exposure and lack this protection against sunburn.

By and large, environmental characteristics that a species or race frequently meets in its normal habitat evoke adaptive reactions; rare and unusual environments often fail to do so. Human skin is injured by very high intensities of ultraviolet light, which are produced artificially but do not occur in nature; and it has no protection against X rays and radium rays. Until recently, these rays were encountered by the human species only in very low intensities. Species of animals that feed on snakes are immune to snake venoms that are fatal to other species. Many tropical plants are killed by frosts easily withstood by plants native to cold countries.

HEREDITARY DISEASE

At this point we may inquire, what is a hereditary disease? To a man in the street, a hereditary disease is an inborn and incurable taint, a scourge against which there is no appeal and no relief. This notion arises from a confusion of the genotype with its manifestation in the phenotype. True enough, there is no known way of changing one's genotype in a desired direction, and hence no way of removing the genotypic basis of a hereditary disease. But health and disease are, after all, conditions of the phenotype, not of the genotype. Since the phenotype is always a product of a heredity as well as of

an environment, it is modifiable by either. The distinction between a hereditary and a nonhereditary disease, like the more general distinction between hereditary and nonhereditary characters of any kind, is more subtle.

Some infectious diseases, such as malaria, measles, and syphilis, are said to be nonhereditary, since all men are more or less susceptible to them and it depends chiefly on the environment whether one gets them or not. But these diseases develop only in man and a few other animals. Only possessors of human genotypes contract malaria, and not all human genotypes are equally susceptible.

Consider now two rather rare human traits, albinism and xeroderma pigmentosum. Albinos have little or no dark pigment in their skin, hair, or the irises of their eyes; when exposed to intense sunshine they may suffer dangerous sunburns. Xeroderma pigmentosum is a more serious condition; when exposed to the sun, persons with this gene become strongly freckled; these freckles are so sensitive that they may, in extreme cases, develop into skin cancers. Both albinism and xeroderma pigmentosum are clearly hereditary—the first is due to the presence in double dose of a recessive gene and the second to a dominant gene (see Chaps. 3 and 5). However, if albinos protect themselves from sunburn they suffer little inconvenience from their inherited peculiarity; and avoidance of light also permits persons with xeroderma pigmentosum to live a reasonably normal life. Obviously, they retain their inherited tendencies, but the "disease" as such is no longer there.

There is, then, no clear-cut distinction between hereditary and nonhereditary diseases. As a general rule it may be said that a "hereditary disease" is due to a more or less rare genotype that reacts to produce ill-adapted phenotypes in environments in which the common or normal genotypes give rise to healthy phenotypes. There are, of course, hereditary diseases for which no adequate environmental corrections (remedies) are yet known. But unless the relations of genotype and phenotype are recognized, attempts at amelioration will not have a rational basis.

The curability of a disease, whether hereditary or environmental, depends upon whether or not environments suitable for the afflicted persons can be devised. When a patient consults a physician, he wants a prescription for environmental conditions in which his phenotype will be satisfactory to himself and to others. Myopia, some forms of which are hereditary, can be corrected by wearing glasses, and glasses obviously come from the environment. But there are many hereditary eye diseases for which no adequate remedies are known, just as there are many incurable nonhereditary diseases. Diseases of the heart and the circulatory system are likely to develop in old age, when some homeostatic adjustments of the body are weakened. Changes in living habits and certain drugs may furnish environments in

which life is prolonged, or the disease may be incurable and lead to death.

PHENOCOPIES

To cure hereditary diseases, or, more generally, to obtain the best possible phenotypes on the basis of existing genotypes, we would need to know the norms of reaction of these genotypes. This is an unattainable ideal, but it is worth keeping in mind as a stimulus for scientific investigation. The norms of reaction of some genotypes contain striking and unexpected potentialities. The normal body color of the vinegar fly *Drosophila melanogaster* is light brown with black markings on the abdomen (Fig. 2.6). However, a hereditary variant of this fly, a mutant found by Morgan in 1910, has a yellow body color. For years the distinction between the normal and the yellow variant of the fly seemed unconditional—normal flies had brown bodies in all environments in which they were

Fig. 2.6. The vinegar fly, *Drosophila melanogaster*, male at left and female at right. (*After Bridges*)

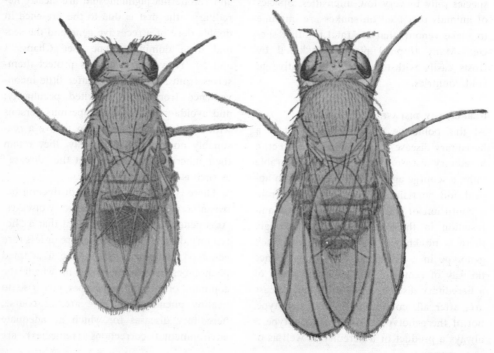

raised, and yellow flies had yellow bodies. Then in 1939 Rappoport found that when normal flies are raised as larvae on food containing silver salts, they develop into yellow flies. The yellow variant raised on silver-containing food also yields yellow flies. Thus a genotypically normal fly has the potentiality of developing a yellow phenotype when raised in a certain environment, namely, when given silver salts in its food.

The yellow-bodied but genotypically normal fly is a *phenocopy* of the yellow mutant. Regardless of how similar a phenocopy may be to the yellow mutant in body color, the two are easy to distinguish. The offspring of a phenocopy have the normal brown body color unless raised again on food containing silver salts; the offspring of the yellow mutant have yellow bodies. One can say that a woman with dark hair chemically bleached is a phenocopy of a blonde, but this condition is even more temporary. A phenocopy lasts no longer than the generation exposed to the inducing environment, and it may last an even shorter time. At any rate, what Rappoport discovered is simply a hitherto unknown potentiality of the norm of reaction of Drosophila flies; he did not discover a way of modifying their genotype.

We can now see clearly just what is needed to "cure" a hereditary disease: an environment must be found which makes an abnormal, aberrant genotype produce a phenocopy of a normal, healthy phenotype. Of course, such environments are rare, but in principle at least, they may be discovered. Some forms of diabetes mellitus in man are conditioned by heredity. The disease involves a grave disturbance of the metabolism of sugars, which in the ill persons are excreted in large amounts in the urine. No reliable treatment of diabetes mellitus was known until it was discovered that the disturbance is due to the failure of the pancreas gland of the diabetic to produce adequate amounts of the hormone insulin. Once this became known, it was a logical step to supply the insulin to the diabetics by injection of pancreas extracts obtained from animals.

A diabetic is cured as long as he receives proper doses of insulin at proper intervals. Similarly, a myopic is cured as long as he wears proper eyeglasses. Neither of them is, however, cured in the absolute sense, since to exhibit a normal phenotype they need special environments—insulin in the case of diabetics, eyeglasses in that of myopics—which the carriers of other "normal" genotypes do not require.

It is evident that "normal" and "abnormal" are relative terms. Normal genotypes and normal phenotypes are simply those that occur frequently among the representatives of a given animal or plant species. The noteworthy thing about them, however, is that they show homeostatic responses to the range of environments that the species usually encounters and are well adapted to live and to reproduce in these environments. This adaptedness is a result of an age-long process of selection of fit genotypes in the course of evolution, as we shall see in Chapter 20.

WHAT CHARACTERS OR TRAITS ARE HEREDITARY?

The question is frequently asked whether a given trait or characteristic of man or of some other species is hereditary or environmental. We can now see how misleading such an alternative may be. Is skin color or toothache hereditary or environmental? Obviously the body must have a skin to have a color in it and must have teeth that may become diseased and ache. Skin and teeth arise in the process of development, which is controlled by genes. However, development is influenced also by the environment, on which skin color and the health of the teeth depend in part. There is simply no hard-and-fast distinction between hereditary and environmental traits; all characteristics are really both.

The question must be stated differently to make it meaningfully answerable. To what extent is the *difference* between the skin colors of persons A and B or between the conditions of the teeth in persons M and N due to their genotypes, and to what extent has it been caused by the environments in which these persons live? No character or trait is inherited ready-made; all of them arise in the process of development of the individual. It is when we observe that different individuals have developed differently

that the question of the relative roles of heredity and environment legitimately arises. As we have seen, this question can be answered most reliably by observing the development of individuals with similar or with different genotypes in uniform environments or in environments differing in known respects. In the special case of man, where such experiments are rarely possible, indirect methods have to be used, as we shall see in Chapter 11.

QUESTIONS FOR DISCUSSION

2.1 Drosophila larvae that have plenty of food and grow at moderately low temperatures develop into larger flies than do similar larvae that grow at high temperatures and on a semistarvation diet. The fly species *Drosophilia miranda* is larger than *D. pseudo-obscura* if the larvae develop at the same temperature and with plenty of food. But *D. miranda* developed at a high temperature and with little food is smaller in body size than *D. pseudoobscura* grown at a lower temperature and with abundant food. Is body size a hereditary trait in these flies?

2.2 What experimental procedure can you suggest to test whether two strains of Drosophila flies (or of any other organism) are genotypically different in body size?

2.3 How could the problem in Question 2.2 be studied in animals such as man, which cannot be subjected to breeding experiments?

2.4 Some races of teasel have spirally twisted stalks if grown in rich soil but normal straight ones if grown in poor soil. How does a normal plant from such a race differ genetically from a normal plant of a race that never shows twisting?

2.5 The chestnut-bark fungus, introduced some years ago into the United States, has exterminated the native American chestnut trees over a wide area. The species of chestnut that grow in China, the native home of this fungus, are almost immune to its at-

tack. How do you explain this difference between American and Chinese chestnut trees?

2.6 The usual method of propagating some important crop plants, e.g., potatoes, is by cuttings of tubers. What methods of crop improvement would be useful with such plants?

2.7 What lessons for crop-improvement programs can be derived from the experiments with cinquefoil described on p. 22?

2.8 How would you set about determining parts of the norm of reaction of a human genotype in respect to (a) musical ability; (b) mathematical ability?

2.9 What do you think might be the importance for medical practice of a clear understanding of the norm-of-reaction concept?

2.10 What are some of the advantages and limitations of the use of inbred lines of laboratory animals in testing (a) susceptibility to cancer; (b) value of particular nutritional factors; (c) learning ability?

2.11 If inbred lines cannot be obtained—as in man, for example—how would you ensure comparability of organisms subjected to different environments?

2.12 If, as stated on page 25, what is inherited in the case of the Himalayan rabbit is the ability (in a certain range of environments) to form or not to form pigment in certain parts, what do you think may explain the differing abilities of the different parts, as in the ears compared to the trunk?

2.13 Do you think that ability to adjust to high altitudes by producing more red blood cells is an inherited or an acquired character? Criticize the question.

2.14 Give some arguments for and against the view that tuberculosis is a hereditary disease.

2.15 Why may members of the same pure line "not necessarily have identical genotypes"?

MENDEL'S LAW OF SEGREGATION

THE CHIEF CONCLUSION to be drawn from the previous chapters is that the appearance, structure, physiology, and behavior of any plant or animal—in short, the characteristics that make up its phenotype—are determined by the interaction of its genotype with the environment. It is now logical to inquire into the nature and composition of the genotype, which plays such a fundamental role in the phenomena of life. Before Mendel's time, heredity was supposed to be transmitted as though it were a miscible fluid, like blood in animals and man. The "bloods" of the parents were assumed to mix or fuse in the offspring. Attribution of such properties to blood survived in such expressions as "pure-blooded" and "half-blooded" even after it had become clear that blood as such has nothing to do with fertilization or heredity.

Mendel provided the first proof for a theory that explained heredity by the transmission of units in the reproductive cells and thus put an end to vague notions such as those concerning "bloods." The genotypes

of all organisms, according to this theory, consist of genes. Because of the universal applicability of this theory throughout the range of life from viruses to man, the gene may be regarded as the fundamental unit of life. Genes in biology are to this extent comparable with other structural units of matter, such as molecules and atoms.

Historically the first and still the most conclusive evidence for the existence of genes comes from the phenomena of segregation of traits observed in the offspring of hybrids between individuals or strains that differ in some recognizable respect. The principle of segregation was formulated by Gregor Mendel in 1866 under such peculiar circumstances that the scientific world failed to recognize or to appreciate it until after a lapse of 34 years. In the first place, Gregor Mendel was not primarily a biologist but a monk in the Augustinian monastery at Brünn, Austria (now Brno, Czechoslovakia) (Fig. 3.1). He had come as a poor boy to the monastery in 1843, was ordained priest in 1847, and in 1851 was sent by his order to study natural science at the University in Vienna. He did not make a brilliant record in physics or mathematics, but when he returned to Brünn as substitute teacher of science in 1854, he gave evidence of those qualities of mind which mark great scientists.

In 1857 he began to collect the varieties of the garden pea which seedsmen offered for sale and to study the differences among

Fig. 3.1. Gregor Mendel (1822–1884), the founder of genetics. From the painting by Flatter. (*Courtesy of Hugo Iltis*)

them. After seven years of experimental work in the monastery gardens, he presented the results of his experiments, together with the generalizations we now know as "Mendel's laws," at two meetings of the Natural History Society of Brünn (Naturforschender Verein) in the spring of 1865. The results and the theory were printed in the annual proceedings of the society, which appeared and were distributed to libraries in Europe and America in 1866. (For an English translation of this paper, see the Appendix.)

It is safe to say that no one who heard Mendel's paper and no one who read it in the nineteenth century appreciated its significance, for it lay neglected until 1900, when the law of segregation was rediscovered almost simultaneously by three different investigators, who had obtained results like Mendel's. These three—De Vries in Holland, Correns in Germany, and Tschermak in Austria—found Mendel's forgotten paper and proclaimed its importance. Immediately his conclusions began to be confirmed and extended by experiments carried on in various parts of the world on many kinds of animals and plants. In his later years, Mendel turned to experiments with other plants and with bees and to meteorological observations, but gradually he became more and more concerned with the administration of the monastery, of which he had become abbot in 1868. He died in 1884, long before his scientific work came into its own.

MENDEL'S METHODS

In order to understand Mendel's work we must examine his methods. Other investigators had made hybridization experiments with plants, and Mendel was familiar with the work of his predecessors. The reason why it remained for Mendel to discover the laws now bearing his name lies in his wise choice of material and methods of study.

Mendel avoided the complexities that had troubled the earlier students by simplifying the problem as far as possible. When plants of different species or varieties are crossed, great variability appears in the progeny, as is apparent also from breeding mongrel animals. However, the early investigators made observations upon the plant or animal as a whole, studying at once all the traits and structures in which hybrids differed from the parents and from each other. Mendel confined his attention to a single character at a time (Fig. 3.2)—flower color, for example. When the behavior of each single trait was established, he then studied two traits together, such as flower color and vine height.

Moreover, he counted the numbers of each type of progeny which resulted from the cross, thus reducing the phenomena of inheritance to a measurable, quantitative basis.

The garden pea proved to be a very satisfactory subject for experiments on hybridization. Its flowers are so constructed that pollen from a flower normally falls on the stigma of the same flower and thus effects self-fertilization. Mendel could open a flower bud and remove the stamens before any pollen had been shed, thus preventing self-pollination. He could then place on the stigma of this "castrated" flower pollen from the plant which he wished to use as the other parent in a cross. The artificially fertilized flowers were guarded against contamination by pollen of unknown origin by preventing the access of insects to these flowers. If he wished to observe the second hybrid generation following the cross, he had only to allow the flowers to fertilize themselves normally.

Mendel's procedure was to cross two plants differing in a pair of contrasted characters and to observe the appearance of the first hybrid, or "F_1," generation.[1] He then crossed hybrid plants together (or allowed them to effect self-fertilization) and raised a second generation, or F_2. In the F_2 offspring he counted the numbers of plants possessing each of the contrasted traits, such as different flower colors, seed colors, or vine lengths, in which the parents (P_1 generation) differed. Most important of all, from a study of such comparatively simple data he formulated working hypotheses, or theoretical explanations of the events he observed. The validity of these hypothetical explanations was tested by further experiments, first by Mendel himself and later by other experimenters using other plants and animals. Mendel's theoretical explanations

---

[1] The parental generation is technically known as the P_1, the first generation following a cross as the F_1 (first filial generation), the second as the F_2, and so on.

of his results are now firmly established as Mendel's laws of inheritance. These include two major principles of segregation and independent assortment of genes, together with some less fundamental generalizations such as that concerning the dominance and recessiveness of traits in the hybrids. Mendel's paper (see the Appendix) should be consulted in the original to appreciate fully the clarity and force of his reasoning. It is a true classic of the methodology of experimental science.

DOMINANCE

When Mendel crossed a true-breeding red-flowered plant with a true-breeding white-flowered one, the progeny was found to resemble the red-flowered parent (Fig. 3.2). The whiteness seemed to be suppressed and the redness to dominate. Mendel therefore called such traits as redness of flowers *dominant* and their alternatives, such as whiteness, *recessive*. All the seven characters in peas studied by Mendel behaved in this way, one of each pair of contrasting traits appearing to be dominant and the other recessive. Thus the round form of seed was found to be dominant over the wrinkled; the yellow color of the cotyledons over the green; the inflated form of pod over the constricted; the green color of the unripe pods over the yellow; the axillary position of the flowers and pods over the terminal; and the tall-vine habit over the dwarf.

Later investigators have found many other characters that show similarly complete or practically complete dominance. In very many other cases, however, dominance is absent, and the hybrid individuals resemble neither parent exactly but are more or less intermediate between the two. In the snapdragon, for example, a crimson plant crossed with a white one gives first-generation hybrids that are all pink in flower color (Fig. 3.3). In the same way a black Andalusian fowl bred with a splashed white one produces offspring with "blue" plumage (Fig.

3.4); and in Shorthorn cattle the cross of red coat with white gives "roan" offspring, their coats consisting of a mixture of red and white hairs. In other instances the hybrid offspring may resemble one parent much

type, microscopic examination reveals two kinds of starch grains in them, one kind representing the effect of the wrinkled parent. There may thus be all stages between complete dominance and the absence of domi-

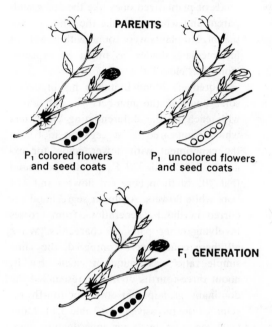

PARENTS

P₁ colored flowers and seed coats

P₁ uncolored flowers and seed coats

F₁ GENERATION

Fig. 3.2. Outcome of one of Mendel's first experiments. Colored flowers, colored spots in leaf axils, and colored seed coats constitute one "differentiating character" as contrasted with the colorless conditions. This character is inherited as a unit. (*After Iltis*)

F₂ GENERATION

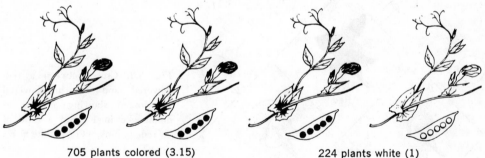

705 plants colored (3.15)

3

224 plants white (1)

1

more closely than the other but may not resemble it exactly, so that dominance is incomplete.

In one of the pairs of contrasted traits studied by Mendel, round versus wrinkled seeds, later investigators have found that although the F₁ seeds from the cross of round with wrinkled are round in external pheno-

nance; and these various conditions may all be found among the different traits of a single individual. The rule that holds regardless of whether dominance is or is not complete is, however, this: provided that the parents belong to true-breeding varieties, the first generation (F₁) hybrids are all uniform with respect to the trait in question.

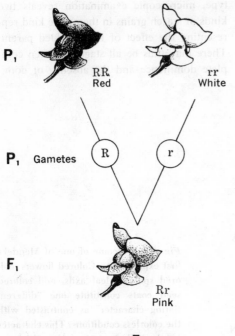

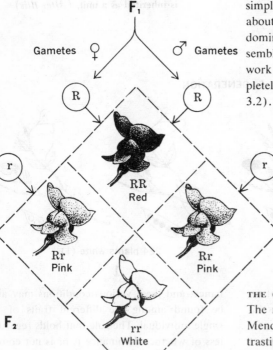

In contrast to the uniformity of the first-generation hybrids, the second generation, produced by self-fertilization of the F_1 red-flowered plants, consisted of two different kinds of plants: red ones like the red grandparent and white ones like the white grandparent. No plants were found with flowers of intermediate shades, as might be expected from the "blood" theory.

Moreover, Mendel, unlike his predecessors, *counted* the numbers of individuals with each of the differentiating characters which reappeared by segregation in F_2. In the experiment with flower color, for example, he raised 929 F_2 plants and found that 705 of them bore red flowers and 224 bore white flowers. A similar segregation occurred in the F_2 generations from crosses involving other pairs of characters. When all these counts were compared, the same simple ratio was found in each—that is, about three-fourths of the F_2 resembled the dominant grandparent and one-fourth resembled the recessive one (Table 3.1). Later work on peas by other investigators completely confirmed Mendel's results (Table 3.2).

Fig. 3.3. Cross between a red-flowered and a white-flowered snapdragon showing absence of dominance in F_1 and a ratio of $\frac{1}{4}$ red, $\frac{1}{2}$ pink, and $\frac{1}{4}$ white in F_2.

THE GENE HYPOTHESIS
The results observed in his experiments led Mendel to the following hypothesis. Contrasting characters, such as the red and the white flower colors in peas, are determined by something that is transmitted from parents to offspring in the sex cells, or gametes. This "something" is now called a *gene*. The

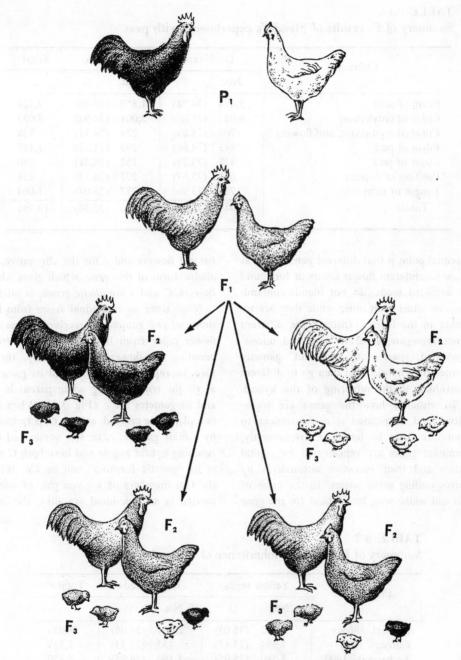

Fig. 3.4. **The inheritance of plumage color in Andalusian fowls.
Crosses of black with white produce only blue-gray progeny in
F₁. These, when bred together, produce in F₂: ¼ black, which
breed true; ½ blue, which breed like the F₁ blue-grays; ¼
white, which breed true.**

TABLE 3.1

Summary of F$_2$ results of Mendel's experiments with peas

Character	Dominant		Recessive		Total
	No.	%	No.	%	
Form of seed	5,474	(74.74)	1,850	(25.26)	7,324
Color of cotyledons	6,022	(75.06)	2,001	(24.94)	8,023
Color of seed coats, and flowers	705	(75.89)	224	(24.11)	929
Form of pod	882	(74.68)	299	(25.32)	1,181
Color of pod	428	(73.79)	152	(26.21)	580
Position of flowers	651	(75.87)	207	(24.13)	858
Length of stem	787	(73.96)	277	(26.04)	1,064
Totals	14,949	(74.90)	5,010	(25.10)	19,959

essential point is that different genes, such as those for different flower colors or for round or wrinkled seeds, do not blend, contaminate, or affect each other while they are together in the hybrid. Instead, the different genes *segregate*, separate pure and uncontaminated, pass into different gametes formed by a hybrid, and then go to different individuals in the offspring of the hybrid.

To visualize how the genes are transmitted and distributed it is convenient to symbolize them by letters. Conventionally, dominant genes are represented by capital letters and their recessive alternatives by corresponding small letters. In the cross of red and white peas, let *C* stand for the gene

for red flowers and *c* for the alternative, or allelic, form of this gene, which gives white flowers. *C* and *c* are *allelic* genes, or *alleles*.

Now, since an individual arises from the union of two gametes, it receives a gene for flower color from both parents. The true-breeding red-flowered parent may, therefore, be represented as *CC* and its gametes as *C;* the true-breeding white parent is *cc*, and its gametes are *c* (Fig. 3.5). When the two plants are crossed, an egg, *C*, is fertilized by a male gamete, *c*, or vice versa; and the resulting hybrid zygote will have both *C* and *c;* its "genetic formula" will be *Cc*. When the two members of a given pair of alleles carried in an individual are alike, the indi-

TABLE 3.2

Summary of F$_2$ results in inheritance of seed color in peas

Investigator	Yellow seeds		Green seeds		Total
	No.	%	No.	%	
Mendel, 1865	6,022	(75.05)	2,001	(24.95)	8,023
Correns, 1900	1,394	(75.47)	453	(24.53)	1,847
Tschermak, 1900	3,580	(75.05)	1,190	(24.95)	4,770
Hurst, 1904	1,310	(74.64)	445	(25.36)	1,755
Bateson, 1905	11,902	(75.30)	3,903	(24.70)	15,806
Lock, 1905	1,438	(73.67)	514	(26.33)	1,952
Darbishire, 1909	109,060	(75.09)	36,186	(24.91)	145,246
Totals	134,706	(75.09)	44,692	(24.91)	179,399

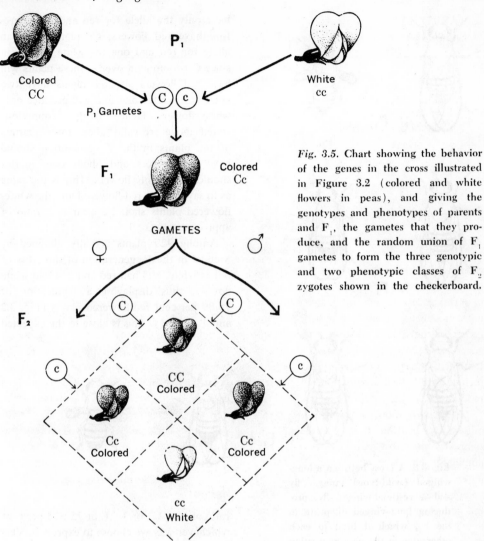

Fig. 3.5. Chart showing the behavior of the genes in the cross illustrated in Figure 3.2 (colored and white flowers in peas), and giving the genotypes and phenotypes of parents and F_1, the gametes that they produce, and the random union of F_1 gametes to form the three genotypic and two phenotypic classes of F_2 zygotes shown in the checkerboard.

vidual is said to be a *homozygote;* the true-breeding red (*CC*) and white (*cc*) plants are homozygotes. When the two members of an allelic pair are unlike, the individual is a *heterozygote*. The red-flowered plants obtained by Mendel in the F_1 generation (*Cc*) were heterozygotes; they were red because the allele *C* is dominant over *c*.

MENDELIAN RATIOS

According to the principle of segregation, the two alleles borne in the heterozygous *Cc*

plants do not fuse, blend, or contaminate each other, despite the fact that the phenotype of this hybrid shows only the red flower color and fails to give any visible indication of the presence of the gene *c* in the genotype. These alleles segregate when the hybrid organism forms its gametes, so that approximately half the gametes will carry *C* and the other half *c*. Let us assume that in fertilization the gametes combine at random, so that there is no preference for or avoidance of unions of gametes that contain

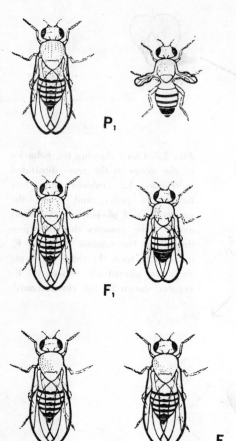

P₁

F₁

F₂

Fig. 3.6. A cross between a long-winged (wild-type) vinegar fly and a vestigial-winged fly, producing long-winged offspring in the F₁, which if bred to each other give in the next generation (F₂) ¾ long to ¼ vestigial. (*After Morgan*)

have only the allele for red and will therefore have red flowers; *Cc* plants have an allele for red and one for white color, but since *C* is dominant over *c*, these plants will have red flowers also; *cc* plants have two alleles for white color and will produce only white flowers. Hence, if the assumptions stated above are valid, about three-quarters of the plants in the F₂ generation should have red flowers and about one quarter should have white flowers. This is the same as to say that the red-flowered and the white-flowered plants should appear in a ratio of approximately 3 : 1.

Among 929 plants actually obtained by Mendel in the F₂ generation of the cross of red × white, 705 had red and 224 had white flowers, thus displaying a segregation of 75.89 per cent red-flowered plants (Fig. 3.2 and Table 3.1). This is close to the expected

like or unlike genes. Finally, let it be supposed that the plants of all genotypes, *CC, Cc,* and *cc,* are equally viable, so that the relative proportions of these plants grown from seeds are the same as the proportions formed at fertilization. Figure 3.5 shows the outcome of these assumptions. Since each of these four combinations is just as likely to occur as any of the others, each should give rise to approximately one-fourth of the progeny. The homozygous *CC* plants

ratio of ¾ : ¼, or 3 : 1, or 75 : 25 per cent whichever way we choose to express it. Very similar ratios were obtained by Mendel in crosses involving all the other characters studied. The actual counts that Mendel obtained in these various crosses are set forth in Table 3.1. In the crosses involving yellow seeds and green seeds, F₂ generations totaling 179,399 seeds have been recorded by other investigators (Table 3.2). Among these seeds, 134,707, or 75.09 per cent, were yellow and 44,692, or 24.91 per cent, were green. Other examples of this Mendelian ratio are shown in Figure 3.6.

Of course, the results of breeding experiments are not exact ratios any more than the results of the tossing of coins or throwing of dice are always exactly the same; and the reason in each case is the same. It must not be expected, for example, that with every three red-flowered plants there will always be associated one plant with white flowers, any more than that in tossing coins heads will invariably alternate with tails. The ratio 3 : 1 and other Mendelian ratios merely indicate the expectation on the basis of probability. And indeed, the larger the number of individuals raised, the closer the ratios observed tend to approach the ideal ones (Table 3.2). Chapter 29 describes methods for testing whether departures from exact 3 : 1 and other ratios are too great to have occurred by chance.

TESTING THE VALIDITY OF THE GENE HYPOTHESIS

Mendel was not content to leave the matter here but applied further and very rigorous tests to his working hypothesis. Indeed, the virtue of his hypothesis lies precisely in that it permitted him to devise further experiments by means of which it could be confirmed or disproved.

In the F_2 of his cross of red-flowered to white-flowered peas, there were approximately 76 per cent of plants with red and 24 per cent with white flowers. The red and white phenotypes appeared in a ratio approaching 3 : 1. But Mendel's interpretation of these results, illustrated in the chart in Figure 3.5, requires that there be two kinds among the red-flowered F_2 plants. About one-third of them should be genotypically CC—that is, homozygous for the allele for red—and about two-thirds should be heterozygotes, Cc, carrying both the dominant allele C and the recessive c. The white-flowered plants should all be recessive homozygotes, cc. The validity of these predictions can be tested by experiments. The homozygous white-flowered plants should all breed true to white flower color through all subsequent generations if self-fertilized or crossed with each other. The red-flowered plants, however, although they look alike,

should not all behave in the same way. About one-third of them, namely those homozygous for C (hence having the genotypic formula CC, see Fig. 3.5) should breed true to red. But two-thirds of the reds, namely, the heterozygotes, Cc, should breed exactly like the F_1 hybrid plants, that is, they should produce red and white offspring in the ratio of about ¾ red : ¼ white. This is, indeed, what happened in the experiments.

The phenotypic segregation ratio in the F_2 of the cross of red to white is, therefore, ¾ red : ¼ white, but the genotypic ratio is ¼ homozygous red : $\frac{2}{4}$ heterozygous red : ¼ homozygous white (or ¼ CC : ½ Cc : ¼ cc, or 25 : 50 : 25 per cent). The difference between the visible and the actual ratios is due to dominance of C over c, which causes the same phenotype to develop from the CC and Cc genotypes. This has also been confirmed in actual experiments.

THE BACKCROSS RATIO

Another correct prediction made and verified by Mendel concerned the behavior of alleles in *backcrosses* or *test crosses*. Suppose that the red-flowered F_1 hybrid from the cross of red × white peas is crossed back with the recessive white-flowered parental variety. According to Mendel's theory, the red-flowered F_1 hybrid is a heterozygote Cc and the white-flowered parent is a homozygote cc. The gametes produced by a hybrid, a heterozygote, are always pure. A gamete may carry either the allele C or c but never a mixture of the two or a hybrid genotype. One-half of the gametes of a red-flowered heterozygous plant should, accordingly, carry C, and the other half should have c. The gametes of the recessive white-flowered plant are, of course, all c. Therefore, if the pollen from the hybrid is placed on the stigma of a white-flowered plant, or vice versa, about half the zygotes formed will be Cc and the other half will be cc. The progeny of this backcross must, if Mendel's theory is right, consist of heterozygous red-flowered (Cc) and of white-flowered (cc)

plants in about equal numbers. Mendel showed that this is actually what happens. Thousands of analogous test crosses made by Mendel's followers produced 1 : 1 ratios in the offspring.

SEGREGATION IN CROSSES WITHOUT DOMINANCE

As we have seen, dominance does not always occur, and many hybrids are intermediate in their phenotype between the parental varieties crossed. An example of this is the cross of red and white snapdragons (Fig. 3.3), which gives hybrids of an intermediate pink color. Have we here, then, a case of transmission of heredity by miscible bloods instead of by segregating genes? It can be demonstrated conclusively that genes are involved, because sharp segregation is observed among the hybrids in the F_2 and in backcross generations.

Figure 3.3 shows that the F_2 generation of the cross of red $\times$ white snapdragons contains individuals of three kinds. Some are red and some white like the parents, whereas some are pink like the F_1 hybrids. They appear with frequencies approaching the ratio ¼ red : ¾ pink : ¼ white. This is exactly what would be predicted on Mendel's theory. The alleles R and r produce red and white colors respectively; since neither allele is dominant, the heterozygote Rr is pink-flowered. A quarter of the F_2 offspring are, then, red homozygotes, RR, one-half pink heterozygotes, Rr, and a quarter white homozygotes, rr. Other examples of Mendelian segregation in crosses in which no dominance is observed are shown in Figure 3.4.

The validity of the gene hypothesis can be tested further. Suppose that pink snapdragons Rr are backcrossed to the red variety RR. We can predict that the offspring will consist of red- (RR) and pink- (Rr) flowered plants in about equal numbers (a ratio of 1 : 1). This is what is actually observed. Or, else, the pink (Rr) may be back-

crossed to the white (rr) variety. It can be predicted that pink- and white-flowered plants will appear with about equal frequency among the progeny. This prediction is also verified by experiments.

LACK OF RELATION BETWEEN DOMINANCE AND VIGOR

Here we may as well anticipate an error that beginners in genetics are prone to make. Dominance of a trait does not imply that its possessors are healthier or more vigorous than the recessives. There is no constant relation between dominance or recessiveness of a character and its usefulness or harmfulness. It will be shown later (Chap. 10) that many serious and fatal diseases in man and other organisms are inherited in accordance with Mendel's laws; some of these diseases are due to dominant genes, whereas the normal, healthy state is conditioned by the recessive alleles of these genes. Again, some diseases and malformations are due to homozygosis for recessive genes and the normal state to the corresponding dominants.

It should also be understood that dominant genes may be rare in populations and that recessives may occur frequently, or vice versa. There is no relation between dominance of a gene and its frequency, nor is there a tendency for a dominant to spread and to become more frequent with time, nor for a recessive to become rare. As will be shown in Chapter 18, a gene, dominant or recessive, may have any frequency, from very high to very low, and may conserve this frequency indefinitely. Suppose, for example, that in a population such as that of Norway most persons have blue eyes but some have brown eyes. It would not be legitimate to conclude that blue eye color is dominant to brown. In fact, the opposite happens to be the case. Furthermore, human populations range all the way from those in which blue-eyed persons are very numerous to those in which they do not occur at all.

PROBLEMS

NOTE: In peas, tall plant habit is dominant over dwarf.

3.1 If a plant homozygous for tall is crossed with one homozygous for dwarf, what will be the appearance of the F_1; of the F_2; of the offspring of a cross of F_1 with its tall parent; with its dwarf parent?

3.2 Let the allele for tall be represented by T and the allele for dwarfness by t. What will be the gametes produced by the parents and the height of the offspring (tall or dwarf) from each of the following crosses: $Tt \times tt$; $TT \times Tt$; $Tt \times Tt$?

3.3 A tall plant crossed with a dwarf one produces offspring of which about one-half are tall and one-half dwarf. What are the genotypes of the parents?

3.4 If the tall parent in Problem 3.3 is self-fertilized, what is the probability that the first offspring will be tall; that it will be dwarf?

3.5 A cross between a tall and a dwarf plant produces 20 offspring, all tall. What is the probability of this happening if the tall parent is TT; if it is Tt?

NOTE: In cattle, the polled, or hornless, condition, P, is dominant over the horned, p.

3.6 A certain polled bull is bred to three cows. With cow A, which is horned, a polled calf is produced; with cow B, also horned, a horned calf is produced; with cow C, which is polled, a horned calf is produced. What are the genotypes of the four parents, and what further offspring, in proportions, would you expect from these matings?

NOTE: In four-o'clock flowers, red flower color, R, is incompletely dominant over white, r, the heterozygous plants being pink-flowered.

3.7 In the following crosses, in which the genotypes of the parents are given, what are the gametes produced by each parent, and what will be the flower color of the offspring from each cross: $Rr \times RR$; $rr \times Rr$; $RR \times rr$; $Rr \times Rr$?

3.8 If a red-flowered four-o'clock plant is crossed with a white-flowered one, what will be the flower color of the F_1; of the F_2; of the offspring of a cross of the F_1 with its red parent; with its white parent?

3.9 How would you produce four-o'clock seeds *all* of which would yield pink-flowered plants when sown?

NOTE: In Andalusian fowls, the heterozygous condition of the alleles for black plumage (B) and white (b) is blue.

3.10 What offspring will a blue Andalusian fowl have if bred to birds of the following plumage colors: (a) black; (b) blue; (c) white?

NOTE: In poultry, rose comb is dominant over single comb.

3.11 A farmer believes that some of his rose-combed Wyandotte fowls may carry a factor for single comb. Can you suggest a method for finding out which fowls are heterozygous?

3.12 Two black female mice are crossed with a brown male. In several litters, female 1 produced 9 blacks and 7 browns; female 2 produced 57 blacks. What deductions can you make concerning inheritance of black and brown coat color in mice? What are the genotypes of the parents in this case?

3.13 Assume that in a particular species of plants, colored flowers are dominant over white ones and that (as in beans) the flowers are self-fertilized in nature. Assume that one heterozygous colored-flowered plant, Cc, becomes established on an island where no other individuals of this species exist and that its offspring thrive and multiply there in great numbers. Assume also that it is an annual plant and that thus there is no chance for members of one generation to cross with those of another and that white and colored plants are equal with respect to natural selection. What will the fifth generation of descendants look like as to flower color, in proportions?

3.14 Make the same assumptions as in Problem 3.13, except that the plant in question (like sunflowers and many other plants and animals) is self-sterile and must be crossed with another plant to set fertile seed; that two heterozygous plants, *Cc* and *Cc,* are the original invaders; and that the individuals of each generation breed freely together. What will the fifth generation of these plants look like as to flower color, in proportions?

NOTE: It is assumed at this point that the student has studied Chapter 29 in detail.

3.15 A certain population consists of 20 individuals of phenotype *A* and 10 of phenotype *aa* (e.g., albinos). Using a table of binomial distribution (cf. Table 29.2) test whether this result is compatible with a 3 : 1 ratio; with a 1 : 1 ratio.

3.16 Repeat Problem 3.15 using the chi-square method of Section 29.9, and compare with the results above.

3.17 Repeat Problem 3.15 using the normal-curve method of Section 29.29, and compare.

3.18 Repeat Problem 3.15 using Figure 29.2.

3.19 Out of the first 10 plants whose seeds were counted by Mendel (cf. p. 425, Appen-

dix), the one with the largest percentage of green seeds had 13 green and 24 yellow seeds. Does this differ significantly from 25 per cent green? How would the choice of this plant affect your interpretation of a significant result?

3.20 From a certain backcross, 1 colored-flowered and 9 white-flowered plants were observed. Using Formula 29.6, test the hypothesis that the true ratio in this cross is 1 : 1. Check your result by Figure 29.2 (Secs. 29.4 and 29.5).

3.21 Test the hypothesis of a 3 : 1 ratio for Mendel's data on color of cotyledons, form of pod, and color of pod (Table 3.1) by the chi-square method.

3.22 Obtain a confidence interval for the ratio of dominants to recessives in the pod-color experiment of Table 3.1, using Figure 29.2.

3.23 Using the combined data of Table 3.2, test the hypothesis of a ratio of 3 yellow : 1 green. Use the chi-square method and the normal approximation method and obtain approximate confidence interval .999 confidence coefficient by the method of Section 29.27 (also Sec. 29.29).

4 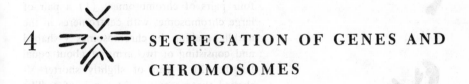 SEGREGATION OF GENES AND CHROMOSOMES

THE CONCLUSION that heredity is transmitted by the nuclei of egg and sperm cells had already been reached before the rediscovery of Mendel's work in 1900. It was derived from observations of the behavior of nuclei and chromosomes at cell division and at fertilization. As we have seen, Mendel showed that the hereditary materials consist of genes that segregate instead of "bloods" that mix. The chromosomes can be seen under a miscroscope, whereas the existence of genes is inferred from observation of the behavior of various traits in hybridization experiments. After 1900, it was quite natural to ask what the relation between the chromosomes and the genes is.

Indeed, this problem was faced and solved simultaneously and independently in 1902 by W. S. Sutton, at that time a graduate student at Columbia University, and by Theodor Boveri, the eminent German cytologist. Both reached the conclusion that the genes are contained in the chromosomes. Allelic genes in a heterozygote segregate because

the chromosomes that carry these genes segregate when the sex cells are being formed. The conclusion of Sutton and Boveri has been amply verified by further studies of geneticists and cytologists. To follow the reasoning leading to this conclusion, however, we need to review some facts that cytologists have discovered concerning the behavior of the chromosomes.

INDIVIDUALITY OF CHROMOSOMES

We have seen in Chapter 1 that the pioneer students of cell biology and fertilization discovered in the 1870s and 1880s that the nuclei of the sex cells that fuse at fertilization contain similar numbers of chromosomes. The nuclei of the gametes contain haploid (n) and those of the zygotes diploid ($2n$) numbers of chromosomes. Very soon van Beneden (1883), Boveri (1887), and others began to compare the sets of chromosomes in different cells in individuals of the same and of different species. It was found that within a species the chromosome num-

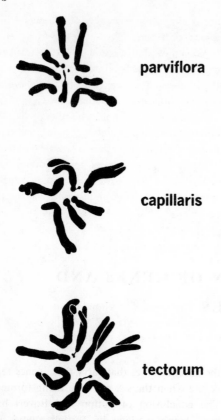

parviflora

capillaris

tectorum

Fig. 4.1. Diploid chromosome complements of Crepis, a plant of the family Compositae, showing chromosome individuality. (*After Hollingshead and Babcock*)

bers are, as a rule, constant in different cells and individuals (except, of course, that gametic nuclei contain only half as many chromosomes as zygotic nuclei). In distinct species, the chromosome numbers may be either similar or different. Moreover, it is important that in many organisms chromosomes in the same nucleus are visibly different in size and shape. Each kind of chromosome can be recognized in the nuclei of different cells and individuals of a species. This suggests at once that chromosomes in the nucleus are not merely different lumps of the same material; they are qualitatively distinct from each other.

For example, *Crepis capillaris* (a relative of the common dandelion) has in its nuclei

three pairs of recognizably different chromosomes. In the longest pair (Fig. 4.1), the *centromere,* the position of which is marked by a constriction, divides the body of the chromosome into two "arms," one of which is about three times as long as the other. Members of another pair of chromosomes are shorter and carry at one end a small stalked piece, or *satellite.* The third pair is the shortest, and the centromeres are near one of the ends, making this end look like a "knob."

Diploid cells of the fly *Drosophila melanogaster* (Fig. 4.2) contain the following four pairs of chromosomes: (1) a pair of large chromosomes with centromeres in the middle, making the chromosomes V-shaped and consisting of two arms of about equal length; (2) a pair of slightly shorter V-shaped chromosomes; (3) a pair of rodlike chromosomes with centromeres very near one of the ends; and (4) a pair of very short rodlike, or dotlike, chromosomes. In the diploid cells the corresponding (homologous) chromosomes, members of a pair, usually lie close together. This "somatic pairing" of chromosomes is characteristic of Drosophila and other flies; in most other organisms the homologous chromosomes in cells not undergoing meiosis lie at random with respect to each other in the nucleus. In the nuclei of the gametes of Drosophila there are, of course, only four chromosomes, one of each of the four kinds just described.

As we have seen, the diploid cells of the human body have been believed to contain 24 pairs of chromosomes, but recent observations suggest that there may be only 23 pairs. Some of the human chromosomes, at any rate, are individually recognizable because of their sizes and shapes. In Indian corn (maize) (Fig. 4.3), each of the 10 pairs of chromosomes can be identified by its length relative to the other chromosomes in the same nucleus, by the location of the centromeres, and by "secondary" constrictions in the body of the chromosome which make the latter resemble a series of beads (Figs. 4.4 and 4.5). Of course, the appearance of the chromosomes as seen under a microscope varies at different stages of cell division and also in different tissues; individual chromosomes can nevertheless be recognized in favorable materials despite these variations.

MEIOSIS

Very important information for understanding the transmission mechanism of hered-

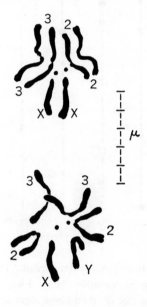

are dealing here with very fundamental biological processes.

We know that the nucleus of a fertilized egg (zygote) arises through the fusion of the nucleus of the egg with that of the male gamete and therefore contains twice as many chromosomes (diploid number) as the gametes (haploid number). Now, the chromosome number within a species remains constant from generation to generation. Obviously, the diploid chromosome complement must be reduced in some way to the

Fig. 4.2. The metaphase chromosomes of *Drosophila melanogaster*, female above, male below. The scale in the figure represents 5 microns.

haploid number. This process is called *meiosis*. In animals, meiosis occurs in the sex glands, or gonads, during *spermatogenesis* and *oogenesis,* by which spermatozoa and egg cells are formed. In plants it occurs at *sporogenesis* (spore formation). Meiosis is, however, basically similar in both animals and plants.

ity came from studies of the behavior of chromosomes during the formation of gametes in animals and of spores in plants. These studies were initiated by Boveri (1887) and developed by Montgomery (1901), Janssens (1909), Darlington (1931), and many others. The behavior of the chromosomes during these processes is extremely variable in different organisms, and there is still much to be learned about it. It is important, however, to see beyond these variations the significant common features that occur in most organisms in which sexual reproduction is observed. Indeed, the existence of these common features suggests that we

MEIOTIC PAIRING OF CHROMOSOMES

Spermatogonia and *oogonia* are diploid cells from which the sperms and the eggs eventually develop. Being diploid, they are in this respect like other body, or somatic, cells. A diploid chromosome complement consists of a number of pairs of chromosomes. The members of each pair look alike under a microscope. They are derived from the maternal and the paternal sex cells that came together at fertilization, and, as will be shown later, they contain similar (homologous) genes. The chromosomes of a pair

Fig. 4.3. Schematic representation of the chromosomes of maize, illustrating relative lengths, positions of the centromeres (clear, oval-shaped), the deeply staining knobs (black), and the nucleolar organizer on the sixth chromosome (dotted). The heteropycnotic regions adjacent to the centromeres are represented by solid lines, and the euchromatic portions of the chromosomes are shown by broken lines. (*From M. M. Rhoades*)

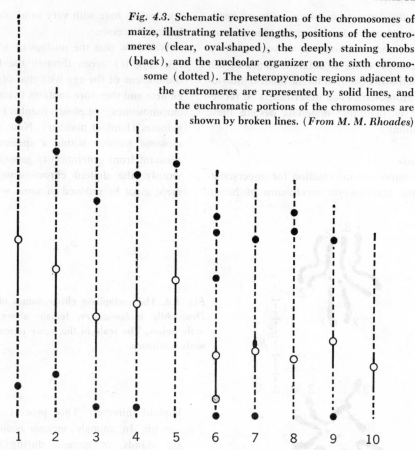

that contain similar genes are homologous chromosomes, or *homologues*. The essence of meiosis is that the two members of each pair, that is, the homologues, approach each other and become tightly *paired* (or *synapsed,* or *conjugated*). Eventually the paired chromosomes disjoin, the cell divides, and the daughter cells receive only one of the two members of the synapsed pair. The diploid, 2n, number is thus reduced to the haploid, n, number. In more detail, what happens is as follows.

Spermatogonia and oogonia increase in size, often manyfold, and become primary spermatocytes and oocytes. The nuclei of these cells then enter a prophase, during which the diploid number of chromosomes appears in each nucleus in the form of long,

apparently single, slender threads. This stage is known as *leptotene* (Fig. 4.6). The homologous threads then come together in synapsis and unite in a haploid number of pairs, or *bivalents* (Figs. 4.4 and 4.5), in which the threads contract and become shorter and thicker. This is the *zygotene,* or *pachytene,* stage. Each chromosome in the bivalent then splits lengthwise into two halves, or *chromatids.* The four homologous chromatids thus formed remain united in a four-strand structure, or *tetrad.* This is the *diplotene* stage (Fig. 4.6).

CHIASMATA
Something very important happens during the transition from pachytene to diplotene. The homologous chromatids break in one or

more places, and the partner strands exchange parts so that new chromatids are formed consisting of sections of the two synapsed chromosomes. The chromosomes formed as a result of this consist of some parts that belonged to the maternal and some that belonged to the paternal homologous chromosomes (Figs. 4.4 and 4.6). Just what is the mechanism of this breakage and reunion remains unclear, and different investigators offer different interpretations of these phenomena. Under the microscope, one can see that the pairs of chromatids in the tetrad are held together at the places where two of the chromatids cross each other at the points where exchange of sections has taken place. Such cross-shaped configurations of chromatids are called *chiasmata* (singular, *chiasma*). The number of chiasmata in each bivalent is variable. In some bivalents only one chiasma is formed, in others two or several, whereas in some exceptional cases no chiasmata have been observed.

THE MEIOTIC DIVISIONS

Following the diplotene stage, the tetrads become shorter and more compact (*diakinesis*, Fig. 4.4), and in the metaphase of this first meiotic division, each of the tetrads breaks into two *dyads,* which separate and pass to opposite poles of the division spindle (Fig. 4.4). After a brief interphase, the second meiotic division occurs. The centromere of each dyad divides, and the dyad separates into two single chromatids (Figs. 4.5 and 4.6), which pass to opposite poles.

The two meiotic divisions result, then, in the formation of four nuclei, each carrying one chromatid from each bivalent, that is, the haploid number of chromosomes. It must, however, be noted that, where chiasmata occur, the chromosomes resulting from meiosis may no longer be like the maternal and paternal chromosomes that underwent pairing at the pachytene stage; instead, the chromosomes coming out of meiosis may be compounded of sections of the maternal and

paternal homologues. Furthermore, the different (nonhomologous) maternal and paternal chromosomes undergo segregation independently of each other. As a consequence, a gamete formed by an individual will virtually never include all the maternal or all the paternal chromosomes. Far more commonly, it will contain various mixtures of maternal and paternal elements (Fig. 4.6).

In animals, meiosis results in the formation of four haploid nuclei that become the nuclei of gametes. In spermatogenesis in the male, each nucleus enters a spermatid cell, which then becomes transformed into a spermatozoon. In oogenesis in the female, three of the nuclei form polar bodies that usually degenerate, and the fourth becomes the female pronucleus of the egg cell. Fertilization restores the diploid condition, which then is retained in the somatic cells, including the cells that give rise to the sex glands.

REPRODUCTION IN PLANTS

The life cycle in plants is more complicated than in animals, and the formation of gametes, instead of following meiosis directly, may be considerably deferred. Plants in the lowest of the four main divisions in the plant kingdom, the thallophytes, show a considerable diversity in this regard. In most of the green algae, meiosis occurs in the first two divisions of the fertilized egg, and thus the vegetative cells of the plant, as well as its gametes, have the haploid number of chromosomes. In the brown alga Fucus, almost exactly the opposite is true, since meiosis takes place just before the formation of the gametes, and the cells of the plant body are thus all diploid, a condition essentially like that in animals. In many of the red algae the fertilized egg produces a group of spores (*carpospores*) each of which develops into a nonsexual plant, and these in turn bear nonsexual spores (*tetraspores*), in the formation of which meiosis is accomplished.

50

CHAPTER 4

The tetraspores develop into haploid sexual plants that ultimately bear gametes.

In plants higher than the thallophytes, the "alternation of generations" is even more definite, a nonsexual diploid generation or plant, the *sporophyte,* bearing spores, in the formation of which meiosis occurs. These in turn grow into haploid sexual plants, *gametophytes,* which ultimately bear gametes, the fertilized egg developing into a sporophyte plant. There is thus an entire "generation" intercalated between meiosis and gamete production.

Among the seed plants, the gametophytic generation has become very greatly reduced and is no longer an independent plant but is contained wholly within the reproductive structures of the sporophyte, which is the "plant" we see. These reproductive structures are the flowers (Fig. 4.7). Each consists, typically, of four sets of structures. Outside is a circle of protective parts, the calyx, and within this another circle of often conspicuously colored parts, the corolla. Next is a series of "male" sexual organs, the stamens, each bearing an anther, which produces within itself a mass of single-celled pollen grains. Strictly speaking, however, the anther is not a sexual organ but a sporangium, and the pollen grains are really microspores rather than gametes, although they give rise directly to gametes. In the center of the flower is the "female" organ, the pistil, consisting of an ovary, a style, and a stigma. Within the ovary are one or more ovules, which after fertilization develop into seeds. The ovule is really a sporangium, also, and produces within itself a megaspore, which develops into a very much reduced female gametophyte, or embryo sac, containing at least one egg cell, the true female gamete.

DOUBLE FERTILIZATION IN PLANTS

When the pollen grain (microspore) germinates on the stigma of the same flower or another of the same species, it gives rise to

METAPHASE I

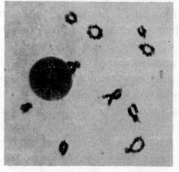

DIAKINESIS

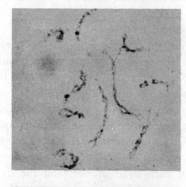

DIPLOTENE

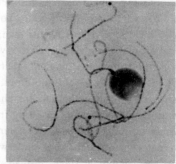

PACHYTENE

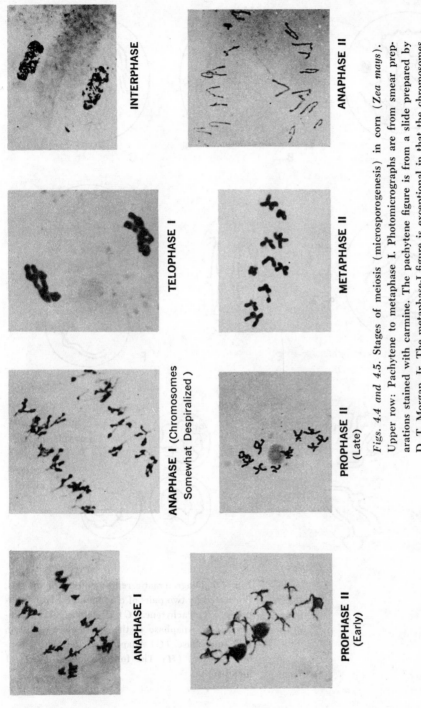

INTERPHASE

ANAPHASE II

TELOPHASE I

METAPHASE II

ANAPHASE I (Chromosomes Somewhat Despiralized)

PROPHASE II (Late)

ANAPHASE I

PROPHASE II (Early)

Figs. 4.4 and 4.5. Stages of meiosis (microsporogenesis) in corn (*Zea mays*). Upper row: Pachytene to metaphase I. Photomicrographs are from smear preparations stained with carmine. The pachytene figure is from a slide prepared by D. T. Morgan, Jr. The metaphase-I figure is exceptional in that the chromosomes are less contracted than usual.

Middle row: Anaphase I to interphase. In anaphase I, two disjoining dyads are still connected by a persistent chiasma. The other dyads have fallen apart. The formation of the cell plate can be seen in interphase.

Lower row: The monads in anaphase II are more extended than usual. (*Courtesy of M. M. Rhoades*)

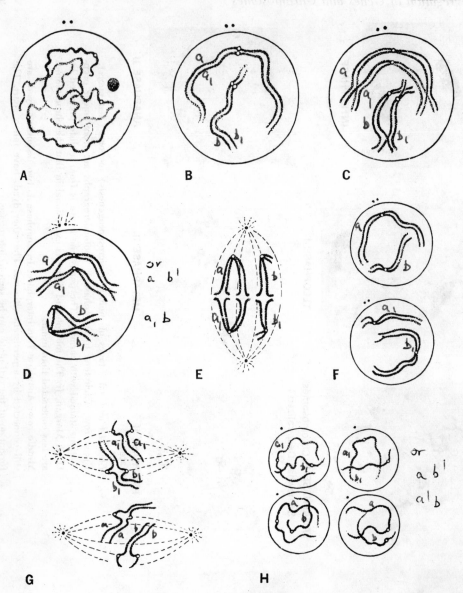

Fig. 4.6. Diagrammatic representation of meiosis, illustrated by two pairs of chromosomes. (*A*) Interphase. (*B*) Pachytene. (*C*) Diplotene. (*D*) Diakinesis. (*E*) Anaphase of the first meiotic division. (*F*) Interphase. (*G*) Anaphase of the second meiotic division. (*H*) The four haploid products of meiosis.

a small group of cells (in the higher plants only three) which represent the last vestige of the male gametophyte. From the pollen grain develops a pollen tube that penetrates the style and enters the ovule in the ovary. Down this tube pass the contents of the pollen grain—one nonsexual nucleus and two other nuclei, the true male gametes. One of

an ear of maize from a type normally bearing white endosperm is pollinated by pollen from a yellow race (yellow endosperm color being dominant over white), the endosperm of the seeds produced will be yellow. This direct effect of the male gamete on tissues other than embryonic ones is known as *xenia*.

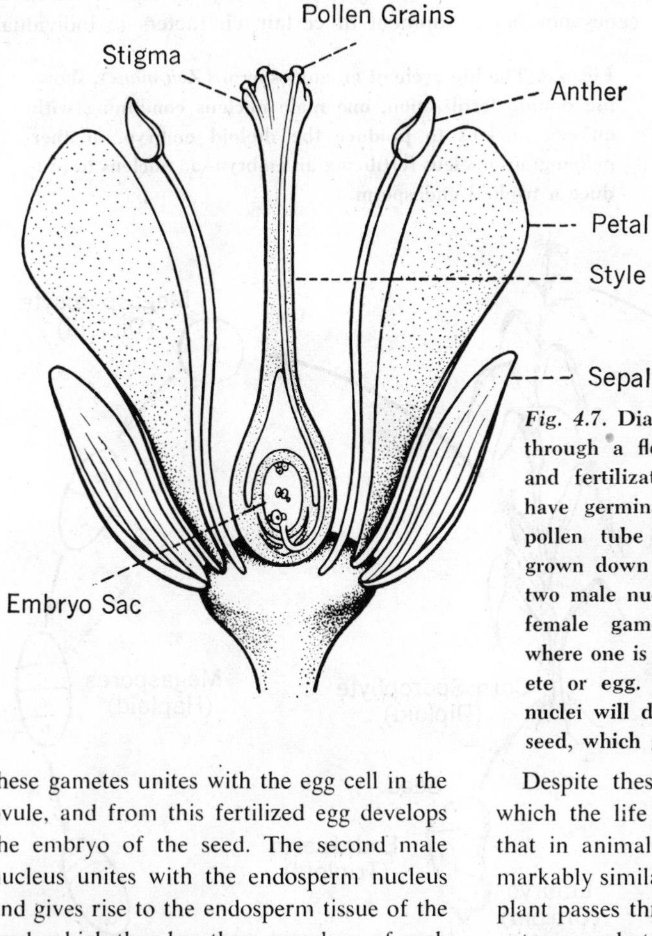

Fig. 4.7. Diagram of a vertical section through a flower, showing pollination and fertilization. Three pollen grains have germinated on the stigma. The pollen tube from one of these has grown down the style and carried the two male nuclei to the embryo sac, or female gametophyte, of the ovule, where one is fertilizing the female gamete or egg. From the union of their nuclei will develop the embryo of the seed, which grows into a new plant.

these gametes unites with the egg cell in the ovule, and from this fertilized egg develops the embryo of the seed. The second male nucleus unites with the endosperm nucleus and gives rise to the endosperm tissue of the seed, which thus has three members of each chromosome set (triploid). This remarkable process of "double fertilization" (Fig. 4.8) results in the formation of endosperm tissue, which partakes of both paternal and maternal inheritance; and in plants where the ovary wall and seed coat are thin and transparent, as in the kernel of corn (maize), a direct effect of the male gamete on the character of the endosperm is evident. Thus, if

Despite these manifold complications in which the life cycle of plants differs from that in animals, the meiotic stages are remarkably similar in both. Meiosis in the corn plant passes through the same leptotene, zygotene, pachytene, diplotene, and diakinesis stages as it does in animals. Chiasmata are usually formed in the chromosomal bivalents, and the two meiotic divisions result in formation of four nuclei that contain haploid sets of chromosomes, these chromosomes being compounded of sections of the maternal and the paternal chromosomes that were present in the diploid cell before meiosis.

Sutton and Boveri concluded in 1902 that Mendelian genes must be carried in the chromosomes. The behavior of the chromosomes at meiosis and fertilization resembles in a very striking way the behavior of genes as observed in breeding experiments.

It should be clearly understood that we are sure of the existence of genes not be-

cause we have seen them or analyzed them chemically (genetics has so far not succeeded in doing either of these things), but because Mendel's laws can be satisfactorily understood only on the assumption that genes exist. For the purpose of studying the inheritance of traits, it is sufficient to define the gene as a unit transmitted from parents to offspring, which is responsible for the development of certain characters in individuals

Fig. 4.8. The life cycle of an angiosperm (*Zea mays*), showing double fertilization, one male nucleus combining with an egg nucleus to produce the diploid embryo, another pollen-grain nucleus fertilizing an embryo-sac nucleus to produce a triploid endosperm.

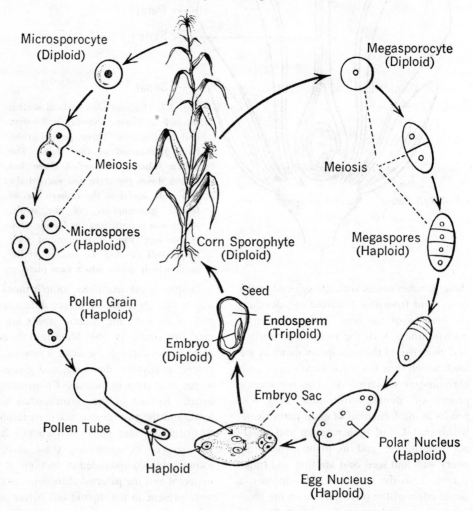

living in certain environments. The gene so defined is a hypothetical unit, and the body of knowledge concerned with these genes has come to be known as *formal genetics*. The theory of formal genetics could have been developed even if chromosomes had been unknown and the microscope did not exist. Compared with pre-Mendelian theories, it represented a great advance in the understanding of the phenomena of heredity. Formal genetics developed in essentially its modern form during the first quarter of the current century.

But the matter could not be allowed to rest there. The ideas of formal genetics constituted a challenge to investigators to discover just where in the organism the genes are located, what they are, and how they function—in other words to discover the material, or physical, basis of heredity. The efforts of these investigators have been brilliantly successful, and it is now known that genes are particles borne in the chromosomes of cell nuclei. Although they are too small to be seen even with the aid of the best existing microscopes, the behavior of the chromosomes can be studied visually, and such studies reveal many things about the genes. Thus genetics has joined forces with cytology, the science dealing with cell structures and cell functions. This union of genetics and cytology has become so intimate that in many studies it is impossible to delimit the concepts and theories of one science from those of the other; for such studies the hybrid name *cytogenetics* is sometimes used. In the nineteenth century, however, the study of cells was largely independent of the study of heredity, and thus the pioneers of cytogenetics in the early years of the present century found an appreciable body of knowledge ready to be interpreted.

The parallelism between the behavior of genes and of chromosomes can be summarized as follows:

1. Both the chromosomes and the genes behave in inheritance as though they were individual units. The individuality of the chromosomes can be directly observed under the microscope. Each pair of chromosomes can be seen, in favorable material, to be different from every other pair. Each gene, likewise, has an individuality that is inferred from its emergence intact and unaltered after a cross.

2. The facts of inheritance can be explained only on the assumption that the genes that make up the genotype of every individual occur in pairs (allelic pairs) and that one member of each pair was contributed by one parent of this individual and the other by the other parent. This is precisely the situation observed in the case of the chromosomes, for these are also definitely associated in pairs, each member of which has been derived from one of the two parents.

3. Each gamete contains only one member of each pair of chromosomes, and each gamete likewise contains but one member of each pair of allelic genes. That the gametes contain the reduced or haploid number of chromosomes is known from actual chromosome counts, especially at the meiotic divisions. That each gamete contains only one of a pair of genes was found to be a necessary inference from breeding experiments. In fact, the most important of Mendel's principles assumes a process of segregation by which, in the formation of gametes, each gene separates sharply from its alternative or allele, the two members of the pair always entering different gametes so that the gametes are "pure" genetically. Such a separation is actually found to take place between the two members of a pair of chromosomes at the meiotic divisions, resulting in the inclusion of each member of the pair in different daughter cells (gametes). Both genes and chromosomes, then, undergo segregation, and in respect to both each gamete is pure, containing only one member of a pair.

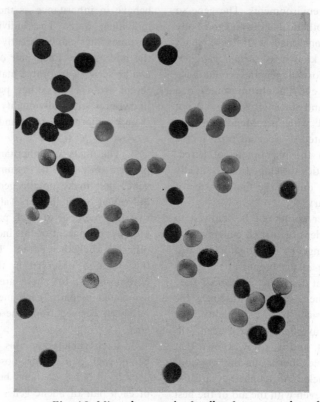

Fig. 4.9. Microphotograph of pollen from an anther of a maize plant heterozygous for the starchy-waxy gene pair, showing segregation for this gene. The pollen has been treated with iodine, making the starchy grains appear dark in contrast to the waxy ones, which are light. (*From M. Demerec*)

TIME OF SEGREGATION

The law of segregation, or Mendel's first law, states that allelic genes in a zygote do not blend or contaminate each other but segregate and pass into different gametes. The time when segregation takes place has been inferred from studies of the behavior of chromosomes at meiosis; it occurs at the meiotic divisions. However, in some organisms it is possible to prove by direct observation that the segregation has taken place as predicted by Mendel's first law (Fig. 4.9).

In maize, rice, peas, and some other plant species, there exist varieties that differ from each other in the kind of carbohydrate reserve materials that accumulate in the cells. For example, "starchy" maize varieties have starch grains that stain intense blue with iodine solutions, whereas the starch grains of "waxy" varieties stain red. The difference is due to a single pair of alleles, starchy being dominant over waxy. The F_1 generation from a cross of starchy with waxy consists of starchy plants, and in F_2 a segregation of 3 starchy : 1 waxy is observed. Carbohydrate reserves are laid down in many cells, including those of the pollen grains. Therefore, pollen grains of starchy maize stain blue, and pollen grains of waxy maize stain red with iodine. The noteworthy fact is that the pollen grains of F_1 hybrid plants, which must be heterozygous for starchy and waxy, fall clearly into two classes of about the same size, some staining blue and others red (Fig. 4.9). Among the starchy plants obtained in F_2, about one-third should the-

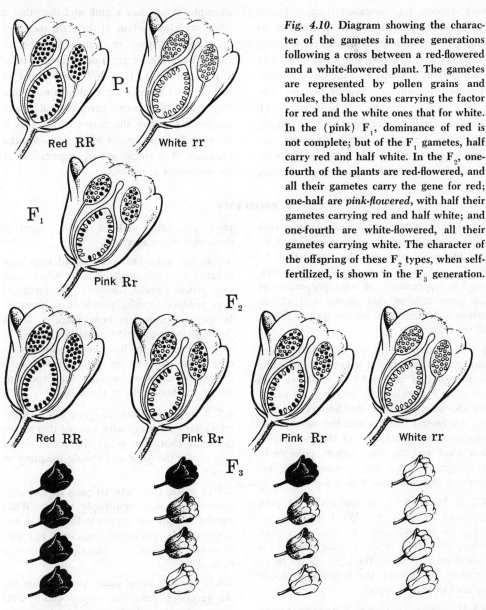

Fig. 4.10. Diagram showing the character of the gametes in three generations following a cross between a red-flowered and a white-flowered plant. The gametes are represented by pollen grains and ovules, the black ones carrying the factor for red and the white ones that for white. In the (pink) F_1, dominance of red is not complete; but of the F_1 gametes, half carry red and half white. In the F_2, one-fourth of the plants are red-flowered, and all their gametes carry the gene for red; one-half are *pink-flowered*, with half their gametes carrying red and half white; and one-fourth are white-flowered, all their gametes carrying white. The character of the offspring of these F_2 types, when self-fertilized, is shown in the F_3 generation.

oretically be homozygous for starchy and two-thirds should be starchy-waxy heterozygous. This prediction is fully confirmed by the discovery that the pollen grains of about a third of the plants stain uniformly blue, whereas about two-thirds of the plants give blue and red pollen grains in about equal numbers.

Mendelian segregation is even clearer in spores of certain fungi. In some species of the pink bread mold (Neurospora) numerous varieties occur, differing in such traits as color of mycelia and manner of growth and especially in nutritional requirements for certain substances such as vitamins. The varieties can be crossed, because if two mycelia of opposite "sex" are brought in contact they establish fusions in which the cell nuclei derived from the two individuals unite to form zygotic nuclei. The cells with zygotic nuclei then develop into so-called fruiting bodies (*perithecia*), which contain a number of sacs, or *asci,* each ascus having eight spores (Fig. 23.5). It is known that each spore, like each gamete, has only half the chromosomes that were present in a zygotic nucleus. The eight spores of an ascus can be isolated with the aid of delicate needles under a microscope, and mycelia from each spore can then be grown in separate cultures. If the individuals crossed differ in a single trait—for example, if one has a pink and the other a white mycelium—four of the eight spores of an ascus give pink mycelia and the other four white. The segregation ratio is, hence, 1 pink : 1 white. It is noteworthy that in this case the segregation is always such that four spores of an ascus carry one allele and the other four the alternative allele. This is because the eight spores of an ascus are the products of a single act of segregation of chromosomes at meiosis.

PROBLEMS

4.1 Assume that, in an animal with four pairs of chromosomes, centromeres A, B, C, and D have come from the father and A', B', C', and D' from the mother. If assortment is independent, in what proportion of the germ cells of this animal will all the paternal centromeres be present together; all the maternal?

4.2 In a species with 10 pairs of chromosomes, a plant is found in which one of the homologues of pair 9 has a knob whereas the other is knobless; the members of pair 5 are also heteromorphic, one homologue having a terminal satellite and the other none. Diagram the constitution of the gametes of this plant and the constitutions possible in its progeny when self-fertilized, with respect to chromosomes 9 and 5.

4.3 In Neurospora, let the allele for pink be *P* and for white be *p*. What are the genotypes of the following: mycelia of a pink strain; of a white strain; zygotic nuclei of a hybrid between these; the eight spores of an ascus of this hybrid; the mycelia produced by each of these spores?

4.4 If a given character *A* pertains to the *gametophyte* and the gametophyte of one plant shows it whereas that of another plant shows its allele *a,* and if gametes from these two gametophytes unite, what will be the appearance of the succeeding generation of gametophytes with respect to this character?

4.5 If one gametophtye displays characters *A* and *B* and is crossed with another that displays *a* and *b,* what will the next gameto-phyte generation look like with respect to these two characters?

4.6 In the honeybee, unfertilized eggs may develop by parthenogenesis, in which case they produce males (drones). The fertilized eggs produce females (workers or queens). In spermatogenesis in bees, there is no reduction division. If the females contain 32 chromosomes in the body cells and if oogenesis is the same as in other species, how many chromosomes would you expect to find in the body cells of the males?

4.7 A queen bee heterozygous for a dominant character mates with a drone that shows the same character. What characters would you expect the male and female offspring to show?

4.8 In maize there are 10 pairs of chromosomes in normal sporophyte tissues. What number would you expect to find in (a) endosperm; (b) pollen-tube nucleus; (c) embryo sac; (d) leaf; (e) root tip; (f) embryo of seed?

4.9 If rows of sweet corn, homozygous for the recessive gene for sugary endosperm, *sn sn,* are planted alternately with starchy corn, *Sn Sn,* some seeds on the sweet corn plants are found to have starchy kernels. Frame a hypothesis to account for this, and indicate how you would test it.

4.10 In man, assuming that the somatic number of chromosomes is 46, what is the probability that any egg selected at random will contain only the chromosomes (centromeres) received from the father?

5 SIMPLE MENDELIAN TRAITS
IN MAN

MENDEL DISCOVERED the law of segregation by analyzing the data obtained in breeding experiments with peas. Soon after the rediscovery of Mendel's work in 1900, it became clear that Mendelian inheritance occurs in all kinds of organisms. At present it would be hard to count the number of species of animals and plants in which Mendelian segregation has been observed. Chromosomes and genes are present in living beings from bacteria to trees and from infusoria to mammals, and units showing segregation have been shown to be present even in viruses. The laws discovered in peas are just as valid for man; indeed, the laws of heredity show a generality rarely met with in biology. In this chapter we shall give examples of human traits that show Mendelian inheritance of the simplest kind, without attempting to list all the traits for which such inheritance has been established with varying degrees of certainty. Some of the more complex cases of human inheritance will be discussed in later chapters.

PEDIGREES

It is obvious that in man one cannot make genetic experiments in the same sense as one can in peas, flies, or cattle. Mating and reproduction in man are intimate personal matters and cannot be directed to suit the convenience of geneticists. However, it does not necessarily follow that man is unfavorable as a subject for genetic studies. The mass of observations on human traits recorded in medical, anthropological, and biological literature is great and growing rapidly. Human heredity is, of course, more interesting to most men than that of any other species, and differences among human beings have always attracted curiosity and attention. However, the methods of studying human heredity must of necessity be different from those applicable elsewhere. One of these methods is that of collecting family trees or pedigrees, examples of which are shown in Figure 5.1 and elsewhere in this book.

In pedigrees it is conventional to symbolize females by circles and males by squares.

59

The symbols of parents are joined by a "marriage line" and the symbols of their children are placed usually below those of the parents under a horizontal line joined to the marriage line by a short vertical line. It is often convenient to number the generations with Roman numerals and individuals within generations with Arabic ones. The characteristics of each individual may be distinguished by such means as black or white color, lacking the dark melanin granules of pigmented hair. Albinos are sensitive to bright light and their skin is easily sunburned.

In Figure 5.1 and in most such pedigrees, albino children have parents neither of whom is an albino. Moreover, whenever one member of a pair of identical (monozygotic) twins is an albino, the other member is also albino (Fig. 5.2), whereas among fraternal

Fig. 5.1. A pedigree of albinism. Squares represent males, circles females. Open symbols represent persons not showing the trait in question; black symbols, persons showing the trait (albinos).

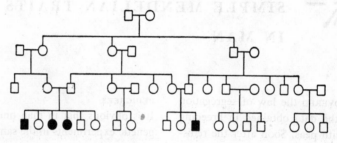

symbols. Figure 5.1 gives a sample pedigree of albinism in man.

THE INHERITANCE OF ALBINISM
Albinism, the complete or nearly complete absence of pigment from skin, hair, and eyes, is a condition found occasionally in many species of mammals. Usually it behaves as a simple Mendelian trait recessive to normal pigmentation. In man albino individuals occur, with some rarity, in many different races. In the English population, for example, about one out of 20,000 babies born is an albino. In such albinos the skin is pale reddish white, the reddish tinge depending upon the color of blood which shows through the superficial layer of skin, whereas in nonalbinos it is obscured by some dark (melanic) pigment. The iris of the eye in albinos is red for the same reason: the color of the blood vessels is not hidden by pigment in the iris. The hair is pale straw

(dizygotic) twins, one member may be albino and the other not (Fig. 11.2). This provides some evidence that albinism is due to heredity, since monozygotic twins come from one egg and thus inherit the same genes.

Pedigrees such as that in Figure 5.1 show us that albinism is due to homozygosis for a recessive allele, *a*. Its dominant allele, *A*, is necessary for the development of pigment. Nonalbinos are thus either homozygous, *AA*, or heterozygous, *Aa*. Marriages of albinos with normally pigmented persons nearly always produce only nonalbino children, since the albino allele is rare and most people do not carry it.

Figure 5.1 illustrates another fact frequently observed in pedigrees in which homozygotes for rare recessive genes appear. The parents of both the sibships that include albino children are first cousins. All four parents are *Aa,* and the albino allele in each was thus probably derived from one of the grandparents. Since such heterozygotes must be rare in the general population, marriages between two unrelated persons, both heterozygous, would be very rare indeed. Hence if a trait is rare and if many of the pedigrees in which it appears show consanguinity (marriages of related persons, usually cousins), it can be assumed to be due to segregation of a recessive gene.

This is to be expected in the case of a dominant, since only one allele, *S*, is required for the development of the trait. All matings that produced spotted children are between heterozygotes *Ss* and unrelated normal persons *ss*. The phenotype of the homozygote *SS* is not known, since no matings *Ss × Ss*, required to produce *SS*, have been recorded. The allele *S* probably arose by mutation from *s* in a germ cell of one of the parents

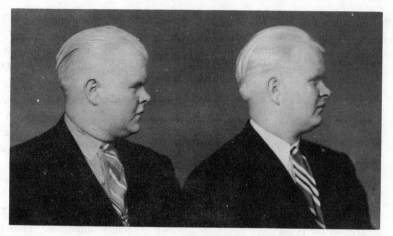

Fig. 5.2. Albinism, a recessive mutation, in a pair of identical twins. (*From Rife, Schonfeld, and Humstead in Journal of Heredity*)

INHERITANCE OF SKIN SPOTTING

In several populations (those of Norway and Holland and the American Negro) individuals are occasionally seen with a "blaze" or forelock of pure white hair. Sundför in Norway has studied the descendants of a man with this form of white spotting, including his 78 great-grandchildren. In this family, individuals with the white forelock are also spotted on other parts of the body, as shown in Figure 5.3 The full pedigree, shown in Figure 5.4, clearly indicates the inheritance of a dominant allele *S* for white spotting. The condition for developing this form of spotting is having one parent who showed it. It does not "skip a generation," as albinism was seen to do. Although the gene is rare, there is no consanguinity in the pedigree.

of the spotted man in generation I, since the trait had not been known before his birth.

TASTE BLINDNESS FOR PTC

Two chemists working with a substance called phenyl-thio-carbamide (PTC for short) discovered by chance that although this substance had an intensely bitter taste to one of them, it was virtually tasteless to the other. Snyder, Blakeslee, and others subsequently found that in the American white population, about 70 per cent of the persons examined are "tasters" and 30 per cent are "nontasters." A summary of pedigree data showing the inheritance of the ability versus the inability to taste the PTC substance is presented in Table 5.1.

The data are consistent with the assump-

TABLE 5.1
Inheritance of the ability to taste the PTC substance
(*After Snyder*)

Parents	Number of families	Children	
		Tasters	Nontasters
Taster × taster	425	929	130
Taster × nontaster	289	483	278
Nontaster × nontaster	86	5	218

tion that the ability to taste PTC is due to a dominant gene, *T*, and those unable to taste it are homozygous for the recessive allele of this gene, *t*. On this assumption, the mar-

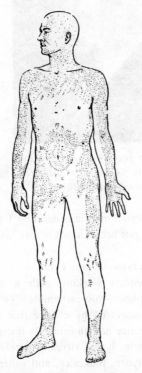

Fig. 5.3. Sketch of a man showing the type of piebald spotting which arose by mutation in a Norwegian family. The white "blaze," or fore-lock, on the forehead and white hairs in irregular patterns on the ventral body surfaces are constant features of the character. The same type of spotting has appeared independently in unrelated families in other parts of the world. (*After Sundför*)

riages in which both parents are nontasters should produce only nontaster children; 86 families of this sort had 218 children who were nontasters but also 5 children who were tasters. In this case there is no need to suppose that all these 5 children were illegitimate, since, as will be shown in Chapter 11, the distinction between tasters and nontasters is not quite sharp, and some persons who had the allele *T* in their genotype might have been misclassified as nontasters, and vice versa.

There is another feature in Table 5.1 which requires attention. The marriages taster × taster have produced children 12 per cent of whom are nontasters and 88 per cent tasters; the marriages taster × nontaster produced about 66 per cent tasters and 34 per cent nontasters among the children. These figures do not suggest the classical Mendelian 3 : 1 or 1 : 1 ratios with which we are familiar. A moment's consideration will show, however, that these classical ratios are not expected in this case. Indeed, because of the dominance of the taster allele *T* over the nontaster allele *t*, some of the persons who are tasters are the homozygotes *TT*, and others are the heterozygotes *Tt*. Now, marriages in which one of the parents is a homozygous taster (*TT* × *TT*, *TT* × *Tt*, and *TT* × *tt*) produce only taster children, regardless of the genotype of the other parent. Marriages of heterozygous tasters (*Tt* × *Tt*) produce taster and nontaster children in the ratio 3 : 1; and marriages of heterozygous tasters with nontasters produce equal numbers of tasters and nontasters among children, i.e., the classical 1 : 1 ratio. Among the observed marriages of taster × taster there were, accordingly, some in which at least one of the parents was a homozygote, some in which at least one of the parents was a heterozygote, and some in

brown to almost black; this is one of the genetically variable human traits that one notices most frequently in everyday life. The inheritance of this trait in most families appears to be simple, blue eyes being recessive to dark eyes (usually brown). Accordingly, blue-eyed parents usually have blue-eyed

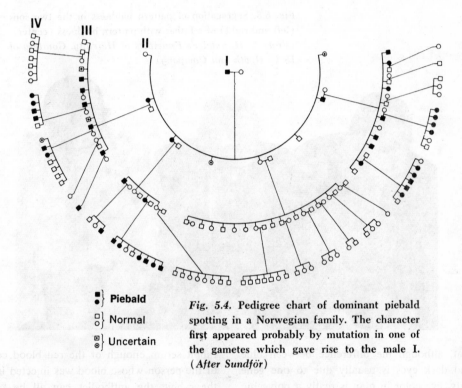

IV III II I

Piebald
Normal
Uncertain

Fig. 5.4. Pedigree chart of dominant piebald spotting in a Norwegian family. The character first appeared probably by mutation in one of the gametes which gave rise to the male I. *(After Sundför)*

which both parents were heterozygotes. Among the marriages taster × nontaster there were some in which the taster parent had the genotype *TT* and others in which he was *Tt*. As will be shown in Chapter 18, the observed proportions of the tasters and nontasters among the children born from these marriages are actually in accord with expectation based on Mendel's law.

BROWN AND BLUE EYE COLORS
The color of the iris of the eyes in non-albinos varies from blue through shades of

children, whereas both blue and dark or dark eyes only appear in families in which one or both parents have dark eyes, depending on whether the parents are homozygous or heterozygous. Blue-eyed persons should, then, always be homozygous recessives. Since the allele for blue is common, consanguinity does not usually appear in pedigrees containing blue-eyed persons. Unfortunately, this simple scheme does not work in all families because the variability of human eye color cannot be adequately divided into only two classes, dark and blue. There exist also irises in intermediate shades—greenish, gray, and speckled gray. It is difficult to decide whether persons with such eyes should be classed as carriers or as noncarriers of the dominant gene for dark eye pigmentation. Dark-eyed children are born in some families in which both parents seem to have light eyes. One is forced to conclude

contain antibodies (agglutinins) which cause agglutination (clumping) of human erythrocytes. This can be shown by mixing on a slide or in a small test tube a drop of the immune rabbit serum and a drop of human blood; the human red cells rapidly form irregular clumps because they stick together by their surfaces. By adding to the immune

Fig. 5.5. Segregation of pattern baldness in the two sons (left and right) of a father with pattern baldness (center). (From L. H. Snyder's Principles of Heredity. Courtesy of D. C. Heath and Company)

that, although the difference between blue and dark eyes is usually due to one gene only, eye color in man is really a polygenic character (see p. 101).

An example of another phenotypic difference which is rather common in men only is shown in Figure 5.5. There is some evidence that a gene for pattern baldness is dominant in men but recessive in women.

M-N BLOOD GROUPS

If human blood, or the red blood cells (erythrocytes) which it contains, are injected into a rabbit or other susceptible animal, the animal becomes immunized against human red cells. The serum (the liquid part of the blood) of the immunized rabbit comes to

rabbit serum enough of the red blood cells of the person whose blood was injected into the rabbit, the antibodies can all be "absorbed" by these cells, and the serum will no longer agglutinate the cells of that person. But if the absorption is done by cells of a different person, it may happen that the serum will continue to agglutinate the red cells of the original donor. In other words, one person may contain in his blood cells some antibody-inducing substances (antigens) which other persons do not contain.

Landsteiner and Levine discovered that by using immune sera against the blood of different persons, all human beings may be divided into three blood groups, or blood types, called M, N, and MN respectively.

The red blood cells of M people carry an antigen denoted M, and these cells can be agglutinated by immune sera of rabbits injected with (immunized against) the blood of other M persons (anti-M sera). The red cells of N people have the N antigen, and they are agglutinated by anti-N sera. Finally, the blood cells of MN people carry both M and N antigens and are agglutinated by both anti-M and anti-N sera (Table 5.2). Given a drop of blood from any person, a competent technician can within a matter of min-

are, in accordance with this hypothesis, homozygous for the allele M^M ($M^M M^M$). Therefore, marriages in which both parents belong to the M blood type should produce exclusively M children. Table 5.2 lists 24 such families which produced 98 M children. People with N blood are $M^N M^N$ homozygotes; marriages of N parents should give only N children. Six such families with 27 N children have been observed. Marriages in which one parent is M and the other N should yield only MN children

TABLE 5.2

Inheritance of the M and N blood groups in man
(After Wiener)

Blood groups of parents	Number of families	Blood groups of children		
		M	MN	N
M × M	24	98	1	
N × N	6	...	...	27
M × N	30	...	43	1
M × MN	86	183	196	
N × MN	71	...	156	167
MN × MN	69	71	141	63

utes make the proper tests with anti-M and anti-N sera and determine the blood type.

The inheritance of the qualities that cause people to have M, N, and MN blood is very simple. Table 5.2 summarizes the data on the bloods of 286 families in which the parents and children were tested as to blood type. These data show that the presence of the antigen M is due to a gene which may be denoted as M^M, and the presence of the antigen N to an allele of this gene which may be denoted as M^N. These two alleles show no dominance; therefore, persons who are heterozygous for both of them, $M^M M^N$, will have both M and N antigens in their red blood cells and will consequently belong to the MN blood type.

Let us, however, examine the data in Table 5.2 in more detail from the standpoint of the gene hypothesis. People with M blood

$(M^M M^M \times M^N M^N \rightarrow M^M M^N)$. The table shows 30 such marriages with 43 children of the expected type.

Marriages of an M person with an MN should give in the offspring a segregation in the ratio approximately 1 M : 1 MN ($M^M M^M \times M^M M^N \rightarrow 1$ $M^M M^M : 1$ $M^M M^N$). Table 5.2 lists 86 such marriages with 183 M and 196 MN children. This is close enough to the expected 1 : 1 ratio; the ideal ratio would be 189.5 children of each of the two types. Marriages of N with MN should give a segregation of 1 N : 1 MN in the progeny ($M^N M^N \times M^M M^N \rightarrow 1$ $M^N M^N : 1$ $M^M M^N$). The actual numbers observed are 167 N and 156 MN; this is close to the ideal ratio of 161.5 of each type. Finally, marriages in which both parents are heterozygous, MN, should yield children of all three types (1 $M^M M^M : 2$ $M^M M^N : 1$ $M^N M^N$). In fact,

71 M, 141 MN, and 63 N children were observed; this is quite close to the ideal ratio 68.75 M : 137.5 MN : 68.75 N. (The differences between the calculated and the actual ratios in the above comparisons may be judged by the methods of Chapter 29.)

DISPUTED PATERNITY

It may be noted that Table 5.2 contains two "exceptions"—children who had blood types not expected among the progeny of parents of certain genotypes. Such "exceptions" occur in almost any large collection of human pedigrees; provided that they are not due to mistakes in classifying the blood types of the persons concerned, they arise from two sources, namely, illegitimacy and mutation. Ignoring mutation as too rare an event (see Chap. 16), the simple rules of Mendelian inheritance permit certain deductions that are put to use particularly in cases of doubtful paternity. Suppose that a child with MN blood is born to an M mother. The father of this child must, then, have either N or MN blood; he cannot have M blood, since M × M marriages produce, barring mutation, only M children. Similarly, M × N marriages produce only MN children, and M × MN marriages produce M and MN but no N children, etc.

The limitations of this method are obvious. It may be used only for paternity exclusion, i.e., to prove that a given couple could not (except by mutation) have produced a child of a certain blood type. It can never prove that a given child is a child of a given couple, because every blood type occurs in many persons. Moreover, certain combinations of parental genotypes can produce children of any of the three blood groups. Thus, MN × MN marriages produce M, N, and MN children. No paternity exclusion is then possible. However, the M–N blood groups are not the only genetic traits of human blood the inheritance of which is reasonably well known at present. In Chapter 10, other blood antigens will be discussed. Through the use of all genetically well-studied human traits, the possibilities of paternity exclusion are much wider than through the use of any single trait.

COUNTING GENES IN HUMAN POPULATIONS

The persons listed in Table 5.2 were white Americans. With the M–N blood groups, the heterozygotes ($M^M M^N$) are distinguishable from the homozygotes ($M^M M^M$ and $M^N M^N$) by standard blood-group tests, because the genes M^M and M^N show no dominance. Therefore, it is easy to count the numbers of the alleles M^M and M^N which were carried in the 286 pairs of parents (572 persons, 1144 gene alleles) listed in Table 5.2 (the second column from the left). The counts turn out to be 623 (or 54.5 per cent) of M^M and 521 (or 45.5 per cent) of M^N genes.

People choose their mates evidently without regard to the blood groups of the prospective partner. Therefore, it is reasonable to assume that in human populations the genes responsible for these blood groups combine at random. We have found that in the population studied for the M–N blood groups (Table 5.2), 54.5 per cent, or 0.545 of the total, of the gametes carry the allele M^M. The chance that two such gametes will meet and form an $M^M M^M$ zygote is, then, 0.545^2, or 0.297 of the total number of persons. In a group of 572 persons, the expected number with M blood is, then, $572 × 0.297 = 170$. The number of parents with M blood listed in Table 5.2 is $(2 × 24) + 30 + 86 = 164$. The expected and the observed numbers are in substantial agreement. The observed and the expected numbers of persons with each of the three blood groups, calculated in a similar manner, are as follows:

Blood group	M	MN	N	Total
Persons observed	164	295	113	572
Persons expected	170	284	118	572

The agreement between the observed and the expected numbers can be tested by the chi-square method (see Problem 5.14). Other human populations show different frequencies of the genes for the blood groups. Thus tests of an Eskimo population gave 91.3 per cent M^M and 8.7 per cent M^N, whereas Australian aborigines showed 17.6 per cent M^M and 82.4 per cent M^N. Such genes, which vary in frequency in different human populations, are very useful in making scientific comparisons of different populations and races, a use to which they are being increasingly put by anthropologists and biologists (see Chap. 20).

MENDELIAN RATIOS OBSERVED IN HUMAN PEDIGREES

Suppose that two heterozygous carriers of the gene for albinism marry and produce children. It is easy to predict that among these children there should be albino and nonalbino individuals in a ratio 1 : 3. However, if we examine a collection of pedigrees in which albino children are born from normally pigmented parents, it will appear that the albinos make up considerably more than the expected one quarter of the total number of children. Furthermore, the fewer children in the family, the greater proportion of albinos among them, as shown in the following tabulation (after Roberts):

Families with 1 to 4 children—0.9 nonalbino : 1 albino

Families with 5 to 7 children—1.6 nonalbino : 1 albino

Families with 8 or more children—2.3 nonalbino : 1 albino

This is, however, exactly what Mendelian segregation in small families should yield. The point is simply that some families in which both parents are carriers of the albino gene ($Aa \times Aa$) produce only nonalbino children (AA or Aa); since the heterozygotes Aa are not phenotypically identifiable, such families are not included in our collection of pedigrees showing albinism. In other

words, by selecting only the families which have produced one or more albino children, we introduce a bias in our data in favor of a higher proportion of albinos. How strong this bias is can be estimated quite simply.

Consider that marriages of two carriers should produce ¾ nonalbino and ¼ albino children. Suppose, however, that such a marriage produces only a single child; evidently ¾ of these will not contain albinos and will not be included in our collection of pedigrees, while the single-child families in this collection will have 100 per cent albinos. Among the families with two children, $\frac{3}{4} \times \frac{3}{4} = \frac{9}{16}$ will have two nonalbinos; $\frac{3}{4} \times \frac{1}{4} \times 2 = \frac{6}{16}$ will have one albino and one nonalbino child; and $\frac{1}{4} \times \frac{1}{4} = \frac{1}{16}$ will have two albino children. Since we study only families that have produced albinos, the proportion of albinos in the two-child families will be 4 albinos : 3 nonalbinos (since families with one albino are three times as frequent as those with two albinos). Probability theory (Chap. 29) permits calculation of the expected proportions of families with any number of children having from no albinos at all to those producing only albinos. The formula for this calculation is:

$$\frac{n!}{x!(n-x)!} \left(\frac{3}{4} \text{ dominants}\right)^x \left(\frac{1}{4} \text{ recessives}\right)^{n-x}$$

In this formula, n is the number of children in the families and x is the number of children showing the dominant trait. The sign ! indicates the product (factorial) of all integers from 1 to n or from 1 to x. Suppose that we wish to calculate the proportion of families with 5 children which produce 2 albino and 3 nonalbino individuals (both parents are assumed, as before, to be heterozygous carriers). Substituting 5 for n and 3 for x, we have:

$$\frac{5!}{3!2!}\left(\frac{3}{4}\right)^3\left(\frac{1}{4}\right)^2 = \frac{20}{2}\frac{27}{64}\frac{1}{16} = 0.264$$

In other words, 26.4 per cent of the families with 5 children, whose parents are Aa, are expected to contain 2 albino and 3 non-albino siblings. A similar formula can, of course, be used to compute the probability of having various numbers of dominants and recessives in families in which a 1 : 1 segregation is expected (for example, in families in which one parent is an albino and the other is Aa). This will be:

$$\frac{n!}{x!(n-x)!}\left(\frac{1}{2}\right)^n$$

For example, among families having 5 children, the proportion of families having 2 albinos and 3 nonalbinos, and also of families having 3 albinos and 2 nonalbinos, will be:

$$\frac{5!}{3!\,2!}\left(\frac{1}{2}\right)^5 = \frac{120}{12}\frac{1}{32} = 0.3125, \text{ or } 31.25\%$$

Using these formulas, the observed segregation ratios in families with different numbers of children can be "corrected" for the loss of the families in which no segregation has been observed (all children have the dominant trait) and which consequently are not included in the data.

GENETIC PROGNOSIS

A geneticist is often asked to predict the characteristics of the progeny to be expected from a given marriage. Such prognoses are especially desired when the characteristics concerned are diseases or malformations, some of which, as will be shown in Chapter 10 and elsewhere in this book, are conditioned by the genotype. The advice of a geneticist may then either allay unjustified

fears that the prospective parents may have, or, alternatively, it may help them reach a decision as to whether they should take the risks of parenthood if their children may be abnormal.

The rules of Mendelian inheritance make some predictions possible, but it is important to realize their limitations. Suppose that both parents have some trait due to homozygosis for a recessive gene; it can be foreseen that, ignoring the possibility of mutation, which is rare for most genes, all the children born of this marriage will be also homozygous for the gene in question. But suppose that a couple with normal pigmentation have given birth to an albino child, or a child with some disease known to be due to homozygosis for a recessive gene. We know, then, that the parents are both heterozygous for the recessive gene in question. Therefore, one-quarter of their children are expected to be recessive homozygotes. But all that one can say is that any child from this marriage runs a risk of 1 out of 4 of being a homozygote. We certainly cannot tell which particular child will be a homozygote; the fact that the marriage had already produced one or more homozygous children neither decreases nor increases the chance that the next child will also be a homozygote. When the characteristic concerned is a grave disease or malformation, a genetic counselor performs a worthwhile service when he presents the facts as he understands them to the prospective parents and leaves to them the responsibility of making a decision.

PROBLEMS

5.1 In Figure 5.1, assuming that persons from the general population (that is, not descended from I 1 and I 2) are not heterozygous for albinism (Aa), what are the genotypes of all persons whose genotypes are known?

5.2 In Figure 5.1, what is the probability that the following persons are of genotype

Aa: III 4; III 10; III 14; IV 2; IV 7; IV 13; IV 18?

5.3 In Figure 5.1, what is the probability that the first child from each of the following marriages would be albino: IV 2 × IV 7; IV 5 × IV 10; IV 7 × IV 13; IV 9 × IV 17?

5.4 In Figure 5.4, the persons in generation IV can be identified by counting in order from left to right. What is the probability that the first child from each of the following marriages would be spotted: IV 1 × IV 8; IV 12 × IV 23; IV 9 × IV 24? (Persons homozygous for this form of spotting have not been identified; you may assume, however, that such persons would be viable and spotted.)

NOTE: In the following four human pedigrees the individuals that are solid black possess the trait mentioned. Squares represent males and circles females. For each pedigree, state your opinion concerning the probability that the trait is dominant or recessive, taking into account the commonness or rarity of the trait in the general (unrelated) population, and, as far as possible, determine for that trait the genotype of each individual in the pedigree.

5.5 Taste blindness

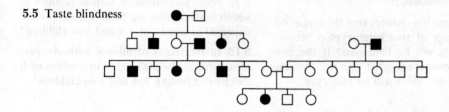

5.6 Polydactyly

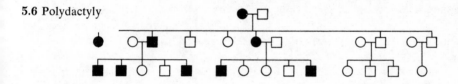

5.7 Monilothrix

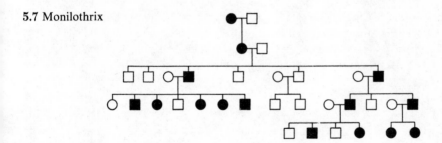

5.8 Muscle atrophy

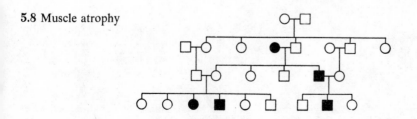

NOTE: Assume that in the families in Problems 5.9, 5.10, and 5.11, the allele for brown eyes is dominant to that for blue.

5.9 A brown-eyed man marries a blue-eyed woman, and they have eight children, all brown-eyed. What are the genotypes of all the individuals in the family?

5.10 A blue-eyed man both of whose parents were brown-eyed marries a brown-eyed woman. They have one child, who is blue-eyed. What are the genotypes of all the individuals mentioned?

5.11 What are the chances that the first child of a marriage of two heterozygous brown-eyed parents will be blue-eyed? If the first child is brown-eyed, what are the chances that the second child will be blue-eyed?

5.12 What is the probability that the first child from a marriage of MN × MN (cf. Table 5.2) will be MN?

5.13 In a case of disputed parentage, the mother of an illegitimate child is blood type N, the child MN, and one suspected father is N and the other MN. How would you decide the case?

5.14 Test the agreement of the results of the matings MN × MN in Table 5.2 with a 1 : 2 : 1 ratio by the chi-square method.

5.15 What proportion of 6-child families in which both parents are heterozygous *Aa* are expected to consist of 3 *A* and 3 *aa* children?

5.16 In marriages of albinos with *Aa* persons, what is the probability in families of 6 children of finding 3 *A* and 3 *aa* children?

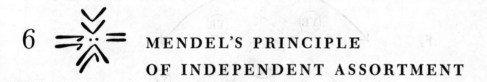

6 MENDEL'S PRINCIPLE
OF INDEPENDENT ASSORTMENT

WE SAW in Chapter 3 how Mendel's wisdom
in studying the inheritance of one character
at a time in varieties of the garden pea led
him to the discovery of the law of segregation. This discovery is the basis of the theory
of the gene, according to which the heredity transmitted from parents to offspring,
the genotype, consists of genes. It was shown
in Chapter 4 that the segregation of genes
is due to segregation of chromosomes at meiosis. Allelic genes in a heterozygote segregate because they are carried in homologous
chromosomes that pass to different gametes
formed as a result of the meiotic divisions.

Now, gametes and zygotes usually carry
several chromosomes, which are often different in appearance and presumably also in
contents. The genotype consists of many
pairs of genes. Although Mendel was not
familiar with chromosomes, he saw the need
of finding out how different characters would
behave in relation to each other in their passage from generation to generation.

DIHYBRID CROSS

Mendel studied seven pairs of characters in
peas, involving seed color, seed surface,
flower color, vine height, color of unripe
pods, pod shape, and position of flowers.
One of his crosses was between a pea plant
with round and yellow seeds and one with
wrinkled and green ones (Fig. 6.1). Such
a cross, which involves two character differences separable in inheritance, is called a
dihybrid cross (a cross involving a single
pair of alleles is *monohybrid*). The F_1 hybrids all had yellow and round seeds, since
the yellow color is dominant over the green
and the round shape is dominant over the
wrinkled. When the F_1 hybrid plants were
crossed to each other or allowed to self-fer-
tilize, an F_2 generation was obtained, consisting of 556 seeds. Among these seeds the
expected segregation in the ratio of 3 domi-
nants : 1 recessive ($\frac{3}{4}$: $\frac{1}{4}$) was observed
both for seed color and for seed shape, as
follows:

71

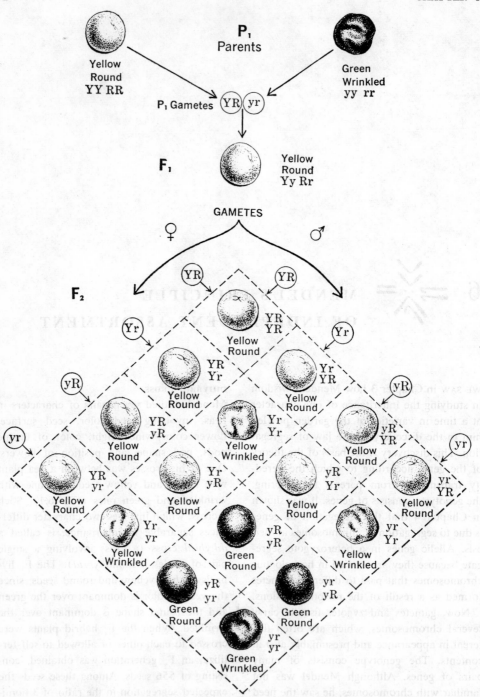

Fig. 6.1. Diagram showing the independent assortment in peas of two pairs of characters in which dominance is complete. In a cross between a plant homozygous for yellow and round seeds and a green, wrinkled-seeded one, the appearance, genotype, and gametes of the parents and the F$_1$ are shown. The results of random union between the four types of gametes formed by the F$_1$ heterozygote are presented in the F$_2$ checkerboard.

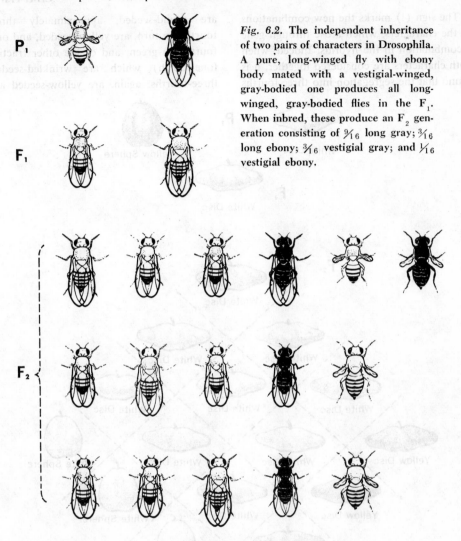

P₁

F₁

F₂

Fig. 6.2. The independent inheritance of two pairs of characters in Drosophila. A pure, long-winged fly with ebony body mated with a vestigial-winged, gray-bodied one produces all long-winged, gray-bodied flies in the F₁. When inbred, these produce an F₂ generation consisting of $\frac{9}{16}$ long gray; $\frac{3}{16}$ long ebony; $\frac{3}{16}$ vestigial gray; and $\frac{1}{16}$ vestigial ebony.

416, or 74.82%, yellow seeds
140, or 25.18%, green seeds
423, or 76.08%, round seeds
133, or 23.92%, wrinkled seeds

However, the question is this: Is the segregation of the seed-color characters independent of that of the seed shape, or are the two characters somehow tied together? Since the original varieties crossed had yellow round and green wrinkled seeds respectively, will the yellow color continue to be associated with the round shape and the green color

with the wrinkled shape of the seeds? Or will all combinations of the characters appear? Mendel found that the segregation of the seed color is independent of the seed shape and that both the old (parental) and new combinations of the characters appear in the F₂ offspring. Classifying the 556 seeds for both characters at once (cf. Appendix), he obtained:

315 round yellow seeds
108 round green seeds (!)
101 wrinkled yellow (!)
32 wrinkled green

The sign (!) marks the new combinations of the characters, which arose through gene recombination in the hybrids. Indeed, when both characters are considered together, it is found that the segregation into three-fourths are round-seeded, approximately three-fourths, in turn, are yellow-seeded, and one-fourth are green; and of the other fraction (one-fourth) which are wrinkled-seeded, three-fourths, again, are yellow-seeded and

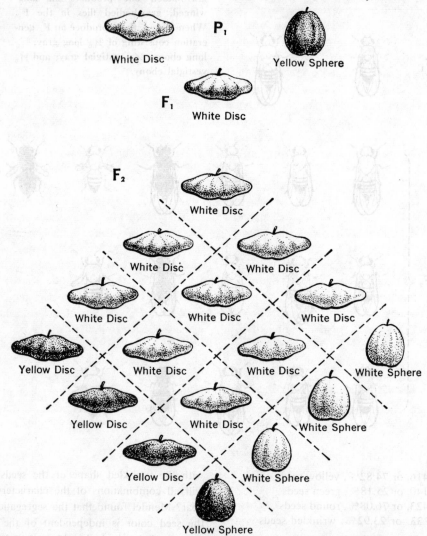

Fig. 6.3. **The inheritance of two pairs of characters in summer squashes, illustrating Mendel's law of independent assortment. White is dominant over yellow and "disk" shape over "sphere." In the F$_2$ there result $\frac{9}{16}$ white disk plants; $\frac{3}{16}$ white sphere; $\frac{3}{16}$ yellow disk; and $\frac{1}{16}$ yellow sphere.**

and one-fourth which occurs in each pair when considered alone is entirely independent of the similar segregation that takes place in the other pair. Thus, of the three-fourths of the entire group of plants which one-fourth green. This leads to the result that three-fourths of three-fourths of the entire number of plants in the F$_2$ generation, or nine-sixteenths of the entire number of plants, show both dominant characters (round and yellow); one-fourth of three-fourths, or three-sixteenths, show one dominant and one recessive (round and green); three-fourths of one-fourth, or again three-sixteenths, show the other combinations of dominant and recessive (wrinkled and yellow); and only one-fourth of one-fourth, or one-sixteenth, show both recessive characters (wrinkled and green). The counts which Mendel actually obtained in his experiment (315 : 108 : 101 : 32) came very close to these proportions, and he therefore inferred that the second generation from a cross involving two character pairs shows four kinds of individuals, approximately in the ratio of $\frac{9}{16} : \frac{3}{16} : \frac{3}{16} : \frac{1}{16}$, or 9 : 3 : 3 : 1. The actual ratio may be compared with the perfect ratio by multiplying the total number of plants, in this case 556, by $\frac{9}{16}, \frac{3}{16}, \frac{3}{16}$, and $\frac{1}{16}$. The perfect ratio in this case would be 312.75 : 104.25 : 104.25 : 34.75. Similar cases of dihybrid inheritance in Drosophila and in squashes are shown in Figures 6.2 and 6.3.

This independent assortment of two character pairs is made still more manifest by the fact that the particular combination in which the characters are brought into a cross makes no difference at all in the manner in which they are assorted and recombined in the F_2. In the example cited (Fig. 6.1), both dominant characters were brought in by one parent and both recessives by the other, but exactly the same results are obtained in the F_2 if, instead of crossing round and yellow with wrinkled and green, round and green is crossed with wrinkled and yellow. The F_1 is round and yellow; and the F_2 is again $\frac{9}{16}$ round and yellow; $\frac{3}{16}$ round and green; $\frac{3}{16}$ wrinkled and yellow; and $\frac{1}{16}$ wrinkled and green.

INDEPENDENT ASSORTMENT

Let the gene for the round seeds be represented by R and its allele for wrinkled seeds by r; and the gene for yellow seeds by Y and for green seeds by y (Fig. 6.1). Mendel's original yellow round-seeded parent thus had the genes $RRYY$, and the green

wrinkled parent $rryy$. The gametes produced by these parents were respectively RY and ry, and consequently the F_1 hybrid zygote formed by their union had the genotype $RrYy$. Now, the crux of the problem lies in the kinds of gametes produced by the F_1 individuals. When the seed surface alone is considered, it is found that the F_1 Rr individuals produce gametes half of which carry R and half r. It is clear, however, that every gamete must necessarily contain within itself not only a gene for seed surface but one for seed color as well, and, indeed, genes affecting every other character of the plant. Half these same gametes must, therefore, contain the allele Y and half the allele y; but in any given gamete it is a matter of chance as to whether the gene for round seeds is associated with that for yellow seeds or with that for green seeds. The assortment of the genes is independent. Of that half of the gametes which carry the gene for round seeds, a half in turn (or a quarter of the whole) carry yellow and a half carry green; and of that half that carry the gene for wrinkled seeds, a half also carry yellow and a half green. The F_1 hybrid produces four kinds of gametes in approximately equal numbers: RY, Ry, rY, and ry.

Now if two such F_1 plants, each of them producing four kinds of gametes, are crossed, there will obviously be 16 possible combinations among their gametes, for there will be four kinds of pollen grains and four kinds of egg cells. The union of these gametes in fertilization is here, too, a random one, any type of pollen grain being as likely to effect fertilization as any other; and any type of egg cell being as likely to be fertilized as any other, no selective preference being exhibited between them. The 16 possible combinations that appear among the F_2 offspring will, therefore, be equally numerous. The parents, the F_1, and the F_2 of the cross that has been used as an example are represented diagrammatically in Fig. 6.1 as to both their genotypes and their appearance, the 16 squares in F_2 representing the 16 possible

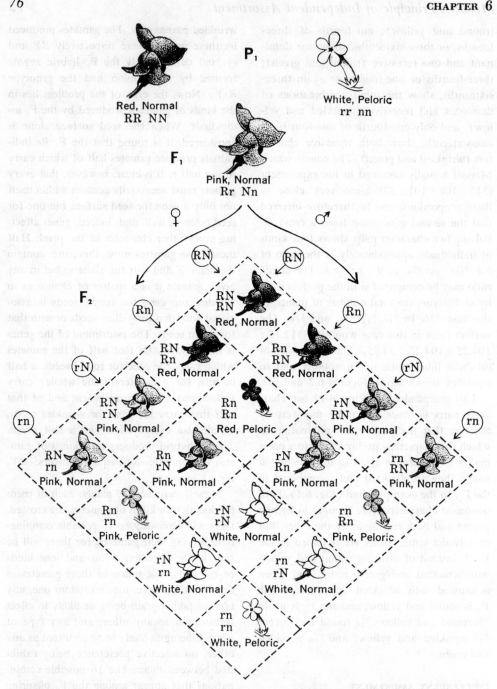

Fig. 6.4. Diagram showing the independent inheritance in snapdragons of two pairs of characters, in one of which dominance is complete and in the other of which it is lacking. In a cross between a plant homozygous for red flowers of normal shape and one with white and abnormal (peloric) flowers, the appearance and genotype of the parents, the F_1, and the F_2 are shown.

combinations of gametes. A count of these squares makes clear how the 9 : 3 : 3 : 1 ratio arises, for 9 out of these 16 individuals are in appearance round and yellow, 3 are round and green, 3 are wrinkled and yellow, and only 1 is wrinkled and green.

DIFFERENCE BETWEEN GENOTYPE AND PHENOTYPE

It is obvious, however, that in the F_2 generation the 16 types will not all be visibly different, since some of the combinations will look alike, as dominance causes heterozygous individuals to look like homozygous dominant ones. As far as actual appearance goes, therefore, there will be only four kinds of individuals, and some of these groups will be much more numerous than others. There are four kinds of round-seeded and yellow-seeded individuals: those with the genotype *RR YY*, which are homozygous for both round and yellow and will breed true if inbred; those with the genotype *RR Yy*, which are homozygous for round but heterozygous for yellow and will therefore breed true to round but not to yellow; those with the genotype *Rr YY*, which are heterozygous for round and homozygous for yellow and will breed true to yellow but not to round; and those with the genotype *Rr Yy*, which are heterozygous for both and will breed true to neither character but will produce a segregating offspring exactly like the F_2. A study of the squares in Fig. 6.1 shows that these four types should be found not in equal numbers but in the proportion of 1 : 2 : 2 : 4, respectively. Mendel tested this assumption experimentally and selfed all his 315 F_2 plants that bore round and yellow seeds. He obtained offspring from 310 of them, of which 38 produced plants bearing round and yellow seeds; 65 produced plants bearing round seeds but some yellow and some green; 60 produced plants bearing yellow seeds but some round and some wrinkled; 138 produced plants of all four types.

Of course, the 9 : 3 : 3 : 1 ratio is to be found only when both characters show complete dominance. If dominance is partial or absent, the heterozygous individuals are different in appearance from the homozygous ones, and more than four F_2 groups will be visibly distinguishable. The results of a dihybrid cross in which one character pair shows complete dominance and the other does not are shown in Fig. 6.4. The presence or absence of dominance, however, has no bearing whatever on the fundamental fact of the independence of assortment of genes in the gametes.

DIHYBRID TEST CROSS

The validity of the assumption that different genes assort independently can be submitted to a further test. The plants grown from the yellow-round seeds of the F_1 generation (Fig. 6.1) may be test-crossed (backcrossed) to the double recessive parent that produces green and wrinkled seeds. The F_1 hybrid plants carry, as we know, the genes *Rr Yy* and form four kinds of gametes in equal numbers, namely, gametes with the genes *RY*, *rY*, *Ry*, and *ry*. The green-wrinkled parent forms only one kind of gamete, *ry*. The expected result in the progeny of the test cross may, then, be found in the lowermost line of squares of the checkerboard in Figure 6.1. We should obtain yellow-round seeds (genotypically *Rr Yy*), yellow-wrinkled (*rr Yy*), green-round (*Rr yy*), and green-wrinkled ones (*rr yy*) in equal numbers, that is, in a ratio approaching ¼ : ¼ : ¼ : ¼. This is what is actually obtained in experiments, which, accordingly, confirm Mendel's theory.

Similarly, one can predict the results to be obtained in Drosophila if the F_1 hybrids of gray-vestigial and ebony long-winged flies (Fig. 6.2) are test-crossed to double-recessive ebony-vestigial ones. The F_1 hybrids are phenotypically normal, that is, they have gray body color and long wings, but they carry the genes for the ebony body color and for vestigial wings in heterozygous condition. The progeny of the test cross will, then, consist of normal (gray and long-winged), gray-vestigial, ebony long-winged, and ebony-vestigial flies in a ratio approximately 1 : 1 : 1 : 1. Test-crossing the F_1 hybrids in summer squashes (Fig. 6.3) to plants with yellow spherical fruits will produce segregation in a ratio of 1 white disk : 1 yellow disk : 1 white sphere : 1 yellow sphere. Finally, a test cross of the pink and normal-flowered snapdragons from the F_1 generation of the cross in Figure 6.4 to white peloric plants will produce a segregation in a ratio of 1 pink normal : 1 pink peloric : 1 white normal : 1 white peloric plants.

TRIHYBRIDS

When lines differing in three or more independently inheritable characters are crossed, the situation is naturally more complex, but the principle of independent assortment still holds good. Using Mendel's peas, a cross may be arranged between a variety with yellow-round seeds and red flowers and a variety with green-wrinkled seeds and white flowers. Using the same letters for the gene symbols as those used above, the genotypes of the parents may be represented as *RRYYCC* and *rryycc* respectively. Their gametes will contain the genes *RYC* and *ryc,* and the triply heterozygous (trihybrid) F_1 will be *Rr Yy Cc.* Because of dominance, it will have round-yellow seeds and red flowers. Given an independent assortment of the genes, this hybrid will produce eight kinds of gametes, as follows:

RYC	*rYC*
RYc	*rYc*
RyC	*ryC*
Ryc	*ryc*

In the F_2 generation produced by random union among these eight kinds of gametes, there will evidently be 64 possible combinations, as can be seen by constructing a checkerboard representing the trihybrid cross. Taking dominance into account, it

will be found that eight phenotypically different kinds of peas will appear with approximately the following frequencies:

> 27 round-yellow-red
> 9 round-yellow-white
> 9 round-green-red
> 9 wrinkled-yellow-red
> 3 round-green-white
> 3 wrinkled-yellow-white
> 3 wrinkled-green-red
> 1 wrinkled-green-white

As in the monohybrid and dihybrid crosses, some of the F_2 individuals that look phenotypically alike will prove to be genotypically diverse. This can be shown by inbreeding them and obtaining an F_3 generation of hybrids. Table 6.1 shows the results to be expected in the F_2 and F_3 generations.

POLYHYBRIDS

The situations obtained in the offspring of hybrids heterozygous for many genes (*polyhybrids*) may be quite complex. As the number of genes involved in a given cross increases, the number of possible gene combinations increases rapidly. Every added gene multiplies by 2 the number of different classes of gametes formed, by 3 the number of genotypes produced in the F_2 generation, and by 4 the number of possible combinations of gametes in F_2. A simple mathematical expression of these relations is found in Table 6.2.

Furthermore, as the number of genes involved increases, the chance of recovering one of the original parent types in the F_2 grows rapidly less. When a single pair of alleles is involved, 1 in 4 of the F_2 will resemble each one of the original parents in appearance and genotype; when two pairs are involved, 1 in 16; when three, 1 in 64; when four, 1 in 256; and so on.

When the number of genes (n) involved in a cross reaches tens or hundreds, the total number of genotypes, 3^n, and even the number of homozygous genotypes, 2^n, which

TABLE 6.1
The theoretical number of individuals, with their genotypes and breeding behavior, expected in F$_2$ from a trihybrid cross of a round, yellow-seeded, red-flowered variety of pea with a wrinkled, green-seeded, white-flowered one

Number of individuals	Genotype class	Phenotype class	Ratio of phenotypes	Breeding behavior when self-fertilized
1	*RR YY CC*			Breeds true
2	*Rr YY CC*			Segregates round-wrinkled, 3 : 1
2	*RR Yy CC*			Segregates yellow-green, 3 : 1
2	*RR YY Cc*	Round		Segregates red-white, 3 : 1
4	*Rr Yy CC*	Yellow Red	27	Segregates round-wrinkled, yellow-green, 9 : 3 : 3 : 1
4	*Rr YY Cc*			Segregates round-wrinkled, red-white, 9:3:3:1
4	*RR Yy Cc*			Segregates yellow-green, red-white, 9 : 3 : 3 : 1
8	*Rr Yy Cc*			Segregates round-wrinkled, yellow-green, red-white, 27 : 9 : 9 : 9 : 3 : 3 : 3 : 1
1	*RR YY cc*	Round		Breeds true
2	*RR Yy cc*	Yellow	9	Segregates yellow-green, 3 : 1
2	*Rr YY cc*	White		Segregates round-wrinkled, 3 : 1
4	*Rr Yy cc*			Segregates round-wrinkled, yellow-green, 9 : 3 : 3 : 1
1	*RR yy CC*	Round		Breeds true
2	*RR yy Cc*	Green	9	Segregates red-white, 3 : 1
2	*Rr yy CC*	Red		Segregates round-wrinkled, 3 : 1
4	*Rr yy Cc*			Segregates round-wrinkled, red-white, 9:3:3:1
1	*rr YY CC*	Wrinkled		Breeds true
2	*rr Yy CC*	Yellow	9	Segregates yellow-green, 3 : 1
2	*rr YY Cc*	Red		Segregates red-white, 3 : 1
4	*rr Yy Cc*			Segregates yellow-green, red-white, 9 : 3 : 3 : 1
1	*rr yy CC*	Wrinkled Green	3	Breeds true
2	*rr yy Cc*	Red		Segregates red-white 3 : 1
1	*rr YY cc*	Wrinkled Yellow	3	Breeds true
2	*rr Yy cc*	White		Segregates yellow-green, 3 : 1
1	*RR yy cc*	Round Green	3	Breeds true
2	*Rr yy cc*	White		Segregates round-wrinkled, 3 : 1
1	*rr yy cc*	Wrinkled Green White	1	Breeds true
64				

TABLE 6.2

The relation between the number of genes involved in a cross and the number of phenotypic and genotypic classes in F_2

Number of genes involved in the cross	Number of visibly different F_2 classes of individuals if dominance is complete	Number of different kinds of gametes formed by the F_1 hybrid	Number of genotypically different combinations	Number of possible combinations of F_1 gametes
1	2	2	3	4
2	4	4	9	16
3	8	8	27	64
4	16	16	81	256
n	2^n	2^n	3^n	4^n

may arise in the progeny of a heterozygote become enormous. In fact, these numbers are likely to be greater than the existing number of individuals of a species. It follows that the process of sexual reproduction, with its twin consequences of gene assortment and gene recombination, creates enormous amounts of new genetic variability. We shall return to this point in discussing the genetic basis of evolution in Chapter 16.

THE "BLOOD" THEORY AND THE GENE THEORY
Mendel obtained hybrids or heterozygotes by crossing varieties of peas which were "pure," or homozygous. Such pure or homozygous varieties exist in peas because the pea plant reproduces chiefly by self-fertilization (self-pollination). But many organisms reproduce sexually and by cross-fertilization, by mating of different individuals most of whom are genetically unlike. In cross-fertilizing species, most or all individuals are polyhybrid heterozygotes. Man is obviously such a species. All humans are hybrids, heterozygous probably for dozens or for hundreds of genes, though we have no way of determining the exact number.

The obsolete "blood" theory of heredity supposed that a parent transmits to his child something of all his hereditary qualities. The heredity that a parent transmits to different children, according to this theory, would evidently have to be about the same; full brothers and sisters would have to be geno-

typically rather similar or even identical. Mendel's findings led to quite different ideas. In the first place, a gamete, being haploid, contains only one-half the chromosomes and genes present in the diploid organism that produced the gamete. Suppose that the parent is a triple heterozygote, $AaBbCc$, and suppose that the gamete that gives rise to a child has the genes aBc. The child has, then, failed to inherit the genes A, b, and C, which are present in the parent. It follows that parents transmit to each of their children only one-half the genes they themselves have and fail to transmit the other half.

Furthermore, parents transmit a different set of genes to each child. Consequently, brothers and sisters usually have different genotypes. This is because different sex cells produced by the same individual are quite unlikely to carry identical sets of genes. In man, a single ejaculation contains between 200,000,000 and 500,000,000 spermatozoa. These are very large numbers, but consider that an individual heterozygous for only 30 genes is capable of producing $2^{30} = 1,073,741,824$ kinds of gametes. Only one more gene added would make the number of possible gametes (2^{31}) close to the number of human beings—men, women, and children —now living on earth (about two and a half billion persons).

Consider further that two gametes, one maternal and one paternal, unite at fertilization to form the genotype of the child. If

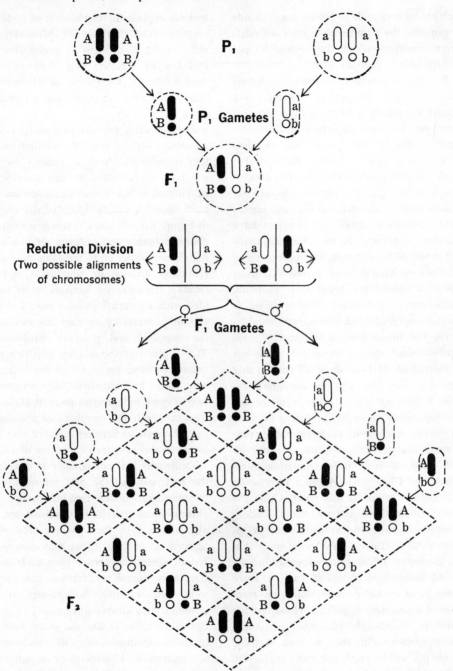

Fig. 6.5. Diagram showing independent assortment of two pairs of chromosomes, A-a and B-b. Note that at the meiotic division there are two possible alignments of chromosomes, producing four types of gametes. By random union these produce the sixteen different chromosome combinations shown in the F₂ checkerboard.

each parent is capable of producing 2^{30} kinds of gametes, the number of zygotes with different genotypes which they would be potentially able to produce would be $2^{30} \times 2^{30}$, or 2^{60}. This is a number so immense that its only meaning is that siblings (brothers and sisters) are utterly unlikely to have identical genotypes. The only exceptions to this statement, in the human species, are identical twins, which arise by asexual division of a single sexually produced zygote. The conclusion is no less valid for persons who are not closely related: no two human individuals, identical twins excepted, are likely to have identical genotypes, and even identical twins live in somewhat different environments and become somewhat different persons. Genetics has thus upheld the belief dear to many philosophers, that every human being is unique, unprecedented, and nonrecurrent.

The conclusion that an individual's genotype is unique applies not to man alone but to individuals of most or of all species that reproduce sexually and by cross-fertilization. It does not apply to the forms of life that reproduce asexually, by fission or similar means. A clone of bacteria arising from a single isolated cell consists of genotypically identical cells, unless mutation intervenes (see Chap. 16). Another reservation that must be made at this point is that the above calculations assume that Mendel's principle of independent assortment is always valid. Actually, only those genes that are carried in different cnromosomes are assorted independently. When two or more genes lie in the same chromosome, the freedom of assortment is limited. However, the numbers of possible genotypes calculated above remain valid, though some of these genotypes will be produced more frequently than others.

INDEPENDENT ASSORTMENT OF GENES
AND CHROMOSOMES

As we saw in Chapter 4, the pairing and disjunction of homologous chromosomes at meiosis explain the mechanism of gene segregation (the first law of Mendel). The independent assortment of genes (the second law of Mendel) can likewise be deduced from a knowledge of chromosome behavior as observed in microscopic preparations.

Diploid cells contain two sets of chromosomes, derived from the mother and father respectively. Now, at meiosis the various pairs of chromosomes are assorted and distributed to the gametes independently of each other. A careful study of the diagram in Figure 6.5 will show that it is a matter of chance whether two maternal or two paternal chromosomes go to the same pole at the reduction division or whether a maternal (black) chromosome happens to be associated with a paternal (white) one. The gametes may, therefore, contain any mixture of the maternal and paternal chromosomes. This is precisely the manner in which genes behave in inheritance, for in the formation of gametes by individuals heterozygous for two or more independent pairs of alleles, the way in which the members of the various pairs happen to become assorted and associated in the gametes is a matter of chance.

Ordinarily it is not possible to distinguish the maternal and the paternal homologous chromosomes under the microscope. The chromosomes that pair at meiosis are usually identical in their cytologically visible features, even though they may contain different alleles of certain genes. However, Carothers found in certain grasshoppers some heteromorphic homologues, that is, chromosomes which pair regularly at meiosis but which differ in size and shape sufficiently to be distinguishable. By observing the segregation of different pairs of heteromorphic chromosomes present in the same individual, Carothers found that different chromosomes assort independently. This furnishes the cytological evidence of independent assortment of maternal and paternal chromosomes.

PROBLEMS

NOTE: In guinea pigs, rough coat R is dominant over smooth coat r, and black coat B is dominant over white b. R and B are independent genes.

6.1 Cross a homozygous rough black animal with a smooth white one. What will be the appearance of the F_1; of the F_2; of the offspring of a cross of the F_1 back with the rough black parent; with the smooth white one?

6.2 In the F_2 generation in the preceding question, what proportion of the rough black individuals may be expected to be homozygous for both characters?

6.3 A rough black guinea pig bred with a rough white one gives 28 rough black; 31 rough white; 11 smooth black; and 10 smooth white. What are the genotypes of the parents? Test the validity of your explanation by the chi-square method.

6.4 Two rough black guinea pigs bred together have two offspring, one of them rough white and the other smooth black. If these same parents were further bred together, what offspring would you expect from them?

NOTE: In poultry, feathered legs F are dominant over clean legs f and pea comb P over single comb p.

6.5 Two cocks A and B are bred to two hens C and D. All four birds are feathered-legged and pea-combed. Cock A with both hens produces offspring that are all feathered and pea. Cock B with hen C produces both feathered and clean but all pea-combed, but with hen D he produces all feathered but part pea-combed and part single. What are the genotypes of these four birds?

6.6 The offspring of a feathered-legged, pea-combed cock bred to a clean-legged, pea-combed hen are all feathered-legged. Most of them are pea-combed, but some singles appear among them. What are the genotypes of the parents? What would be the offspring expected from a cross of this hen with one of her feathered-legged, single-combed male offspring?

6.7 In man, assume that spotted skin (S) is dominant to nonspotted (ss) and that woolly hair (W) is dominant to nonwoolly (ww). List the genotypes and phenotypes of children to be expected from a marriage of a spotted $Ssww$ man and a woolly-haired $ssWw$ woman. If S and W assort independently, in what proportions should the different phenotypes appear in the children?

6.8 The first child of a normal woman of blood group M is of blood group MN and albino. Assign tentative genotypes to the mother and the normal father. Using your assumed genotypes, predict the probability, among subsequent children born to this couple, of the phenotypes MN-normal; MN-albino; M-normal; M-albino; N-normal.

NOTE: In snapdragons, red flower color, R, is incompletely dominant over white, r, the heterozygous condition being pink; and normal broad leaves, B, are incompletely dominant over narrow grasslike ones, b, the heterozygous condition being intermediate leaf breadth.

6.9 If a red-flowered, broad-leaved plant is crossed with a white-flowered, narrow-leaved one, what will be the appearance of the F_1 and the F_2?

NOTE: In garden peas, tall vine, T, is dominant over dwarf, t; green pods, G, over yellow, g; and round seed, R, over wrinkled seed, r.

6.10 If a homozygous dwarf, green, wrinkled pea plant is crossed with a homozygous tall, yellow, round one, what will be the appearance of the F_1? What gametes does the F_1 form? What is the appearance of the offspring of a cross of the F_1 with its dwarf, green, wrinkled parent; with its tall, yellow, round parent?

6.11 What will be the appearance of the offspring of the following crosses, in which the genotypes of the parents are given:

TT Gg Rr × *tt Gg rr*   *tt gg Rr* × *Tt Gg rr*
Tt GG Rr × *Tt Gg Rr*   *Tt gg rr* × *tt Gg Rr*

NOTE: In the following four questions, all of which concern garden peas, find the genotypes of the parents as to vine height, pod color, and seed shape.

6.12 A tall, yellow, round plant crossed with a dwarf, green, round one produces offspring three-eighths of which are tall, green, and round; three-eighths dwarf, green, and round; one-eighth tall, green, and wrinkled; and one-eighth dwarf, green, and wrinkled.

6.13 A tall, green, wrinkled plant crossed with a dwarf, green, round one produces offspring three-fourths of which are tall, green, and round, and one-fourth of which are tall, yellow, and round.

6.14 A tall, green, round plant crossed with a tall, yellow, round one produces 26 tall, green, round offspring; 10 tall, green, wrinkled; 9 dwarf, green, round; and 3 dwarf, green, wrinkled.

6.15 A tall, yellow, round plant crossed with a dwarf, green, round one produces 58 tall, green, round offspring; 61 tall, yellow, round ones; 62 dwarf, green, round ones, 59 dwarf, yellow, round ones; 19 tall, green, wrinkled ones; 20 tall, yellow, wrinkled ones; 21 dwarf, green, wrinkled ones; and 20 dwarf, yellow, wrinkled ones.

6.16 In tomatoes, red fruit is dominant over yellow, two-loculed fruit over many-loculed, and tall vine over dwarf. A breeder has pure races of red, two-loculed, dwarf plants and of yellow, many-loculed, tall ones. He wants a race of red, many-loculed, tall plants. If he crosses his two races and raises an F_1 and an F_2, what proportion of this F_2 will be, in appearance, the type he desires? What proportion of these will be homozygous for all three characters? How can he determine which are the homozygous plants?

6.17 In poultry, the white plumage of Leghorns is dominant over colored plumage, feathered shanks over clean, and pea comb over single. If a homozygous white, feathered, pea bird is crossed with a colored, clean, single one, what proportion of the white, feathered, pea birds in the F_2 from this cross will prove to be homozygous if mated to colored, clean, single birds?

6.18 In snapdragons, normal flowers are dominant over peloric ones and tallness over dwarfness. Red flower color is incompletely dominant over white, the heterozygous condition being pink. If a homozygous red, tall, normal-flowered plant is crossed with a homozygous white, dwarf, peloric-flowered one, what proportion of the F_2 will resemble the F_1 in appearance?

6.19 By finding the values of χ^2 and P, determine how closely each of the five following F_2 populations fits a $9 : 3 : 3 : 1$ ratio. Which are to be regarded as examples of this ratio, and which are not?

Population	AB	Ab	aB	ab
1	315	108	101	32
2	51	11	16	2
3	860	315	340	117
4	75	35	41	9
5	1770	610	618	202

6.20 Determine the goodness of fit of the following F_2 population to a $3 : 1$ ratio, using the normal curve, or binomial (Sec. 29.9), and chi-square methods. Which do you think is the more satisfactory method?

A	a
1,182	418

6.21 The following results of an experiment with rats were reported by Roberts, Dawson, and Madden in Biometrika, 31, 56–66.

P_1 Wild color (agouti, dark-eyed, solid color) $\times$ dilute, ruby-eyed, spotted black.

F_1 All wild color.

$F_1 \times$ dilute, ruby-eyed, spotted black:

wild color	41	black	50
dilute agouti	36	dilute black	29
ruby-eyed agouti	41	ruby-eyed black	38
spotted agouti	29	spotted black	30
ruby-eyed, dilute agouti	39	ruby-eyed, dilute black	34
spotted, dilute agouti	33	spotted, dilute black	34
spotted, ruby agouti	35	spotted, ruby-eyed black	32
spotted, ruby, dilute agouti	25	spotted, ruby, dilute black	30

Explain the inheritance of the differences observed. On the basis of your hypothesis predict the proportions of the different phenotypes from the cross $F_1 \times F_1$.

7   THE EXPRESSION AND INTERACTION OF GENES

ALTHOUGH MENDEL's laws of segregation and independent assortment were immediately confirmed following the rediscovery of his work in 1900, it was by no means certain that these laws were to apply universally to all heredity in all organisms. In fact, it looked as though Mendelian inheritance might be rather an exception, and that most heredity might be of the blending type, in which the heredities of the parents mix or blend in the offspring. Indeed, the classical Mendelian ratios, such as 3 : 1, 9 : 3 : 3 : 1, etc., do not by any means occur in all crosses.

It was soon found, however, that most of the apparent exceptions could be explained by assuming that many characters are influenced by two or more pairs of genes the expressions of which interact. Depending upon the form of interaction, phenotype ratios are modified in various ways, although the fundamental laws of the transmission of heredity remain the same. During roughly the first quarter of a century of the existence of

genetics (1900–1925), much effort was devoted to analyses of such apparently complex forms of inheritance. As case after case fell into line, it became evident that with the exception of some traits inherited through the cytoplasm (see Chap. 26) the transmission of chromosomal genes accounts for all biological heredity. Some of the more important forms of gene expression and interaction will be discussed in this and the following chapters.

COMBS IN FOWLS

A classical case of two genes influencing the same character was discovered about half a century ago by Bateson and Punnett in fowls. Each variety of poultry possesses a characteristic type of comb. The Wyandotte breed, among others, has a comb known as the "rose" comb; Brahmas and some other varieties have a comb known as the "pea" comb; Leghorns and breeds of similar origin have "single" combs. Each of these types can be bred true (Fig. 7.1). Crosses be-

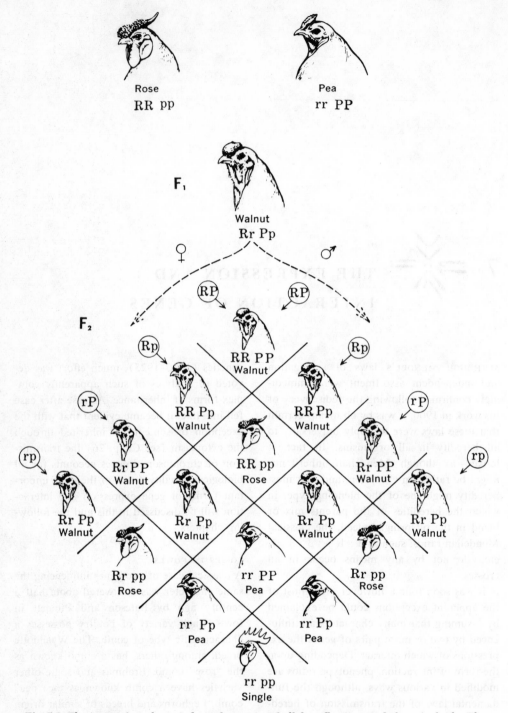

Fig. 7.1. The interaction of two independent pairs of alleles affecting comb form in fowls. The sixteen possible combinations of the F₁ gametes and the genotypes and phenotypes of the resulting zygotes are shown in the F₂ checkerboard.

tween rose-combed and single-combed varieties showed that rose was dominant over single and that there was a segregation into three-fourths rose and one-fourth single in the F_2. In crosses between pea-combed and single-combed birds, pea was dominant over single, and a 3 : 1 ratio appeared in the F_2. A new and interesting result, however, was obtained when rose was crossed with pea, for the F_1 birds showed a new comb form known as "walnut," previously noted as characteristic of the Malay breed of fowls, a race unrelated to those from which the new walnut comb was obtained. When the F_1 walnut-combed birds were bred together, a still more remarkable result was manifest, for in the F_2 generation there appeared not only walnut-, rose-, and pea-combed fowls but single-combed ones as well. These types occurred in the proportions $\frac{9}{16}$ walnut, $\frac{3}{16}$ rose, $\frac{3}{16}$ pea, $\frac{1}{16}$ single.

This ratio is expected in F_2 from a cross of parents differing in two genes. The doubly dominant class in F_2 was walnut, whereas the numbers of singles obtained indicated that this type contained both the recessive genes involved, a conclusion supported by the fact that the F_2 singles, when bred together, produced only single-combed progeny in subsequent generations. The walnut comb depends on the presence of two dominant genes, R and P. One of these genes alone (R) produces the rose comb; the other alone (P) produces the pea comb. The combination of the recessive alleles of these genes produces the single type of comb, rp. These assumptions are illustrated in the diagram in Figure 7.1.

The mode of inheritance of the genes for rose and pea does not differ at all from the usual Mendelian scheme. The differences that distinguish this and similar cases from ordinary dihybrid inheritance are that (1) the F_1 resembles neither parent, and (2) apparently novel characters appear in F_2. One of these new characters (walnut comb) evidently results from an interaction between two independently inherited dominant genes, and the other (single comb) results from the interaction of their two recessive alleles. These peculiarities are due not to a new method of inheritance but simply to the circumstance that both genes involved happen to express themselves in the same part of the organism, in this case in the comb.

COMPLEMENTARY GENES FOR COLORS IN CORN

Indian corn (maize) occurs in a number of varieties, some of which have colorless seeds, others seeds of a purple color (due to the presence of a purple substance known as *anthocyanin* in the aleurone layer of the seeds), and still others seeds of various other colors. Some varieties have green leaves, stems, and husks, due to the presence of the common plant pigment, chlorophyll. Others have, in addition, a brownish or a purple anthocyanin pigment in these parts. The inheritance of the colors in crosses between strains of corn seemed bewilderingly complex until it was worked out by R. Emerson of Cornell University and other geneticists and shown to be satisfactorily explicable by a relatively simple scheme, a part of which can be summarized as follows.

The crux of the whole matter is that in order to develop the purple anthocyanin pigmentation the plant must carry the dominant alleles not of one but of several genes; plants homozygous for the recessive alleles of any one of these genes have no anthocyanin, at least in the seeds, and therefore have colorless seeds. To state it differently, the purple anthocyanin color is elaborated owing to interaction of the dominant alleles of several genes; the action of these dominant alleles is complementary; that is, each allele controls a step essential for the production of the pigment. The absence of any one of them throws the whole anthocyanin-forming machinery in the plant out of order.

A true-breeding variety of maize with purple seeds and with purple pigment in the

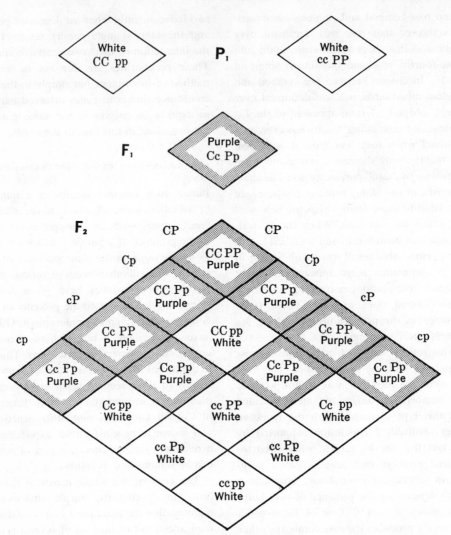

Fig. 7.2. The 9 : 7 ratio. Checkerboard showing the expected composition of the F_2 from a cross of two white-flowered sweet peas which produces all purple-flowered plants in the F_1.

body of the plant is homozygous for at least three dominant genes, denoted *A*, *C*, and *R*. The genetic "formula" of such a plant is, accordingly, *AA CC RR*. The recessive allele *a*, in the presence of the dominant *C* and *R*, gives colorless seeds but a plant of a brownish-green color, *aa CC RR*. The recessive alleles *c* and *r* give colorless seeds and green plants, so that *AA cc RR* and *AA CC rr*

genotypes produce plants devoid of purple or brown pigments. The simplest results are obtained when plants with colored seeds, *AA CC RR*, are crossed to any one of the three kinds with colorless seeds, *aa CC RR*, *AA cc RR*, or *AA CC rr*. The purple color behaves as a dominant, and the F_1 seeds are purple. In F_2 the classical segregation in 3 purple : 1 colorless ratios are observed.

Suppose, however, that a colorless-seeded maize plant lacking the gene *A* (i.e., of the composition *aa CC RR*) is crossed with another plant that is colorless but of the composition *AA cc RR*. The F_1 hybrid seeds will have all three color genes, *Aa Cc RR,* and will be purple in color. Because the genes *A, C,* and *R* are *complementary,* the F_1 hybrids are here unlike either parent. The same will happen if a colorless *aa CC RR* is crossed to a colorless *AA CC rr* or a colorless *AA cc RR* is crossed to a colorless *AA CC rr*. The resulting F_1 hybrid seeds will all be purple.

THE 9 : 7 RATIO

The F_2 generation from all these crosses will consist of purple and colorless seeds in a ratio of 9 : 7. The origin of this ratio can be easily seen in Figure 7.2, which illustrates the outcome of the cross that first revealed the complementary interaction of two independent pairs of alleles. Each parent in this cross was from a *different* true-breeding, white variety of sweet pea. The interpretation was that in each white variety, failure to form pigment was due to a different recessive gene and that the presence of both dominant alleles was necessary for the completion of the chain of biochemical processes (Chap. 24) leading to the formation of a colored substance.

Applying this interpretation to seed color in corn, we can assume that all seeds that inherit the dominant alleles of the two color genes, either in homozygous or heterozygous condition, will be purple; the proportion of such seeds will be nine-sixteenths. All seeds that lack the dominant alleles of at least one of the color genes will be colorless; there will be seven-sixteenths of such seeds. The validity of this interpretation can easily be tested by a number of experiments of which the outcomes are predictable. For example, we may make the assumption that among the purple seeds there must exist four different genotypes. One-ninth of the

purple seeds are homozygous, *AA CC RR,* and the plants grown from them will breed true, i.e., will produce only purple F_3 seeds if selfed or crossed to each other. Four-ninths are double heterozygotes *Aa Cc RR;* they will again give a ratio of 9 purple : 7 colorless seeds if selfed or crossed to each other. Two-ninths are heterozygous for just one color gene, *Aa CC RR,* and two-ninths heterozygous for another color gene, *AA Cc RR.* These will give, when selfed or intercrossed, segregation ratios of 3 purple : 1 colorless.

GENETIC "FORMULAS"

In this explanation, only the genes *A-a* and *C-c* need be indicated, and *R* may be omitted, although we know that its presence and the presence of still other genes is necessary if purple pigment is to be formed. Such an omission is customary, for otherwise the genetic "formulas" would be confusingly complex. One includes in a formula the genes that are known to be segregating in a cross and disregards the rest. But there are crosses in which more than two genes must be taken into account. Thus, a colorless-seeded maize of the composition *aa CC RR* can be crossed with a colorless *AA cc rr,* or a colorless *aa cc RR* with a colorless *AA CC rr,* or a purple-seeded *AA CC RR* with a triply recessive colorless *aa cc rr.* In all these crosses, the F_1 hybrids have purple seeds and have identical genotypes, *Aa Cc Rr.* To predict the result obtained in the F_2 generation of these crosses, a checkerboard diagram should be constructed having 64 cells (the trihybrids form, as shown in Table 6.1, eight kinds of gametes). There will be 27 out of 64 genotypes that will contain all three color genes, and these will produce purple-colored seeds. The remainder, 37 out of 64, will lack one, two, or all three dominant alleles of the color genes and will consequently produce colorless seeds. Such a 37 : 27 ratio has, indeed, been observed in experiments.

REVERSION

The inheritance of seed color in maize and similar situations in other organisms suggest an explanation for the numerous instances among domesticated animals and plants in which crosses between true-breeding varieties produce progeny resembling a remote ancestor more than they do either parent. Plant and animal breeders had noted these peculiar "throwbacks," "atavisms," or "reversions," but in the absence of any satisfactory explanation they regarded reversion as the expression of some mysterious force that caused the retention and subsequent reappearance of a remote ancestral trait. The reappearance of an old trait is usually due to the reunion of the two or more genes, necessary for its production, which had become separated in the history of the species. Thus, in maize, it is plain from the experiment cited above that purple seed color depends on at least three genes and that colorless seeds result when any of them is lost. It is easy to imagine that one colorless variety arose when, in the purple type, a mutation occurred from C to c, and the second arose when R changed to r. Thus the two elements necessary for purple color became separated into two different strains. When these strains were crossed, the two genes were reunited, and the primitive, or "reversionary," color appeared.

COAT COLOR IN RODENTS (THE 9 : 3 : 4 RATIO)

A similar but more complex case of gene interaction and reversion has been worked out in breeding experiments with "fancy" varieties of the common house mouse, in which a number of genes have been found to interact in producing what appears to be a simple character. The ancestral coat color of this species is that of the ordinary wild mouse. Upon close examination, this coloration is found to be due to the presence of two pigments in the fur. The individual hairs are for the most part black with a narrow yellow band near the tip. The underside of the animal is usually much lighter, the hairs being cream or yellow, with some black or gray at the base. This inconspicuous and hence protective coloration, which is known as the *agouti* pattern, characterizes many of the wild rodents, such as the Norway rat, the meadow vole, the guinea pig, the gray squirrel, and many others.

A number of variations that have taken place in this wild gray, or agouti, coat coloration have been preserved under domestication and have given rise to the many color varieties of mice. The commonest and most familiar variation is the albino, in which the coat is white and the eyes are pink because of the absence of pigment from the iris. Albinos always breed true, and this variation has been found to behave as a simple recessive to any color. Another variation in coat color arose through the disappearance of the yellow pigment from the agouti pattern, leaving the fur solid black. Black is recessive to the wild gray type and breeds true. When black mice are crossed with ordinary albinos, the progeny are usually all agouti like the wild type. When these F_1 agoutis are inbred, their progeny consist, on the average, of nine-sixteenths agouti animals, three-sixteenths black, and four-sixteenths albino (Fig. 7.3). This, like the 9 : 7 ratio encountered in maize, indicates a difference of two genes. Here, however, the last two terms of the ordinary 9 : 3 : 3 : 1 ratio have been added together, indicating that two of the ordinarily different classes of the dihybrid F_2 zygotes cannot be distinguished. The results are explained on the assumption that the parents differ in (1) a gene, C, necessary for the development of any color, which the black mice contain but which is lacking in the albinos; and in (2) a gene for the agouti pattern, A, which results in a banding of the black hairs with yellow. Since the black mice cannot contain this gene A (if they did, they would appear agouti), it must have come from the albino parent,

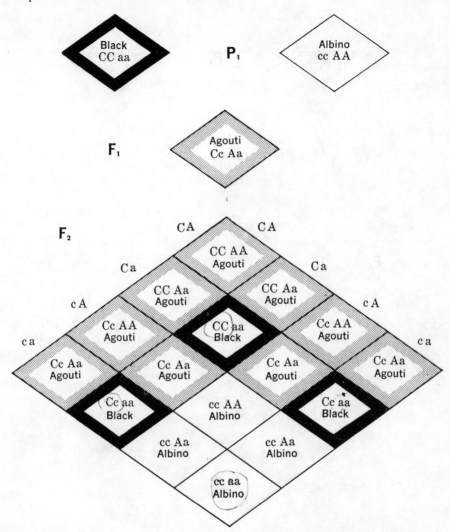

Fig. 7.3. The 9 : 3 : 4 ratio. Checkerboard showing the expected composition of the F_2 from a cross of black and albino mice which produces all agouti animals (wild-type) in the F_1.

where, in the absence of the ability to develop any color at all, it could have no visible expression. The recombination of these two genes, one for color and the other for the agouti pattern, reconstitutes the genotype of the wild mouse, and a "reversionary" type results. Reversions also occur in other ways, as by return of a mutant gene to its original form (reverse mutation).

EPISTASIS

Owing to dominance, the presence of the recessive allele in a heterozygote may be obscured or hidden. It sometimes happens that when two different genes, which are not alleles, both affect the same part or trait of the organism, the expression of one covers up or hides the expression of the other. A gene that thus masks or prevents the expres-

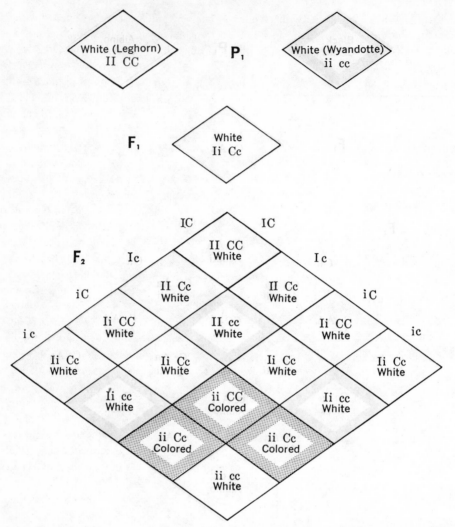

Fig. 7.4. The 13 : 3 ratio. Checkerboard showing the expected composition of the F_2 from a cross between two varieties of fowls, one with dominant white plumage and one with recessive white plumage.

sion of another is said to be epistatic to it, and the gene that is hidden is said to be hypostatic.

The white plumage of White Leghorn fowls is almost completely dominant over the colored plumage of black, barred, or other colored varieties. The white plumage of some other white varieties, however, such as White Wyandottes or White Plymouth Rocks, has been found to be recessive to

colored plumage and to be due to a gene distinct from that which produces the white of Leghorns. Experiments show that White Leghorns contain a color gene and with it a gene that inhibits its expression. They are genetically colored birds that are unable to develop their true color. Denoting such an inhibitor by *I* and the color gene by *C*, the White Leghorn is *IICC* and the White Wyandotte is *iicc*. A test of this hypothesis made by crossing White Leghorns with White Wyandottes produces a curious result. The F_1 chickens from such a cross are white with small, dark flecks and resemble the F_1 birds produced by crossing White Leghorns with colored fowls. When these F_1 whites are bred together, however, white and colored chicks appear in F_2 in the proportion of about $13/16$ white (or white with small, dark flecks) to $3/16$ colored (see Fig. 7.4). The "color genes" are hypostatic to the white of Leghorns, which is thus epistatic to the variety of genes determining colors and patterns.

The complications introduced by epistasis are comparable to those produced by dominance; that is, two or more genotypes are indistinguishable in appearance. In cases of epistasis, however, there are always two or more genes involved, each of which affects the same part of the organism. This same condition occurred in cases of interaction such as that observed in comb shape in fowls, but in fowls both genes are expressed, producing a new or different condition of the part. In epistasis, on the contrary, the competition of two genes for expression in one part results in the apparent triumph of one and the suppression of the other, so that the original traits are recovered but in modified ratios.

ANALYSIS OF COAT COLOR IN MICE

A thorough study of the variations in a group of related characters in any organism will usually reveal an intricate series of interactions between the component genes. As an example we shall choose the house mouse. As we have just seen, C is the fundamental color gene, necessary for the production of any pigment in the coat. Another gene, A, determines the development of the agouti pattern. Its recessive allele, a, is present in the nonagouti mice, such as blacks or browns. Still another, B, governs the development of black pigment and is dominant over its allelic condition of brown or choco-

late, b. Many varieties are spotted with white in a blotched, or piebald, pattern, and such mice contain a gene, s, which is recessive to self-, or solid, color, S. Another gene, d, brings about a clumping of the black and brown pigment granules in the hairs and makes these colors appear faded, or dilute, as opposed to the normal, fully pigmented form, D. Another gene reduces the amount of black and brown pigment in the fur, giving it a pale, washed-out appearance, and also reduces the pigment in the iris, making the eyes appear reddish or pink like the eyes of albinos. This gene, which is called pink eye (p) from its most noticeable effect, is recessive to the normal dark-eyed, intense-colored condition, P. These genes all segregate sharply and may occur in any combination. There are also several other genes affecting coat color which, in order to simplify the problem, will not be discussed here. Some of these combinations result in characters that are distinctive and have been given names of their own. Thus the non-black agoutis are called "cinnamon" or brown agouti; the dilute blacks, "blue"; the dilute browns, "silver fawn"; and so on. Table 7.1 lists these various gene combinations, together with the type of coat color produced by each.

All these types are recessive to the wild coat and appear to have arisen from it by mutation of one or more genes. Thus at any time the wild type may be reconstituted by bringing into combination all the dominant alleles of the genes responsible for these new types. In fact, the wild coat color itself is found to depend on the presence and interaction of all of the genes named. Thus in order to produce the agouti pattern there must be present the genes for color (C), agouti (A), black (B), dark eye (P), dense color (D), and solid color (S). With regard only to these genes the genotype of the wild mouse may be written AA BB CC DD PP SS. These genes all show essentially complete dominance, so that their heterozygous con-

TABLE 7.1

Interaction of genes for coat color in mice

Genes					Gametic formula	Phenotype
C	A	B	D	P	S	CABDPS	Wild-type agouti
					s	CABDPs	Spotted agouti
				p	S	CABDpS	Pink-eyed agouti
					s	CABDps	Pink-eyed, spotted agouti
			d	P	S	CABdPS	Dilute agouti
					s	CABdPs	Spotted, dilute agouti
				p	S	CABdpS	Pink-eyed, dilute agouti
					s	CABdps	Pink-eyed, spotted, dilute agouti
		b	D	P	S	CAbDPS	Cinnamon
					s	CAbDPs	Spotted cinnamon
				p	S	CAbDpS	Pink-eyed cinnamon
					s	CAbDps	Pink-eyed, spotted cinnamon
			d	P	S	CAbdPS	Dilute cinnamon
					s	CAbdPs	Spotted, dilute cinnamon
				p	S	CAbdpS	Pink-eyed, dilute cinnamon
					s	CAbdps	Pink-eyed, spotted, dilute cinnamon
	a	B	D	P	S	CaBDPS	Black
					s	CaBDPs	Spotted black
				p	S	CaBDpS	Pink-eyed black
					s	CaBDps	Pink-eyed, spotted black
			d	P	S	CaBdPS	Dilute black
					s	CaBdPs	Spotted, dilute black
				p	S	CaBdpS	Pink-eyed, dilute black
					s	CaBdps	Pink-eyed, spotted, dilute black
		b	D	P	S	CabDPS	Brown
					s	CabDPs	Spotted brown
				p	S	CabDpS	Pink-eyed brown
					s	CabDps	Pink-eyed, spotted brown
			d	P	S	CabdPS	Dilute brown
					s	CabdPs	Spotted, dilute brown
				p	S	CabdpS	Pink-eyed, dilute brown
					s	Cabdps	Pink-eyed, spotted, dilute brown
c	with any other genes					c..........	Albino, may be of any of 32 genotypes above

dition will give the same result as is produced by the homozygous form here given. Thus an animal with the genotype *Aa Bb Cc Dd Pp Ss* would also be agouti in appear-

ance. The genes named do not include all that are known, nor is it believable that more than a small sample of the genes affecting coat color in mice has been studied. If our knowledge of the subject were complete, it is probable that the list of genes necessary for the production of the agouti pattern would be much longer and that the letters of the alphabet would be exhausted in the attempt to write the genotype of the wild mouse. Here, then, is a clear and convincing example of gene interaction. In order that the apparently simple pattern characteristic of wild house mice may be developed, there must be present at least six genes (probably many more) each of which has a definite effect on coat color. If any single gene is missing or changed, a coat pattern differing more or less widely from the wild type results.

GENE INTERACTION IN CATS

The work of geneticists has disclosed numerous examples of gene interaction in many species of animals and plants. We shall certainly not attempt to review all of them here, but it may be useful to describe briefly some further examples to show how great is the variety of the situations encountered and at the same time how simply they are explained in terms of the theory of the gene. The validity and importance of a scientific theory are attested by its capacity to provide an intellectually satisfying account of many facts of nature and to help one predict the results of observations and experiments not yet carried out.

It has already been pointed out that the agouti color pattern occurs not only in the house mouse but in other rodents as well. Other genes having effects similar to or identical with those described for the mouse occur also in some of these other species of rodents. In fact, more or less parallel situations are known in remotely related mammals as well. Thus, in domestic cats there is a gene one allele of which gives, when homozygous, a yellow coat color, whereas the other allele, when homozygous, gives a black color. But in contrast to mice, this gene is carried in cats in the sex-determining X chromosome (see Chap. 12). In the heterozygous female cats, neither allele is dominant and instead a "tortoise-shell" coat, consisting of patches of black and yellow fur, results. Males cannot normally be heterozygous for genes carried in the X chromosomes, and for this reason male cats are either yellow or black but not "tortoiseshell." Another gene, possibly parallel to the agouti gene in rodents, gives in cats the "tabby" coat color, consisting of alternating darker and lighter stripes. This is the color pattern characteristic of the remote wild ancestors and some living relatives of domestic cats. A recessive gene gives the "Maltese dilution," which transforms black into a smoky gray, tabby into a gray with traces of the tabby pattern, and yellow into a pale sandy coat. The large irregular white spots are due to a dominant gene for spotting.

ALBINISM AND SPOTTING IN MAN

In man, there exists a gene that acts like the fundamental color gene described above for mice. A recessive allele of this gene gives, when homozygous, the albinotic condition described on page 60. The dominant allele of this gene allows pigmentation to develop, and several further genes control its amount, thus causing variations in skin colors ranging from that of the white race to that of the black (see Chap. 8). There exist also several genes that increase the pigmentation of the hair from blond to black and the eye color from blue to brown or black. The interrelations between the genes that increase the pigmentation of the skin, hair, and eyes are not well understood. It is probable that some of these genes affect the pigmentation of all these parts, whereas others act on the hair without changing the eye color or on the eyes without changing the hair color. A dominant gene that is rare in human populations causes the skin to be irregularly spotted or pied with darker and lighter areas. The effects of this gene are especially striking in human races that normally have a darkly pigmented skin (Fig. 5.3). The analogy between this human gene and the spotting genes in mice, cats, horses, and other mammals is rather striking.

GREEN COLOR IN CORN

In corn (maize), many genes affecting the development of the green chlorophyll pigment are known. The normal green color of maize results from the combined action of the normal alleles of these genes. If one of these genes mutates to a recessive allele, the seedlings are *albinotic* (virtually without chlorophyll); unable to carry on photosynthesis, they soon die. There are at least 15 different genes susceptible to this type of change, which means that there are at least 15 genetically different types of albinos. In another group of recessive mutants, known as lutescents, only yellow pigment develops; in another group are more than twenty recessive genes, each of which, when homozygous, produces virescent seedlings that are albinotic but eventually develop enough chlorophyll to keep them alive. Other recessive genes are responsible for pale-green color (10 known), zebra striping (4 known), piebald spotting (4 known), golden color (4 known), yellow-green color (3 known),

yellow striping (2 known), fine white striping (3 known), and many other modifications of chlorophyll composition and arrangement. It must be true, therefore, that the normal development of chlorophyll in maize depends on interaction among at least 75 different genes. If any one of these changes by mutation of the recessive allele from the normal one, some essential step in the process fails and the chlorophyll is absent or deficient in some way. The results of the analysis of such cases as those described above suggest that many of the characters of organisms are the end products of long chainlike series of related steps, $a \rightarrow b \rightarrow c \rightarrow d \rightarrow n$. Separate genes seem to affect separate steps so that if the gene affecting step b does not perform its task, then c and all later steps that depend upon it cannot take place and the character, such as normal chlorophyll, cannot appear. Other evidence for this view of the mechanism of gene interaction will be presented in Chapter 24. Whatever the means by which the genes interact, it may be accepted as a general rule that the hereditary characters of a plant or animal depend upon the balanced cooperation during development of a large number of genes.

PROBLEMS

NOTE: In poultry the genes for rose comb, *R,* and pea comb, *P,* if present together, produce walnut comb. The recessive alleles of both, when present together in homozygous condition, produce single comb.

7.1 What will be the comb character of the offspring of the following crosses, in which the genotypes of the parents are given:

    Rr Pp × *Rr Pp*   *Rr Pp* × *Rr pp*
    RR Pp × *rr Pp*   *Rr pp* × *rr Pp*
    rr PP × *Rr Pp*   *Rr pp* × *Rr pp*

NOTE: In the following five questions, all of which concern comb form in poultry, determine the genotypes of the parents:

7.2 A rose crossed with a walnut produces offspring three-eighths of which are walnut, three-eighths rose, one-eighth pea, and one-eighth single.

7.3 A walnut crossed with a single produces in F_1 one-fourth walnut, one-fourth pea, one-fourth rose, and one-fourth single.

7.4 A rose crossed with a pea produces six walnut and five rose offspring.

7.5 A walnut crossed with a single produces one single-comb offspring.

NOTE: In poultry, feathered shanks, *F,* are dominant over clean, *f;* and the white plumage of Leghorns, *I,* is dominant over black, *i.*

7.6 What will be the appearance of the offspring of the following crosses, in which the genotypes of the parents are given:

$$ff\ Rr\ Pp \times Ff\ Rr\ pp$$
$$Ff\ ii\ Rr\ pp \times ff\ II\ Rr\ Pp$$

7.7 A feather-shanked, rose-comb bird crossed with a clean-shanked, pea-comb one produces 25 feathered, pea offspring; 24 feathered, walnut; 26 feathered, rose; and 22 feathered, single. What are the genotypes of the parents?

7.8 A breeder has a homozygous race of feathered-legged, black, rose-comb birds and another of clean-legged, white, pea-comb ones. He wants a race of black birds with clean legs and walnut combs. What proportion of the F_2 raised from a cross between these two races will be what he desires in *appearance?* What proportion of these birds will be homozygous for the desired characters?

NOTE: In sweet peas, genes C or P alone produce white flowers, the purple color being due to the presence of both these factors.

7.9 What will be the flower color of the offspring of the following crosses, in which the genotypes of the parents are given:

$$Cc\ Pp \times cc\ Pp \qquad cc\ Pp \times CC\ pp$$
$$Cc\ Pp \times Cc\ PP \qquad Cc\ pp \times cc\ Pp$$

NOTE: In the following three crosses of sweet peas, what are the genotypes of the parents?

7.10 A white-flowered plant crossed with a purple produces offspring of which three-eighths are purple and five-eighths white.

7.11 A purple-flowered plant crossed with a white one produces offspring of which one-half are purple and one-half white.

7.12 A white-flowered plant crossed with another white produces offspring of which three-fourths are white and one-fourth purple.

7.13 In maize, plant A when crossed with plant B produced 255 green and 89 white offspring but when selfed produced 153 green and 118 white offspring. What are the genotypes of these two plants? What should plant B produce when selfed?

7.14 A green maize plant when selfed produces about fifteen-sixteenths green and one-sixteenth white (lethal) seedlings. Explain.

NOTE: In maize, C and R are both necessary for the production of red aleurone color, the absence of either resulting in white aleurone. If P is present in addition to C and R, the aleurone is purple, but P has no effect in the absence of either C or R or both.

7.15 In maize, what is the aleurone color of the offspring of the following crosses, the genotypes of the parents being given:

$$Cc\ Rr\ \ pp \times cc\ Rr\ Pp \qquad CC\ rr\ \ Pp \times Cc\ Rr\ pp$$
$$cc\ RR\ Pp \times Cc\ Rr\ pp \qquad Cc\ Rr\ Pp \times Cc\ Rr\ Pp$$

NOTE: In the following three questions, all of which refer to aleurone color in maize, find the genotypes of the parents.

7.16 A purple plant crossed with a white produces offspring of which one-eighth are purple, one-eighth red, and three-fourths white.

7.17 A purple plant crossed with a red produces offspring of which nine thirty-seconds are purple, nine thirty-seconds red, and seven-sixteenths white.

NOTE: The effect of the C, A, B, D, P, and S and their recessive alleles on coat color in mice is as follows (see Table 7.1): C, colored; c, albino; AB, black agouti (wild type); Ab, cinnamon (brown agouti); P, normal dark eyes; p, pink eyes; aB, black; ab, brown; D, normal dark color; d, dilute color; S, solid color, or self color; s, spotted with white.

7.18 In mice, what will be the coat color of the offspring of the following crosses, in which the genotypes of the parents are given:

$$Cc\ Aa\ Bb \times CC\ aa\ Bb$$
$$Cc\ Aa\ BB\ Dd \times cc\ Aa\ Bb\ Dd$$
$$CC\ aa\ Bb\ dd\ Pp \times Cc\ aa\ Bb\ Dd\ pp$$
$$CC\ AA\ BB\ Dd\ Pp\ SS \times Cc\ aa\ Bb\ DD\ Pp\ ss$$

NOTE: In the following three crosses, which deal with coat color in mice, find the genotypes of the parents.

7.19 An agouti animal crossed with another agouti produces offspring of which nine-sixteenths are agouti, three-sixteenths black, three-sixteenths cinnamon, and one-sixteenth brown.

7.20 A black animal crossed with an agouti produces offspring of which nine thirty-seconds are agouti, nine thirty-seconds black, three thirty-seconds cinnamon, three thirty-seconds brown, and one-fourth albino.

7.21 A dilute agouti animal crossed with a pink-eyed, spotted black produces three agouti offspring, one spotted agouti, two dilute agouti, two dilute spotted agouti, four cinnamon, one spotted cinnamon, and four albinos.

7.22 What will be the plumage color of the offspring of the following crosses in poultry, the genotypes of the parents being given:

$$Ii\ Cc \times ii\ Cc \qquad ii\ Cc \times Ii\ CC$$
$$II\ cc \times ii\ cc \qquad Ii\ cc \times ii\ Cc$$

7.23 In each of two different strains of maize, plants have been found which, when selfed, produce about three-fourths normal green and one-fourth lethal white ("albino") seedlings. If two such albino-producing plants, one from each strain, are crossed,

the F_1 is found to be all green, but certain of the F_2 populations are approximately nine-sixteenths green and seven-sixteenths white. Explain, giving genotypes.

7.24 In maize, the scutellum develops color only when certain aleurone genes and any two of the three genes S_2, S_3, and S_4 are present. Thus, $S_2S_2s_3s_3s_4s_4$ and $s_2s_2S_3S_3s_4s_4$ have colorless scutellum. What ratios in respect to scutellum color are to be expected in F_2 from

  a. Colorless × colorless
    $(S_2S_2s_3s_3s_4s_4 \times s_2s_2S_3S_3s_4s_4)$
  b. Colored × colored
    $(S_2S_2s_3s_3S_4S_4 \times s_2s_2S_3S_3S_4S_4)$

Would you classify the interaction of these genes as duplicate or complementary?

7.25 By calculating χ^2, determine whether the following F_2 population fits better a 3 : 3 : 1 : 1 ratio or a 27 : 21 : 9 : 7 ratio:

AB	Ab	aB	ab
290	225	97	92

On the basis of this test, what hypothesis would you adopt concerning the genotypes of the parents and the action of the genes involved, assuming that they affect aleurone color in maize?

8   MULTIPLE–FACTOR INHERITANCE

MENDEL WAS the first to offer a simple and reasonable explanation of the process of heredity in terms of the gene theory. His success was, as we have seen, due in part to his use of pea varieties that differed in clear-cut, visible traits. The flower color in his peas was either red or white, the seeds either yellow or green, either smooth or wrinkled, etc. This permitted Mendel to make accurate counts of individuals showing one or the other of these alternative traits. Mendel's successors continued to deal in the main with such clear-cut qualitative differences, and, as described in Chapter 7, they succeeded in unraveling many complex cases of gene interaction.

However, not all differences between individuals and between varieties or races are of this kind. Variations such as those in stature, weight, or intelligence in man, economically important traits in domestic animals and cultivated plants such as yield of fruits, seeds, or eggs and amount of milk or meat produced, do not usually fall into clear-

cut classes. These characters are quantitative rather than qualitative. All gradations occur between large and small, heavy and light, high-yielding and low-yielding. Mendel's methods of analysis are hard to apply to such continuously varying traits, because they seem to mix or blend, instead of segregate, in the offspring of hybrids. The inheritance of skin color in mulattoes, hybrids between Negroes and whites, seemed to be a striking example of such blending non-Mendelian heredity.

The problem of the inheritance of quantitative characters had sooner or later to be faced. The trail was blazed by the Swedish geneticist Nilsson-Ehle (1908) and the American geneticist East (1910, 1916), who showed that the apparently "blending" inheritance can be accounted for by supposing that continuously varying traits are due to joint action of several or many genes, each of which has individually only a small effect on the trait in question. Mather in England has in recent years evolved statis-

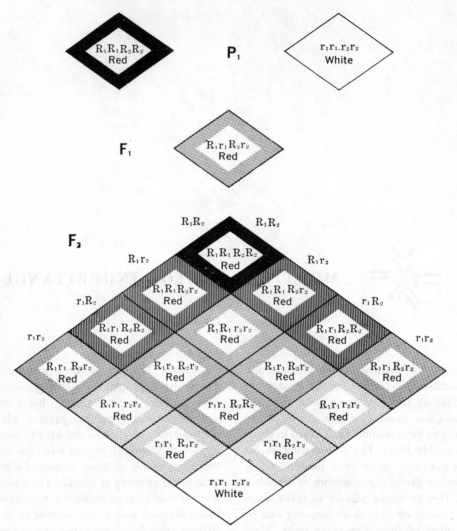

Fig. 8.1. Diagram showing the result of a cross between a red-kerneled and a white-kerneled wheat, where the red color is due to the operation of either or both of two genes, R_1 and R_2. The intensity of the red color is indicated by the density of the crosshatching.

tical methods for analysis of such multiple genes, which he calls *polygenes*. Undoubtedly much is to be revealed by further research on polygenic inheritance.

QUANTITATIVE AND QUALITATIVE TRAITS
Obviously no sharp dividing line can be drawn between these two kinds of traits. Mendel himself crossed tall and short peas

and showed that the difference in size was very simply inherited and caused by just one pair of alleles of a single gene. The tall and the short plants were so distinct that no measurements were needed. It is not precisely the "quantitative" nature of these variations which sets them apart from "qualitative" ones, but the fact that some variations are gradual or continuous so that clear-cut classes can be distinguished only with difficulty or not at all. Thus there occur all kinds of skin colors intermediate between that in nonalbino whites and that in the darkest Negroes.

Moreover, quantitative traits are often susceptible to environmental modification. The skin color of one person can be lighter or darker depending upon the amount of exposure to sunlight. Animals and plants grow larger and heavier with abundant food and on good soil. Polygenes, the genes that bring about heritable variations in quantitative traits, are not a separate category of genes. They are simply genes the different alleles of which produce small phenotypic differences, of about the same order of magnitude as the differences caused by usual environmental fluctuations. Polygenic inheritance is not a separate kind of heredity; it is heredity that must be studied with the aid of statistical techniques (cf. Chap. 29) rather than by simply counting the numbers of individuals belonging to a few easily distinguishable classes.

SEED COLOR IN WHEAT

Nilsson-Ehle crossed several varieties of wheat, some of which had red and others white kernels. Red is incompletely dominant over white, and the heterozygotes may have somewhat lighter red kernels than the homozygotes. In some crosses of red and white a simple ratio of 3 red : 1 white is found among the F_2 hybrids, indicating a single gene difference. In other crosses a ratio of 15 red : 1 white is found in the F_2. The conclusion is obvious (and verified by a study of F_3 generations raised from the red seeds of the F_2) that there are two pairs of genes for red, either of which can produce red kernels. These genes are *duplicates* of each other. The checkerboard in Figure 8.1 shows the genotypes of the F_2 plants with the numbers of red genes (capital R letters) possessed by each genotype. Only 1 of the 15 reds has all four genes for red and has dark-red seeds;

4 classes have three red genes; 6 have two; 4 have one red gene and have pale red seeds.

In still other crosses, 63 out of 64 of the F_2 wheat kernels were red and only 1 of 64 was white, a condition which suggested that three genes each capable of producing the red color were involved. If the red parent is represented by $R_1R_1R_2R_2R_3R_3$ and the white by $r_1r_1r_2r_2r_3r_3$, the F_1 generation has three color genes, $R_1r_1R_2r_2R_3r_3$. The genotypes that appear in the F_2 generation can easily be predicted by constructing a checkerboard with 64 cells. About 1 in 64 individuals will be like the red grandparent and will have six color genes; 6 in 64 will have five, 15 in 64 will have four, 20 in 64 will have three, 15 in 64 will have two, 6 in 64 will have one, and 1 in 64 will have no genes for the red color.

SKIN COLOR IN NEGRO AND WHITE CROSSES

The wheat seeds heterozygous for the R genes have only slightly less intense red colors than do the homozygotes, but Nilsson-Ehle noticed that the variation in the seed color observed in the F_2 generation was greater than in the F_1. This is expected, since the F_1 consists of individuals that are genotypically uniform, whereas in the F_2 a segregation takes place. The hypothesis of multiple factors, proposed to explain the inheritance of quantitative characters, assumes that some character differences are determined by series of independent genes. The effects of these genes are *cumulative*, or *additive*; i.e., each gene contributes a certain quantity of color, or height, or weight, or fertility, and the phenotype that develops shows a simple summation of these quantities. Dominance is usually absent or incomplete; the F_1 generation appears to have a blend of the characteristics of the parents. In the F_2 generation most individuals are still intermediate between the grandparents, and usually resemble the F_1 parents, as though the heredities of the strains crossed were thoroughly mixed or fused But some F_2 individuals are

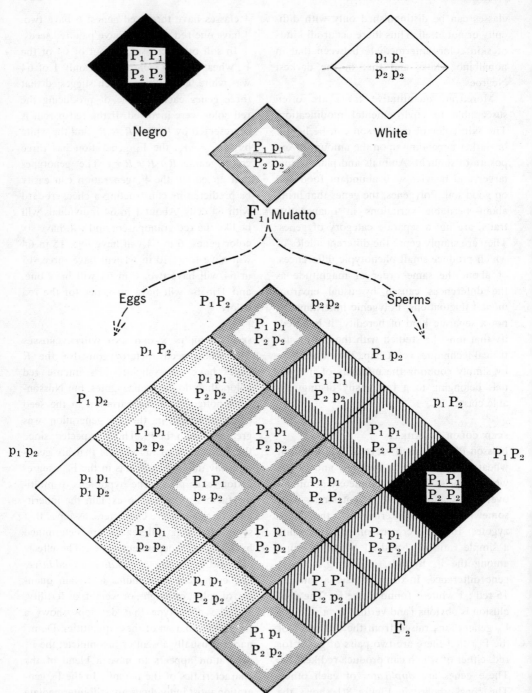

Fig. 8.2. The interaction of two hypothetical independent pairs of alleles (multiple factors) affecting skin color, as in matings of Negroes and whites. The sixteen possible combinations of F_1 gametes with their genotypes and phenotypes are shown in the F_2 checkerboard.

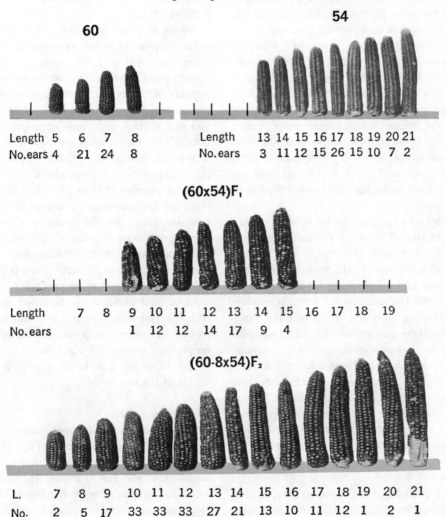

Fig. 8.3. The inheritance of ear length in maize, as shown by the results of crossing a short-eared variety of popcorn with a long-eared variety of sweet corn. Ears showing the range in length of the parent types are pictured above, with the F_1 and F_2 generations below. (*From East*)

60

54

Length	5	6	7	8
No. ears	4	21	24	8

Length	13	14	15	16	17	18	19	20	21
No. ears	3	11	12	15	26	15	10	7	2

(60x54)F_1

Length	7	8	9	10	11	12	13	14	15	16	17	18	19
No. ears				1	12	12	14	17	9	4			

(60-8x54)F_2

L.	7	8	9	10	11	12	13	14	15	16	17	18	19	20	21
No.	2	5	17	33	33	33	27	21	13	10	11	12	1	2	1

intermediate between the F_1 and the grandparents, and, finally, a minority of individuals may resemble the grandparents.

Davenport (1913) saw that the hypothesis of multiple factors explains the inheritance of a character which seemed baffling and even incompatible with the gene theory, namely skin color in mulattoes. He thought that the situation might be satisfactorily ac-

counted for by assuming that Negroes native to central and western Africa differ from whites in two pairs of pigment-forming genes showing no dominance (Fig. 8.2). Assume, then, that Negroes have four color genes, $P_1P_1P_2P_2$, and whites no color genes, $p_1p_1p_2p_2$. The first-generation mulattoes have two color genes, $P_1p_1P_2p_2$, and their color is intermediate between the parents.

The offspring of mulattoes (the F_2 generation of the Negro × white cross) would be like that shown in Figure 8.1 for the color of wheat kernels. More than a third (6 out of 16) of individuals among the F_2 mulattoes have two color genes and hence resemble the F_1 mulattoes in skin pigmentation. But 4 out of 16 have three color genes, and 4 out of 16 have only one (Fig. 8.2). These people will be intermediate in skin pigmentation between the F_1 mulattoes and the original Negro parents, and between the mulattoes and the original white parents respectively. Finally, 1 out of 16 F_2 individuals will have 4 color genes, and a pigmentation as dark as Negroes, and 1 out of 16 will have no color genes and a light skin resembling that of whites.

It is easy to predict also the skin pigmentation in the offspring of the backcrosses of the F_1 mulattoes $(P_1p_1P_2p_2)$ with whites and with Negroes. In the backcross mulatto × white, half the offspring will have one pigment gene (either P_1 or P_2) and a skin color intermediate between F_1 mulattoes and whites. One-quarter of the offspring will have two pigment genes and will resemble the F_1 mulattoes, and one-quarter will have no pigment genes and will resemble the whites. In the backcross mulatto × Negro, half the offspring will have three pigment genes, one-quarter two, and one-quarter four pigment genes. These people will range in skin pigmentation from that in F_1 mulattoes to that in Negroes.

It is probable that Davenport's hypothesis oversimplifies the situation. The difference in skin color between Negroes and whites seems to be due to more than two pairs of pigment genes, possibly to four or even more pairs. After all, considerable variation in skin color is observed among whites, and the variation is no less pronounced among African Negroes. Some of this variation assuredly has a genetic basis. These pigment genes are not necessarily equally potent; some may cause production of more pig-

ment than others. But Davenport's hypothesis is essentially correct in that the heredity of skin pigmentation in man is due to the action of several color genes with incomplete or with no dominance and with additive effects.

Owing to gene segregation, some persons in the offspring of mulattoes resemble in skin color, and also in other traits, people of "pure" white ancestry. One of the persistent popular beliefs is that such persons nevertheless carry Negro traits in their "blood" and that a black child may occasionally be born if they marry white persons. It is easy to see that this belief conflicts with Davenport's hypothesis. A "throwback" or "atavism" is possible if both parties to a marriage are heterozygous carriers of the same recessive gene. But the genes that govern skin pigmentation in man apparently show no dominance. If both parents carry such genes (for example, if their genotypes are $P_1p_1p_2p_2$ and $p_1p_1P_2p_2$ respectively), then some of their children can be either darker $(P_1p_1P_2p_2)$ or lighter $(p_1p_1p_2p_2)$ than either parent. But when one of the parents carries no pigment genes $(p_1p_1p_2p_2)$, no individual in the offspring can be darker than the darker of the two parents.

EAR SIZE IN MAIZE

One of the first successful applications of the polygene hypothesis was in East's study of the inheritance of the length and other dimensions of the ear in maize. He worked with two varieties: long-eared Black Mexican sweet corn and short-eared Tom Thumb popcorn. Figure 8.3 shows the parental varieties and the F_1 and F_2 generations following a cross between them. The ears have been arranged in classes differing by 1 cm in length, and under each class is given the number of individuals in that class. Thus in the F_1 there was 1 plant in which the ear was 9 cm long, there were 12 in which it was 10 cm long, and so on. Each of the parental varieties varied somewhat in ear length, and

TABLE 8.1

Frequency distributions expected in F_2 populations from crosses of parents differing in a dimensional trait by 12 units when the difference in the parents is determined by one, two, three, and six pairs of independent genes, with equal additive effects

Gene pairs	P_1	Class Centers F_1											P_2	n
	101	102	103	104	105	106	107	108	109	110	111	112	113	
1	1,024	...	...	.....	...	...	2,048	...	...	.....	...	...	1,024	4,096
2	256	...	...	1,024	...	...	1,536	...	...	1,024	...	...	256	4,096
3	64	...	384	.....	960	...	1,280	...	960	.....	384	...	64	4,096
6	1	12	66	220	495	792	924	792	495	220	66	12	1	4,096

the F_1 shows about the same degree of variability, although it is essentially intermediate between the two parents. In the F_2, however, there is a much greater range, from plants with ears as short as the shorter-eared grandparent to those with ears as long as the longer-eared grandparent. There are relatively few of these extreme types and a relatively large number of those that have intermediate ear length essentially like that of the F_1. This situation is similar in its essentials to that of kernel color in wheat, and although segregation into a series of distinct classes is impossible to demonstrate, the marked increase in variability of the F_2 as compared with the F_1 finds its simplest explanation in the segregation of a series of "multiple factors," each affecting ear length and all of them cumulative in their effect.

A size difference between two strains of plants or animals may be due to one, two, or several gene differences. A comparison of the kinds of segregations to be expected in the F_2 from parents whose differences in a quantitative trait such as size are due to 1, 2, 3, and 6 pairs of independent genes with equal and cumulative effects and without dominance is shown in Table 8.1. The frequencies will be recognized as proportional to the coefficients in the expansion of $(a + b)^n$ for the even powers from 2 to 12 corresponding to the number of alleles contributing to the total result. As the number of alleles increases, the relative frequency of the parental types recovered in the F_2 declines sharply and the different F_2 phenotypes are spread much more evenly over the range, approaching the type of continuous distribution obtained from the measurements of a continuously variable trait such as size in actual F_2 populations. A further discussion of the nature of observed distributions of quantitative characters is given in Chapter 29, especially in Sections 29.13, 29.20, and 29.21.

WHITE SPOTTING IN MICE

With polygenic inheritance, the number of genes segregating in the offspring of a cross may be hard to determine in the usual hybridization experiments. The reasons are that, first, the effects of individual genes on the phenotype may be obscured by variations due to environment, and, second, that the effects of one gene often interfere with the expression of other genes. In other words, the gene effects may not be simply additive, and gene interaction may complicate the situation.

Among mice homozygous for the gene, *ss,* for pied spotting, animals occur ranging from those with only a small white spot on the belly to those with an entirely white coat (Fig. 8.4). By selection it is possible to produce strains of mice which differ in the range of the spotted types they produce.

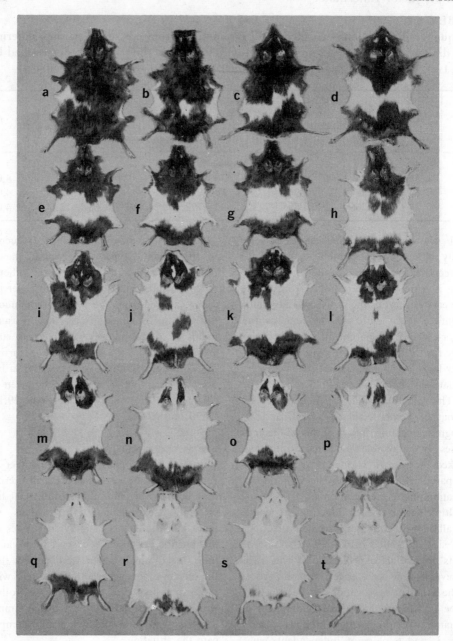

Fig. 8.4. Variation in piebald spotting in laboratory strains of mice, due to multiple factors interacting with each other and with *ss*, which is homozygous in all the varieties above. (*From Dunn and Charles*)

TABLE 8.2
Inheritance of quantitative differences in pied spotting
(*From Dunn and Charles*)

	Per cent of dorsal white																				
	0	5	10	15	20	25	30	35	40	45	50	55	60	65	70	75	80	85	90	95	100
P_1 line 118 (F_{7-14})	..	7	89	35	2	1															
P_1 line 19 (F_{7-8})	..	..	..	..	..	..	..	..	..	..	..	..	..	..	..	..	..	1	9	29	134
F_1 line 19 × line 118	..	..	..	..	1	1	4	3	3	10	7	9	9	7	1	1					
F_2 line 19 × line 118	..	..	1	2	6	15	10	12	14	19	27	29	28	19	34	21	14	2	3	2	
BC F_1 × line 19	..	..	..	..	..	..	..	..	..	..	..	..	5	16	33	24	15	10	9		12
P_1 line 190a (F_{10-17})	..	..	3	10	22	23	31	27	28	15	5										
P_1 line 19 (F_{7-8})	..	..	..	..	..	..	..	..	..	..	..	..	..	..	..	..	..	1	9	29	134
F_1 line 190a × line 19	..	..	..	..	..	..	..	..	..	..	..	..	1	5	4	1					
F_2 line 190a × line 19	..	..	..	..	..	..	..	..	..	2	5	1	7	16	29	45	10	3	2	3	2

The results of crossing some of these strains are shown in Table 8.2. As in the cross of corn varieties differing in ear length, the F_1 is intermediate, whereas the F_2 is more variable, and a few individuals within the range of the parent types are recovered. In a backcross of the F_1 with animals of the nearly all-white stock, the parental type was recovered with about the frequency that would be expected if three or four genes with quantitative effects were segregating in the F_1. The results suggest that the lighter and darker spotted strains differ by several genes $s_1 \ldots s_n$, whose effects cumulate with each other and with those of ss, the pied gene being common to all these strains. This conclusion was later confirmed by separating the $s_1 \ldots s_n$ genes from s and analyzing them in outcrosses. Similar evidence has been obtained for the multiplicity of white-spotting factors in guinea pigs, in rats, and in rabbits.

MODIFYING FACTORS

The type of interaction in which several genes with small expression, such as $s_2 s_2$, $s_3 s_3$ above, exert their chief actions by changing the magnitude of effect of a major gene, such as ss above, is sometimes referred to as modifying effect, and the minor genes as modifiers. In this case the modifiers have a small effect even when the major gene is not present, so that the effects of the modifiers and of the major gene are qualitatively similar. An analysis of genes producing white spotting in the guinea pig by Wright and Chase indicates a similar situation there, though probably with more genes concerned. Castle, by selecting lighter and darker variants of the hooded (white-spotted) rat, produced strains that apparently differed by many modifiers with small effects, and this type of interaction is probably a common one. The complex of modifiers in a stock, which determines small effects and alters the expression of other genes introduced into it, is sometimes referred to collectively as the residual heredity of the stock. Because of the number of genes involved, it is usually difficult to analyze such complexes into single gene components.

SPECIFIC MODIFIERS

In a few cases it has been shown that multiple genes, or polygenes, exist which have little or no effect themselves on the particular trait under consideration, except in the presence of some specific main gene that they modify. Thus, in certain strains of mice, there occurs a form of spotting known as

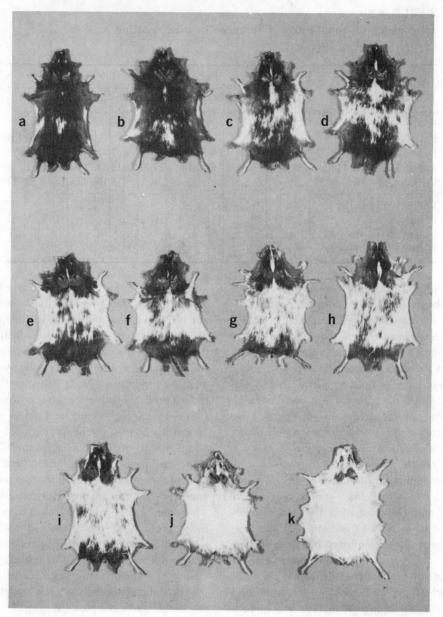

Fig. 8.5. Variation in variegated white spotting in laboratory strains of mice differing in the number of mutant modifiers of the heterozygous effect of the gene W (in WwSs) from few (upper left) to many (lower right).

TABLE 8.3
The effects of specific modifiers $m(W)$ on the dominance of the spotting mutation W in house mice

Parents	Genotype for W and s	Progeny: Condition of $m(W)$ loci	Progeny: Phenotype in per cent dorsal white	Progeny: Proportions
Light variegated	*WWSS*	$m_1m_2 \ldots m_x$	100	¾ white
WwSS × *WwSS*	*WwSS*		90–95	
	wwSS		0–5	¼ unspotted
Unspotted	*WWSS*	$M_1M_2 \ldots M_x$	100	¼ white
WwSS × *WwSS*	*WwSS*		0	¾ unspotted
	wwSS		0	
Medium variegated	*WWSS*	$M_1m_2M_3m_x$	100	¼ white
WwSS × *WwSS*	*WwSS*		20–80	½ spotted
	wwSS		0	¼ unspotted
Black-eyed white	*WWss*	$m_1m_2 \ldots m_x$	100	¾ white
Wwss × *Wwss*	*Wwss*		100	
	wwss		50–90	¼ spotted
Intermediate spotted	*WWss*	$M_1M_2 \ldots M_x$	100	¼ white
Wwss × *Wwss*	*Wwss*		50–100	¾ spotted
	wwss		0–50	

variegated (Fig. 8.5). Such variegated mice are heterozygous for a dominant gene *W*, which is lethal when homozygous, *WW* mice usually dying shortly after birth with a severe anemia. When, rarely, they live long enough to develop hair, they are seen to be entirely white with black eyes; that is, the white spotting covers the entire coat. The degree of white spotting of the heterozygotes, however, depends not only on *W* but on a complex of polygenes, each with a small effect, which determine the effect of *W* (Table 8.3). If many of these modifiers are present, the *Ww* coat is nearly all white; if a few or none are present, *Ww* mice have little or no white. These modifiers have, however, little or no effect in *ww* mice; even with the maximum number present, the animal is unspotted unless *W* is also present.

One effect of these modifying genes is thus to determine the degree of expression or dominance of *W*. When all of the modifiers are present, the cross of *Ww* × *Ww* produces offspring in the ratio of ¾ white (¼ *WW*, ²⁄₄ *Ww*): ¼ unspotted (*ww*); when part of them are present, the offspring consist of ¼ white (*WW*), ½ variegated (*Ww*), and ¼ unspotted (*ww*); and when none is present, the progeny are ¼ white (*WW*) and ¾ unspotted (*Ww* and *ww*). This is a clear-cut demonstration of the fact that dominance in a pair of alleles is determined by the interaction of other genes.

Modifiers like these may be referred to as specific, since their expression seems to depend upon interaction with one specific genotype. This type of interaction probably intergrades imperceptibly with the more general, less specific modifying effects of other genes with quantitative effects. Because of the mutual interaction among many genes in producing a phenotype, it is probable that most genes may function as modifiers.

PROBLEMS

8.1 The F_1 generation from pure parent types differing in a size character is usually no more variable than the parents. Explain.

8.2 If two pure types, differing in a size character, are crossed, is it possible for individuals in the F_2 to be more extreme than either grandparent? Explain.

8.3 Why is it, when selection has ceased to be effective in producing changes in a given stock, that if this stock is crossed with another similar one, selection among the subsequent offspring is often able to produce a marked change?

8.4 As a result of crosses involving a size character, it is often found that F_3 families raised from selfed F_2 plants differ markedly in their variability. Some are almost as low as the original parents, some a little higher, and some as high as the F_2 itself. None exceeds the F_2 in variability, however. Explain these facts.

8.5 It frequently happens that one character of a plant, such as number of seeds, is much more variable than another character, such as weight of seeds. What explanations for this difference can you suggest?

8.6 Certain groups of individuals, when their frequency distribution for some continuously variable character is plotted, show a bimodal or multimodal curve. What different explanations can you make for this fact?

NOTE: Assume that in man the difference in skin color between Negro and white is due to two pairs of factors; that *AA BB* is "black" and *aa bb* "white"; and that any three of the color-producing factors produce "dark" skin; any two, "medium"; and any one, "light."

8.7 What will be the skin color of the offspring from a mating of white with black; from a mating of two individuals genotypically like these F_1 offspring?

8.8 What are the genotypes of the parents in the two following matings of Negroes: medium × light, giving one-eighth dark, three-eighths medium, three-eighths light, one-eighth white; medium × light, giving one-half medium and one-half light?

8.9 Can two mulattoes have white-skinned offspring? Can two white-skinned people have dark-skinned offspring? Explain.

8.10 Assume that the red kernel color of a certain race of wheat is due to the presence of three independent genes R_1, R_2, and R_3. Any one of the genes singly will cause the red color. White is $r_1r_1r_2r_2r_3r_3$. What are the genotypes of the parents in each of the following crosses: red × red giving 3 red : 1 white; red × red giving 15 red : 1 white; red × red giving 63 red : 1 white; red × red giving 7 red : 1 white; red × white giving 1 red : 1 white; red × white giving 3 red : 1 white; red × white giving 7 red : 1 white; red × white giving all red?

8.11 Assume that the difference between a race of oats yielding about 4 grams per plant and one yielding 10 is due to three equal and cumulative multiple-factor pairs *AA BB CC*. Cross one type with the other. What will be the phenotypes of the F_1; of the F_2?

8.12 Assume that in squashes the difference in fruit weight between a 3-pound type and a 6-pound type is due to three factor pairs *AA*, *BB*, and *CC*, each factor contributing ½ pound to fruit weight. Cross a 3-pound plant (*aa bb cc*) with a 6-pound one. What will be the phenotypes of the F_1; of the F_2?

8.13 In the following squash crosses, what will be the range in fruit weight of the offspring, on the assumption made in the previous problem:

> *Aa Bb CC* × *aa Bb Cc*
> *AA bb Cc* × *Aa BB cc*
> *Aa Bb Cc* × *Aa Bb Cc*
> *aa BB cc* × *AA BB cc*

8.14 Assume in the following three problems that the difference between a corn plant 10 decimeters high and one 26 decimeters high is due (in so far as it is caused by inheritance) to four pairs of equal and cumulative multiple factors, the 26-decimeter plant being *AA BB CC DD* and the 10-decimeter one *aa bb cc dd*. What will be the size and genotype of an F_1 from a cross between these two pure types? Give the limits of variation in height which the offspring of the following crosses will show:

> *Aa BB cc dd* × *Aa bb Cc dd*
> *aa BB cc dd* × *Aa Bb Cc dd*
> *AA BB Cc DD* × *aa BB cc Dd*
> *Aa Bb Cc Dd* × *Aa bb Cc Dd*

8.15 Two 14-decimeter corn plants, when crossed, give nothing but 14-decimeter offspring. Two other 14-decimeter plants give one 18-decimeter, four 16-decimeter, six 14-decimeter, four 12-decimeter, and one 10-decimeter plants. Two other 14-decimeter plants when crossed give one 16-decimeter, two 14-decimeter, and one 12-decimeter plants. What genotypes for each of these 14-decimeter parent plants would explain these results? By selection in any of these families would it be possible to get a plant taller than 18 decimeters?

8.16 A breeder has a 26-decimeter starchy and a 10-decimeter sweet corn. Starchiness is dominant over sweetness and is due to a single factor. He wants a 26-decimeter sweet corn. Assume that height is due to four factor pairs, as before. If he wants this new type of corn in two years, how many plants should he raise in the F_2 of the cross between

tall starchy and short sweet to be reasonably sure of getting it? If he has more time, what would you advise him to do in order not to have to raise such a big crop in the F_2 and subsequent generations?

NOTE: Problems 8.17–8.23 refer to the cross of line 19 × line 118 in Table 8.2.

8.17 Calculate the mean and standard deviation of the distribution of per cent of dorsal white for the F_1 and the F_2.

8.18 Obtain confidence intervals with .95 confidence coefficient for the mean of F_1 and the mean of F_2 by the method presented in Section 29.25. (Cf. Sec. 29.22)

8.19 Test the hypothesis that the true means of F_1 and F_2 are the same. What is the confidence interval with .95 confidence coefficient for the difference by the method presented in Section 29.27?

8.20 Test the hypothesis that the standard deviation is the same in F_1 and F_2, using the method presented in Section 29.31 or the F test explained in statistics textbooks.

8.21 What is the confidence interval with .99 confidence coefficient for the standard deviation of the F_2?

8.22 Calculate the mean and variance for each of the two P_1's and the average of the two P_1 means (often called the *mid-parent value*). Calculate a confidence interval with .95 confidence coefficient for the difference between the mid-parent value and the F_1 mean, using as your estimate for the standard error of the difference

$$s_{\text{diff.}} = \sqrt{\frac{s^2}{N}(19) + \frac{s^2}{N}(119) + \frac{s^2}{N}(F_1)}$$

8.23 In Problem 8.22, what value would you expect the difference to take in the absence of dominance and epistasis? How might dominance and epistasis affect it?

9 ALLELISM AND PLEIOTROPISM

HOW DO WE know that genes exist? Their existence is inferred from observations of segregation and recombination of bodily characters in the offspring of hybrids and heterozygotes. The behavior of flower color in crosses between red and white varieties of peas is the evidence that in peas there is a gene for flower color. If all pea plants were red-flowered or all were white, one could not observe segregation in flower color in hybrids and consequently would not know that a gene for flower color exists. Similarly, if all men were brown-eyed or all blue-eyed, the eye-color genes would not be known in man. Now, genetically different flower colors are found in peas because the genes influencing flower color changed by mutation at some time in the past, giving rise to two variants, or alleles, of these genes. Similarly, somewhere in the ancestry of the human species an eye-color gene underwent a change giving rise to the allele for blue eyes and the allele for brown. Only those genes are known which have mutated to give rise

to at least two distinguishably different alleles. Of course, the mutations may have taken place many generations in the past. However, at present there is no way to detect genes that have not mutated at all or genes which have changed but of which only one allele survives.

MULTIPLE ALLELES

The examples of Mendelian heredity discussed in the preceding chapters dealt with segregation of genes each of which had only two alternative expressions, or *alleles*. However, many and possibly all genes can change in several or in many different ways. These changes give rise to several alternative states or variants of the gene, which are called *multiple alleles*.

THE ALBINO SERIES OF COAT COLORS IN RABBITS

The pink-eyed white (albino) condition in rabbits (Fig. 9.1, top) is recessive to the colored condition. Crosses of albinos with colored rabbits produce colored F_1 progeny, which when inbred produces an F_2 generation with segregation in the ratio ¾ colored : ¼ albino. Color, C, and albinism, c^a, thus form a pair of alleles. There is another form of albinism in rabbits known as *Hima-*

Fig. 9.1. Three alleles of a gene for coat color in rabbits (bottom, fully colored, C^+C^+; *center*, Himalayan albinism, c^hc^h; top, complete albinism c^ac^a). (*From Castle*)

are ¾ colored and ¼ Himalayan. Himalayan albinism, c^h, and color, C, are alleles. The critical experiment is, then, crossing Himalayan with albino rabbits. If Himalayan and albino are due to changes in different genes, each type should carry the domi-

layan albinism (Fig. 9.1, center). Himalayans have pink eyes, and their fur is white except for the feet, tail, ears, and the tip of the nose, which are black or dark brown. When these are crossed with fully colored rabbits, the F_1 is colored and in the F_2 there

nant allele of the other and reversion to full color should occur in F_1. Actually, the cross of Himalayan with albino produces all Himalayan in F_1 and ¾ Himalayan to ¼ albino in F_2. Reversion does not occur. The Himalayan allele and the albino allele are never present in the same gamete; a colored animal may carry either Himalayan or albino but never both. It is evident that Himalayan and albino are allelic to each other and that both are allelic to full color. The colored, Himalayan, and albino alleles are three variants of the same gene.

Several other light coat colors in rabbits also behave as alleles of albino and of Himalayan. These show absence of dominance with each other. An example is chinchilla, which is less intense in color than the wild gray (agouti) type. When chinchilla is crossed with albino, the F_1 animals are light gray, intermediate between the parents, and the F_2 consists of 1 chinchilla : 2 light gray : 1 albino. This shows that F_1 is heterozygous for chinchilla (c^{ch}) and for albinism (c^a) alleles. The genotypes of these members of the albino series of coat colors in rabbits may therefore be written as follows:

Genotype	Phenotype
$C\,C$	wild type
$C\,c^{ch},\ C\,c^{h},\ C\,c^{a}$	wild type
$c^{ch}\,c^{ch}$	chinchilla
$c^{ch}\,c^{h},\ c^{ch}\,c^{a}$	light gray
$c^{h}\,c^{h}$	Himalayan
$c^{h}\,c^{a}$	Himalayan
$c^{a}\,c^{a}$	albino

There are, in addition, several other alleles that are lighter than the wild type but darker than Himalayan. The wild-type allele is dominant to all the mutant alleles. Otherwise, the compounds of most of the alleles are intermediate in coat color. All the mutant alleles and their compounds show the temperature sensitivity of Himalayan which was described on page 25.

ALBINISM IN OTHER ANIMALS

Similar series of alleles of the albino gene are known in the mouse, the rat, the guinea pig, and the cat. In the cat, one of the alleles of the albino series gives the so-called Siamese color highly prized by cat fanciers. In man, it is possible that some persons with very little pigment in the hair and skin also contain an allele of albinism. Human albinos, like the full albinos of other mammals, are homozygous for the lowest member of this allelic series. The mutation from full color, C, to the albino allele, c^a, has occurred in nearly all mammals; but because of the weakness of eyesight and the sensitiveness of unpigmented skin, albinos are known chiefly in domesticated animals and are seldom found in the wild state.

One series of alleles among the many known in *Drosophila melanogaster* is the series called "white-eye" because it consists of alleles of white, one of the first mutants. The homozygotes form a series of eye colors of increasing intensity from white, through yellowish, to red, as shown in the partial list in Table 9.1. In this series, the eye colors of the heterozygous compounds are about intermediate between those in the parent homozygous types, whereas the wild-type allele is dominant to all others.

TABLE 9.1
Alleles of white in *Drosophila melanogaster*

Allele	Symbol	Allele	Symbol
white	w	apricot	w^a
ivory	w^i	cherry	w^{ch}
pearl	w^p	eosin	w^e
tinged	w^t	blood	w^{bl}
buff	w^{bf}	coral	w^{co}
honey	w^h	red (wild type)	W

MOSAIC DOMINANCE

Members of a series of multiple alleles may affect different combinations of traits or body parts of the organism. Stadler investigated a series of alleles of the gene R in maize which determine the purple (anthocyanin) coloration of different parts of the plant. Four of these alleles have the following effects

R^r—colored seed (aleurone), colored plant
R^g—colored seed (aleurone), colorless plant
r^r—colorless seed (aleurone), colored plant
r^g—colorless seed (aleurone), colorless plant

In compounds, the colored condition is dominant over the colorless. Thus $R^g r^r$ plants have both colored aleurone and colored leaves and stalks. This gene behaves

as though it consists of at least two parts or components, one of which determines aleurone color and the other plant color. Furthermore, the aleurone color component may change (mutate) separately from the plant color component, although the two kinds of changes are not independent.

Different alleles of the gene scute in Dro-

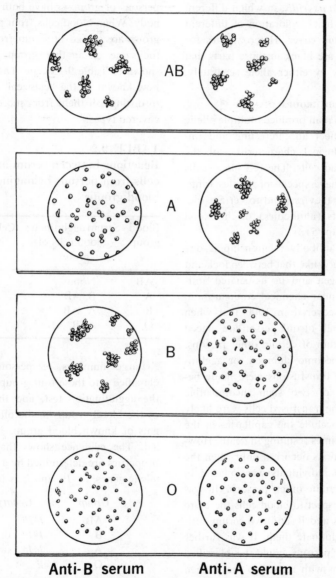

Anti-B serum   **Anti-A serum**

Fig. 9.2. Appearance of red blood cells of the four "classical" blood groups when tested by anti-B serum from a person of blood group A (left) and anti-A serum from a person of blood group B (right).

sophila remove different combinations of bristles on the fly's body. Serebrovsky and Dubinin showed that the heterozygous compounds have all the bristles that are present in homozygotes for either allele and lack only those bristles that are removed by both alleles. An even more remarkable case of this sort has been described by Tan in the beetle *Harmonia axyridis,* in which different alleles produce black coloration of different parts of the wing cover. Heterozygotes for any two alleles are black in those parts that are made black by either allele separately.

THE O-A-B BLOOD GROUPS IN MAN

Several genes in man produce multiple allelic series which affect an interesting and important physiological characteristic of the human red blood cells. The red blood cells (erythrocytes) have special properties (antigens) by which they respond to certain specific components (antibodies) of the blood serum (see Chap. 5).

The antigen-antibody relationship is one of great specificity, like that between lock and key. Each antigen and its associated antibody has a peculiar chemical configuration. Landsteiner discovered in 1900 that when the red blood cells of one person are placed in the blood serum of certain other persons, the cells may become clumped, or agglutinated. If blood transfusions were made between persons of two such incompatible blood groups, the transfused cells were likely to clump and occlude the capillaries in the recipient, sometimes resulting in death. However, such reactions occurred only when the cells of certain individuals were placed in serum from certain other persons. It was found that in respect to blood cells there are two antigens, A and B, and two serum antibodies that agglutinate them. It was further found that all persons could be classified into four groups with regard to the antigen property of the blood cells, those with antigen A (group A), those with antigen B (group B), those with both A and B (group

AB) and those with neither antigen (group O) (Fig. 9.2). Persons of group A have the antigen A but no antibody that agglutinates A cells; however, they do have antibodies that agglutinate B cells; persons of group B have no antibodies that agglutinate B but do have antibodies that agglutinate A; persons of group AB have neither type of antibody; persons of group O have both types of antibody. When blood cells from persons of one group are placed in serum from persons of the same or another group, the reactions shown in Table 9.2 occur. These groups are now known as the "classical" blood groups to distinguish them from more recently discovered types.

TABLE 9.2
Reactions between serum and red blood cells from persons belonging to different blood groups

Blood group	Serum agglutinates blood cells of group	Cells agglutinated by serum of group
AB	None	O, A, B
A	B, AB	O, B
B	A, AB	O, A
O	A, B, AB	None

Large numbers of persons have been classified into these four groups by means of the agglutination test, and the distribution of the blood groups in the offspring of parents of known blood groups has been studied. The evidence shows that these blood properties are determined by a series of three allelic genes, I^A, I^B, and i, as follows:

Group	Genotype
AB	$I^A I^B$
B	$I^B I^B$ or $I^B i$
A	$I^A I^A$ or $I^A i$
O	ii

I^A is a gene for the production of the antigen (isoagglutinogen) A, I^B for antigen B, and i for neither antigen. Additional alleles

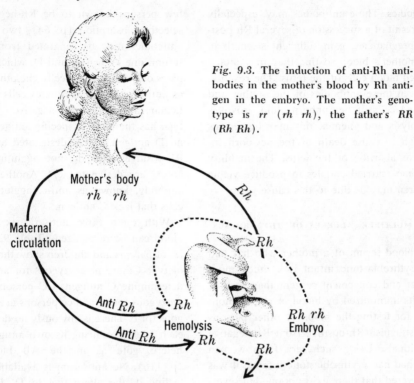

Fig. 9.3. The induction of anti-Rh antibodies in the mother's blood by Rh antigen in the embryo. The mother's genotype is *rr* (*rh rh*), the father's *RR* (*Rh Rh*).

are known but are omitted for the sake of simplicity.

The existence of these alleles in man and the ease with which the blood groups can be identified have obvious practical applications in blood transfusion, cases of disputed parentage, and description of human populations (see Chaps. 5 and 20). The alleles of these genes, which affect a variety of biochemical properties of the blood, act in such a way that in the heterozygous compound $I^A I^B$ each allele produces its own characteristic and specific effect; the cells of the heterozygote contain both antigens A and B. On the other hand, I^A and I^B both show complete dominance over *i*, which lacks both antigens.

THE DISCOVERY OF THE "RHESUS" ALLELES IN MAN

A very interesting series of alleles affecting the antigens of human blood has been discovered through the work of Landsteiner,

Wiener, Levine, Mourant, Race, Sanger, and several others. The original discovery was that the red cells of about 85 per cent of the population of New York City are Rh-positive; that is, they are agglutinated by a serum prepared by immunizing rabbits against the blood of rhesus monkeys. The antigen responsible for this reaction was consequently called the *rhesus factor,* and the gene that causes this property was denoted as *R-r* (or *Rh-rh*).

Interest in this factor was stimulated by Levine's study of a characteristic form of anemia, known as *erythroblastosis fetalis,* which occurs occasionally in newborn infants. It was found that the infants suffering from this anemia are usually Rh-positive and so are their fathers; but their mothers are Rh-negative. The origin of the disease was explained as follows (Fig. 9.3). The Rh-positive fetus developing in the uterus of an Rh-negative mother causes the formation in the mother's blood stream of anti-Rh antibodies. These antibodies may, especially as a result of a succession of several Rh-positive pregnancies, gain sufficient strength in the mother's blood so that they may attack the red blood cells of the fetus. The reaction between these antibodies of the mother and the red cells of her unborn child provokes hemolysis and anemia; this may be serious enough to cause death of the newborn infant or abortion of the fetus. The inability of some married couples to produce viable children may be due to this cause.

THE MULTIPLE ALLELES OF THE "RHESUS" SERIES

The blood serum of a mother who has had an erythroblastotic infant is a much more potent and convenient reagent than sera of rabbits immunized by blood of rhesus monkeys for testing the blood of other persons to distinguish Rh-positive from Rh-negative individuals. Using such sera from women who had had erythroblastotic infants, it was discovered that there exist not one but several kinds of Rh-positive and negative persons. The situation is most easily described by saying that there is not one Rh antigen but there are several different ones detected by specific antisera. Thus an Rh-negative woman, immunized during pregnancy by her Rh-positive children, may have in her blood serum antibodies that agglutinate not only Rh-positive red cells but also cells from a

few persons known to be Rh-negative. By selective absorption (p. 64), two kinds of antibodies may be separated from such a serum, one known as anti-D, which agglutinates only Rh-positive cells, the other known as anti-C, which agglutinates cells of a particular rare type of Rh-negative. The latter type has therefore a specific antigen, C, but no D antigen, and is designated as Cd; the Rh-positives that do not agglutinate with anti-C are designated cD. Another specific antibody, known as anti-c, agglutinates all cells that lack C antigen.

With these three antisera six types of blood can be recognized (Table 9.3). Studies of parents and children show that persons of type Cc are heterozygous for an allele *C* determining C antigen; CC persons are homozygous for *C*, and cc persons are homozygous for *c*. There is obviously no dominance, each allele producing its own antigen in the heterozygote as in the AB blood type (p. 116). No antiserum is available for detecting d, the alternative to D; D-positive persons may be heterozygous or homozygous. However, the genotypes of such persons may be diagnosed from their progeny: for example, a D-positive person who has a d-negative child is thereby shown to be *Dd*.

Two other specific antibodies, anti-E and anti-e, have been found; these detect the antigens E and e determined by a pair of alleles *E* and *e*. The three elementary types

TABLE 9.3
Agglutination reactions of red cells of different persons to three specific Rh antisera

Positive reactions +, negative reactions —

Anti-D	Anti-C	Anti-c		Rh type
+	+	+	*CcD*	(Rh-positive)
+	+	—	*CCD*	(Rh-positive)
+	—	+	*ccD*	(Rh-positive)
—	+	+	*Ccd*	(Rh-negative)
—	+	—	*CCd*	(Rh-negative)
—	—	+	*ccd*	(Rh-negative)

of antigens, C-c, D, and E-e, occur in fixed combinations that are always inherited together, as alleles of a single gene. Two systems of nomenclature are used for the alleles of this gene, one devised by Fisher and the other by Wiener (Table 9.4).

TABLE 9.4
The Rh system of alleles

Fisher's symbols	Wiener's symbols	
CDE	R^z	
CDe	R^1	Rh-positive
cDE	R^2	
cDe	R^0	
CdE	r^y	
Cde	r'	Rh-negative
cdE	r''	
cde	r	

Some of the genotypes in which these alleles occur can be detected directly from the phenotypes, that is, from the reactions of the red cells to antisera. Thus red cells with the reactions C+, c−, D−, E−, and e+ must be from a person of type *CCdee;* the genotype must be *Cde/Cde(r'/r');* red cells with the reactions C−, c+, D−, E−, e+ indicate the genotype *cde/cde(r/r)*, etc. Other genotypes can be deduced only from knowledge of the phenotypes of both parents and children. Thus where a child is *cde/cde(r/r)*, although neither parent is, both parents must be heterozygous for this allele as in the mating [*CDe(R^1)/cde(r)*] ×[*cDE(R^2)/cde(r)*].

The existence of such a series of eight different alternative arrangements of three kinds of antigens has of course led to the suspicion that these are not allelic states of the same gene but rather that the Rh locus consists of a cluster of three closely associated genes C-c, D-d, E-e. At present, the inheritance of these properties in families can be explained by assuming that they are multiple alleles; only future research will determine whether another interpretation is necessary.

SELF-STERILITY ALLELES

Other multiple allelic series that are especially interesting are those causing self-sterility and self-incompatibility in certain plants. Most higher plants and many lower animals are, as we know, hermaphrodites that produce normally functioning gametes of both sexes. In some hermaphrodites, such as the peas used by Mendel, self-fertilization occurs normally, and no barrier exists to the union of the male and female gametes of the same individual and the same flower. In other hermaphrodites, such as the sea-squirt Ciona, a peculiar self-sterility, or self-incompatibility, prevents the union of egg and sperm of the same individual. Among the higher plants, some species are entirely self-sterile and will set seed only when pollinated by a different individual of the same species. With certain other individuals, however, these same plants are also cross-sterile.

In the genus Nicotiana (tobacco), these self- and cross-incompatibilities are due to the existence of a long series of alleles of one gene, designated as $S^1, S^2, S^3, \ldots, S^n$. Pollen grains containing a certain allele, say S^1, fail to grow properly in the style of a plant that carries the same allele. Thus, if a plant S^1S^2 is pollinated by its own pollen or by the pollen of another S^1S^2 plant, no pollen grains will reach the ovules in time to effect fertilization. A cross of S^1S^2 ♀ with S^2S^3 ♂ yields offspring of classes S^1S^3 and S^2S^3 only. S^2S^3 ♀ × S^1S^2 ♂ gives offspring S^1S^3 and S^1S^2. In all crosses in which the parents have one allele in common, the mother's class is not found among the offspring; this means that the presence of an allele in the mother's tissue prevents the growth of pollen grains that carry that same allele. If, however, a plant S^1S^2 is crossed with S^3S^4, the crosses yield offspring of all four types, S^1S^3, S^1S^4, S^2S^3, and S^2S^4. This hypothesis, which is illustrated in Table 9.5, has been tested in

TABLE 9.5
Progeny obtained from representatives of three genotypic classes in *Nicotiana*

Female parent	Male parent		
	S^1S^3	S^1S^2	S^2S^3
S^1S^3	No offspring	S^1S^2 S^2S^3	S^1S^2 S^2S^3
S^1S^2	S^1S^3 S^2S^3	No offspring	S^1S^3 S^2S^3
S^2S^3	S^1S^2 S^1S^3	S^1S^2 S^1S^3	No offspring

various ways and gives a satisfactory explanation of the results not only in Nicotiana, where 15 alleles have been found, but in several other genera as well. In *Oenothera organensis,* Sterling Emerson found 37 different compatibility alleles in 500 plants. Even longer series have been detected in red clover.

The alleles that determine self-sterility apparently produce their effects by controlling the rate of pollen-tube growth. In compatible combinations the pollen tubes grow more and more rapidly as they approach the ovule, but in incompatible ones they grow so slowly that before the gamete reaches the ovule the flower has withered. This is probably due to a gene-controlled reaction between the diploid tissue of the female sporophyte and the haploid gametophytic tissue of the pollen tube. In this reaction each allele acts separately. Thus, a plant S^1S^3 discriminates against both S^1 and S^3 pollen by opposing the growth of S^1 and S^3 pollen tubes, whence such alleles have been called oppositional alleles. The separate action of such alleles resembles that of I^A and I^B in the blood group AB, in which two separate antigens are produced.

UNIT CHARACTERS
Mendel's great contribution to biology was the demonstration that heredity is transmitted from parents to offspring in the form of separable units called genes. An individual may receive from his father and his mother two unlike alleles of the same gene. For example, a person may inherit a gene responsible for the production of the antigen A in his blood cells from one parent and its allele for the antigen B from the other parent. As we know, in such a heterozygote the unlike alleles do not fuse or mix but segregate cleanly when the hybrid produces its gametes. Furthermore, different nonallelic paternal and maternal genes are assorted freely in the hybrid and form new combinations in the offspring of a heterozygote.

However, it should be understood clearly that the existence of genes in the chromosomes of sex cells and other cells is inferred from observations of the characters or traits, that is, from the phenotypic manifestation of the genes in the parents that are crossed and in the offspring they produce. What we actually see are not genes but the colors of flowers or of seeds in peas, production or nonproduction of seeds in tobacco plants, blood cells agglutinated or free in certain human sera, etc. What, then, are the relations between the genes in the chromosomes and the visible characters of the organism?

In the early years of the study of genetics following 1900, some authorities liked to speak of the inheritance of "unit characters" determined by unit genes. In Mendel's experiments with peas, the color of the flowers behaved as a unit character, and it proved to be separable from the color of the seeds, from the shape of the seeds, etc. This way of speaking and writing is, however, fraught with danger, since it may suggest that genes are, like Darwin's hypothetical gemmules (1868) or Weismann's determinants (1892), representatives in the sex cells of separate body parts of the organism that develops from them, in other words that the body is preformed in the sex cells (see Chap. 1). In reality the body develops from the fertilized egg epigenetically, by a series of successive transformations of the whole organism, not by a gradual assembling of independent unit characters. Therefore, when we speak of genes "for" a flower color, or for size, or for blood antigens, or for intelligence, or for a certain disease, etc., we are using shorthand expressions which should not be taken too literally.

The body develops as a whole, not as a mosaic of independent characters. A "character" such as body size is actually an abstraction, a convenient word to describe our observations concerning how different bodies are built and how these differences are inherited. Obviously, "body size" does not exist apart from a body, and intelligence does not exist apart from a person with all his other characters and qualities. We do not inherit stature or intelligence as such. As explained in Chapter 2, we really inherit the genes contained in the sex cells of our parents. However, these genes make the development of the individual follow certain paths from fertilization to death. These developmental paths lead, in certain environmental conditions, to the attainment at a certain age of a definite body stature and a certain intellectual capacity. The path which the development takes is conditioned by all the genes which the organism has, although changes in some of these genes produce alleles that influence chiefly skin color, others that influence the composition of the blood, still others the body size, eyesight, or intelligence, etc.

PLEIOTROPISM

We have seen, especially in Chapters 6 and 7, that many characters are determined not by single genes but by cooperation, or interaction, of several or many genes. This is probably true of all characters when they are investigated in detail. Now it must be pointed out that the reverse is also true, since many, and possibly all, genes influence several or many characters.

Mendel himself noted that one of the genes he studied affected simultaneously the color of the flowers (red or white), the color of the seeds (gray or brown), and the presence or absence of reddish spots in the axils of the leaves (Fig. 3.2). Similarly, the inheritance of wing length in crosses of normal and vestigial-winged Drosophila flies (Fig. 3.7) is described by saying that the dominant normal allele of the "vestigial gene" produces long wings and the recessive allele gives rise to vestigial wings. This gene is sometimes called a "wing gene." Indeed, the change which first strikes our eye when the recessive allele is substituted for the dominant one is the reduction in size of wings. Yet when normal and vestigial flies are carefully compared, many differences come to light. Apart from short wings, vestigial flies have also modified balancers (*halteres*); the bristles of a certain pair on the dorsal side of the fly are erect instead of horizontal; the shape of the spermatheca is changed; the number of egg strings in the ovaries is decreased compared to normal when the vestigial larvae are well fed but relatively increased when they are poorly fed; length of life and fecundity are lowered; and there are still other differences.

When an allele or alleles cause changes in two or more parts or characters that are not obviously related, the gene is called *pleiotropic* or is said to have multiple, or manifold, effects. The "vestigial gene" might just as well be called a "bristle gene" or a "fecundity gene" as a "wing gene." Careful studies show that many, perhaps all, genes are pleiotropic, although as a rule one trait produced by a gene change appears more striking than others. It must also be remembered that when red-flowered peas, homozygous for the dominant allele *C*, are compared with white-flowered ones, *cc*, the comparison discloses only the changes in the phenotype due to the difference between *C* and *c*. In other words,

such a comparison does not necessarily tell us what the sum total of effects of either *C* or *c* is upon the organism. In order to find out all the effects of these genes one would have to compare *CC* and *cc* plants with others in which neither *C* nor *c* is present, which carry no allele of *C* at all. Such physical absences of a gene or genes are called *deficiencies* and will be discussed in a later chapter. In most cases, they lead to the death of the organism and thus act as lethals (cf. p. 126).

PROBLEMS

9.1 In rabbits, full color (*C*), Himalayan albinism (*c^h*), and albinism (*c^a*) form a series of multiple alleles with dominance in the order given. What will be the appearance of the offspring of the following crosses:

    a. colored × Himalayan (both homozygous)
    b. F$_2$ from a
    c. Himalayan × albino (both homozygous)
    d. F$_2$ from c
    e. F$_1$ from a × F$_1$ from c

9.2 What are the genotypes of the parents in the following crosses in rabbits:
    a. wild type × wild type, giving ¾ wild type : ¼ Himalayan
    b. wild type × wild type, giving ¾ wild type : ¼ light gray
    c. wild type × Himalayan, giving ½ wild type : ¼ Himalayan : ¼ albino

9.3 What will be the appearance of the offspring from the following crosses in rabbits (*c^{ch}c^{ch}* is chinchilla; *c^{ch}c^h* and *c^{ch}c^a* are light gray):

    a. *Cc^{ch}* × *Cc^a*
    b. *c^{ch}c^h* × *c^hc^h*
    c. *c^hc^a* × *c^{ch}c^{ch}*
    d. *Cc^h* × *c^{ch}c^a*

NOTE: In mice the following genes affecting coat color form a series of multiple alleles: *A^Y*, yellow; *A^L*, agouti (light belly); *A*, agouti (gray belly, wild type); *a^t*, black and tan (black back, light belly); *a* (black, non-

agouti). *Aa^t* animals are agouti with light belly; otherwise dominance is complete in order given. *C* is colored; *cc*, albino.

9.4 What will be the appearance of the offspring of the following crosses:

a. *A^LA* × *AA*	**e.** *A^YA* × *aA^L*
b. *A^LA^L* × *Aa*	**f.** *A^Ya* × *Aa^t*
c. *Aa^t* × *Aa*	**g.** *A^Ya^t* × *Aa^t*
d. *A^LA* × *a^ta*	

9.5 What are the genotypes of the parents in the following crosses:
    a. Agouti light belly × agouti light belly, giving one-fourth agouti, one-half agouti light belly, one-fourth black and tan.
    b. Agouti light belly × agouti, giving one-half agouti light belly; one-fourth agouti, one-fourth black.
    c. Albino × agouti, giving all agouti light belly in F$_1$; and in F$_2$ three-sixteenths agouti, three-eighths agouti light belly, three-sixteenths black and tan, and one-fourth albino.

9.6 In maize there are several factors that affect plant color. Three of these are sun red, weak sun red, and dilute sun red, with decreasing intensities in the order named. Following are the results of crosses between these three types (data from Emerson): sun red × dilute sun red gave all sun red in F$_1$ and 998 sun red : 314 dilute sun red in F$_2$; weak sun red × dilute sun red gave all weak sun red in F$_1$ and 1,300 weak sun red : 429 dilute sun red in F$_2$; sun red × weak sun red gave all sun red in F$_1$ and 71 sun red : 16

weak sun red in F_2. Explain these results, stating the relationship among these three plant colors.

9.7 What will be the phenotype, as to blood groups, of offspring of parents of the following genotypes for blood groups: $I^A i \times I^B i$; $I^A I^B \times I^B i$; $I^B i \times I^B i$

9.8 If a person of blood group AB marries one belonging to group O, what will be the blood groups of their children?

NOTE: In the three following problems on blood groups, determine the genotypes of the parents.

9.9 One parent is group A and the other group B, but all four groups are represented among the children.

9.10 Both parents are group A, but three-fourths of the children belong to group A and one-fourth to group O.

9.11 One parent is AB and the other B, but of the children, one-fourth are A, one-fourth AB, and one-half B.

9.12 In the two following cases of disputed paternity, determine the probable father of the child:

9.13 In the choice of donors for blood transfusion, a patient's brother or sister is often selected. Would these be more likely to be successful donors if both parents belonged to blood group AB or if both belonged to group O? Explain.

9.14 In Nicotiana, if $s^1 s^2$ is crossed with $s^4 s^5$, calculate the proportion of wholly or partly cross-sterile (incompatible) combinations in crosses between F_1 individuals.

9.15 If the progeny plants from Table 9.5 are allowed to cross at random in large numbers, what should be the distribution of genotypes in the next generation, assuming that all genotypes are equally viable and fecund and that there are large numbers of individuals of each genotype in both F_1 and F_2?

9.16 In Nicotiana, 100 plants tested among themselves for self- and cross-sterility were found to fall into groups that had the relationships with respect to offspring shown in Table 9.6. Give the allelic constitutions of A, B, C, and D which would explain these relationships.

9.17 In about 85 per cent of Europeans, known as *secretors*, antigen A or B is found in saliva and other body fluids if it occurs in the blood, whereas 15 per cent do not have an antigen in saliva and are known as *nonsecretors*. If S (secretor) is dominant to

TABLE 9.6

Male parent	Female parent			
	A	B	C	D
A	—	½A, ½C	½A, ½B	¼B, ¼C ¼E, ¼F
B	½B, ½C	—	½A, ½B	½B, ½E
C	½B, ½C	½A, ½C	—	½C, ½F
D	¼B, ¼C ¼E, ¼F	½D, ½E	½D, ½F	—

a. The mother belongs to group B, the child to O, one possible father to A, and the other to AB.

b. The mother belongs to group B, the child to AB, one possible father to A, and the other to B.

s (nonsecretor) and S and s are inherited independently of the classical blood-group alleles, calculate the proportion of offspring from the following matings which would be expected to give A or B reactions in the saliva:

AB secretor (Ss) × O (Ss)

O ss × AB secretor (Ss)

9.18 A sibship of seven children gave the following reactions to Rh-testing sera:

Child	Anti-C	Anti-c	Anti-D	Anti-E	Anti-e
1	−	+	−	−	+
2	+	+	+	+	+
3	−	+	−	−	+
4	−	+	+	+	+
5	+	+	+	−	+
6	+	+	+	+	+
7	−	+	+	+	+

Give the probable genotypes of the children and the two parents and predict the reactions of parent 1 and parent 2 to the testing sera.

9.19 Which of the following matings would run the risk of having a baby with erythroblastosis foetalis?

$$A \quad \frac{\text{♀}}{\text{CDe}} \quad \frac{\text{♂}}{\text{cde}} \qquad C \quad \frac{\text{♀}}{\text{Cde}} \quad \frac{\text{♂}}{\text{CDe}}$$
$$\frac{}{\text{cde}} \quad \frac{}{\text{cde}} \qquad \frac{}{\text{cde}} \quad \frac{}{\text{cDE}}$$

$$B \quad \frac{\text{cde}}{\text{cde}} \quad \frac{\text{cDe}}{\text{cde}} \qquad D \quad \frac{\text{cDe}}{\text{CDe}} \quad \frac{\text{Cde}}{\text{cde}}$$

In which mating would the risk be greatest?

9.20 Assuming that the three main AB blood-group alleles *IA*, *IB*, and *i* are inherited independently of the eight Rh alleles (R^1, R^2, R^z, R^0, r^y, r', r'', r), how many genotypes with respect to these two blood characters are theoretically possible?

10 LETHAL GENES, PENETRANCE, AND EXPRESSIVITY

IT HAS BEEN repeatedly pointed out above that in studying the transmission of genes, geneticists have usually preferred to work with clear-cut alternative traits. Consider, for example, the O–A–B–AB blood groups in man. Every person has blood belonging to one of these groups, and no one has blood intermediate between, say, A and B. The presence or absence of the A and B antigens can be ascertained in the fetus, at any time during the postnatal life, and even in bones for many years after death, until the organic material of the bone is entirely replaced by mineral matter. It is easy to follow the inheritance of such "unit characters" from generation to generation and to secure good pedigrees and unambiguous statistical data. Many characters do not, however, behave so conveniently. As shown in Chapter 7, some character differences are determined by the cooperation of many genes, each of which has by itself so small an effect on the phenotype that it is difficult or impossible to distinguish different genotypic classes by their phenotypes. Still other character differences are caused by genes whose phenotypic manifestation is very sensitive to environmental variations. Carriers of the same genotype may have different phenotypes, and it may be hard to tell to which genotype an individual belongs by a simple inspection of his appearance. Such irregularities in the external expression of genes are particularly frequent among gene mutations that produce hereditary diseases in man and other organisms, and investigating them is of considerable practical as well as theoretical importance (see Chap. 11).

LETHAL GENES

Let us consider first a classical example of a gene the phenotypic manifestation of which is not interfered with by environmental variations but which nevertheless alters the usual Mendelian ratios. The classical Mendelian segregation of ¾ dominants : ¼ recessives occurs when the gametes that carry different alleles of the same gene unite at random and when different gametes and zygotes are equally viable and vigorous (cf. Figs. 3.5 and 3.8). These conditions are not always realized.

Not long after the rediscovery of Mendel's work, Cuénot noticed that matings between two mice with yellowish fur produced progenies with yellow and nonyellow individuals in a ratio of 2 : 1. The combined results of a number of investigators are shown in Table 10.1. Furthermore, it was found that the litters born from matings between yellows are smaller by about one-fourth than litters from yellow × nonyellow. Both these facts are consistent with the hypothesis that the zygotes homozygous for yellow are in-

The inheritance of yellow may be represented as follows:

$$A^Y = \text{a dominant gene for yellow fur}$$
$$a = \text{its recessive allele for nonyellow}$$

Parents:
Yellow A^Ya ×   Yellow A^Ya
   Progeny:
¼A^YA^Y :   ¾A^Ya :   ¼aa
die   yellow   nonyellow

Thus a mouse homozygous for A^Y dies before birth. The allele A^Y is *lethal*, i.e., produces death, in homozygous condition. When heterozygous, it merely modifies the color of the fur, which assumes a yellowish tinge. The effects of the allele A^Y on fur

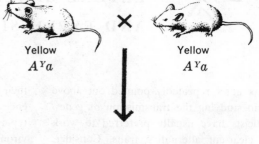

Fig. 10.1. Inheritance of a lethal gene in mice.

Yellow
A^Ya

Yellow
A^Ya

Dies
A^YA^Y

Yellow
A^Ya

Yellow
A^Ya

Black
aa

viable and die before birth. The hypothesis has been verified by several investigators who found that some embryos in the uterus of a yellow female mated to a yellow male die in an early embryonic stage (Fig. 10.1).

TABLE 10.1
Inheritance of the difference between yellow and nonyellow in mice

Parents	Offspring	
	Yellow	Nonyellow
Yellow × yellow	2,396	1,235
Yellow × nonyellow	2,378	2,398

color are dominant over those of a, and its lethal effects are recessive; mice heterozygous for A^Y do not seem to be particularly handicapped by having fur of a different color. This is an example of some of the effects of one gene's being dominant while others are recessive to those of its allele. Such situations are not rare among lethal as well as nonlethal genes. Dominant and recessive alleles are not sharply distinct categories.

LETHAL HEREDITARY DISEASES IN MAN
Lethal genes are known in many species of experimental animals and plants. In Dro-

sophila many hundreds of them have been detected (see Chap. 18), and in man they are also numerous. The gene causing the disease called juvenile amaurotic idiocy may serve as an example. Infants homozygous for this gene appear to be normal at birth. However, their eyesight begins to fail between the ages of 4 and 7, resulting gradually in blindness. Deterioration of mental and physical powers leads inexorably to death before or during adolescence. Another recessive lethal gene produces, when homozygous, the so-called Tay-Sachs disease, or infantile amaurotic idiocy, which results in early death of the homozygotes.

Mendel, one quarter of their children will be homozygous *aa* and will die of the disease. Among the surviving children, two-thirds will be the carriers *Aa,* and one-third will be the normal homozygotes, *AA.* It stands to reason that marriages in which only one of the parties is a heterozygote run no risk of producing afflicted children.

Sickle-cell anemia is caused by a gene with a lethal effect when homozygous and with only a slight but discernible effect when heterozygous. The name of this disease refers to a property of the red blood cells of the carriers, which assume abnormal shapes when placed in media deficient in oxygen—

Fig. 10.2. Sickle cells in man. Left, red blood cells from a patient with sickle-cell anemia (homozygous); right, cells from a person with sickle-cell trait (heterozygous). (After Neel)

In contrast to the A^Y gene in the mouse (see above), the genes for the juvenile and the infantile forms of amaurotic idiocy have no known effects in heterozygotes with their normal alleles. The parents of amaurotic idiots are normal people, usually quite unaware of being heterozygous carriers of the recessive genes capable of producing a dreadful disease when homozygous. Denoting the recessive allele responsible for the disease by *a* and its normal allele by *A*, the parents of the afflicted children are heterozygotes, *Aa.* According to the first law of

under a sealed cover slip of a microscopic preparation, for example (Fig. 10.2) The homozygotes usually die of a fatal anemia before the advent of sexual maturity (although they may occasionally survive). The heterozygotes are healthy people, occasionally showing signs of a mild anemia. Since the heterozygotes are identifiable by means of a microscopic examination of their blood, the birth of children with the fatal anemia could be prevented by avoidance of marriages among the carriers.

A somewhat analogous condition, revealed by abnormalities of the red blood cells in the heterozygotes, is known as *thalassemia,* or *microcytemia.* The gene in homozygous condition causes a fatal anemia (Cooley's anemia). It was thought to occur chiefly among peoples native to countries near the Mediterranean Sea (Italians, Greeks, and Syrians), but is found also in Persia, India, and Thailand.

PHENYLKETONURIC IMBECILITY

Many forms of idiocy or imbecility are known in man and in some cases the causative gene has been identified. One of these, *phenylketonuric imbecility* (cf. p. 336), was identified by the discovery of a peculiar reaction of the urine of some inmates of homes for mentally defective children. The urine of certain patients developed a temporary deep bluish-green color upon addition of a few drops of a 5 per cent solution of ferric chloride. This reaction revealed the presence of phenylpyruvic acid, which is excreted by these patients but metabolized in normal persons. All persons who continuously excrete this substance have some degree of mental impairment, their muscular reflex reactions are accentuated, and they have a characteristic posture and a dilution of skin and hair pigments. They have a reduced life expectancy and seldom have children.

All these characteristics are associated with a defect in metabolism (inability to oxidize phenylalanine to tyrosine) caused by a gene that was thought until recently to have no effect in the heterozygote's parents, which appear perfectly normal. This gene could therefore be classed as a recessive, lethal when homozygous. Recently, however, it has been found that parents of phenylketonuric idiots have a slightly different tolerance level for the amino acid phenylalanine when they are fed large quantities of it. They cannot metabolize it as rapidly and efficiently as persons who do not carry a gene for phenylketonuria. Thus a means may be provided for diagnosing such

heterozygotes, just as persons carrying the sickling and thalassemia genes are identified by blood tests. This would be the first step in reducing the frequency of such deleterious genes in human populations.

It is probable that many prenatal deaths (stillbirths, abortions) in man are due to lethal genes, but genes of this sort have received much less attention and study than those that cause illness and death after birth. Genes that produce lethal changes in embryos have been more extensively studied in other animals—mice, rats, cats, swine, horses, and others. Many genes with lethal or deleterious effects have been identified in the vinegar fly, Drosophila.

SEMILETHAL AND SUBVITAL GENES IN MAN

With the possible exception of sickle-cell anemia, the genes that we have described as lethal to mice and men kill all or nearly all homozygous individuals before they reach sexual maturity. These genes are complete lethals. However, genes are also known which kill some of the afflicted persons but permit others to survive long enough to have families. Such genes are called *semilethal* or *subvital.* The distinction between these categories is not sharp, especially since genes that are lethal under some conditions may permit survival under others, e.g., with special medical treatment. Conventionally, genes that kill fewer than 100 per cent but more than 50 per cent of their victims are called semilethals, whereas those that cause less than 50 per cent mortality are known as subvital genes.

An example of a dominant semilethal in man is a rare disease called *epiloia.* Its victims are heterozygous carriers of a gene that causes a combination (syndrome) of morbid traits, including severe mental deficiency, abnormal growths on the skin, and tumors in internal organs. Most persons with epiloia die during childhood, but some of them manage to survive, marry, and beget children. Half these children are expected to inherit the dominant semilethal and to develop epiloia. But most of the cases of epiloia are born to parents both of whom are free of the disease; their appearance is due evidently to mutation of the normal gene to a dominant allele responsible for the disease. The frequency of such mutation is estimated at about ten per million gametes (see Table 16.1). Surviving carriers of epiloia are so rare in most populations that unions of two carriers have not been observed; it is not known what effects the semilethal would have in homozygous condition.

Retinoblastoma is due to another dominant human gene; it causes malignant tumors in the eyes, and almost always leads to death in early childhood. This gene acts as an almost complete lethal. According to Neel and Falls, about forty-nine babies born in the state of Michigan between 1936 and 1945 developed retinoblastoma, most of them being children of normal parents. These "new" cases were assumed to be due to mutation; if the gene were a complete lethal, all cases of retinoblastoma would be due to recent mutations. Occasionally, however, an infant with retinoblastoma survives the critical phase of the disease and grows to maturity. Consequently, the gene for it, like those for sickle-cell anemia and thalassemia must be classed as a semilethal rather than a complete lethal.

SUBVITAL EFFECTS IN MUTANTS OF DROSOPHILA

Any hereditary disease or malformation that incapacitates its carriers and causes among them a higher mortality during the preadult years or during maturity than that among persons free of that disease may be regarded as a semilethal or a subvital condition. Of course, semilethal and subvital genes occur not only in man but also in other animal and plant species, wild and domesticated. Many of the classical mutants of Drosophila produce subvital effects along with their more conspicuous effects on the external appear-

ance of the flies. Thus vestigial-winged flies (Fig. 3.7) are less sturdy than the normal-winged ones. This can be demonstrated by making counts of the vestigial and normal segregants in the F_2-generation flies from the cross vestigial $\times$ normal (Fig. 3.7). When the experiment is carried out under favorable culture conditions (ample food, optimal temperature, etc.), the deviations from the segregation ratio of 3 normal : 1 vestigial are no greater than those expected from sampling errors (cf. Chap. 29). But if the cultures are handled roughly, and especially if the flies develop in crowded cultures in which the amount of food is small for the number of larvae that grow on it, the proportion of the vestigial flies may fall appreciably below the theoretically expected 25 per cent. The percentages of vestigial-winged flies observed in cultures in which the total numbers of the flies hatched were between the figures indicated are shown in the following tabulation (based on experiments performed by students in the genetics course at Columbia University):

Total flies per culture	*Per cent vestigial*
Less than 50	24.9
50–100	25.2
100–200	20.8
More than 200	16.0

In crowded cultures, in which only a part of the eggs deposited by the parent flies develop successfully to produce adult progeny, the mortality among the vestigial homozygotes is significantly greater than among the normals. The vestigial class is significantly deficient in such cultures.

PENETRANCE AND EXPRESSIVITY

Every Drosophila fly that is homozygous for the gene vestigial has wings strikingly shorter than normal as well as certain other characteristics (see p. 121). Such genes are said to have a complete *penetrance,* that is, every individual of the proper genotype develops a phenotype that makes him distinguishable from individuals with other genotypes. Such genes also have a fairly constant *expressivity*—their phenotypic effects, at least in the usual environments, are more or less uniform. But the gene for epiloia has an incomplete penetrance, at least as far as its lethal effects are concerned; some persons who carry this gene die early, but others live long enough to raise families. It has also a somewhat variable expressivity, since some of its carriers do not develop certain of the morbid symptoms shown by others. The following examples will illustrate some of the problems met with in studying genotypes with incomplete penetrance and variable expressivity.

HUNTINGTON'S CHOREA

Persons who carry the dominant gene for Huntington's chorea may enjoy good health for most of their lives. The disease starts with involuntary twitchings of the head, limbs, and body and goes on to degenerative changes in the nervous system, loss of mental and physical powers, and death. However, as shown in Table 10.2, the age of onset of this disease, i.e., the age at which it becomes first noticeable, varies from infancy to old age.

TABLE 10.2
Age of onset of Huntington's chorea in man (*After Julia Bell*)

Years	Number of cases	Years	Number of cases
0–4	4	40–44	57
5–9	5	45–49	42
10–14	15	50–54	28
15–19	24	55–59	12
20–24	38	60–64	7
25–29	57	65–69	7
30–34	83	70–74	1
35–39	80	Total	460

It is virtually certain that some persons who are carriers of the gene for this disease die of other causes before they develop any symptoms of Huntington's chorea. The gene may, then, be said to have an incomplete penetrance. Its expressivity is also variable. When the victim of the disease dies young, before producing children, the gene may be said to have a lethal effect. When the victim dies in the midst of the reproductive period of life, the gene acts as a semilethal or a subvital. When incapacitation and death occur in old age, after the close of the reproductive period, the gene (and this may seem a paradox) is not lethal at all. Health or disease in old age are, however, not under direct control of natural selection in the evolutionary process (see Chap. 18). Death after the close of the reproductive age may, from the standpoint of genetics, be regarded as "natural death."

The variable age of onset of a grave disease such as Huntington's chorea raises serious problems for afflicted persons as well as for their families. A carrier of the gene for the disease may be quite unaware of being a carrier and may become a parent of many children. Each of these children has a 50–50 chance of being a carrier, and all of them may suffer throughout their entire conscious lives from the apprehension, which will be as often groundless as it will be warranted, of becoming victims of the disease.

TASTE BLINDNESS FOR PTC

Incomplete penetrance and variable expressivity occur not only among genes that produce hereditary diseases but among those that cause differences among "normal" persons. In Chapter 5 we discussed ability and inability to taste the PTC substance (phenyl-thio-carbamide). Harris and Kalmus have studied the taste sensitivity of different people to different solutions of PTC. When they used solutions containing between 20.3 and 40.6 mgm of PTC per liter of water, about 70 per cent of the persons tested were "tasters" and about 30 per cent were nontasters. With most persons there was no doubt at all whether they were tasters or nontasters. Some experienced an intensely bitter taste in the solution of this concentration and others no taste at all. A few of them were in doubt; they found the solution slightly acid, salty, or bitter. However, most of these persons found somewhat stronger solutions (81, 162, or 325 mgm of PTC per liter of water) distinctly bitter. These people had a higher taster-sensitivity "threshold" for PTC. How greatly people differ with respect to the height of this threshold is shown in Table 10.3. One person detected a bitter taste in a solution with only 0.16 mgm of PTC per liter, whereas 31 persons still could not taste a solution with 1300 mgm PTC per liter. The sensitivity of the former was at least 10,000 times greater than that of the latter.

TABLE 10.3
Taste thresholds for phenyl-thio-carbamide (PTC) in 441 Englishmen (*After Harris and Kalmus*)

The figures on the left indicate the concentration of PTC (in mgm per liter of water) in the different solutions used; the figures on the right show the numbers of persons who first detected a bitter taste in a solution of a given concentration.

Solution mgm/l	Persons
> 1300	31
1300	37
650	21
325	26
162	23
81.2	10
40.6	13
20.3	29
10.2	51
5.1	73
2.5	73
1.3	29
0.6	18
0.3	6
0.16	1
Total	441

To sum up: Most people are either very sensitive or very insensitive to the bitter taste of PTC solutions. It appears that these differences in sensitivity are due mostly to possession of either the dominant or the recessive allele of the single gene *T-t*. However, the existence of a minority of persons who are intermediate in sensitivity raises a difficulty. The expressivity of the alleles *T* and *t* is variable. This causes the apparent exceptions to the simple rules of Mendelian inheritance, such as the birth of children who are tasters to parents both of whom appear to be nontasters.

CAUSES OF VARIABLE PENETRANCE AND EXPRESSIVITY

The existence of genes with variable penetrance and expressivity surely does not change the validity of the gene theory. As we have seen, we do not inherit "characters" or "traits." We inherit a genotype, the sum total of the genes that jointly determine our norm of reaction in various environments and consequently the paths that the development of our body and mind may take under various environmental circumstances. The characters that develop thus depend upon the genotype as well as upon the environment. It is evident that the expression of the genes depends upon the environment in which the organism develops, and the expression of some genes may be less sensitive to environmental variations normally encountered by the organism in the course of its life than that of other genes. (See Chap. 2 for genotype-environment interactions.)

Variations in penetrance and expressivity may also be caused by genetic factors. In Chapter 8 we have seen that the phenotypic effects of a gene such as that for white spotting in mice may be more or less striking depending upon the genetic milieu, i.e., upon what other genes the animal has. The other genes, modifiers, may be said to influence the penetrance and the expressivity of the gene for white spotting.

PROBLEMS

10.1 Calculate the goodness of fit of the actual ratios in Table 10.1 to expected ratios of 1 : 1 (second line) and 3 : 1 and 2 : 1 (first line). What conclusions can be drawn from the P values?

NOTE: For Problems 10.2 and 10.3, see the notes above Problems 7.18 and 9.4. Yellow is epistatic to agouti, black, and brown.

10.2 A cross of two yellow mice gave the following result: 24 yellow, 12 black, 12 albino. What were the genotypes of the parents?

10.3 In mice, what will be the appearance of the offspring from the following crosses (A^Y = yellow):

$$CC \ A^Y A \ BB \times CC \ A^Y A \ bb$$
$$Cc \ A^Y A \ BB \times Cc \ A^Y A \ Bb$$
$$cc \ A^Y A \ BB \times Cc \ A^Y A \ BB$$

10.4 If a large population of yellow mice is allowed to mate at random, permitting matings only among members of the same generation, what would be the expected frequency of yellows and nonyellows in the F_1–F_5 generation? Plot graphically the changes in the frequency of the gene A^Y during this period. Assume that yellow and nonyellow have equal fecundity.

10.5 In Drosophila, crosses of Dichaete-winged flies × Dichaete always give two-thirds Dichaete to one-third normal-winged offspring. Dichaete × normal gives one-half Dichaete and one-half normal. How would you explain these results?

10.6 In poultry the following results were obtained:

	Progeny	
	Short-legged	Normal
a. Short-legged		
× short-legged	1,972	955
b. Short-legged		
× normal	1,676	1,661

Explain these results, giving genotypes of animals involved. Explain how you would test your hypothesis (a) by statistical methods; (b) by obtaining what additional facts?

10.7 What proportion of homozygotes for sickle-cell anemia would you expect to find at birth in a population in which 20 per cent of the adults are heterozygous for this gene?

10.8 Assume that the genes for sickle-cell anemia, *Si*, and the gene for thalassemia, *Th*, show independent assortment and that the double heterozygote has normal viability. Predict the phenotypes and viability of the offspring from the following matings:

a. *Si si th th* × *si si Th th*
b. ·*Si si Th th* × *si si th th*
c. *Si si Th th* × *Si si Th th*

The following observations have been made as part of a test of these assumptions. In five families, in which one parent was known to have both sickle-cell and thalassemia traits and the other parent to have neither, eighteen children were tested. Ten of these had thalassemia only, and eight had sickle-cell trait only. What is the probability of this result on the assumption of independent assortment? How would you explain the result?

10.9 What is the probability that a sibling of a juvenile amaurotic idiot is heterozygous for this gene? Estimate for such a person the risk he will run of having an amaurotic-idiot child (a) if he marries a first cousin and (b) if he marries an unrelated person.

10.10 If the genes for phenylketonuric imbecility and for juvenile amaurotic idiocy are independent in inheritance, what will be the risk encountered by the children of the person in Problem 10.9 if he marries a sibling of a phenylketonuric imbecile?

10.11 In cattle, short-legged animals of the Dexter-Kerry breed occasionally produce abnormal calves dead at birth or dying shortly thereafter. Outline an experimental test of the hypothesis that such deaths are due to homozygosis for a lethal gene.

NATURE–NURTURE PROBLEM IN MAN: TWIN STUDIES

WE SAW in Chapter 5 that many traits in which healthy persons differ from one another show complete penetrance and straightforward Mendelian inheritance. The same is true of many hereditary diseases. Other traits, such as skin color, are polygenic; studying them is more laborious. The inheritance of still other traits is complicated further by variable penetrance and expressivity as well as by polygenic inheritance. Such traits are most difficult to study.

The relative contributions of heredity and environment to the variation observed in some of man's most important traits—intelligence, temperament, special abilities, behavior, and predispositions to diseases—have long been matters of dispute. Some have regarded them as primarily genotypic, others as chiefly environmental; Francis Galton (1822–1911) used the terms *nature* and *nurture* to represent these two types of influences. The polemics aroused by these questions have been due chiefly to confusion of biological with legal inheritance (see Chap.

2) and to the belief that if variation in a trait can be induced by environmental agencies, it cannot also be induced by genetic differences. This confusion, supplemented occasionally by bias and prejudice, has made it difficult for many people to understand that human traits influenced by social and cultural environments may nevertheless be conditioned by heredity.

TWINS

The study of the nature-nurture problem in plants by dividing the same individual into parts and subjecting these parts with identical genotypes to different environments has already been described (p. 23). Plants that grow from parts of the same individual are members of a clone; barring mutation, they have the same genotype. The nearest approach to this kind of experiment in man is through observations of identical twins.

There are two kinds of human twins. Identical or *monozygous* twins arise from a single zygote formed by fertilization of a single egg by a single sperm. In such cases the developing egg cleaves at an early division, by some sort of developmental accident, to form two separate embryos instead of the usual one. Twins arising in this way are members of a clone and should have the same genotype (Figs. 11.1 and 5.2). Fraternal, or *dizygous*, twins come from two

mice, etc.) such multiple ovulation is the rule, and in some human races (Japanese) it is less frequent than in others (whites, Negroes). The matter is, thus, partially conditioned by the genotype.

Identical twins, on the other hand, appear sporadically in man and some other animals, and the causes of such accidents

Fig. 11.1. Monozygous twins separated at birth. George (left) and Millan (right) were born in Salt Lake City, where Millan remained while George grew up in New York City. Neither knew he had a twin. In addition to their physical resemblance, their responses to mental tests are quite similar. (*From F. E. Stephens and R. B. Thompson, Courtesy of Journal of Heredity*)

different eggs, each fertilized by a different sperm. Since different gametes from the same parent will in general have different sets of genes, fraternal twins have different genotypes (Fig. 11.2). The genotypes of such twins need not be any more or any less different than the genotypes of siblings— brothers or sisters who are not twins. Fraternal twins are simply siblings born simultaneously.

The causes of multiple births are not completely understood. Fraternal twins arise from the simultaneous release of two eggs from the ovaries of the mother which are fertilized by two different spermatozoa. In many animals (for example, dogs, cats,

are not well understood. In the armadillo, at least, a single egg regularly produces four embryos resulting in identical quadruplets, and the process is thus under genotypic control.

Fraternal twins are of different sexes about as often as they are of the same sex. When twins are of the same sex, there arises the problem of how to distinguish the identicals from the fraternals. Fraternals usually are enclosed in separate birth membranes and have separate placentae, whereas identicals are generally enclosed in one membrane and are attached to one placenta; however, there are exceptions to both rules. A more conclusive diagnosis can be made by comparing the members of the pairs in traits known to be determined by genes (such as the blood-group genes) which express themselves wherever they are present. If members of a twin pair differ in such a known genotypic trait—for example, if they are of different blood groups or of different sexes they are fraternals; if alike in all such traits, they are probably identicals. Obviously, the greater the number of independently inherited traits examined, the less the proba-

++ or ——); when only one of the twins shows the trait, they are called discordant (symbol +—). Obviously, identical twins are always concordant with respect to fully penetrant hereditary characteristics, whereas fraternal twins are sometimes discordant with respect to such characteristics. This fact is, as pointed out above, used to distinguish the identical from the fraternal twins. If the variation in a trait is due entirely to the environment, the frequency of concordance

Fig. 11.2. Dizygous, or fraternal, twins. Mrs. Olivia Strong with her twins, Eddie Ray, an albino, and Lucy May, normally colored. (*International News Service*)

bility that siblings such as fraternal twins will happen just by chance to be alike in all of them.

CONCORDANCE AND DISCORDANCE

The simplest kind of data which studies on twins can yield is qualitative comparison of various traits in pairs of identical and fraternal twins. When members of a twin pair both show or fail to show the trait in question, they are called concordant (symbols

and discordance should be alike among identical and fraternal twins, within the limits of statistical errors of observation. Table 11.1 shows a comparison of various diseases as they appear in identical and fraternal twins.

Measles, scarlet fever, and tuberculosis are infectious diseases that come from the environment. Nevertheless, the proportion of twins concordant with respect to tuberculosis is significantly greater among the iden-

TABLE 11.1

Percentage of concordance (++) and discordance (+−) with respect to certain traits in pairs of identical and fraternal twins, of which one member was affected (*After Stern, Verschuer, and other sources*)

Traits	Twin pairs studied		Identical		Fraternal	
	Identical	Fraternal	++	+−	++	+−
Measles	189	146	95	5	87	13
Scarlet fever	31	30	64	36	47	53
Tuberculosis	190	427	74	26	28	72
Tumors (all types)	62	27	61	39	44	56
Tumors (specific kinds)	62	27	58	42	24	76
Diabetes mellitus	63	70	84	16	37	63
Feeble-mindedness	126	93	91	9	45	55

ticals than it is among the fraternals. There is evidently a genotypic predisposition to this disease; the carriers of some genotypes are more likely than others to develop tuberculosis. It is not known whether this is the case with scarlet fever; and for measles the frequency of concordance is so high both among the identicals and the fraternals that all, or nearly all, genotypes in this sample evidently make their carriers susceptible to infection with the virus that produces this disease.

The data on tumors, collected by M. T. Macklin, are presented in two ways. First, the presence in a pair of twins of any one of the many kinds of tumors that occur in man is entered as "concordance," and only cases in which one of the twins had a tumor and the other had none are regarded as "discordant." Secondly, only cases in which both members of a twin pair had the same kind of tumor are listed as "concordant." It can be seen that concordant identical twins usually had tumors of the same kind, whereas among fraternal twins both similar and different types of tumors arose. There may thus be a genotypically induced predisposition to develop certain kinds of tumors. However, this predisposition is far from complete or uniform, so that individuals with the same genotype may or may not develop a tumor.

Diabetes mellitus and feeble-mindedness show a much greater frequency of concordance among identical than among fraternal twins. The presence or absence of these traits is strongly conditioned by the genotype. Nevertheless, some of the identical twin pairs are discordant; this clearly means that the manifestation of the genotypes concerned is not fully penetrant and is influenced by the environment.

In the case of mongoloid idiocy, all thirteen cases reported are concordant—where one twin was a "mongoloid," the other was, too. But in this case another fact must be recognized—that in addition to an inherited predisposition, the age of the mother is also important, the frequency of "mongoloids" in affected families rising with the increasing age of the mothers. Members of twin pairs obviously have been subjected to the same conditions that depend on maternal age, so the environmental requirement for the expression of the genotype is met equally for both members, increasing the likelihood of concordance.

INTRAPAIR DIFFERENCES, VARIANCES, AND CORRELATIONS

The traits in Table 11.1 are qualitative and can be described simply as presence or absence of a certain characteristic. Other traits are quantitative—they can be measured or weighed and expressed as a greater or lesser amount of something (see Chap. 8). One may thus compute the mean differences in a given trait between members of a pair of identical and of fraternal twins. If the variability in the trait studied is conditioned to some extent by the genotype, these mean intrapair differences will be significantly greater among fraternal than among identical twins. For traits whose variability in a given sample is purely environmental, the differences among fraternal twins should be as large as those among identicals.

A better method is to use not the average intrapair differences but the intrapair variance (cf. Chap. 29) of a given trait. This is computed as the sum of the squares of the differences observed between the two twins of each pair divided by the number of twin pairs of each kind studied. If the observed variation of a given trait is purely environmental, then the intrapair variance for the fraternal twins should be about as great as that for the identicals: the ratio of the two variances should be around unity. The greater the relative importance of heredity, the higher will this ratio become, and a stat-istician can easily estimate whether or not the ratio observed is significantly different from unity. The degree of correlation between the measurements obtained in the pairs of twins can also be computed. For a trait the variation of which is due entirely to heredity, identical twins should show a perfect correlation (a correlation coefficient close to or equal to 1), whereas fraternal twins will show a lower correlation. For an environmental trait, the correlations for identical and fraternal twins should be about equal.

AMINO-ACID EXCRETION IN URINE

Table 11.2 deals with the variances of concentrations of certain amino acids in the urine of a small collection of twins (15 pairs of identicals, 11 pairs of fraternals). The table shows the ratios of these variances, i.e., the observed variance for the fraternal twins divided by that for the identical twins. The highest ratio is for the substance known as beta-amino-isobutyric acid. Some persons excrete much more of this substance in their urines than others; identical twins excrete usually about the same amounts, whereas fraternal twins may differ greatly in this re-

TABLE 11.2

Ratios of the intrapair variances of the observed concentrations of certain amino acids in the urines of identical and fraternal twins (*After Berry, Dobzhansky, Gartler, Levene, and Osborne*)

Amino acid	Variance ratio	Probability (per cent)
Beta-amino-isobutyric	14.9	< 0.5
Valine	7.4	< 0.5
Threonine	5.9	< 0.5
Lysine	4.6	< 0.5
Tyrosine	3.2	1.0
Taurine	2.8	< 5.0
Alanine	1.4	< 5.0
Leucine	1.3	> 5.0
Glutamine	0.5	> 5.0

spect. The probability that so high a ratio (14.9) happened to occur merely by chance is much less than one-half of 1 per cent (<0.5 per cent). Obviously, the concentration in which this substance is excreted in the urine is to a considerable extent under genetic control.

Three other amino acids, valine, threonine, and lysine, gave variance ratios lower than that for beta-amino-isobutyric acid but still so high that the chances that these ratios were not really different from one are also less than 0.5 per cent (i.e., less than 1 in 200). The excretion rates of these substances among the persons examined is influenced to a significant extent by their genotypes. Alanine, leucine, and glutamine show, however, variance ratios that may well not be different from unity; in each case, the probability that the apparent differences could arise by chance alone is above 5 per cent. The conclusion is that the data examined give no evidence that the observed variations in the excretion rates of these three substances are controlled to any appreciable extent by the genotype.

TWINS REARED APART

Twin children are usually raised together in the same family, and they usually receive similar treatment from their parents and other people. Objection has been raised against the use of twins for nature-nurture studies on the ground that this similarity of environments may be greater for identical than for fraternal twins, since the former are so nearly identical in appearance, habits, and experience. This is not a serious objection, because if the identicals really have more nearly similar environments than the fraternals, this greater similarity of environments is itself an indirect result of their greater genotypic similarity. Nevertheless, it is unquestionably desirable to see how great a phenotypic difference can arise in persons of the same genotype. The relatively rare cases in which twin children are separated within a few months or years after birth and raised apart from each other offer an opportunity for such studies. The team of Newman (a geneticist), Freeman (a psychologist), and Holzinger (a statistician) collected and published (1937) data on 19 such pairs, comparing them with twins and siblings reared together and apart.

It can be seen in Table 11.3 that identical twins resemble one another a great deal more in such traits as stature, head length, and head width than fraternal twins, regardless of whether the identicals were raised together or apart. This means that these traits —and, incidentally, other physical traits by which people recognize each other, such as facial appearance and expression—are more strongly influenced by hereditary variations than by the environmental variations that

TABLE 11.3
Mean differences between identical and fraternal twins in various traits (*After Newman, Freeman, and Holzinger*)

Trait	Identicals reared together	Identicals reared apart	Fraternals reared together	Siblings reared together
Body height (cm)	1.7	1.8	4.4	4.5
Body weight (lbs)	4.1	9.9	10.0	10.4
Head length (mm)	2.9	2.2	6.2	
Head width (mm)	2.8	2.9	4.2	
IQ (raw data)	5.9	8.2	9.9	9.8
IQ (corrected)	3.1	6.0	8.5	

commonly differentiate people from one another. The name "identical twins" refers, of course, to just these striking similarities that people notice between these genotypically similar persons.

The situation is rather different for body weight, since here the identical twins reared and living together resemble each other considerably more than do such twins reared apart, and the latter may be about as different as fraternal twins reared together and siblings who are not twins. Here the influence of environmental differences is apparent. The intelligence quotient (IQ) in this material shows the influence of both genotypic and environmental variations. Even computing the mean difference in the IQs from the raw data, it is clear that the "intelligence" thus measured is most similar in identicals reared together, less so in identicals reared apart, and in these more similar than in fraternals or in siblings, which show about equal average differences. The estimation of IQ is, however, subject to some experimental error; repeated tests of the same person produce slightly different results. "Correcting" the mean IQ differences for these experimental errors, Newman, Freeman, and Holzinger obtained the figures shown in the bottom line of Table 11.3. It is again evident that IQ is conditioned both by nature and by nurture.

IS CRIMINALITY INHERITED?

Although psychologists are not all in agreement concerning the nature and significance of the human abilities measured by IQ testing, we are clearly dealing here with what are usually referred to as "psychic" traits. In the heat of polemics concerning the nature-nurture problem, some people doubted and even denied that psychic traits can be inherited. To bring out more clearly the meaning of the results obtained through twin studies, we shall consider perhaps the most controversial of all investigations of this sort, namely, that of the inheritance of criminality.

Several investigators in different countries have sought in prisons persons who were members of twin pairs. Anybody confined in a prison was considered to have a criminal record, irrespective of what law he had broken. The investigators then determined whether the co-twin also had a criminal record of any kind and at any time. If so, the twins were scored as concordant; if not, they were entered as discordant. Identical and fraternal twins were distinguished, using (as in all such studies), fraternal twins only of like sex. The results are summarized in Table 11.4. It is obvious that the proportions of concordant twin pairs is in every case higher among the identicals than among the fraternals.

TABLE 11.4

Concordance $(++)$ and discordance $(+-)$ for criminality in twins (*After Stern*)

Investigator and country	Identical		Fraternal	
	$++$	$+-$	$++$	$+-$
Lange (Germany)	10	3	2	15
Rosanoff et al. (USA)	35	10	6	21
Legras (Holland)	4	0	0	5
Kranz (Germany)	20	11	23	20
Stumpfl (Germany)	11	7	7	12
Total	80	31	38	73
Percentage	72	28	34	66

It does not follow from these data that "crime is destiny," as some people hastily concluded. There is nothing in the data to show that the persons who committed crimes (and were caught) would have done so had they lived in different environments. There is likewise nothing to show that other persons, whether the co-twins who had no criminal records or unrelated people, would not have become criminals if their life experiences had been like those of the actual criminals. Least of all do the data show that crimes are committed only by persons having a special genotype not found in noncriminals. What is shown is simply this: people having similar genotypes are more likely to behave similarly in certain environments than people with different genotypes. Criminality as such is not inherited. A tendency toward a similar behavioral conditioning is inherited.

CRITIQUE OF THE TWIN METHOD

Very clearly, studies of twins do not permit us to divide characters in which men differ into two sharp classes, those due to nature and those due to nurture; nor do they reveal anything about the mode of inheritance of the inherited characters. Consider again the data in Table 11.2; surely it would be wrong to draw from these data the conclusion that the rates of excretion in human urine of

TABLE 11.5
Observed differences between IQs (Binet) of 19 pairs of identical twins reared apart (*After Snyder, Lehmann, and Verschuer*)

The two columns on the right show the estimates of the magnitudes of the differences between the educational opportunities and the social environments in which the twins were brought up.

Number of the twin pair	Difference in IQ	Difference in education	Difference in social environment
1	12	15	27
2	12	32	14
3	-2	12	15
4	17	22	15
5	4	11	26
6	8	7	10
7	-1	9	27
8	15	14	32
9	6	7	14
10	5	10	15
11	24	37	25
12	7	19	13
13	1	11	13
14	-1	12	15
15	1	9	7
16	2	8	12
17	10	15	15
18	19	28	31
19	9	9	14

valine and threonine are hereditary and those of leucine and glutamine environmental. The most we can say is that the observed differences among the persons (twins) studied were in part genetically conditioned for valine and threonine excretion and showed no evidence of genetic conditioning for leucine and glutamine excretion. It would similarly be wrong to conclude from the data in Table 11.3 that weight in man is not under genetic control. Persons with certain types of body build are inclined to put on weight, and persons with other types of body build are inclined to be slim even without dieting; body build is certainly influenced by heredity.

The mean intrapair difference in the IQ of identical twins reared apart is only some 3 units greater than that of such twins reared together (Table 11.3). Again, it would be fallacious to conclude that environmental differences can raise or lower the IQ by only 3 units. Both the twins reared together and those reared apart were living in more or less similar environments—in the same country, mostly in the same economic stratum, in schools of the same general type, etc. We do not know how great a difference in the IQ could be produced if members of twin pairs were reared in different parts of the world or under greatly different circumstances in the same country, or if one twin suffered a severe disability that his co-twin escaped. Some data relevant to this problem are shown in Table 11.5.

Nineteen pairs of identical twins reared apart were given IQ tests; some of the twins made similar scores, but in other pairs (numbers 11, 18, 4, 8), one of the twins was markedly superior to his co-twin. The educational and social environments in which these twins were brought up were then rated in arbitrary units and the differences between them determined as shown in Table 11.5. It can be seen that where one of the members of a twin pair had an appreciably higher IQ than the other, he had, as a rule, also a markedly superior environment and education. Where the environmental opportunities of the twins were approximately alike, their IQs tended to be also rather similar. In fact, some twins whose environments were rated slightly superior to those of their co-twins scored a little lower on the IQ tests (the negative values in Table 11.5). However, notwithstanding all its limitations, the twin method does give incontrovertible evidence of participation of both heredity and environment in causation of the observed variability of certain human traits which had been supposed by some people to be either wholly hereditary or wholly environmental. It teaches us again that there is no sharp distinction between hereditary and environmental characters, all characters being due both to heredity and to environment.

PROBLEMS

11.1 Design an investigation, using the twin method, of the following question: To what categories of causes may variations in human temperament be due?

11.2 Identical twins often show "mirror imaging," e.g., clockwise hair whorls on one member, counter-clockwise whorls on the other. Should these be scored as concordant or discordant?

11.3 In aminoaciduria, a rare human disease, the excretion levels of many amino acids are greatly increased. What effect would inclusion of one or more such persons among the twins of Table 11.2 have upon the conclusions which might be drawn from it?

11.4 The following percentages of concordance were observed in twins:

Abnormality	Identical	Fraternal
spina bifida	72.2 (13/18)	33.3 (12/36)
Mongolism	88.9 (16/18)	6.7 (4/60)
club foot	22.9 (8/35)	2.3 (3/133)

What inference can be drawn from these data concerning relative roles of heredity and environment in the causation of these abnormalities? How could the inference be further tested?

11.5 Holt, in the Annals of Eugenics, 18, 211–231, counted the number of fingerprint ridges on the right and left hands of six pairs of normal identical twins with the following results:

Determine by the method of Section 29.28 whether there is evidence of a higher ridge count on the right hand than on the left. Give a confidence interval with 95 per cent confidence coefficient for the difference right-minus-left by the method of Section 29.25. (Note: A test of whether the similarities between co-twins are real or due to chance would involve the analysis of variance, a discussion of which can be found in any good statistics textbook.)

Hand	Pairs											
	1		2		3		4		5		6	
Left	62	69	92	90	97	92	28	44	53	51	62	56
Right	62	66	95	89	90	99	44	48	59	53	60	51

12   SEX–LINKED INHERITANCE

THE HYPOTHESIS of Sutton and Boveri that the behavior of chromosomes at meiosis provides the mechanism for segregation and independent assortment of genes, *if it is assumed that the genes are located in chromosomes,* has been amply verified by subsequent research. Microscopic observations on cell division, fertilization, and meiosis have shown that despite multiform variations in detail, these processes are remarkably similar in essential features throughout the animal and plant kingdoms. The phenomena of Mendelian segregation, from which the existence of genes is inferred, have also been observed in the most diverse groups of organisms. However, the chromosome theory of heredity, as it came to be called, was proved not by the general parallelism to which the earlier workers had called attention but by new data obtained from breeding experiments accompanied by cytological examination of the material of the experiments. The crucial evidence was that in which an association was proved between a specific gene and a specific chromosome identified under the microscope. In this chapter we shall examine some of the proofs for the chromosome theory, beginning with the evidence that certain genes in *Drosophila melanogaster,* the vinegar fly, are located in the chromosome concerned with sex determination.

DISCOVERY OF SEX CHROMOSOMES
We must now take account of one important exception to the statements, made in Chapter 4, that (1) the chromosomes in diploid cells appear in pairs of homologous mates and that (2) the disjunction of the members of these pairs at the reduction division in meiosis results in all gametes' receiving exactly equivalent chromosome complements. The discovery of this exception led to the development of the chromosome theory of sex determination, which will be discussed on its own merits in Chapter 22. At present we are interested in sex chromosomes only in so far as they throw light on the

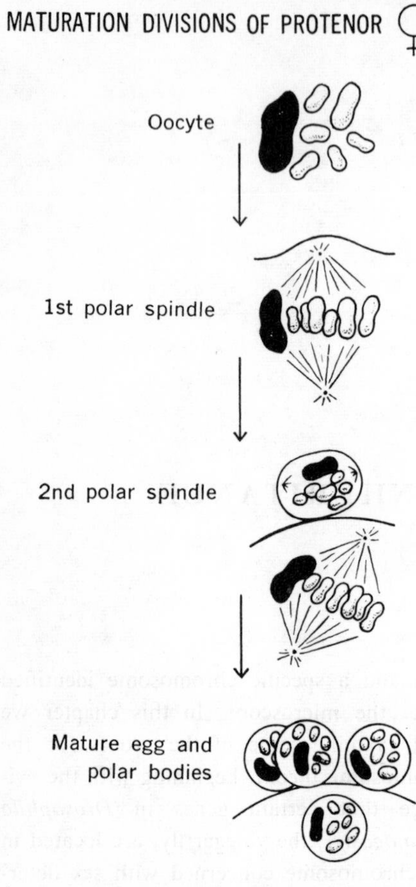

MATURATION DIVISIONS OF PROTENOR ♀

Oocyte

1st polar spindle

2nd polar spindle

Mature egg and
polar bodies

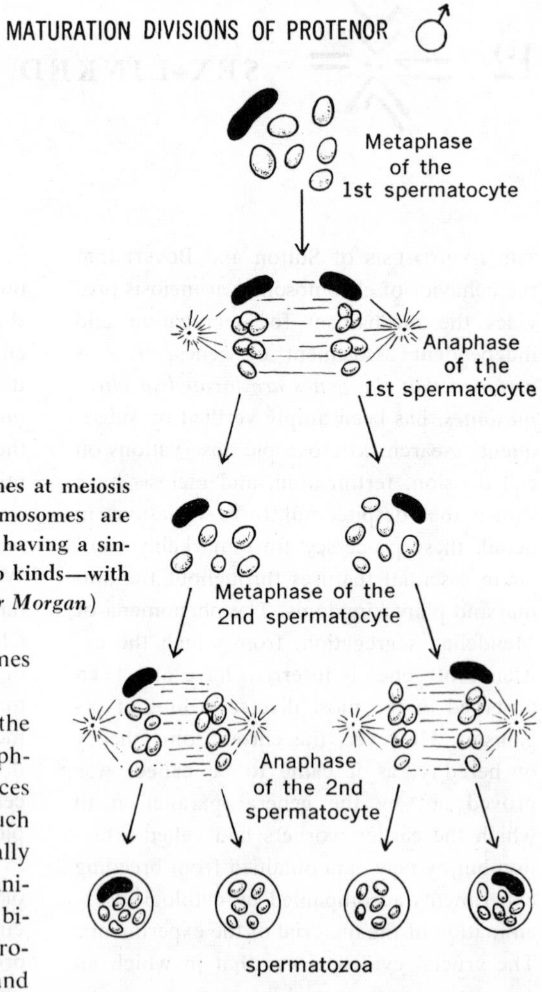

Fig. 12.1. Behavior of sex chromosomes at meiosis in the bug Protenor. The X chromosomes are shown in black. All eggs are alike in having a single X chromosome. Sperms are of two kinds—with and without an X chromosome. (*After Morgan*)

females and males differ visibly in chromosomal constitution. This was shown in the early years of this century by several investigators, among whom Montgomery, McClung, Sutton, Stevens, and especially Wilson must be mentioned.

The precise form of the chromosomal differences between the sexes is not the same in different organisms. Perhaps the simplest arrangement is that found in most grasshoppers and in some bugs, in which the males have one chromosome less than the females (Fig. 12.1). For example, in the squash bug,

MATURATION DIVISIONS OF PROTENOR ♂

Metaphase
of the
1st spermatocyte

Anaphase
of the
1st spermatocyte

Metaphase of the
2nd spermatocyte

Anaphase
of the 2nd
spermatocyte

spermatozoa

problem of the association of chromosomes and genes.

Most of the higher plants and some of the lower animals are monoecious, or hermaphroditic; that is, the same individual produces both female and male gametes. In such organisms, all the chromosomes normally occur in pairs. On the other hand, most animals and some plants are dioecious, or bisexual, and in them eggs and sperms are produced by different individuals, females and males. In some of the bisexual organisms,

Protenor, Wilson found that females regularly have 14 chromosomes in their diploid cells, which unite into 7 pairs (bivalents) at meiosis. All eggs receive, therefore, a haploid set of 7 chromosomes. Males, however, have only 13 chromosomes in diploid cells, which form at meiosis 6 pairs and one odd, unpaired chromosome. At the second meiotic division, the unpaired chromosome passes undivided into one of the two daughter cells, and therefore two kinds of spermatozoa are formed in equal numbers, some with 6 and others with 7 chromosomes. Fertilization of an egg (7 chromosomes) by a sperm with 7 chromosomes produces a female (14 chromosomes); fertilization by a sperm with 6 chromosomes produces a male with 13 chromosomes. The odd chromosome thus determines the sex of the individual receiving it, and it was consequently called the *sex chromosome,* or X chromosome. The other chromosomes, which are alike in males and females, have been called *autosomes.* The case may thus be formulated:

♀ = 6 pairs of autosomes + 2 X
  chromosomes (12 A + 2 X)
♂ = 6 pairs of autosomes + 1 X
  chromosome (12 A + X)

In many other animals and in several plants, males and females have been found to differ, not in the presence or absence of one whole chromosome, but in the presence in one sex of a chromosome that is unlike its mate and unlike any chromosome in the opposite sex. In *Drosophila melanogaster,* the female has four pairs of chromosomes (Fig. 4.2), the members of each pair being alike. In the male there is only one of the straight rodlike chromosomes, the place of the other member of this pair being taken by a rod with a hook-shaped or bent end. The rodlike member, which is alike in both male and female, is the X chromosome; the unlike member of this pair in the male is known as the Y chromosome. The eggs all have four chromosomes (3 A + X); the sperms also have four chromosomes, but half have the rod-shaped X chromosome (3 A + X), and half have the bent Y chromosome (3 A + Y). Fertilization of any egg by an X-containing sperm produces a female (6 A + XX); fertilization by a Y-containing sperm produces a male (6 A + XY).

THE TWO TYPES OF SEX DETERMINATION

The type of sex determination in which the female has two X chromosomes and the male one X and one Y chromosome is very widespread, being found not only in many insects and other invertebrates but also in some fish, in mammals including man, and in many dioecious plants. In man, for example, somatic cells have 48 chromosomes (or, according to newer data, 46 chromosomes), which in the female form 24 (or 23) pairs at meiosis (23 AA + XX). Each egg carries 23 autosomes and an X. In the male, the 48 chromosomes form at meiosis 23 pairs in which the homologues are visibly alike and one pair consisting of members of unequal size, the larger one being the X and the smaller the Y chromosome (23 AA + XY). Two kinds of spermatozoa are formed, half of which carry an X (23 A + X) and the other half a Y chromosome (23 A + Y). The sex of the offspring is determined at fertilization by the kind of spermatozoon that happens to reach and enter the egg; the X-bearing sperms produce girls and the Y-bearing ones boys (Fig. 12.2).

In all the above cases, the male is the heterozygous, or heterogametic, sex, because two kinds of sperm are produced, and the female is homozygous, or homogametic, because all eggs are sexually alike. But in some animals the relations are reversed; that is, the female has an unlike pair of chromosomes (XY) and the male is XX. For such cases a different formulation has often been used: the sex chromosomes have been called Z instead of X and the other member of this pair W instead of Y. Animals of this type are thus called ZW and ZZ, or, briefly, of

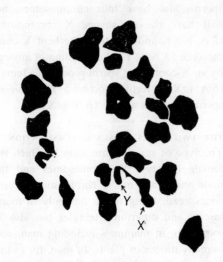

Fig. 12.2. Diagram of diakinesis in a spermatocyte of man. Arrows indicate the X–Y bivalent. (*After J. Schultz*)

the ZW type, to distinguish it from the Drosophila, or XY, type. Here we shall adopt a similar terminology for both types, since the letters are merely symbols and do not indicate homology between X chromosomes in different forms. The two types may be distinguished as male heterogametic and female heterogametic, respectively.

In the domestic fowl, for example, the female forms eggs of two sorts, half with an X chromosome, which when fertilized by any sperm develop into males (XX), and half without an X chromosome, which develop into females. The mechanism is the same as in Drosophila; that is, two types of gametes are formed by one sex and only one by the other sex; and sex is determined at fertilization by the kinds of gametes that unite.

SEX LINKAGE IN DROSOPHILA

Events of crucial importance for the chromosome theory proved to be the discovery of sex-linked genes in Drosophila by Morgan in 1910 and coordinated genetical and cytological study of these cases by Morgan, Bridges, and others. In the course of breeding experiments with the normal wild type, which has red eyes, Morgan found one individual in which the eyes were white. This gave rise to a true-breeding strain of white-eyed flies. When he crossed this new variety with the wild, red-eyed type, the results from a cross of a white male with a red female were different from those obtained from the reciprocal cross of red male with white female. The results were found to depend on the sex of the parent by which the trait was introduced into the cross, whereas with other Mendelian characters, as we have seen, it makes no difference in either the F_1 or the F_2 whether a given character is brought in by the male or female parent. The details of these experiments are shown in Figures 12.3 and 12.4.

From the cross of white-eyed male with red female, the first-generation flies are red-eyed in both sexes (Fig. 12.3). When these are bred together, white reappears in a quarter of the F_2 offspring, indicating that red and white eye colors are due to an allelic pair of genes of which red acts as the dominant. However, of the F_2 offspring all the females are red, whereas half the males are red and half are white. The females, however, are of two kinds genotypically. Half of them give nothing but red offspring; the other half, however, must carry the recessive white, for in their offspring half the males are white-eyed.

When a red male is bred to a white female, however, quite a different result follows (Fig. 12.4). Among their F_1 offspring, all the females are red-eyed and all the males are white-eyed. When these are bred together, their offspring (the F_2) consist of red-eyed and white-eyed individuals in equal numbers in both sexes. All the white-eyed flies are apparently pure, for no red-eyed flies appear in their offspring; and the red-eyed males bred to pure red females also produce only red-eyed descendants. The red-eyed F_1 females, however, must be heterozygous, for when bred to either white or red

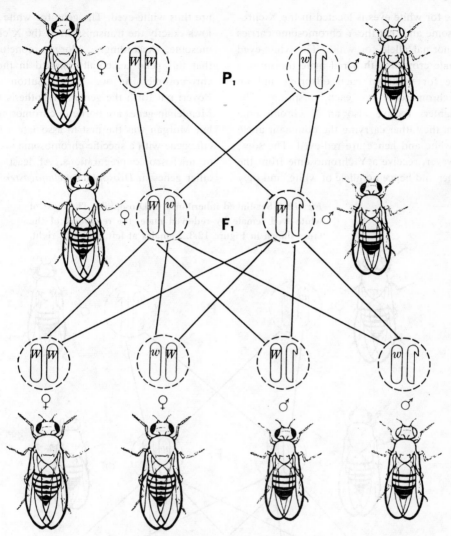

Fig. 12.3. Sex-linked inheritance in Drosophila. The cross of
red-eyed female by white-eyed male. The course of the sex
chromosomes carrying the sex-linked gene W-w is traced
from the parents to the F_2. Females at left, males at right.

males, half their male offspring are always
white-eyed.

In Drosophila, sex-linked traits such as
white eye color follow a crisscross inheritance. The male transmits his sex-linked
traits to his grandsons through his daughters,
never to or through his sons. The trait thus
seems to alternate or cross from one sex to
the other in its passage from generation to

generation. This, of course, is the mode of
transmission followed by the X chromosome, as can be seen in the diagrams. Only
the daughters get an X chromosome from
the father, whereas both sons and daughters
receive an X chromosome from the mother
(Figs. 12.3 and 12.4).

In explaining the inheritance of white eye
color in Drosophila, it was assumed that the

gene for white eyes is located in the X chromosome and that the Y chromosome carries no normal allele for white. The white-eyed female crossed with a red male transmits a gene for white to each offspring and an X chromosome to each offspring. The daughters receive also an X chromosome from the father carrying the dominant allele of white and hence are red-eyed. The sons, however, receive a Y chromosome from the father and hence no allele of white, and they are thus white-eyed. The gene for white follows exactly the transmission of the X chromosome. Accordingly, Morgan concluded that this gene is actually carried in the X chromosome. As we know, Sutton and Boveri put forth the general hypothesis that Mendelian genes are borne in chromosomes, but Morgan was the first to associate a specific gene with a specific chromosome visible in microscopic preparations. At least 140 other genes in *Drosophila melanogaster* fol-

Fig. 12.4. Sex-linked inheritance in Drosophila. The cross of white-eyed female by red-eyed male, the reciprocal of the cross shown in Figure 12.3. Females at left, males at right.

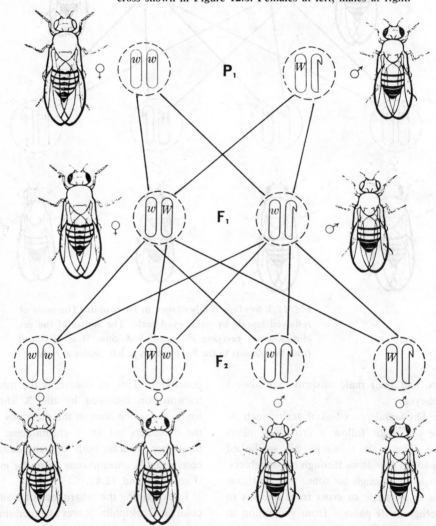

low the same mode of inheritance as white, which indicates that these genes are also carried in the X chromosome.

SEX-LINKED GENES IN MAN

Approximately twenty known genes in man are inherited like the gene white or its normal allele in Drosophila and therefore are presumed to be borne in the human X chromosome (Fig. 12.5).

The commonest sex-linked human trait is red-green color blindness, which in the United States occurs in about 8 per cent of men and only about 0.5 per cent of women. After its peculiar mode of transmission chiefly to sons from the mother's family had been known for at least a hundred years, E. B. Wilson in 1911 pointed out that all the facts about the heredity of color blindness could be explained by the assumption that the recessive gene responsible for this condition is contained in the X chromosome and that in man the male is the heterogametic sex. These are the same assumptions that are made for the white-eye gene in Drosophila (Fig. 12.3 and 12.4).

It is easy to see why color blindness is found more often in men if one remembers that a father transmits his X chromosome to all his daughters but to none of his sons, whereas a mother passes one of her two X's to each of her children. Therefore, all the sons of a color-blind mother are color-blind regardless of what kind of color vision her husband may have; but if the husband has normal vision, all his daughters have normal vision. These daughters are, however, carriers of the gene for color blindness, since they contain this recessive gene covered up by its dominant allele; married to men with normal color vision, they produce all normal girl children, but among the boys about half are normal and the other half color-blind. A color-blind daughter can be produced only if a color-blind man happens to marry a carrier or a homozygous color-blind woman. Since women who are either carriers or

color-blind and color-blind men are less common than those with genes for normal vision, such marriages are rather rare.

Similarly, one of the forms of the disease hemophilia is restricted almost entirely to men, and such men are invariably sons of mothers who are normal but are carriers of a recessive hemophilia gene. This hemophilia manifests itself chiefly in absence of the ability of the blood to clot when exposed to air. In normal persons this ability limits the bleeding from wounds and thus prevents excessive and possibly fatal hemorrhages. In hemophilics, even a small skin injury can lead to death from loss of blood. Mortality among hemophilics is therefore very high, especially in childhood. The disease may be said to be caused by a sex-linked, recessive, semilethal gene.

Hemophilic men, if they survive and reach the reproductive age, produce daughters all of whom are normal but who are carriers of hemophilia, which they transmit to half their sons (grandsons of the male hemophilics). One-half of the daughters of the female carriers are, of course, also heterozygous carriers. A female hemophilic could, theoretically, be produced if a woman who is a carrier marries a man who is a hemophilic. In fact homozygous female hemophilics have been reported. They may be rarer than expected from the gene frequency, but the condition is not always lethal to females as was once thought. Yet this gene can be transmitted from a heterozygous carrier to her daughters, granddaughters, etc., all of whom will have normal blood and yet produce sons half of whom will be afflicted with hemophilia. A famous case of this sort is the transmission of hemophilia in some royal houses of Europe, which is traceable to Queen Victoria of England and her progeny (Fig. 12.6).

HEREDITY THROUGH THE Y CHROMOSOME

The sex-linked genes contained in the X chromosome of Drosophila have no alleles

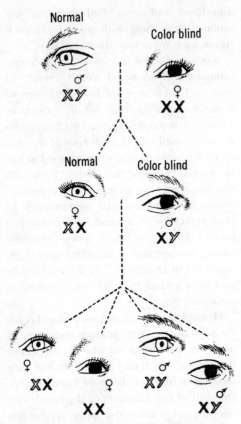

Fig. 12.5. The inheritance of red-green color blindness in man. On the right, the result of marriage of a color-blind man and a normal woman. The defect is transmitted only through the daughters and appears in half their sons, being carried in one of the X chromosomes.

in the Y chromosome; this is the reason why a male that carries a single dose of a recessive sex-linked gene shows its effects in the phenotype. The Y chromosome is, therefore, genetically "empty" or "inert," at least compared with the X chromosome. One gene, bobbed, however, has alleles both in the X and in the Y chromosomes. The recessive mutant allele of bobbed, when present in both X chromosomes of a female, causes the bristles on the body of the fly to be shorter and slenderer than normal. A male carrying bobbed in the X chromosome but a normal

allele of that gene in the Y has normal bristles. If such a male is crossed with bobbed females, all the daughters are bobbed and all the sons have normal bristles; the normal bristles are transmitted from father to sons, just as the Y chromosome is. Several bobbed alleles in the Y chromosome are also known, and males that carry bobbed both in the X and in the Y chromosomes show bobbed bristles. The Y is also necessary for male fertility. There is some evidence that in man also some genes are carried in the Y chromosome.

Color-blind individuals and chromosomes carrying the gene for this character are shown in black. On the left, results of marriage of a color-blind woman and a normal man where the defect is transmitted to all the sons and to both grandsons and granddaughters.

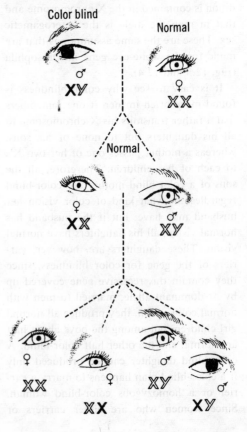

SEX-LINKED GENES IN POULTRY AND IN MOTHS

The kind of sex-linked inheritance described in Drosophila and in man is characteristic of both animals and plants in which the male sex is the heterogametic one; this inheritance is readily understandable if the genes concerned are borne in the X chromosomes. A different kind of sex linkage occurs where females are heterogametic, as in birds, moths, butterflies, and certain other animals.

The inheritance of barred plumage in poultry is a classical example of this type of sex linkage (Figs. 12.7 and 12.8). The barred pattern, as seen in such breeds as the Barred Plymouth Rock, is dominant over black or red unbarred plumage. Breeding evidence indicates that a male may carry two genes for barring but a female only one; and cytological research has shown that there are two X chromosomes in the cells of

nonbarred cock gives, as might be expected, a very different result. Here the F_1 males are all barred and the F_1 hens are nonbarred.

Fig. 12.6. **Pedigree of hemophilia in the descendants of Queen Victoria of England. I-1, Queen Victoria; II-2, King Edward VII; II-3, Princess Alice; II-8, Leopold, Duke of Albany; III-11, Irene; III-13, Prince Frederick William of Hesse; III-14, Alexandra; III-21, Alice; III-24, Victoria Eugenie; III-25, Prince Leopold of Battenberg; III-26, Prince Maurice of Battenberg; IV-18, Prince Waldemar of Prussia; IV-20, Prince Henry of Prussia; IV-25, Tsarevitch Alexis of Russia; IV-27, Viscount Trematon; IV-29, Alfonso, formerly Prince of Asturias; IV-34, Infante Gonzalo. (*After Haldane*)**

◑ **Known to be transmitter**
⊞ **Died in childhood or infancy**

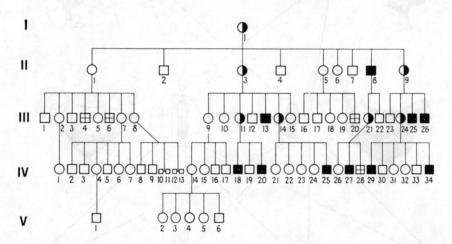

the male but only one in those of the female. In Figures 12.7 and 12.8, the gene for barred plumage is represented by B and nonbarred by b. The cross between a nonbarred hen and a barred cock produces only barred offspring of both sexes. When inbred, these produced only barred males in F_2, but approximately half of the F_2 hens were barred and the other half nonbarred.

The reciprocal cross of barred hen and

whereas in F_2 there are equal numbers of barred and nonbarred birds in both sexes. Barring thus follows the same crisscross mode of inheritance as white eyes, except that in the fowl the sex-linked gene goes from mother (XY) to her sons only, whereas the father (XX) transmits it to both his sons and his daughters. The gene follows the X chromosome in both cases.

In the fowl, pigeon, duck, canary, several

species of moths, and one species of fish, sex-linked characters have been studied and found to resemble barring in their inheritance.

**PRIMARY NONDISJUNCTION OF
X CHROMOSOMES IN DROSOPHILA**
Morgan's identification of the microscopically visible X chromosome as the seat of the genes for white eyes and for other sex-linked traits in Drosophila was still based on an analogy: if one supposes that these genes are borne in the X chromosome, then the ob-

served mode of their inheritance necessarily follows. Bridges, a student of Morgan, completed the proof. He showed that, taking the assumption that genes are carried in the chromosomes as a working hypothesis, one can predict how the chromosomes of certain flies will appear under the microscope. And, conversely, knowing the chromosomes, one can predict the behavior of certain traits of the flies in breeding experiments. When Bridges made the crucial experiments, the results came out as predicted. He published an account of his work in 1916 in a classical

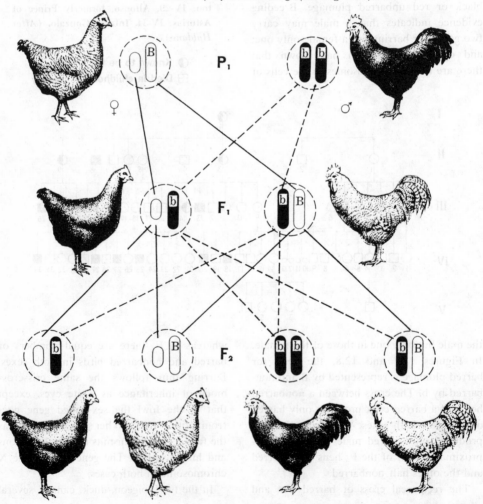

Fig. 12.7. Sex-linked inheritance in poultry. The cross of barred ♀ by nonbarred ♂ (see Fig. 12.8).

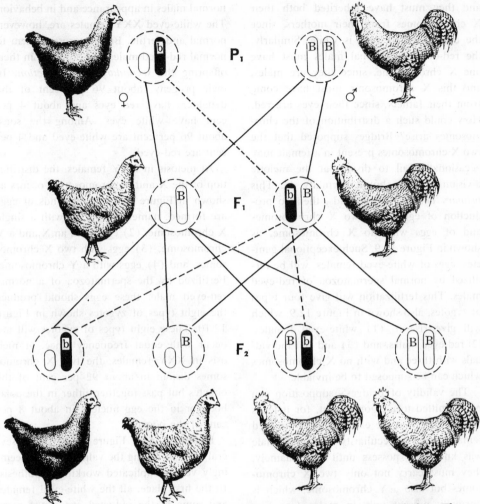

Fig. 12.8. Sex-linked inheritance in poultry. The cross of barred ♂ by nonbarred ♀. The course of the X chromosomes carrying the sex-linked gene *B* (barring) and its recessive allele *b* is traced from parents to F_2. Males at right, females at left.

paper characteristically entitled "Nondisjunction as Proof of the Chromosome Theory of Heredity."

As we have seen (Figs. 12.3 and 12.4), white-eyed Drosophila females crossed with red-eyed males produce red-eyed daughters and white-eyed sons in the F_1 generation. However, there are some exceptions to this rule. About one fly in 2,000 to 3,000 F_1 offspring has the unexpected eye colors, red in

males and white in females. Does the appearance of these exceptional flies, even though they are rare, contradict Morgan's assumption that the gene differentiating the white-eyed flies from the red-eyed is transmitted in the X chromosome? Bridges decided that there is no such contradiction.

His reasoning was as follows. The white-eyed exceptional females must carry two X chromosomes, since their sex is female;

and they must have inherited both their X chromosomes from their mothers, since the color of their eyes is white. Similarly, the red-eyed exceptional males must have one X chromosome, since they are males, and this X chromosome must have come from their fathers, since their eyes are red. How could such a distribution of the chromosomes arise? Bridges supposed that the two X chromosomes present in a female may occasionally fail to disjoin at the meiotic division as they should normally do. This *primary nondisjunction* leads, then, to production of eggs with two X chromosomes and of eggs with no X chromosome, as shown in Figure 12.9. Such exceptional gametes, eggs of white-eyed females, will be fertilized by normal spermatozoa of red-eyed males. This fertilization will give four types of zygotes, also shown in Figure 12.9, which will give rise to (1) white-eyed females, (2) red-eyed males, and (3) and (4) individuals with three and with no X chromosomes which can be supposed to be inviable.

The validity of Bridges's supposition can be submitted to a rigorous test, for it leads us to expect that the exceptional white-eyed females have a peculiarity that no female was known to possess until then, namely, they must carry not only two X chromosomes but also a Y chromosome, which is normally present only in males (see Fig. 12.9). Bridges verified this prediction by examination of the chromosomes of the exceptional white-eyed females under the microscope. They actually have two X chromosomes and a Y chromosome (XXY females). Moreover, the exceptional red-eyed males should have no Y chromosome, which normal males of Drosophila always have. This prediction was also verified by cytological examination.

SECONDARY NONDISJUNCTION OF
X CHROMOSOMES IN DROSOPHILA
The exceptional males without the Y chromosome are sterile, although they are quite

normal males in appearance and in behavior. The white-eyed XXY females are, however, normal and fertile. Bridges crossed them to normal red-eyed males and observed in their offspring the *secondary nondisjunction*. In their progeny, about 96 per cent of the daughters have red eyes and about 4 per cent have white eyes. Among the sons, about 96 per cent are white-eyed and 4 per cent are red-eyed.

At meiosis in XXY females, the distribution of the X and Y chromosomes occurs as shown in Figure 12.10. Four kinds of eggs are formed, namely, (1) eggs with a single X chromosome, (2) eggs with an X and a Y chromosome, (3) eggs with two X chromosomes, and (4) eggs with a Y chromosome. Fertilized by the spermatozoa of a normal red-eyed male, these eggs should produce the eight types of zygotes shown in Figure 12.10. These eight types of zygotes will not occur with equal frequency since, at meiosis in XXY females, the two X chromosomes disjoin in about 92 per cent of the oöcytes but pass together either in the polar body or in the egg nucleus in about 8 per cent of the oöcytes.

Examination of Figure 12.10 shows several ways of testing the validity of this seemingly very complicated working hypothesis. In the first place, all the white-eyed females and some of the red-eyed ones must carry not only two X chromosomes but also a Y chromosome. The red-eyed males, in contrast to those arising from primary nondisjunction, must have a Y chromosome and accordingly ought to be fertile. And finally, some of the white-eyed males must have a hitherto unknown set of chromosomes, namely, one X chromosome and two Y chromosomes. Bridges not only made these predictions but verified them by cytological examination of the proper classes of flies.

ATTACHED X CHROMOSOMES IN DROSOPHILA
In 1922 L. V. Morgan found another exceptional case of inheritance of sex-linked traits

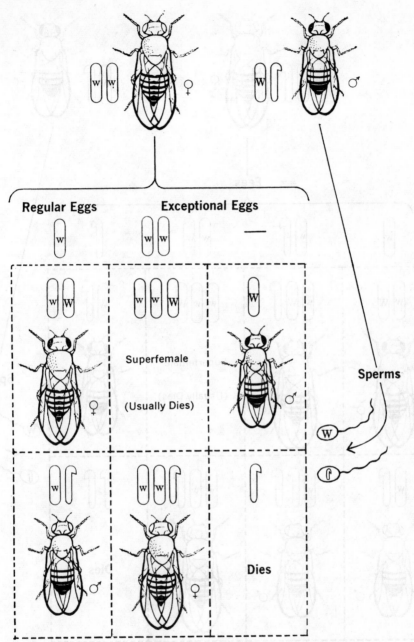

Fig. 12.9. Nondisjunction of the X chromosomes in *Drosophila melanogaster* in a cross of white-eyed female by red-eyed male.

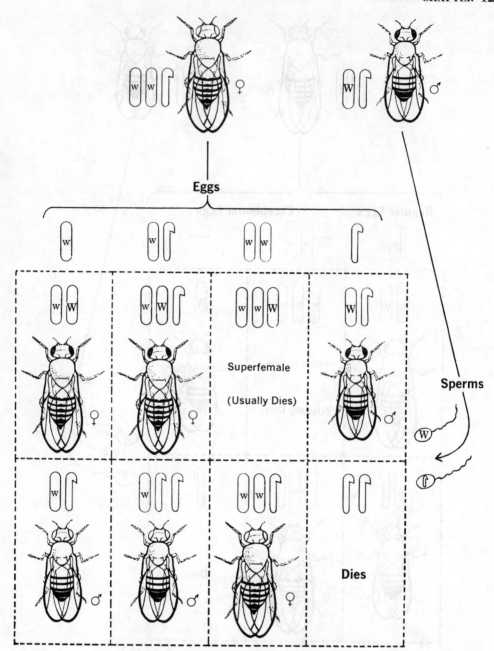

Fig. 12.10. Secondary nondisjunction in *Drosophila melanogaster.* A white-eyed female with an extra Y chromosome (see Fig. 12.9) produces the four kinds of eggs shown above. When these are fertilized by sperm of a normal red-eyed male, the phenotypes and genotypes shown in the checkerboard are produced.

in Drosophila, and analyzed it along lines similar to those followed earlier by Bridges. This analysis proved the same principle, but in an even more diagrammatic way than that used in Bridges's original experiments.

Yellow body color in *Drosophila melanogaster* is, like the white eye color described above, due to a sex-linked recessive gene. Yellow females crossed with normal, brownish-gray males ordinarily give in the F_1 all normal daughters and yellow sons and equal numbers of yellow and gray in both sexes in the F_2. Normal females crossed to yellow males give all normal offspring in the F_1

and in the F_2 all normal females and a segregation 1 yellow : 1 normal among the males (cf. Figs. 12.3 and 12.4). L. V. Morgan found, however, an exceptional yellow female which, when crossed to normal males, produced only yellow daughters and normal sons. These yellow daughters repeated the exceptional performance of their mother; the sons of the original exceptional mother were all sterile, but in subsequent generations the normal sons behaved like the usual normal flies.

What is the explanation for this exceptional behavior? Let us suppose that in the

Fig. 12.11. Inheritance of "attached X" chromosomes in Drosophila. The X chromosomes of the mother each carry the gene yellow, and these are transmitted together. The only surviving sons are those that receive the Y chromosome from the mother and the X from the father. (*After L. V. Morgan*)

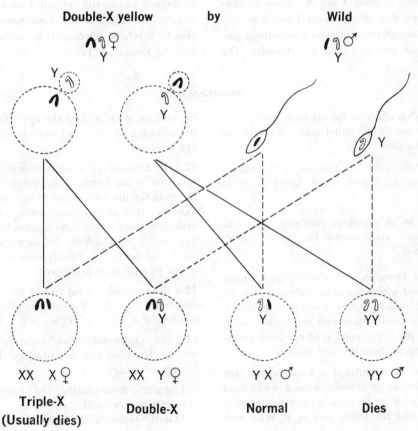

Double-X yellow	**by**		**Wild**

XX X ♀	XX Y ♀	Y X ♂	YY ♂
Triple-X **(Usually dies)**	**Double-X**	**Normal**	**Dies**

exceptional yellow female the X chromosomes become permanently attached to each other so that meiotic disjunction is no longer possible and both X's either remain in the egg or else are extruded in the polar body (Fig. 12.11). The original exceptional yellow female must, therefore, have produced two kinds of eggs: those with the attached X chromosomes carrying the gene yellow, and those without an X chromosome. Fertilized by the sperm of a normal male, the two kinds of eggs will give four kinds of zygotes, namely, (1) with two attached yellow X chromosomes and a normal X chromosome from the male, (2) with two attached yellow X chromosomes and a Y chromosome, (3) with a normal paternal X chromosome and a Y chromosome, and (4) with two Y chromosomes and no X. Zygotes of class 2 are the observed yellow daughters, and those of class 3 are the observed normal sons. Zygotes of classes 1 and 4 usually die, although those of class 1 sometimes survive and give so-called superfemales. The

exceptional yellow females will henceforth carry a Y chromosome; hence the two kinds of eggs produced will have either two attached X chromosomes (100 per cent nondisjunction) or a Y chromosome, as shown in Figure 12.11.

How can the validity of L. V. Morgan's hypothesis be tested? This hypothesis permits us to make several predictions: namely, (1) the females from the exceptional yellow stock must have their two X chromosomes somehow attached to each other; (2) these females must carry not only two X's but also a Y chromosome; (3) about half their eggs can be expected to produce no viable flies, because some of them will have three X chromosomes (duplication) and others will have none and thus will be deficient for all X chromosome genes. These predictions were tested and found to be valid, and the hypothesis was clearly verified. Females with attached X chromosomes have been found also in a related species, *Drosophila simulans,* by Kossikov (1934).

PROBLEMS

12.1 What effect on the sex ratio would a recessive sex-linked lethal factor have in the domestic fowl?

12.2 What effect on the sex ratio would a recessive sex-linked lethal factor have in man?

NOTE: In all problems involving sex-linked characters, state results for the two sexes separately.

12.3 In Drosophila, if a white-eyed female is crossed with a red-eyed male and if an F_1 female from this cross is mated with her father and an F_1 male with his mother, what will be the appearance as to eye color of the offspring of these last two crosses?

12.4 In Drosophila, if a homozygous red-eyed female is crossed with a white-eyed male and if an F_1 female from this cross is mated with her father and an F_1 male with

his mother, what will be the appearance of the offspring of these last two crosses as to eye color?

12.5 In Drosophila, vestigial wings, v, are recessive to the normal long wings, V, and the gene for this trait is not in the sex chromosome. If a homozogous white, long female is crossed with a homozygous red, vestigial male, what will be the appearance of the F_1; of the F_2; of the offspring of a cross of the F_1 with each parent type?

12.6 In Drosophila, what will be the appearance of the offspring of the following crosses: $Ww\ Vv \times w\ vv;\ ww\ Vv \times W\ Vv?$

12.7 In Drosophila, two red-eyed long-winged flies bred together produce the following offspring:

Females: three-fourths red long; one-fourth red vestigial.

Males: three-eighths red long; three-eighths white long; one-eighth red vestigial; one-eighth white vestigial.

What are the genotypes of the parents?

12.8 In Drosophila, a cross between Bar-eyed females and wild-type (round-eyed) males produces only Bar-eyed males and females in the F_1. Wild-type female × Bar-eyed male produces Bar-eyed females and wild-type males. Explain the inheritance of Bar eye, and predict the appearance of the F_2 from each of these crosses.

12.9 A girl of normal vision whose father was color-blind marries a man of normal vision whose father was also color-blind. What type of vision can be expected in their offspring?

12.10 A color-blind man marries a woman of normal vision. They have sons and daughters, all of normal vision and all of whom marry persons of normal vision. Where among the grandchildren may color blindness be expected to appear? If there are cousin marriages among these grandchildren, where among *their* offspring may color blindness be expected to appear? (All persons of normal vision mentioned are homozygous.)

12.11 A man and a woman, both of normal vision, have (1) a color-blind son who has a daughter of normal vision, (2) a daughter of normal vision who has one color-blind and one normal son, and (3) another daughter of normal vision who has five sons, all normal. What are the probable genotypes of grandparents, children, and grandchildren?

12.12 A man's maternal grandmother had normal vision; his maternal grandfather was color-blind; his mother is color-blind; his father is of normal vision. What are the genotypes, as to vision, of the two parents and grandparents mentioned? What type of vision has this man himself? What type have his sisters? If he should marry a woman genotypically like one of his sisters, what type of vision would be expected in the offspring?

12.13 In poultry, if a nonbarred cock is crossed with a barred hen and an F_1 female from this cross is mated with her father and an F_1 male with his mother, what will be the appearance of the offspring of these last two crosses, as to barring?

12.14 In poultry, if a nonbarred cock is crossed with a barred hen and an F_2 from this cross is allowed to interbreed freely, what will be the appearance of the F_3 as to barring; of the F_5?

12.15 A single-comb barred cock crossed with a walnut-comb barred hen produces the following offspring:

- 4 rose barred males
- 5 walnut barred males
- 2 rose barred females
- 3 rose nonbarred females
- 2 walnut barred females
- 2 walnut nonbarred females

What are the genotypes of the parents?

12.16 In Drosophila, vermilion eye color is recessive and sex-linked. In exceptional cases, vermilion female × normal male produces, in addition to the usual vermilion male and red-eyed female, a few vermilion females and red males. Explain this result, and predict what classes of offspring should appear when the vermilion F_1 females from the above are crossed with red-eyed males.

13   LINKAGE AND CROSSING OVER

MENDEL'S PRINCIPLE of independent assortment, as we saw in the preceding chapters, applies both to genes and to chromosomes. The maternal and paternal members of each pair of chromosomes are distributed independently to the gametes at meiosis. It is for this reason that genes carried in different chromosomes undergo independent assortment and produce the ratios of differentiating characters which Mendel discovered and explained so successfully.

It must be evident, however, that the number of genes in most organisms, which may be reckoned in the thousands, exceeds the number of pairs of chromosomes, which seldom reaches 100. In Drosophila, for example, hundreds of genes have been studied, yet there are only four pairs of chromosomes. If all genes are in chromosomes, it follows that each chromosome must contain many genes. Thus genes in the same chromosome will not be assorted independently. Mendel's second law is not universal but is limited to genes in different chromosomes.

Indeed, an exception to this law was discovered not long after Mendel's work was rediscovered, for in 1906 Bateson and Punnett found two pairs of alleles in sweet peas which did not assort independently. Instead, when two alleles, such as *A* and *B,* came from the same parent (*AA BB* × *aa bb*), they tended to enter the same gamete and to be transmitted together; and when the same alleles came from different parents (*AA bb* × *aa BB*), they tended to enter different gametes and to remain apart. The first peculiarity was called *coupling* and the second *repulsion*.

LINKAGE

No satisfactory explanation of coupling and repulsion was developed until Morgan in 1910 found similar situations in Drosophila and saw that coupling and repulsion are but two aspects of a single phenomenon called *linkage*. He supposed that this tendency of linked genes to remain in their original combinations was due to their residence in the

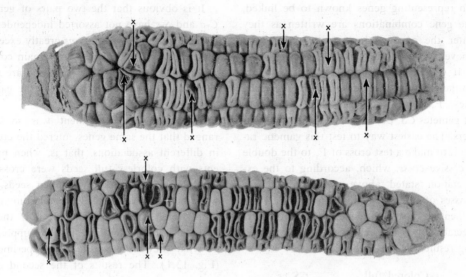

Fig. 13.1. Evidence of linkage between two pairs of alleles in corn. Above, an ear resulting from a cross of a heterozygous plant that had received the genes for colored aleurone (*C*) and full (nonshrunken) endosperm (*S*) from one parent and for colorless (*c*) and shrunken (*s*) from the other with a double recessive colorless shrunken (*cs*) plant. Most of the kernels show the parental combinations of characters, but a few (designated by X) have the new combinations colored shrunken and colorless full. Below, an ear from a heterozygote that had received the genes in different combination—colored and shrunken from one parent, colorless and full from the other—crossed with the double recessive. The recombinations (X) in this case are colored full and colorless shrunken. (*From Hutchison, in the Journal of Heredity*)

same chromosome. Furthermore, he advanced the basic idea that the degree or strength of linkage depends upon the distance between the linked genes in the chromosome. This proved to be a very fruitful idea, for it soon developed into the theory of the linear arrangement of genes in the chromosomes and has led to the construction of genetic or linkage maps of chromosomes.

Linkage in maize. The phenomena of linkage are particularly clear in maize, in which the recombination between linked genes occurs in both sexes and in which traits

visible in the seeds can be easily observed in large numbers, the same ear having several hundred seeds. A good example is the results obtained by Hutchison, who crossed a variety of maize having seeds that were colored and normally filled out (full) to one with colorless and shrunken seeds. In other experiments it had been shown that color, gene *C*, was a simple dominant over colorless, *c*, whereas normal or full endosperm, gene *S*, is dominant over shrunken, *s*. Accordingly, the parents were *CC SS* and *cc ss*, and the F_1, as expected, had colored, full seeds that must have the genotype *CS/cs*.

(In representing genes known to be linked, the gene combinations are written as they enter the zygote, those from one parent above a line, those from the other below it.)

If *C* and *S* assort independently, in accordance with Mendel's second principle, these F_1 plants should produce four types of gametes *CS, Cs, cS,* and *cs* in equal numbers. The easiest way to test this gametic ratio is to make a test cross of F_1 to the double recessive *cc ss,* which, according to the expectation stated above, would yield four classes of progeny in the ratio 1 : 1 : 1 : 1. When the cross was made, however, this expectation was not realized, but the following result was obtained:

Colored full	*CS /cs*
	4,032
Colored shrunken	*Cs /cs*
	149
Colorless full	*cS /cs*
	152
Colorless shrunken	*cs /cs*
	4,035
Total	8,368

The colored full and colorless shrunken seeds are *more* frequent than the colored shrunken and colorless full seeds (Fig. 13.1). Now, the parents had colored full and colorless shrunken seeds. These are *parental combinations* of characters, whereas in the *recombinations* the associations of the characters have changed. In independent assortment the *parental combinations, CS* and *cs,* and *recombinations, Cs* and *cS,* would be equally frequent. But in the experiment shown, the situation is as follows:

Parental $\left\{ \begin{array}{l} CS \ 4,032 \\ cs \ \ 4,035 \end{array} \right.$
combinations

8,067, or about 96.4 per cent of the total

Recombinations $\left\{ \begin{array}{l} Cs \ 149 \\ cS \ 152 \end{array} \right.$

301, or about 3.6 per cent of the total

It is obvious that the two pairs of genes *C-c* and *S-s* have not assorted independently. The *parental combinations* greatly exceed the expected 50 per cent; they remain combined or linked in 96.4 per cent and are recombined in only 3.6 per cent of the gametes.

When another experiment was so arranged that the same genes entered the cross in different associations, that is, when parents with colorless full seeds were crossed with those with colored shrunken seeds, it was found that again the parental combinations were in excess, although now these parental combinations are just the opposite of what they were in the first experiment (Fig. 13.1). The results of the second experiment were as follows:

Colored full	*CS /cs*
	639
Colored shrunken	*Cs /cs*
	21,379
Colorless full	*cS /cs*
	21,906
Colorless shrunken	*cs /cs*
	672
Total	44,595

Here the parental combinations are 21,379 + 21,906 = 43,285, or 97.06 per cent of all, whereas the recombinations are 638 + 672 = 1,310 or 2.94 per cent of the total. The ratio between parental combinations and recombinations is only slightly lower than it was in the first experiment. It is obvious that, whatever the parental combinations of two different pairs of linked genes may be, linkage tends to keep them together in about the same proportion of the gametes of the double heterozygote.

CROSSING OVER

According to the theory of T. H. Morgan, linkage is caused by linked genes being carried in the same chromosome. If, however, the chromosomes remain intact in inheritance, then two genes located in the same

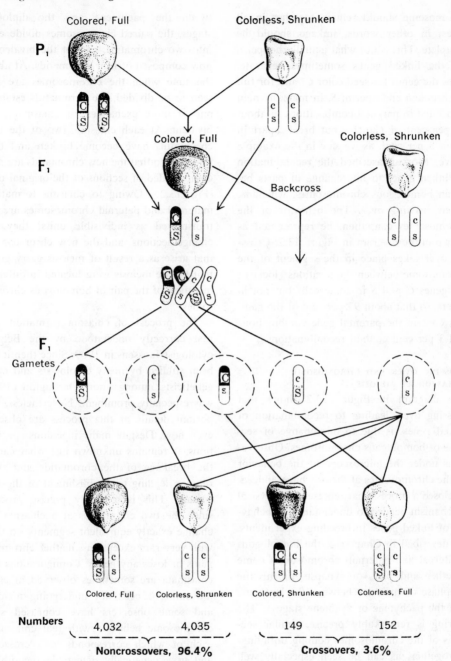

P₁   Colored, Full   Colorless, Shrunken

F₁   Colored, Full   Colorless, Shrunken

                             Backcross

F₁
Gametes

Colored, Full   Colorless, Shrunken   Colored, Shrunken   Colorless, Full

Numbers   4,032   4,035   149   152

        Noncrossovers, 96.4%   Crossovers, 3.6%

Fig. 13.2. The chromosome interpretation of linkage and crossing over, illustrated by the behavior of the genes for colored or colorless aleurone and for full or shrunken endosperm in corn.

chromosome should remain together in all cases; in other words, linkage should be complete. This is not what actually happens, for the linked genes sometimes separate. Thus the genes for seed color *C*, and for full or shrunken endosperm, *S*, in maize remain associated in parental combinations in about 97 per cent of gametes but break apart in about 3 per cent, as we saw in the example above. Morgan ascribed the recombination of linked genes to interchange of parts between homologous chromosomes, which he called *crossing over*. The behavior of the chromosomes can, then, be represented as shown in the diagram in Figure 13.2. Crossing over takes place in the segment of the chromosome between the locations (loci) of the genes *C* and *S* in some cells but not in others, so that about 97 per cent of the gametes contain the parental gene combinations and 3 per cent contain recombinations.

CROSSING OVER AND CHROMOSOME BEHAVIOR AT MEIOSIS

The diagram in Figure 13.2 shows that crossing over, leading to recombination of linked genes, is due to interchange of sections of homologous chromosomes. Observations under the microscope of the behavior of the chromosomes at meiosis have, indeed, disclosed a process that represents a physical mechanism needed to understand the behavior of linked genes in breeding experiments. As described in Chapter 4, the homologous (maternal and paternal) chromosomes come together and pair, or synapse, during the prophase of meiosis (between the leptotene and the pachytene or zygotene stages). The pairing is remarkably precise, similar sections of the chromosomes coming unfailingly together, as can be seen especially well in chromosomes differentiated into chromomeres (Fig. 4.4). This pairing is evidently brought about by mutual attraction of the parts of the chromosomes that are similar or homologous because they contain allelic genes. Further, during the transition between the pachytene and the diplotene stages, the paired chromosomes divide each into two chromatids, so that the bivalent is now composed of four chromatids. At about the time when the chromosomes are first seen to be divided, the chromatids establish one or more exchanges, or chiasmata, per bivalent. At each chiasma, two of the four chromatids have become broken and then rejoined, so that the new chromatids are now compounded of sections of the original ones (Fig. 13.2). Owing to chiasma formation, maternal and paternal chromosomes are not transmitted as indivisible units; they exchange sections, and the new chromosomes that arise as a result of meiosis carry genes that before meiosis were located in different members of the pair of homologous chromosomes.

The process of chiasma formation was first correctly understood by the Belgian cytologist Janssens in 1909. Since then it has been studied by many cytologists and cytogeneticists, among whom Darlington (1937) was especially prominent. Nevertheless, important details of this process are obscure even now. Despite many ingenious speculations, it remains unknown just what causes the breakage of the chromatids and their reunion leading to establishment of the chiasmata. This is a highly precise process, since the two chromatids at a chiasma exchange exactly equivalent segments, so that, with very rare exceptions, neither chromatid gains or loses any genes. Configurations like chiasmata are sometimes observed in chromosomes of cells not undergoing meiosis, and some observers have confused such chromosome behavior with real chiasmata, each of which corresponds to a crossover and to a genetically detectable recombination of linked genes.

ABSENCE OF CROSSING OVER IN DROSOPHILA MALES

In most of the organisms that have furnished the classical materials for genetic studies, such as maize, peas, mice, poultry, man, and others, recombination of linked genes takes place both in females and in males. Similarly, in most organisms favorable for cytological studies, formation of chiasmata is observed in both female and male meiosis. However, the most thorough and extensive studies on linkage and crossing over have been made on species of Drosophila, and it happens that in these insects the situation is very different in the two sexes. In Drosophila, crossing over rarely or never takes place in the male.

If a gray-bodied vestigial-winged fly is crossed to a black-bodied long-winged one,

the F_1 generation consists of gray long-winged (normal) flies (Figs. 13.3 and 13.4). Thus the gene for gray body color, *B*, is dominant over its allele, which causes black body color, *b;* and the gene for long wings, *V*, is dominant over its vestigial allele, *v*. Now, if the F_1 male hybrids are crossed to double recessive females (black-bodied vestigial-winged females), only two kinds of offspring are produced: gray vestigial and black long (Fig. 13.3). The expected types of crossovers—gray long and black vestigial —do not appear at all. If, however, an F_1 female fly is crossed with a black vestigial male, the four expected types (Fig. 13.4)

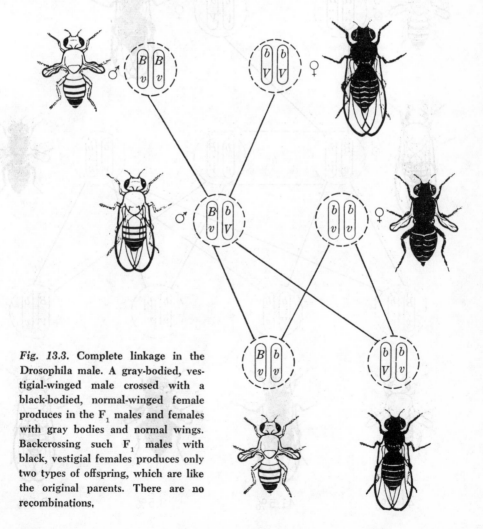

Fig. 13.3. Complete linkage in the Drosophila male. A gray-bodied, vestigial-winged male crossed with a black-bodied, normal-winged female produces in the F_1 males and females with gray bodies and normal wings. Backcrossing such F_1 males with black, vestigial females produces only two types of offspring, which are like the original parents. There are no recombinations.

are produced in the following proportions (data from Morgan, 1919):

Noncrossovers

Gray vestigial   Black long
41.5 per cent   41.5 per cent
83 per cent

Crossovers

Black vestigial   Gray long
8.5 per cent   8.5 per cent
17 per cent

Recombination is evident in about 17 per cent of the gametes. The experiment shows that a perceptible distance separates the genes for black and vestigial and that absence of crossovers in the gametes of the male is not due to the extreme closeness of

Fig. 13.4. Recombination of linked genes in the Drosophila female. Results of a cross similar to that in Figure 13.3 but with the F₁ females backcrossed with black, vestigial males.

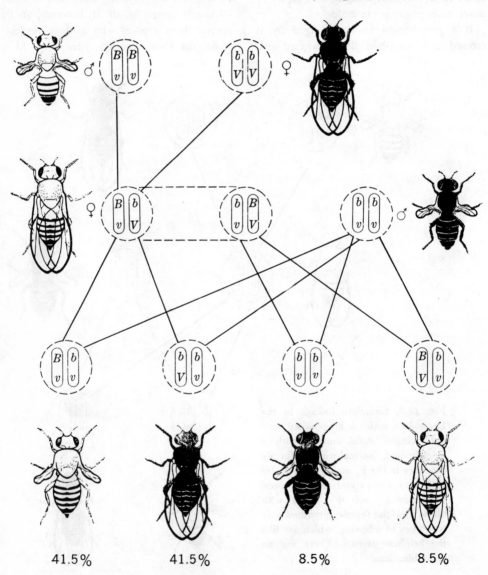

41.5%   41.5%   8.5%   8.5%

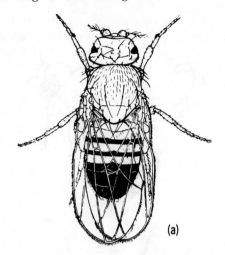

(a)

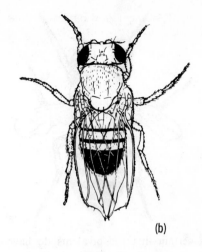

(b)

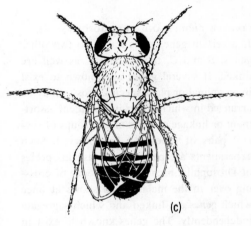

(c)

the genes in the chromosome. It must, therefore, be due to conditions peculiar to the male, such as the nonoccurrence of chiasmata in spermatogenesis.

Only a few cases are known in which linkage is complete in one sex and crossing over occurs more or less freely in the other. In all species of Drosophila so far studied in this respect, crossing over is absent or exceedingly rare in males, whereas in the silkworm moth it seems to be absent in females. Cytological study of spermatogenesis in male Drosophila, made by Darlington and others, discloses that the homologous chromosomes undergo, as usual, pairing in the spermatocytes; however, no chiasmata are established, at least not in the autosomal bivalents. The bivalents eventually come to consist of four chromatids lying parallel to one another. At the first meiotic division, pairs of chromatids go to each pole, and at the second meiotic division, single chromatids pass to each cell, and the cells are transformed into spermatozoa. Female meiosis in Drosophila is unfavorable for detailed cytological study, but it

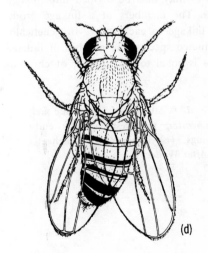

(d)

Fig. 13.5. Mutants of Drosophila melanogaster: (a) Bar eyes; (b) cut wings; (c) rudimentary wings; (d) rotated abdomen. (After Wallace)

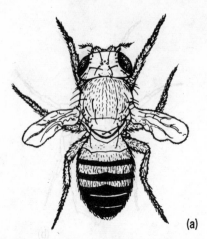

(a)

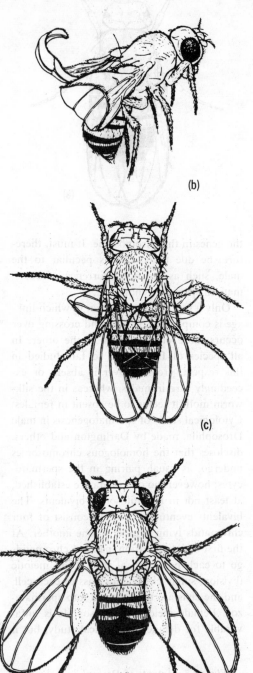

(b)

(c)

(d)

appears certain that the bivalents do have chiasmata.

LINKAGE GROUPS AND CHROMOSOMES

If a certain gene, *A*, is linked to two other genes, *B* and *C*, then *B* and *C* as well are linked. If several genes are known to exist in an animal or plant species, crosses may be arranged in which either independent assortment or linkage of pairs or of groups of several pairs of genes can be observed. Such experiments are particularly easy in species of Drosophila, because the absence of crossing over in the male hybrid shows at once which genes are linked and which segregate independently. The genes known to exist in a species may thus be divided into *linkage groups*. The members of a linkage group show linkage to each other. In genetically well-studied species, the number of linkage groups is equal to the number of chromo-

Fig. 13.6. Mutants of *Drosophila melanogaster:* (*a*) vestigial, (*b*) curly wings, (*c*) bithorax, (*d*) dichaete. (*After Wallace*)

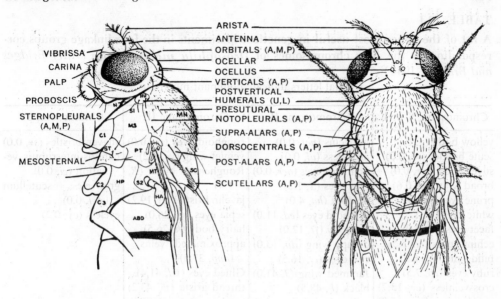

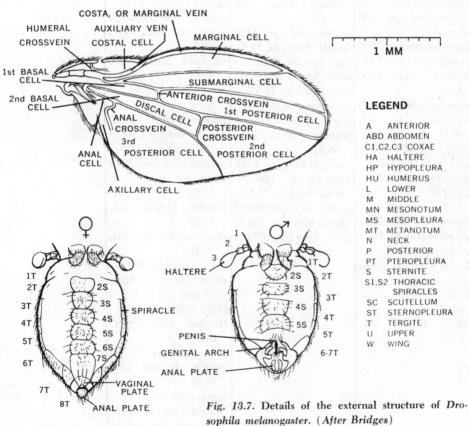

LEGEND

A   ANTERIOR
ABD ABDOMEN
C1,C2,C3 COXAE
HA   HALTERE
HP   HYPOPLEURA
HU   HUMERUS
L   LOWER
M   MIDDLE
MN   MESONOTUM
MS   MESOPLEURA
MT   METANOTUM
N   NECK
P   POSTERIOR
PT   PTEROPLEURA
S   STERNITE
S1,S2 THORACIC
     SPIRACLES
SC   SCUTELLUM
ST   STERNOPLEURA
T   TERGITE
U   UPPER
W   WING

Fig. 13.7. Details of the external structure of *Drosophila melanogaster.* (*After Bridges*)

TABLE 13.1

A list of the genes most useful in genetic experiments in the four linkage groups corresponding to the four chromosomes of *Drosophila melanogaster* (*After Bridges
and Brehme,* 1944)

Capital letters indicate dominant mutations.

Chromosome X or I	Chromosome II	Chromosome III	Chromosome IV
yellow body (*y*, 0.0)	net veins (*net*, 0.0)	roughoid eyes (*ru*, 0.0)	shaven bristles (*sv*, 0.0)
scute bristles (*sc*, 0.0)	aristaless (*al*, 0.0)	veinlet wing (*ve*, 0.2)	cubitus-interruptus ve-
silver body (*svr*, 0.0)	ochracea eyes (*ocr*, 0.0)	Roughened eyes (*R*,	nation (*ci*, 0.0)
broad wing (*br*, 0.6)	Star eyes (*S*, 1.3)	1.4)	grooveless scutellum
prune eyes (*pn*, 0.8)	heldout (*ho*, 4.0)	javelin bristles (*jv*, 19.2)	(*gvl*, 0.0)
white eyes (*w*, 1.5)	echinoid eyes (*ed*, 11.0)	sepia eyes (*se*, 26.0)	eyeless (*ey*, 0.2)
facet eyes (*fa*, 3.0)	fat body (*ft*, 12.0)	hairy body (*h*, 26.5)	
echinus eyes (*ec*, 5.5)	dumpy wing (*dp*, 13.0)	approximated veins	
bifid veins (*bi*, 6.9)	clot eyes (*cl*, 16.5)	(*app*, 37.5)	
ruby eyes (*rb*, 7.5)	Jammed wing (*J*, 41.0)	Glued eyes (*Gl*, 41.4)	
crossveinless (*cv*, 13.7)	black (*b*, 48.5)	thread arista (*th*, 43.2)	
roughex eyes (*rux*, 15.0)	reduced bristles (*rd*,	scarlet eyes (*st*, 44.0)	
carmine eyes (*cm*, 18.9)	51.0)	clipped wing (*cp*, 45.3)	
cut wing (*ct*, 20.0)	purple eyes (*pr*, 54.5)	Wrinkled wing (*W*,	
singed bristles (*sn*, 21.0)	Bristle short (*Bl*, 54.8)	46.0)	
lozenge eyes (*lz*, 27.7)	light eyes (*lt*, 55.0)	inturned bristles (*in*,	
raspberry eyes (*ras*,	straw body (*stw*, 55.1)	47.0)	
32.8)	tarsi fused (*ti*, 55.9)	radius-incompletus	
vermilion eyes (*v*, 33.0)	cinnabar eyes (*cn*, 57.5)	veins (*ri*, 47.1)	
miniature wing (*m*,	engrailed (*en*, 62.0)	pink eyes (*p*, 48.0)	
36.1)	scabrous eyes (*sca*,	blistery wing (*by*, 48.7)	
dusky wing (*dy*, 36.2)	66.7)	curled wing (*cu*, 50.0)	
sable body (*s*, 43.0)	vestigial wing (*vg*, 67.0)	mussed wing (*mu*, 50.0)	
garnet eye (*g*, 44.4)	Lobe eye (*L*, 72.0)	karmoisin eyes (*kar*,	
scalloped wing (*sd*,	curved wing (*c*, 75.5)	52.0)	
51.5)	plexus veins (*px*, 100.5)	Stubble bristles (*Sb*,	
uneven eyes (*un*, 54.4)	brown eyes (*bw*, 104.5)	58.2)	
forked bristles (*f*, 56.7)	speck wing (*sp*, 107.0)	spineless bristles (*ss*,	
Bar eyes (*B*, 57.0)		58.5)	
Beadex wing (*Bx*, 59.4)		Roof wing (*Rf*, 59.0)	
fused veins (*fu*, 59.5)		stripe thorax (*sr*, 62.0)	
carnation eyes (*car*,		glass eyes (*gl*, 63.1)	
62.5)		Delta veins (*Dl*, 66.2)	
bobbed bristles (*bb*,		Hairless bristles (*H*,	
66.0)		69.5)	
		ebony body, (*e*, 70.7)	
		Prickly bristles (*Pr*,	
		90.0)	
		rough eyes (*ro*, 91.1)	
		Beaded wing (*Bd*, 93.8)	
		claret eyes (*ca*, 100.7)	
		brevis bristles (*bv*,	
		104.3)	

some pairs (the haploid number of chromosomes) which the species possesses.

Several species of Drosophila have been widely used for studying linkage. Most of the early work was done on *D. melanogaster,* a vinegar fly, sometimes incorrectly referred to as a fruit fly. These flies are very easy to breed under laboratory conditions; their culture is simple and inexpensive; their life cycle is less than two weeks long at 75°F; their fecundity is so high that a pair of parents may produce hundreds and even thousands of offspring; they produce numerous hereditary variants (mutations); and their chromosomes, especially in the cells of larval salivary glands, are uncommonly favorable for observation. Many mutations have been observed in *D. melanogaster* since about 1909, when this species was first used for such studies by T. H. Morgan and his collaborators. Examples of some of these mutant types are shown in Figures 13.5 and 13.6. Drawings of the chief external details of the normal, or wild-type, fly are shown in Figure 13.7. Studies of the inheritance of these mutant types have shown that they belong to four linkage groups, some of the members of which are listed in Table 13.1.

The numbers of main gene loci belonging to the four linkage groups in *D. melanogaster* are, according to Bridges and Brehme (1944), as follows: first, 141; second, 228; third, 156; fourth, 12. The species possesses, as we know, four pairs of chromosomes (in other words, the haploid chromosome number is n = 4) (see Fig. 4.2). There are two rod-shaped X chromosomes in females and only one in males, the partner of that in the male being the hook-shaped Y chromosome. Since the genes of the first linkage group all show the sex-linked inheritance discussed in Chapter 12, they evidently are localized in the X chromosomes. The fourth linkage group contains the fewest genes; this makes it probable that this group corresponds to the small dotlike pair of chromosomes (Fig. 4.2). The second and the third linkage groups correspond to the two large V-shaped chromosome pairs, called the second and third chromosomes.

In species of Drosophila other than *D. melanogaster,* the haploid chromosome numbers vary from 3 to 6 and the numbers of linkage groups vary accordingly. In other genetically well-studied organisms, a similar correspondence is observed. Thus, maize has 10 pairs of chromosomes, and approximately 400 genes studied in this plant fall into 10 linkage groups, whereas in peas, *Pisum sativum,* there are 7 linkage groups and 7 pairs of chromosomes. As could be expected, in several organisms the number of linkage groups known is less but is nowhere greater than the haploid number of chromosomes. Thus, in the mouse 16 linkage groups are known for 20 pairs of chromosomes, in the rabbit 11 linkage groups for 22 pairs of chromosomes, in the tomato 10 linkage groups for 12 pairs of chromosomes, etc.

RECOMBINATION AND CROSSING OVER

One important fact about crossing over that has been established by cytological observation and then confirmed by breeding experiments is that the exchanges of chromosome segments which cause recombination of linked genes occur at the four-strand, or tetrad, stage, in the prophase of meiosis. At this time, the homologous chromosomes have paired, each homologue has split into two chromatids held together by the undivided centromere, and chiasmata are observed in the tetrad (Fig. 13.8). A careful examination shows that at each chiasma only two of the four chromatids cross over, whereas the two other chromatids preserve their original continuities. In genetic terms, this must mean that of the four chromosomes that emerge from meiosis, only two can show crossing over at any one level. In most animals and plants it is impossible to determine by observing the gene recombination in linkage experiments whether the

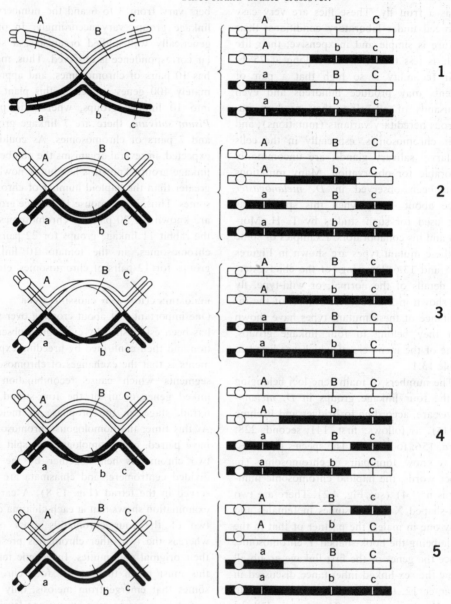

Fig. 13.8. Diagram showing chromosome bivalents with single chiasmata (above) and double chiasmata (below). 1. Single chiasma. 2. Two-strand double crossover. 3. Four-strand double crossover. 4 and 5. Three-strand double crossover.

crossing over that produced this recombination involved two, three, or all four strands of chromatids. The difficulty is that the products of each meiosis—the four haploid nuclei, each with one chromatid of the original four—cannot usually be identified

two meiotic divisions followed by one mitotic division. Dodge showed that these spores are disposed in a regular order in the ascus and developed a technique by which they can be dissected out and grown separately, giving rise to haploid individuals that

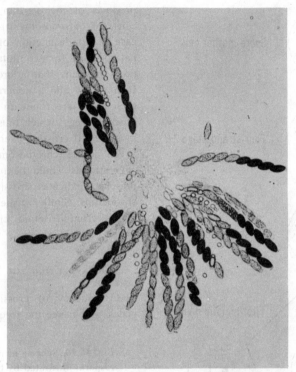

Fig. 13.9. Segregation of a pair of alleles affecting ascospore maturity in Neurospora. Among the eight spores in each ascus, four are colored (mature) and four colorless (immature). (*Courtesy of David R. Stadler*)

among the gametes, in the mass of which the cells coming from different meiotic divisions are inextricably mixed. But in some of the lower plants, all the cells derived from a single meiotic division remain together and the individual gametes can be recognized, separated, and tested individually.

In the bread mold Neurospora, each ascus, or fruiting body, contains eight haploid ascospores, as in Figure 13.9, which have arisen from a single diploid cell through the

show the genetic constitution of each gamete. Lindegren, working with mutant genes in Neurospora, then showed that, when two pairs of linked genes undergo crossing over, exchange in any one region occurs only between two of the four chromatids, that is, between one chromatid of one homologue and one chromatid of the other homologue, as in the diagram in Figure 13.10. The proof that this is what happens is the fact that the four cells resulting from meiosis consist of two with parental combinations (noncrossovers) and two with recombinations of genes (crossovers) which could arise only if two of the four strands exchanged parts between the two loci being studied. Such a proof is possible because in Neurospora and related

organisms all four products of meiosis can be recovered and all four members of a meiotic "tetrad" analyzed in detail.

The same type of proof that crossing over between two loci involves only two of the four chromatids has been obtained from cases in Drosophila in which some of the products of meiosis can be identified because of chromosome irregularities. In the case of nondisjunction of X chromosomes heterozygous for two mutant genes, it sometimes happens that a crossover chromatid such as *Ab* and a noncrossover chromatid such as *ab* are found in the same nondisjunctional egg, which thus has two X chromosomes. If crossing over had occurred between whole chromosomes, no noncrossover strands would be found; hence their presence indicates crossing over between chromatids. Similar evidence has been obtained from trisomic chromosomes with linked genes in maize.

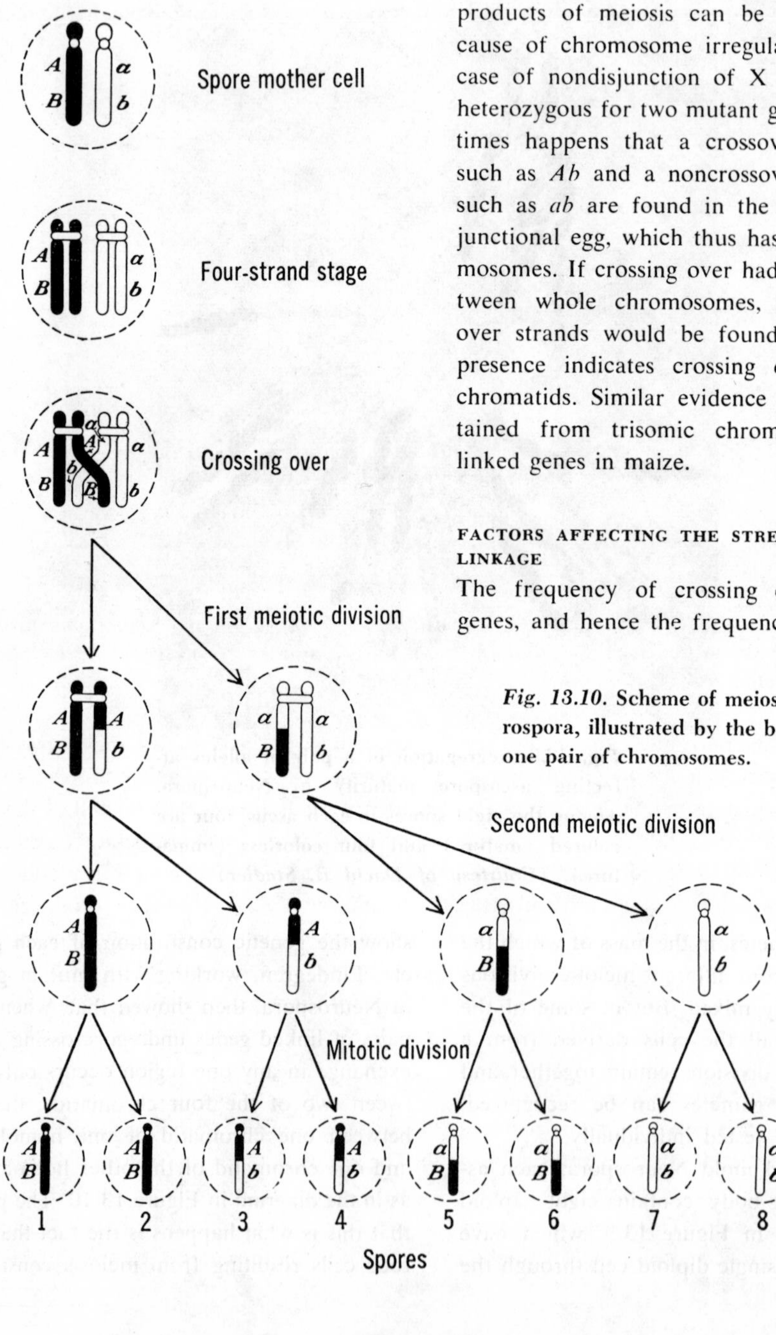

FACTORS AFFECTING THE STRENGTH OF LINKAGE

The frequency of crossing over between genes, and hence the frequency of chiasma

Fig. 13.10. Scheme of meiosis in Neurospora, illustrated by the behavior of one pair of chromosomes.

formation between their loci in the chromosome, may be influenced by a number of physiological and environmental factors. Thus, with the increasing age of the female of *D. melanogaster,* the amount of crossing over in her eggs becomes smaller. Furthermore, this effect is not equally pronounced in all chromosomes but is particularly noticeable in the middle portions of the second and

and by Jones in maize. It results in the appearance of "twin spots" of tissue (Fig. 13.11) somewhere in the body which show complementary genetic constitutions. Suppose, for example, that a Drosophila female carries in one of her X chromosomes the gene for singed bristles, *sn,* and in her other X that for yellow body, *y.* Such a female has,

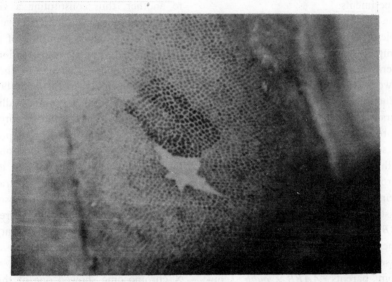

Fig. 13.11. A "twin spot" on the surface of a maize kernel, showing different colorations of the aleurone cells, due to somatic segregation. (*After Jones. Courtesy of Connecticut Agricultural Experiment Station*)

able in the middle portions of the second and third chromosomes in the neighborhood of the loci of the centromeres (see pp. 210–211). Temperature, X rays, and the chemical composition of the food are other agencies that modify the frequency of crossing over.

The frequency of crossing over in Drosophila males is so low as to be negligible under normal circumstances, but Whittinghill has shown that it can be increased by X rays. Although crossing over normally occurs only in gametogenesis or sporogenesis during meiosis, under some exceptional circumstances not yet understood, it may take place in somatic cells. This *somatic crossing over* has been studied by Stern in Drosophila

of course, normal bristles and a gray body, because the genes *sn* and *y* are recessive to their normal alleles. But if a cell of this constitution, $+ sn/y +$, undergoes a meiosislike process, cells homozygous for *y* and others homozygous for *sn* will be produced. The resulting fly will be in general normal but will have on some part of its body a yellow spot with normal bristles and next to it a spot with singed bristles of normal color (see also Fig. 25.10).

MEASUREMENT OF LINKAGE FROM F_2 DATA
The simplest technique for studying linkage is to cross strains differing in two or more linked genes, to obtain F_1 hybrids heterozygous for these genes (AB/ab or Ab/aB),

then to cross these hybrids back to a strain homozygous for the recessive alleles of the genes tested (*ab/ab*). In the progeny of the test crosses, individuals with the parental combinations and with recombinations of the genes are counted, and the frequency of recombination is expressed in percentages of the total number of individuals examined in the experiments.

In some organisms, test crosses are much more difficult to obtain than F_2 progenies. For example, in wheat and some other grasses, crossing requires emasculation of many flowers, which upon artificial pollination produce only a few seeds each. But if the flowers are protected from foreign pollen, they are self-pollinated automatically and many F_2 seeds are formed without further labor on the part of the experimenter. If the parents crossed differ in linked genes *A* and *B* and their alleles *a* and *b*, the F_2 generation will consist of individuals in the phenotypic classes *AB, Ab, aB,* and *ab*. Suppose that the numbers of individuals in these phenotypic classes are **a, b, c,** and **d,** respectively. Then from parents *AABB* × *aabb* (coupling), the parental (noncrossover) and recombination classes will be **ad** and **bc,** whereas in the opposite cross (repulsion *AAbb* × *aaBB*) they will be **bc** and **ad.** The recombination fraction X will be a function of the ratio, $X_1 = $ **bc/ad** for coupling and $X_2 = $ **ad/bc** for repulsion. For other methods of linkage calculations, consult Mather (1938).

CYTOLOGICAL DEMONSTRATION OF CROSSING OVER

Further evidence of association of genes with chromosomes is provided by the demonstration that, where there is an interchange of material between two homologous chromosomes, there is also an interchange of genes by crossing over. This has been shown in a number of cases, but Stern's demonstration in Drosophila is simple and complete (Fig. 13.12). The essential feature

of this demonstration is the use of strains in which it is possible to distinguish under a microscope the two members of a pair of chromosomes from each other and from other chromosomes of the same set. This is possible when, as a result of *translocation* (see Chap. 15), a portion of one chromosome has broken away and become attached to another, thus constituting a visibly different configuration. Stern had a strain of Drosophila in which a portion of a Y chromosome had through translocation become attached to the end of one of the X chromosomes, forming an L-shaped body easily distinguished from a normal rodlike X. In another strain, one of the X chromosomes had been broken into two approximately equal parts. The terminal portion containing the centromere remained in its normal position. The other portion was translocated to one of the small fourth chromosomes. The strain was viable, since the entire material of the X chromosome was present although in two separate pieces. By crossing these strains, females were produced in which one X chromosome showed one of these translocations and the other X the other; it was thus possible to distinguish both the X chromosomes in the same individual from each other and from autosomes (Fig. 13.12).

Stern made such females heterozygous for two sex-linked mutations located in the X chromosome : carnation, *cr,* an eye-color mutant, and Bar, *B,* causing a narrowing of the eye. Carnation is recessive and Bar dominant. Such a fly, therefore, has eyes of wild-type (red) color and Bar shape, with the genotype (*cr B*)/(+ +). It was known from the way in which the stock had been made up that the *cr* and *B* genes were in the broken X chromosome and that their two normal alleles were in the X bearing the translocated Y portion. Such a female was bred to a male having both the recessive genes (*cr* and the wild-type allele of Bar) in its X chromosome. The offspring of such a cross of double heterozygote by double recessive

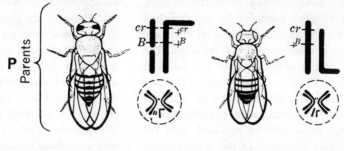

Fig. 13.12. Diagram of recombination of the genes for Bar (*B*, narrow eyes) and carnation (*cr*, an eye color) in females in which the two X chromosomes are distinguishable in appearance under the microscope. (*After Stern*)

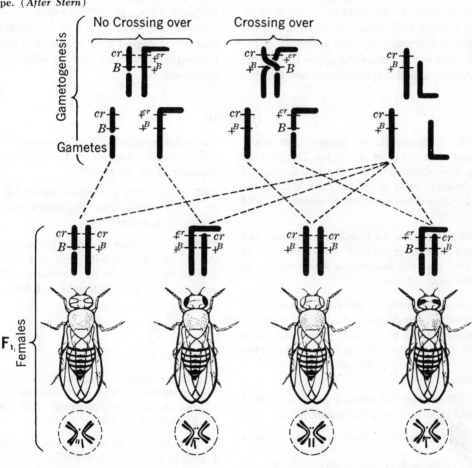

could be classified by inspection into four groups, as in any case of linkage. The females alone were studied. Of these there were two noncrossover classes (carnation Bar and normal) and two crossover classes (carnation with normal shape and Bar with normal color). These may be represented as follows:

Noncrossovers

$$\frac{cr\ B}{cr\ +} \qquad \frac{+\ +}{cr\ +}$$

Crossovers

$$\frac{cr\ +}{cr\ +} \qquad \frac{+\ B}{cr\ +}$$

The X chromosomes of these four classes of females were then studied cytologically. One X chromosome of each female, coming from the father, should evidently be normal. Its mate, coming from the mother, should be distinguishable by its abnormal character and should show the effect of any cytological crossing over in the eggs. The genetic and cytological results are shown in Figure 13.12. It is evident that in the two classes of genetic noncrossovers the maternal X is as it was in the mother, either broken into two or entire and provided with the translocated fragment. In the genetic crossovers, however, the maternal X has evidently resulted from crossing over, since in the Bar noncarnation flies the fragment of the Y is now attached to the upper half of the divided X, and in the carnation non-Bar flies

an apparently normal chromosome is present. These are the results that should obtain if there has been an interchange between the two X chromosomes of the mother at a point near the upper end of the X and between the locations of the *cr* and *B* genes. Of the F_1 female flies, 364 were tested, and in all but 5 (and these presumably the result of experimental error) there was a complete correspondence between the genetic and cytological facts. In other words, genetic recombination was proved to be accompanied by cytological crossing over and actual exchanges of material between homologous chromosomes.

PROBLEMS

13.1 In Drosophila, the genes for red, eosin, and white eye color are alleles. The gene for yellow body is linked with white eye with a crossover value of 1.5 per cent. What is the probable crossover value between eosin and yellow?

13.2 If a factor for high egg production and one for barring are both sex-linked traits, of what practical importance would this be to the poultry breeder?

NOTE: In problems involving linkage it is customary to designate the normal alleles of mutant genes by + (wild type). The genes in each member of a pair of chromosomes are written separately above and below a line.

13.3 Assume that genes *a* and *b* are linked and show 40 per cent of recombination. If a $\dfrac{+\ +}{+\ +}$ individual is crossed with one that is $\dfrac{ab}{ab}$, what will be the genotype of the F_1? What gametes will the F_1 produce, and in what proportions? If the F_1 is crossed with a double recessive, what will be the appearance and genotypes of the offspring?

13.4 If the original cross is $\dfrac{+b}{+b} \times \dfrac{a+}{a+}$, what will be the genotype of the F_1? What gam-

etes will it produce? If the F_1 is crossed back with a double recessive, what will be the appearance of the offspring?

13.5 What will be the appearance of the F_2 ($F_1 \times F_1$) of the crosses described in the two preceding questions?

13.6 An individual homozygous for genes *cd* is crossed with wild type and the F_1 crossed back with the double recessive. The appearance of the offspring is as follows:

$$
\begin{array}{ll}
903 & +\ + \\
897 & c\ d \\
98 & +\ d \\
102 & c\ +
\end{array}
$$

Explain this result, giving the strength of the linkage between *c* and *d*. If assortment between *c* and *d* were independent, what would be the result of this cross?

13.7 If the cross in the preceding question had been between a homozygous $+d$ individual and a homozygous $c+$ one, what would be the result of the cross of F_1 with the double recessive?

13.8 Calculate the percentage of crossing over between the alleles for colorless aleurone and shrunken endosperm in corn from the combined data from both coupling and repulsion (p. 162) experiments.

NOTE: In Drosophila the mutant known as "black," *b*, has a black body in contrast to the wild type, which has a gray body; and the mutant "arc," *a*, has wings that are somewhat curved and bent downward, in contrast to the straight wings of the wild type.

13.9 From the data below, calculate the crossover value between black and arc.

I. Black straight × gray arc
 F_1 ♀ ♀ × black arc ♂ ♂ give:

Gray straight	281
Gray arc	335
Black straight	335
Black arc	239

II. Black arc × wild type
 F_1 ♀ ♀ × black arc ♂ ♂ give:

Gray straight	1,641
Gray arc	1,251
Black straight	1,180
Black arc	1,532

13.10 In cross I of Problem 13.9, test for independent assortment by the chi-square test for a fourfold table.

13.11 In Problem 13.9, give a confidence interval with .95 confidence coefficient for the crossover frequency.

13.12 In the two following crosses the parents are given, as in the previous question, together with the counts of offspring of F_1 females × black vestigial males (data from Bridges and Morgan):

I. Black vestigial × wild type (gray long)
 F_1 females × black vestigial males give:

Gray long	822
Gray vestigial	130
Black long	161
Black vestigial	652

II. Black long × gray vestigial
 F_1 females × black vestigial males give:

Gray long	283
Gray vestigial	1,294
Black long	1,418
Black vestigial	241

From these data calculate the crossover value between black and vestigial.

13.13 Give a confidence interval with .95 confidence coefficient for the crossover frequency in Problem 13.12 for the data in cross I, cross II, and both crosses combined (see Section 29.29).

NOTE: The inheritance of grain color in wheat is described on page 101.

13.14 What would be the F_2 ratio of red and white grains from a cross of red with white if two duplicate factors for red were linked, with a crossover value of 10 per cent? (Assume the red parent to be homozygous for both genes.)

NOTE: In rats, dark eyes are due to the interaction of two genes *R* and *P*, the recessive allele of either producing light eyes. These genes are in the same chromosome.

13.15 When homozygous dark-eyed rats, $\dfrac{++}{++}$, were crossed with double recessive ones, $\dfrac{r\,p}{r\,p}$ and the F_1 crossed back with the double recessive, the following offspring were obtained (data from Castle):

Dark-eyed	1,255
Light-eyed	1,777

When $\dfrac{+p}{+p}$ animals were crossed with $\dfrac{r+}{r+}$ ones and the F_1 crossed back with the double recessive, the following offspring were obtained:

Dark-eyed	174
Light-eyed	1,540

Calculate the crossover value between *r* and *p*.

13.16 In Drosophila, white eye color and club wing are both sex-linked with a crossover value of about 15 per cent. If a wild-type female (red long) is crossed with a white club male, what will be the appearance of the offspring? If both males and females of the F_1 are crossed back to pure white club stock, what will be the offspring in each case?

13.17 In fowl, assume that *e* (early feathering) and *B* (barring) are sex-linked and show 20 per cent of crossing over (in the male only). If a male from a cross of late-feathered barred male × early black female is mated with an early black female, what will be the appearance of their offspring as to feathering and barring?

13.18 Assume that genes *a* and *b* are linked, with a crossover percentage of 20 per cent, and that *c* and *d* are also linked, with a crossover percentage of 10 per cent, but are in another chromosome. Cross a plant homozygous for *AB CD* with one that is *ab cd*, and cross the F_1 back on *ab cd*. What will be the appearance of the offspring of this cross?

13.19 Can you devise a method for obtaining a confidence interval for the crossover frequency in Problem 13.15, using the coupling data only? using all the data? If you find methods, carry them through with .95 confidence coefficient.

13.20 In sweet peas, a cross of a homozygous procumbent, hairy, white-flowered plant with a bush, glabrous, colored-flowered one produces an F_1 that is all procumbent, hairy, and colored-flowered. If this F_1 is crossed on a bush, glabrous, white-flowered plant, the offspring would be expected to show approximately the following distribution (data adapted from Punnett):

	Per cent
Procumbent, hairy, colored	6
Procumbent, hairy, white	19
Procumbent, glabrous, colored	6
Procumbent, glabrous, white	19
Bush, hairy, colored	19
Bush, hairy, white	6
Bush, glabrous, colored	19
Bush, glabrous, white	6

Explain these results, determining the recombination values for such linkages as may be observed.

13.21 In Drosophila, yellow body is sex-linked and recessive to the gray body of the wild fly. Vermilion eye is also sex-linked and recessive to the wild red eye. The genes for yellow and vermilion show about 28 per cent of crossing over. The gene for vestigial wings is in one of the autosomes. If a homozygous yellow-bodied, red-eyed, long-winged female

is crossed with a homozygous gray-bodied, vermilion-eyed, vestigial-winged male and if an F_1 female is crossed with a yellow, vermilion, vestigial male, what will be the proportions in the offspring of this last cross?

13.22 *AA BB* + *aa bb* gives the following segregation in F_2:

AB	*Ab*	*aB*	*ab*
582	172	169	77

Do you think that *a* and *b* are linked or independent? Give evidence for your answer. Compare the actual distribution with the theoretical expectation on the basis of (1) independent assortment of *a* and *b*; (2) 40 per cent crossing over between *a* and *b*, using the chi-square test.

13.23 In Nicotiana, assume that the genes for colored or white flowers (*C-c*) are in the same chromosome with the self-incompatibility locus, *s*, and show 20 per cent crossing over with it. Compare the results to be expected from the following crosses:

    a. $Cs^1/cs^2 \times Cs^3/cs^4$
    b. $Cs^1/cs^2 \times cs^2/Cs^3$

13.24 Penrose in the Annals of Eugenics, 6, 133–138, has shown that linkage can be demonstrated for a pair of traits like those in Problem 13.25, even when we have no pedigrees but only pairs of sibs. If there is linkage, then the sibs are more likely to agree with respect to trait I if they also agree with respect to trait II than if they disagree with respect to trait II. Show why this should be so.

13.25 In the Annals of Eugenics, 19, 319, Renwick and Lawler give the following data for sib pairs:

Type of pair	Nail — patella		
	Like	Unlike	Total
ABO Like	78	44	122
Unlike	30	84	114
Total	108	128	236

Test the hypothesis of independent assortment by the chi-square method for a four-fold table.

GENETIC MAPS OF CHROMOSOMES

THE DISCOVERY of linkage and its interpretation by Morgan have furnished a tool for a combined genetic and cytological study of the internal structure of chromosomes. Whereas before Morgan it was possible to say only in a general way that genes are carried in chromosomes, the work of Morgan and Bridges established the fact that specific genes are borne in specific chromosomes. The next step was to analyze the behavior of combinations of genes of the same linkage group, and to draw from such experiments conclusions concerning the architecture of the chromosome itself.

We have seen in Chapter 13 that the frequency of recombination of a pair of linked genes is, under standardized environmental conditions, constant and characteristic for that pair of genes. T. H. Morgan put forward the hypothesis (1911) that the strength of linkage of a pair of genes—that is, the amount of crossing over and recombination observed—is a function of the distance in the chromosome between the genes in question. The greater this distance, the more likely, in general, that crossing over will occur between these genes. Genes located close to each other in the chromosome are strongly linked. This proved to be a very fertile working hypothesis, and from it grew a whole new chapter of genetics, dealing with genetic maps of chromosomes.

LINEAR ARRANGEMENT OF GENES IN CHROMOSOMES

A very significant regularity is revealed if, instead of observing recombination of two linked genes, an experiment is made in which three or more linked genes are involved. Bridges and Olbrycht crossed *Drosophila melanogaster* flies with rough eyes due to the gene echinus, *ec*, with flies with scute, *sc* (certain bristles missing), and crossveinless, *cv* (absence of the cross veins in the wings). Since these three genes are recessive to the corresponding normal condition and are sex-linked, the hybrid females were normal, or wild type, in phenotype;

that is, they had nonrough eyes, and all bristles and cross veins were present. The hybrid females had one X chromosome carrying the gene echinus and the normal alleles of scute and crossveinless, and another X chromosome with a normal allele of echinus and with mutant alleles of scute and crossveinless. In Drosophila genetics it is convenient to denote the normal alleles (that is, the alleles present in wild flies as they are found outside laboratories) by plus signs; and so X chromosomes of the hybrid females may be written as follows: $\frac{+ \ ec \ +}{sc \ + \ cv}$. These females were backcrossed to males carrying the three recessive genes scute, echinus, and crossveinless (*sc ec cv* males). If these genes were not linked, the offspring of the cross, in accordance with the second law of Mendel, should have contained eight classes of offspring in equal numbers, representing the possible combinations of the three parental genes. In the actual experiment the following results were obtained (Table 14.1).

TABLE 14.1

echinus (+ *ec* +)	810	
scute crossveinless (*sc* + *cv*)	828	1,638
scute echinus (*sc ec* +)	62	
crossveinless (+ + *cv*)	88	150
scute (*sc* + +)	89	
echinus crossveinless (+ *ec cv*)	103	192
wild type (+++)	0	
scute echinus crossveinless		
(*sc ec cv*)	0	0
Total	1,980	

The parental combinations are more frequent than any of the recombination classes; some of the latter, namely, wild type and *sc ec cv*, are altogether missing. Let us now compute the frequencies of recombinations between the three genes involved. The genes scute and echinus and their normal alleles entered the cross from different par-

ents, and they remained in different individuals in 1,638 + 192 = 1,830 flies, which represent, then, the parental combinations of these two genes. But in 62 flies the genes scute and echinus are present together, and in 88 flies their normal alleles are present together. These 62 + 88 = 150 flies represent the recombinations of the genes *sc* and *ec*. The frequency of recombinations of *sc* and *ec* is, accordingly, (150 × 100)/1,980 = 7.6 per cent. Similarly, the genes echinus and crossveinless and their normal alleles entered the cross from different parents. We find, however, 89 flies that have neither *ec* nor *cv* and 103 flies that have both *ec* and *cv*, in other words, 89 + 103 = 192 recombinations for these genes. The frequency of recombination between *ec* and *cv* is, then, (192 × 100)/1,980 = 9.7 per cent. Finally, the genes scute and crossveinless and their normal alleles were introduced into the cross by the same parents; in the progeny one of these genes is present without the other in 62 + 88 + 103 + 89 = 342 flies; the frequency of recombination between *sc* and *cv* is, accordingly, (342 × 100)/1,980 = 17.3 per cent.

To summarize, the frequencies of recombinations between the genes scute, echinus, and crossveinless are

sc-ec	7.6 per cent
ec-cv	9.7 per cent
sc-cv	17.3 per cent

According to Morgan's hypothesis, the frequency of crossing over giving rise to recombination of linked genes is a function of the distance between these genes in the chromosome. Now, the figures show that the "distance" *sc-cv* equals the sum of the *sc-ec* and *ec-cv* "distances." In general, *if the distances between genes* a, b, *and* c *are, respectively,* ab *and* bc, *then the distance between* a *and* c *is equal to either* ab + bc *or* ab − bc Such a relationship results in geometry if the points *a*, *b*, and *c* lie on a straight line, and in genetics this relationship is the basis of the theory according to which *genes are arranged in chromosomes in a single linear series*. In the example under consideration, the genes evidently form a series *sc-ec-cv* (or *cv-ec-sc,* which is equivalent), and we may draw a *genetic map* of the part of the chromosome in which these genes are located, thus:

$$\frac{sc \quad ec \quad cv}{7.6 \quad 9.7}$$

DOUBLE CROSSING OVER

In principle, it is a rather simple matter to add to the above map the positions of more and more genes, until all the genes belonging to the same linkage group have been entered. For this purpose, experiments are planned so that at least two previously known loci[1] and one or more new ones are involved in crosses. Then, using the fact that the distance between genes *a* and *c* is either the sum or the difference of the *a-b* and *b-c* distances, it is determined whether the new gene lies between, or to one side of, the old ones.

---

[1] The term *locus* (plural, *loci*) is used both to indicate the location of a gene on a chromosome map and to designate the unit whose variants act as alleles. In the latter sense, "locus" is almost equivalent to "gene." One speaks, however, of the alleles that determine the red, eosin, and white eye colors in Drosophila as "the gene for red," for "eosin," and for "white eye color," whereas these three genes together are referred to as variants or alleles of the same "white" locus. The locus is usually named for the first variant allele found.

Crossveinless (*cv*) flies were crossed by Bridges and Olbrycht to flies carrying echinus (*ec*) and cut (notched wing margin, *ct,* a sex-linked recessive gene). The hybrid females, which must have had the genetic structure $\frac{+ \ cv \ +}{ec \ + \ ct}$, were crossed to *ec cv ct* males. In the next generation the classes of flies shown in Table 14.2 were obtained.

As in the example presented in Table 14.1, the analysis of the data in Table 14.2 begins by determining which classes represent the parental combinations of each pair of genes and which are recombinations (crossovers) of these genes. It should be noted that two numerically smallest classes of flies, wild type and echinus crossveinless cut, represent recombinations both of the genes *ec* and *cv* and of *cv* and *ct;* these classes are, however, parental combinations as far as the genes *ec* and *ct* are concerned. The frequency of recombinations between the genes *ec* and *cv* is, therefore, 10.1 + 0.1 = 10.2 per cent, between *cv* and *ct* 8.3 + 0.1 = 8.4 per cent, and between *ec* and *ct* 10.1 + 8.3 = 18.4 per cent. From these data the relative positions of their genes can be determined. Since the distance *ec-cv* is 10.2 per cent and the distance *cv-ct* is 8.4 per cent, the distance *ec-ct* may be either 10.2 + 8.4 = 18.6 per cent or 10.2 − 8.4 = 1.8 per cent. The former figure would mean that the gene order is *ec-cv-ct* and the latter that it is *ec-ct-cv*. The actual figure for the *ec-ct* distance is 18.4 per cent, which is very close, although not quite equal, to the sum of the

TABLE 14.2

Noncrossovers	crossveinless (+ *cv* +)	2,207	81.5 per cent
	echinus cut (*ec* + *ct*)	2,125	
Crossovers between *ec* and *cv*	echinus crossveinless (*ec cv* +)	273	10.1 per cent
	cut (+ + *ct*)	265	
Crossovers between *cv ct*	echinus (*ec* + +)	217	8.3 per cent
	crossveinless cut (+ *cv ct*)	223	
Double crossovers	wild type (+ + +)	5	0.1 per cent
	echinus crossveinless cut (*ec cv ct*)	3	
Total		5,318	

ec-cv and *cv-ct* distances. This small discrepancy must be accounted for, but meanwhile the arrangement of the loci in the chromosome, based on the data discussed so far, may be taken to be as follows:

sc		*ec*		*cv*		*ct*
	7.6		9.7		8.4	
			10.2			

The discrepancy just noted arises because the wild-type and *ec cv ct* flies in Table 14.2 are formed when crossing over occurs both between the loci of *ec* and *cv* and between *cv* and *ct;* these flies arise through *double crossing over*. Since the occurrence of double crossing over restores the parental combinations of the genes lying farthest apart, in this case *ec* and *ct,* the frequency of recombination of *ec* and *ct,* and hence the *apparent* distance between them, is smaller than the sum of the recombination frequencies between *ec-cv* and *cv-ct*. In general, the more remote in the chromosome the genes are, the more double crossing over takes place among them. With several linked genes involved in crosses, not only double but triple, quadruple, and even quintuple crossovers may be found. The multiple crossovers may cause wide departure from the rule that frequencies of recombinations between remote genes should be equal to the sum of the recombination frequencies between the intervening genes.

We have seen above (p. 172) that crossing over is caused by exchange of sections of homologous chromatids at meiosis, visibly expressed in the appearance of chiasmata in the meiotic bivalents. A single crossover is, then, the product of a single exchange of sections between the chromatids; double or multiple crossing over results from a chromatid's being involved in two or more exchanges (Fig. 13.8). The number of chiasmata per bivalent is, indeed, variable not only in different chromosomes and in different species but even in the same chromosome in different cells of the same individual. Cytological observations show that this number varies from none to six or more.

INTERFERENCE AND COINCIDENCE

In the experiment the results of which are summarized in Table 14.2, the frequency of single crossing over is 10.2 per cent between the genes *ec* and *cv* and 8.4 per cent between *cv* and *ct*. If the occurrence of crossing over in one part of a chromosome were independent of its occurrence in other parts of the same chromosome, we could predict the frequency of simultaneous occurrence of crossing over between *ec* and *cv* and between *cv* and *ct*. On the assumption of independence, the frequency of such double crossing over should be 10.2 per cent of 8.4 per cent, or 0.86 per cent. In actuality, the observed frequency of double crossovers is only 0.15 per cent (Table 14.2). In the experiment reported in Table 14.1, no double crossovers at all are observed (no wild-type and no *sc ec cv* flies). It seems, then, that the occurrence of crossing over at one point in the chromosome decreases the probability of its occurrence elsewhere in the same chromosome. This phenomenon is called *interference*. An inverse measure of interference is called coincidence and is computed simply as a ratio of the observed number of double crossovers to the expected number of such doubles. For the data in Table 14.2, this ratio is evidently 0.15/0.86 = 0.17; in other words, only 17 per cent of the expected doubles are actually found. For the data in Table 14.1, coincidence is zero, since no double crossovers at all are found.

In general, interference is greatest over short distances in the chromosomes, so that within a certain minimal distance there is no double crossing over (coincidence = 0). Farther apart, interference diminishes and at a certain distance disappears entirely (coincidence = 1). This might mean that at meiosis the chromosomes do not coil tightly about one another but are somewhat rigid, so that if a chiasma is established between the loci of the genes scute and echinus, no other chiasma can appear between echinus and crossveinless (Table 14.1). What takes place at crossing over is exchange of *blocks of genes*, arranged in a linear order. Interference is important in placing genes in the genetic chromosome maps, since where recombination data on distant genes must be used, the figures must be corrected for multiple crossing over before they can be taken to represent the "distances" between the genes. For methods concerning linkage calculations, see Mather (1938).

LINKAGE MAPS OF DROSOPHILA CHROMOSOMES

The extensive study of linkage and crossing over, at first in *Drosophila melanogaster* and later in other organisms, led to the construction of linkage maps, or genetic maps, of chromosomes. These maps are condensed graphic representations of the relative distances, expressed in percentages of recombination, among the genes in one linkage group, consequently located in a single chromosome.

The actual construction of the linkage maps of *Drosophila melanogaster* represents the outcome of a collective effort of many investigators led and coordinated chiefly by C. B. Bridges from the inception of the work until his death in 1938. The maps have gradually included more and more gene loci, and the positions of these loci have become more and more accurate as more carefully controlled crossover data accumulate. One of the last maps constructed by Bridges is shown in Figure 14.1. The genetic lengths of the four chromosomes, measured in terms of percentage frequencies of crossing over between genes, are 66 units for the X chromosomes, 107.3 for the second, 106.2 for the third, and only 0.2 unit for the fourth chromosomes. This corresponds fairly well to the lengths of these chromosomes as observed under a microscope, except that in the fourth chromosome crossing over seems to be excessively rare. It will be asked how distances in excess of 50 units can be possible, since crossing over may vary only from nearly zero (no crossing over) to nearly 50 per cent (independent assortment). It is true that the *amount of recombination* between two genes never exceeds 50 per cent; but because of double crossing over, it is necessary to measure long distances by adding together the sums of the recombination values for intermediate genes, as explained above. These sums frequently exceed 50 in the long chromosomes. In the second chromosome, for instance, the genes for "Star" and "speck" appear on the map as 105 units apart. When Star and speck are crossed, they show less than 50 per cent of crossing over (actually about 48.7 per cent), but this is known to be due to the reduction caused by double crossing over. When the intermediate percentages are added, the sum is in excess of 100, which expresses the true distance between these two genes.

"Map distance," therefore, does not always correspond to recombination percentage as measured directly, and consequently the amount of crossing over between two genes cannot be read directly from the maps, except with genes so near together that no double crossing over occurs in the distance between them.

LINKAGE MAPS OF MAIZE CHROMOSOMES

The most extensively mapped species, after *Drosophila melanogaster,* is the maize plant. Here, thanks to the cooperative work of many geneticists and plant breeders, under the leadership of R. A. Emerson, the locations of several hundred gene loci are known (Fig. 14.2). Each of the 10 linkage groups of this plant has been placed in a particular one of the 10 microscopically visible chromosomes, by means of a combined cytological and genetic study of chromosomal aberrations of the kinds discussed in Chapter 15.

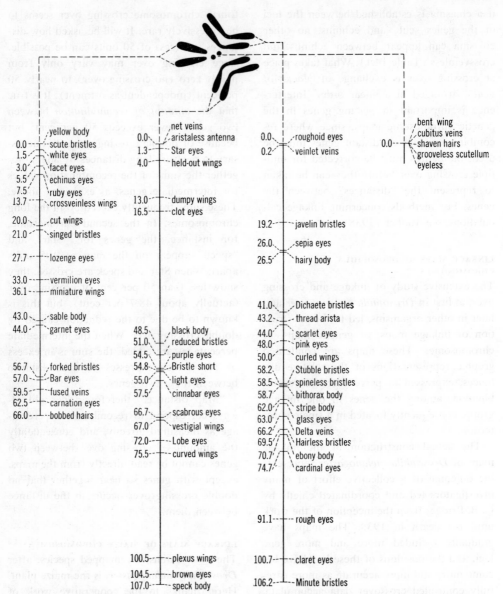

Fig. 14.1. A genetic or linkage map of the four chromosomes of *Drosophila melanogaster*, showing the relative positions of some of the more important genes. Figures refer to distances from the upper end of the chromosome as determined from the percentages of recombination observed in linkage experiments.

MAPS OF HUMAN CHROMOSOMES

In man, a beginning has been made in constructing a linkage map of one chromosome, the X; but this necessarily derives from methods unlike those employed with animals and plants which can be used experimen-tally. It is based on the fact, first noted in the aquarium fish Lebistes (the guppy), that occasionally a gene in the X chromosome (in Lebistes the male is the heterogametic sex, XY) undergoes crossing over and appears to be transmitted in the Y chromosome. Such

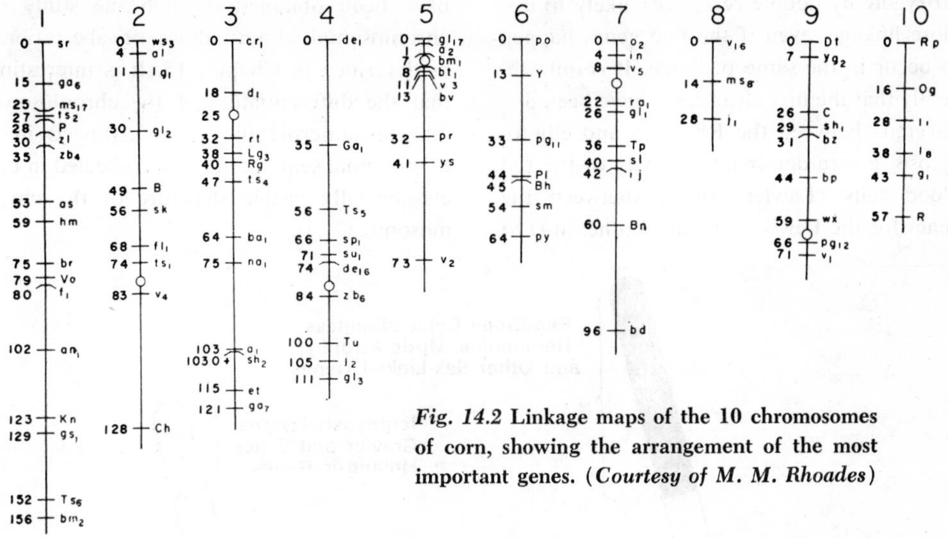

Fig. 14.2 Linkage maps of the 10 chromosomes of corn, showing the arrangement of the most important genes. (*Courtesy of M. M. Rhoades*)

genes have been called partially or incompletely sex-linked. Thus the part of the X chromosome which contains these genes must be homologous with a part at least of the Y. Later (1934) Koller and Darlington showed that chiasmata were probably formed between the X and Y chromosomes in spermatogenesis in man. It occurred to Haldane that, if the human X and Y chromosomes had homologous segments so that crossing over could occur between them, then genes in this segment which entered a zygote on the X chromosome would generally be passed on to offspring in the X, but that, where crossing over had occurred, they would be transmitted in the Y and that the frequency of such exceptions would be a measure of the frequency of crossing over between the gene in question and the differential segment (Fig. 14.3) which carries the completely sex-linked genes. The pedigree in Problem 14.7 illustrates the method of detection of such incompletely sex-linked genes. The first male in the third generation got the gene from his mother, hence in the X, and passed it on to four daughters but not to three sons. On the assumption of incomplete sex-linkage, these would be non-crossovers. However, one son got the gene

from his father, hence in the Y, and two daughters failed to get it in the paternal X chromosome. These must have been crossovers. The analysis of many pedigrees led to an estimate of about 32.6 per cent of crossing over between this gene and the differential part of the X. A modification of the method permitted detection of additional incompletely sex-linked recessives and led to the construction of a map resembling that in Figure 14.3. The accuracy of this map is not comparable with those for Drosophila species and maize, which are based on large numbers of experimentally controlled observations, but it is a useful approximation. Since the most reliable sex-linked mutant genes are rare, it is unlikely that two will often be found in the same pedigree; hence the construction of a map of the differential segment of the X will probably be accomplished only in the distant future. Recently, however, the validity of this analysis and the existence of a homologous segment in man have been questioned.

The detection and measurement of linkage between autosomal genes is beset with special difficulties in man, since the chromosomes are numerous and in few families will the mating be of the type (e.g., double heterozygote by double recessive) likely to disclose linkage, even if the two genes happen to occur in the same pedigree. It is only recently that the first clear cases have been discovered: between the Rh locus and elliptocytosis, a rare dominant anomaly of the red blood cells (Lawler, 1953); between the genes for the Lewis (*Le*) and Lutheran (*Lu*)

have been obtained through the study of chromosomal abnormalities or aberrations, as described in Chapter 15. It is interesting that the differentiation of the chromosome into ultramicroscopic genes arranged in a longitudinal sequence is often reflected in the cytologically visible structure of the chromosome.

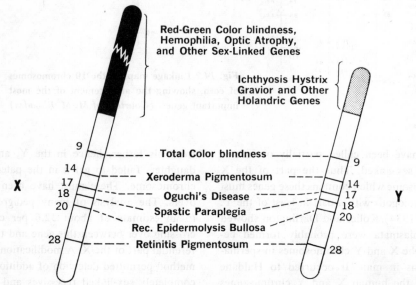

Fig. 14.3. A tentative map of human X and Y chromosomes based on the assumption of partial sex linkage and crossing over between the pairing segment (shown in white) and the differential segment of the X chromosome (shown in black). The differential segment of the Y chromosome is stippled. (*After Snyder*)

blood types (J. Mohr, 1954); and between the ABO blood group locus and a rare dominant, the nail-patella syndrome of abnormalities (Renwick and Lawler, 1955). These mark the beginnings of the autosomal maps of man.

CHROMOSOME MORPHOLOGY AND CHROMOSOMES

Genes are bodies of the order of size of protein molecules; consequently they are not visible directly in any existing microscope. Proofs of the validity of the theory of linear arrangement of genes in the chromosomes

Chromosomes in the prophase stages of mitosis and, especially, meiosis often resemble chains of beads on a string. The beads, or *chromomeres,* are regarded by most cytologists as thickenings of the chromosome string, or *chromonema.* Some cytologists believe, however, that chromomeres are simply places where the chromonema is thrown into a tight springlike coil and that the internodes connecting the chromomeres are places where the chromosome is relatively uncoiled and straightened. However that may be, the appearance of chromosomes attests to their longitudinal differentiation in a very obvious manner. The classical work of Belling (1928) showed that the pachytene chromosomes of the lily *Lilium paradalinum* contain between 2,000 and 2,500 chromomeres. Belling was inclined to believe that there might be a one-to-one correspondence between these "ultimate chromomeres" and genes, but this cannot be considered as proved. The adjacent chromomeres may differ from each other in size, and the seriation of chromomeres of different size is constant and characteristic for each chromosome. At the pachytene stage of meiosis, when homologous maternal and paternal chromosomes are paired, the chromomeres that are in contact are of the same size, and the seriation of the chromomeres in the synapsed homologues is, section by section, exactly the same (Fig. 4.4). This means that every chromomere is qualitatively distinct from every other one, and the attraction forces that bring the chromosomes together and make them pair at meiosis are highly specific ones. The physicochemical nature of these specific attraction forces, which operate between homologous chromomeres in cells undergoing meiosis, is for the time being a matter of speculation.

CHROMOSOMES AND LINKAGE MAPS IN MAIZE

Among organisms that are important as materials for genetic investigations, maize is remarkable in having chromosomes that show many structural details at the pachytene stage of meiosis (Figs. 4.4 and 4.5). Each of the ten pairs of chromosomes can be recognized by its length, the position of the centromere, which divides the body of the chromosome into two arms of more or less equal length, and the pattern, which is formed by the arrangement of larger and smaller, more and less darkly staining chromomeres. The average lengths of the chromosomes and the ratios of the lengths of their longer and shorter arms are given in Table 14.3.

GIANT CHROMOSOMES IN THE SALIVARY GLANDS OF FLIES

Chromosomes of gigantic size, showing a wealth of structural details that permit not only every chromosome but even chromosome fragments to be recognized, occur in the salivary-gland cells of larvae of some species of Diptera. These remarkable chromosomes were discovered as early as 1881 by Balbiani in larvae of the midge Chirono-

TABLE 14.3

Average lengths, in microns, and ratios of the two limbs (separated by the centromeres) in the pachytene chromosomes of maize at meiosis (*After Longley, from Rhoades* **)**

Chromosome	Length	Length of the longer limb / Length of the shorter limb
1	82	1.3
2	67	1.2
3	62	2.0
4	59	1.6
5	60	1.1
6	49	7.1
7	47	2.8
8	47	3.2
9	43	1.8
10	37	2.8

mus. But the significance of this discovery was not appreciated until 1933, when Painter, Heitz, and Bauer, and soon also Koltzoff and Bridges, clarified the nature of these chromosomes and used them for studying problems of genetics.

In Drosophila, as in other flies, the homol-

gonia, or neuroblasts in the larval brain. The salivary-gland chromosomes have the shape of long cylinders or ribbons, which consist of a succession of darkly staining disks or bands and of light internodes (Fig. 14.4). The darkly staining disks consist chiefly of a nucleoprotein containing desoxyribonucleic

Fig. 14.4. Photomicrograph of the nucleus of a salivary-gland cell of *Drosophila melanogaster.* (*Courtesy of Jack Schultz*)

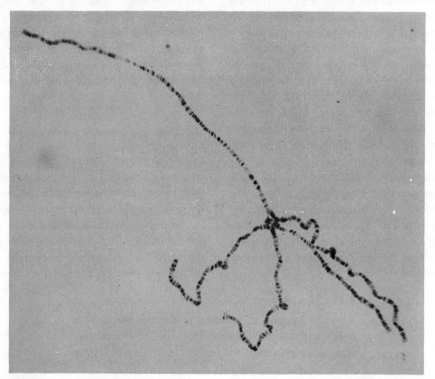

ogous members of each pair of chromosomes tend to lie side by side in the cell nuclei. This *somatic pairing,* which in many ways reminds one of the pairing which the chromosomes undergo in meiotic prophase, is so strong in the salivary-gland cells that the homologous chromosomes are tightly apposed and almost fused with each other. Furthermore, in the salivary-gland cells the chromosomes are 100 or more times longer than in other cells used to study Drosophila chromosomes, such as oögonia, spermato-

acid; some of them are thicker or more darkly staining than others, some consist of dots, and others appear solid. The pattern of disks is diagnostic for each section of each chromosome, as shown in the photo in Figure 14.5. The centromere regions of all the chromosomes are associated together in a mass in which the bands appear to be less discrete than in other parts; this mass is called the *chromocenter.* Owing to the tight somatic pairing and to the association of the centromeres in the chromocenter, the correspondence between the chromosomes in the metaphase plates and in the salivary-gland cells is as shown in Figure 14.6.

Bridges, who entertained the working hypothesis that there is a one-to-one correspondence between the genes and the disks, counted at least 5,149 distinct disks in the salivary-gland chromosomes of *Drosophila melanogaster*.

The cells of salivary glands of fly larvae never divide, and they disintegrate soon after the larva pupates. The giant chromosomes observed in these cells correspond to those

seen at the prophase stage in ordinary cells and thus constitute a "permanent prophase." The giant size of the chromosomes is due to the chromonema, which in ordinary chromosomes is spirally coiled but which is unwound in the salivary chromosomes, and to the lengthened internodes between the chromomeres. Moreover, the chromonema in the salivary-gland cells has undergone repeated division, although neither the nucleus nor the cell has divided at a similar rate. Such a chromosome division, which is not accompanied by nucleus and cell division, is called

Fig. 14.5. Photomicrograph of the salivary-gland chromosomes of a male *Drosophila persimilis*. The spherical dark object at lower center is the nucleolus. (*Courtesy of Eliot Spiess, photograph by David A. Hungerford*)

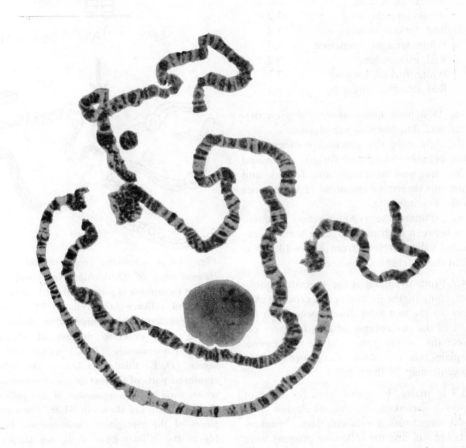

endomitosis and is known to occur in certain tissues in both animals and plants. Owing perhaps to the somatic pairing of chromosomes in flies, endomitosis in the salivary-gland chromosomes results in formation of cablelike bundles of chromonemata, with the homologous chromomeres tightly paired to form the stainable disks, and the internodes forming the light segments between the disks.

PROBLEMS

14.1 In Drosophila, white eyes (w), miniature wings (m), and forked bristles (f) are sex-linked and recessive to the wild-type characters red eyes, long wings, and straight bristles. In a cross of $\dfrac{wfm}{wfm} \times +++$, the F_1 females crossed with *wfm* males gave the following in a large population:

	Per cent
White, forked, miniature	26.8
Red, straight, long	26.8
White, straight, long	13.2
Red, forked, miniature	13.2
White, straight, miniature	6.7
Red, forked, long	6.7
White, forked, long	3.3
Red, straight, miniature	3.3

   a. Designate noncrossover, single-crossover, and double-crossover classes.

   b. Determine the percentage of crossing over between white and forked, white and miniature, and miniature and forked, and from this determine the order of these genes in the chromosome.

   c. Compare the recombination frequencies between each pair of genes with the expected values derived from Table 13.1. Explain the differences observed.

14.2 From the data in the preceding problem, compare the percentage of crossing over between the two most distant genes with the sum of the percentages of crossing over between the two end genes and the center gene. Explain this difference. Construct a chromosome map of these genes.

14.3 In maize, F_1 plants from the cross of colored, shrunken, starchy × colorless, full, waxy were crossed with colorless, shrunken, waxy plants, and the following progeny were observed (data from Hutchison):

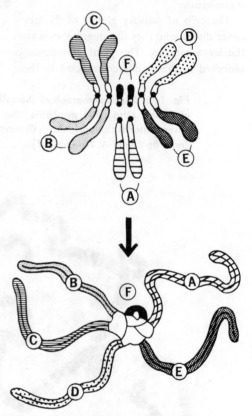

Fig. 14.6 A schematic representation of the chromosomes of *Drosophila melanogaster* as seen at metaphase of mitosis (above) and in the nuclei of salivary-gland cells of fully grown larvae (below). The chromosome limbs are shown with differing degrees of shading. (*A*) X chromosomes; (*B, C*) second chromosomes; (*D, E*) third; (*F*) fourth. The heterochromatic parts of the metaphase chromosomes, which form the chromocenter of the salivary-gland nucleus, are shown in white. The centromeres of the metaphase chromosomes, invisible in the salivary-gland cells, are shown in black.

Colored, shrunken, starchy	2,538
Colorless, full, waxy	2,708
Colored, full, waxy	116
Colorless, shrunken, starchy	113
Colored, shrunken, waxy	601
Colorless, full, starchy	626
Colored, full, starchy	4
Colorless, shrunken, waxy	2

Map the positions of *c, s,* and *w,* and determine the coincidence.

14.4 In Drosophila, the mutant "morula" (*m*) has a peculiar eye modification in which the facets are more irregular in size, shape, and color than are those of the normal eye. (For descriptions of mutants "black" and "arc," see Problem 13.9.) In the four following crosses, the genes for arc, black, and morula entered the crosses in all four possible combinations, as stated. The counts in each case are the results of mating F_1 females with arc, black, morula males. Only the recessive alleles are named, the normal dominant alleles being assumed to be present unless the recessive is mentioned. Thus "black" flies are $b++$, possessing the dominant alleles of arc and morula. The four crosses are as follows:

   I. Arc, black, morula × wild-type; F_1 female × arc, black, morula male
  II. Arc black × morula; F_1 female × arc, black, morula male
 III. Black morula × arc; F_1 female × arc, black, morula male
 IV. Black × arc morula; F_1 female × arc, black, morula male

The results of these four backcrosses are given below (data from Bridges and Morgan):

Determine the crossover percentage between black and arc, arc and morula, and black and morula. Map the chromosome for these three points.

14.5 Below are the data from Bridges and Morgan for the crossovers between the genes black, curved, purple, speck, star, and vestigial in chromosome II of Drosophila. On the basis of the data, map the chromosome for these six genes as accurately as possible. Remember that determinations for short distances are more accurate than for those for long ones.

Genes	Total flies	Crossovers
Black-curved	62,679	14,237
Black-purple	48,931	3,026
Black-speck	685	326
Black-Star	16,507	6,250
Black-vestigial	20,153	3,578
Curved-purple	51,136	10,205
Curved-speck	10,042	3,037
Curved-Star	19,870	9,123
Curved-vestigial	1,720	141
Purple-speck	11,985	5,474
Purple-Star	8,155	3,561
Purple-vestigial	13,601	1,609
Speck-Star	7,135	3,448
Speck-vestigial	2,054	738
Star-vestigial	450	195

Locate also on this map the genes for arc and morula, studied in Problem 14.4. (Arc and morula are on the opposite side of black from Star.)

14.6 In rats, two genes *r* and *p* (referred to in Problem 13.15) are linked. *RR pp* animals have pink eyes and light-colored coats; *rr PP* animals have red eyes and light-col-

	Cross I	Cross II	Cross III	Cross IV
Wild type	613	95	3	164
Black	445	40	13	187
Arc	38	713	113	21
Morula	82	851	107	7
Arc black	55	884	96	8
Black morula	29	666	120	15
Arc morula	467	33	14	187
Arc, black, morula	514	79	2	133

ored coats. *RR PP* animals have dark eyes and dark coats. Albinism, *cc* (pink eyes and white coat), is also linked with *r* and *p*. *ccrr*, *ccR(r)*, *ccpp*, *ccP(p)* are albino and have colorless eyes at birth. Design an experiment to measure this linkage and to map the chromosome containing *r*, *p*, and *c*, giving all the necessary steps and crosses.

14.7 From the following pedigree of dominant retinitis pigmentosa, give the probable genotypes of all individuals, showing whether the mutant gene is probably in the X or in the Y chromosome and discriminating crossovers and noncrossovers.

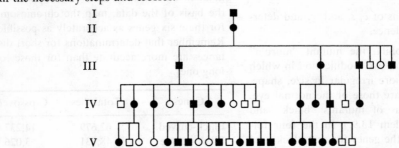

Transmission of a dominant gene for retinitis pigmentosa through five generations. The mates of all persons shown were free from defect. (*From Haldane, after Snell*)

15 CHROMOSOME ABERRATIONS AND CYTOLOGICAL MAPS

THE LINKAGE maps described in the previous chapter are essentially summaries of a large amount of statistical data on recombination of linked genes. The data are expressed in terms of "distances" between the genes in a linear series. It is interesting to speculate that, even if chromosomes as bodies visible under a microscope were unknown, the data of the linkage maps might lead a biologist to infer that there must be, in the germ cells at least, bodies with the essential properties and behavior that chromosomes are known to possess. Microscopic observations on the behavior of chromosomes shed as much light on the transmission of genes as a knowledge of heredity does on cytological processes; and the actual history of genetics and cytology has been one of cooperation and mutual stimulation. As a result, there have developed ingenious combinations of methods of experimental genetics and cytology, and evidence has been obtained which shows that the arrangement of genes in the linkage maps corresponds to their distribution in the actual chromosomes as revealed by the microscope.

CLASSIFICATION OF CHROMOSOMAL ABERRATIONS

Different cells of the same body and different individuals of the same species have, as a rule, identical numbers of chromosomes; within these chromosomes, the genes are arranged in the linear series shown in the linkage maps. But this rule admits exceptions, and the study of these exceptions has been most profitable for the development of genetics. Just as the genes normally reproduce themselves and synthesize their perfect copies, so also do the chromosomes. But the genes occasionally mutate (p. 112 and Chap. 16), and chromosomes produce abnormalities or aberrations. Several kinds of chromosomal aberrations can be distinguished, as shown in the following tabulation.

I. Changes in the number of chromosomes.
   A. Changes involving entire sets; n = basic, or *monoploid,* number.

1. *Haploidy* (n): each chromosome represented singly.
2. *Polyploidy:* each chromosome represented by more than two homologues. *Triploidy* (3n); *tetraploidy* (4n); *pentaploidy* (5n); etc. An *autopolyploid* is a form derived by chromosome multiplication from a single diploid, so that the homologues come from the same source as in pure strains or homozygotes. An *allopolyploid* is a form derived from a hybrid between two diploids, so that the homologues come from different sources.

B. Changes involving the numbers of chromosomes in a set (*heteroploidy*).
   1. *Monosomics* represent the loss of one chromosome from one set. Where this occurs in the diploid, the chromosome complement is 2n -- 1.
   2. *Polysomics* represent the addition of one or more chromosomes to one set. *Trisomic* = 2n + 1, *tetrasomic* = 2n + 2, etc.
   3. *Nullisomics* represent the loss of both chromosomes of a pair.

II. Changes in the number or arrangement of gene loci within a chromosome (Fig. 15.1).
   A. In number.
      1. *Deficiency,* or *deletion*: loss of one or more genes.
      2. *Duplication*: addition of one or more genes, as a result of which the organism carries the same gene repeated in its haploid chromosome complement.
   B. In arrangement.
      1. *Translocation*: exchange of parts between nonhomologous chromosomes to form two new chromosomes. For example, if the original chromosomes were *ABCDEF* and *GHIJKL*, the new ones may be *ABCJKL* and *GHIDEF*.
      2. *Inversion*: within a chromosome, a block of genes may rotate by

Fig. 15.1. Classification of chromosomal aberrations. (*A*) Normal chromosomes. (*B*) Deficiency. (*C*) Duplication. (*D*) Heterozygous translocation. (*E*) Heterozygous inversion. (*F*) Homozygous translocation. (*G*) Homozygous inversion. The centromeres are shown as black circles.

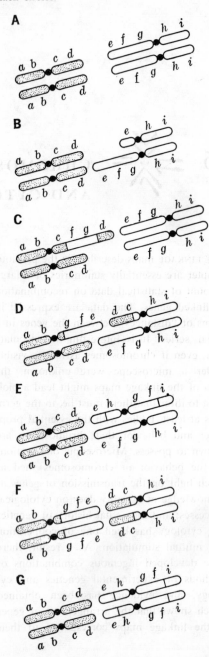

180 degrees. For example, a chromosome with genes in the order *ABCDEFG* may change to *AEDCBFG*.

TRISOMICS AND MONOSOMICS

As shown in Chapter 12, nondisjunction of the X chromosomes in Drosophila leads to the appearance of trisomic individuals with one chromosome more (XXY females, XYY males), or of monosomics with one chromosome less (X no-Y males), than in normal flies. Not only the X chromosomes but also the autosomes occasionally undergo nondisjunction, and Bridges obtained and studied individuals of *Drosophila melanogaster,* some of which had three of the dotlike fourth chromosomes and others only one of these instead of the normal two. Trisomics and monosomics for the large V-shaped autosomes in Drosophila (see Fig. 4.2) are inviable.

A complete series of trisomics has been described in the Jimson weed, *Datura stramonium,* by Blakeslee and his collaborators. Jimson weed has 12 pairs of chromosomes, and 12 different trisomics have arisen, each having one of the chromosomes of the normal set present in triplicate and each recognizable by its appearance (Fig. 15.2) and distinguishable from other trisomics. This is precisely as it should be if each chromosome of the normal set carries genes different from those in the other chromosomes. One might have expected to find also a series of 12 different monosomics, each having lost one of the 12 chromosomes of the normal sets, but such monosomics in Jimson weed are inviable. It is a general rule that having some genes and chromosomes present in numbers in excess of normal is less deleterious to the organism than having the same genes present in subnormal quantities.

However, in some plants both polysomics and monosomics are viable. R. Clausen and his collaborators found in *Nicotiana tabacum* 24 different monosomics corresponding to

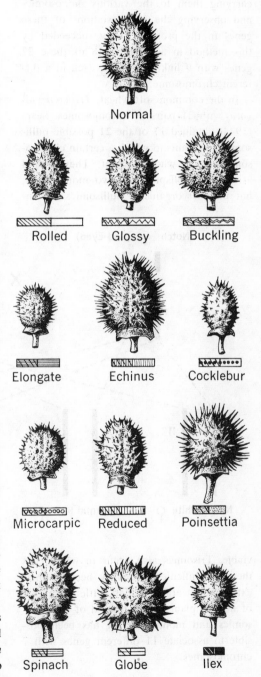

Fig. 15.2. Chromosomal mutants in the Jimson weed (Datura). The capsule of the normal plant is shown at the top, and the results of the duplication of each of the twelve chromosomes of this plant are shown by the other twelve seed capsules. (*After Blakeslee*)

Normal

Rolled　　Glossy　　Buckling

Elongate　　Echinus　　Cocklebur

Microcarpic　Reduced　Poinsettia

Spinach　　Globe　　Ilex

the normal 24 chromosome pairs of this plant. Each of the 24 monosomics is recognizable from the appearance of the plant. Clausen and Cameron have analyzed 22 genes in the tobacco plant by crossing plants carrying them to the various monosomics and observing the manifestations of these genes in the progeny. They succeeded by this method in associating 18 of these 22 genes with 9 linkage groups, each in a different chromosome.

In the common soft wheat, *Triticum vulgare,* with 21 pairs of chromosomes, Sears (1944) obtained 17 of the 21 possible nullisomics, or plants in which a certain chromosome pair is wholly absent. They should arise in the offspring of two monosomics, but in most organisms nullisomics are in-

DEFICIENCY

The classical case of deficiency was discovered and worked out by Bridges (1917) and Mohr (1923). A mutant called Notch produces a notched margin of the wings. It is inherited as a sex-linked dominant in the female but is lethal in the male. Since male zygotes carrying Notch die, the mutant is perpetuated by breeding females with notched wings to normal males. Such sex-linked mutants are not very rare, but studies of Notch revealed an unusual situation. When Notch females with normal red eyes were crossed to white-eyed males with normal wings (*w*, sex-linked recessive; see Fig. 14.1), the F_1 females with Notch wings had

Fig. 15.3. **The inheritance of Notch deficiency in *Drosophila melanogaster.***

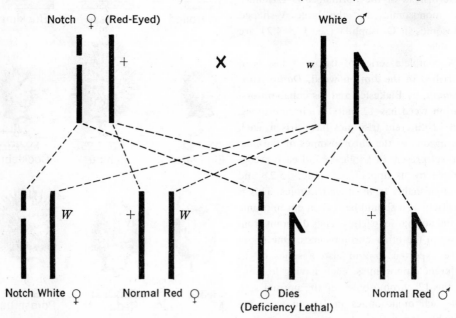

viable. Trisomics also occur in wheat, but they are difficult to identify because their external appearance differs little from that of normal plants. With the aid of the nullisomics and monosomics it has been possible to associate 11 different genes with 7 chromosomes.

also *white eyes* (Fig. 15.3), as though the gene white were dominant in the presence of Notch. Some other recessive sex-linked genes lying in the vicinity of white on the linkage map (Fig. 14.1)—for example, facet (*fa*)—also show this *pseudodominance* in the presence of Notch. A hypothesis was formulated according to which Notch arose as a result of the *loss of a piece of the chromosome* containing the genes that show the pseudodominance. This hypothesis was confirmed when Mohr found that the frequency of crossing over between the genes lying to the left and to the right of the deficient piece was decreased in Notch flies by 3.8 per cent, as was to be expected if the deficient piece was so long that about 3.8 per cent of recombination was due to crossing over in that piece.

Mohr was unable to confirm his hypothesis cytologically because the section of the

as shown in Fig. 15.4. *The genes which, on the basis of the genetic tests, are known to be missing in the deficiency must be located in the part of the chromosome that forms the buckle in the deficiency heterozygotes.* Thus the position of certain genes is determined not in terms of a linkage map but in terms of the chromosome as seen under the microscope. By using this method, a number of genes have been localized in the salivary-gland chromosomes of *Drosophila melanogaster* (Fig. 15.5). For some genes the localization has been narrowed to a very small group of disks, or even to a single disk, in a

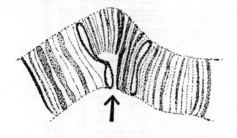

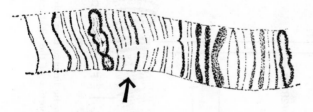

Fig. 15.4. Portions of salivary chromosomes of *Drosophila melanogaster* showing (above) a deficiency of 10 or more bands and (below) a 2-band deficiency.

chromosome deficient in Notch is too small to produce an appreciable shortening of the X chromosome as seen at mitosis. Such a confirmation, for Notch and for other deficiencies discovered meanwhile, became possible when the technique of studying chromosomes in salivary-gland cells was introduced. In individuals heterozygous for a deficiency, one of the two paired homologous chromosomes is shorter than the other, and since the pairing occurs only between homologous disks, the section of the normal chromosome which contains the disks missing in the other chromosome forms a buckle,

chromosome. Deficiencies have been seen also in the pachytene chromosomes in maize by McClintock and others.

In Drosophila, only individuals heterozygous for short deficiencies, generally not exceeding a few dozen disks in the salivary-gland chromosomes, are viable. Even these individuals usually show some external abnormalities, such as the notching of the wing margin in Notch deficiency, which appear to be due to the presence of certain genes in a single dose instead of in the normal double dose. On the other hand, deficiency homozygotes (that is, individuals in which certain

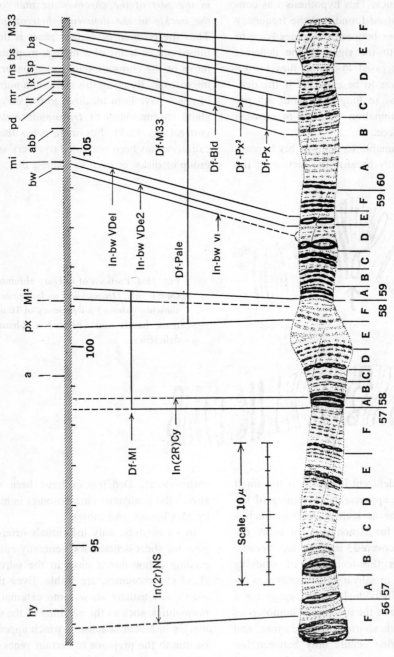

Fig. 15.5. A comparison of the genetic linkage map (above) and a corresponding section of the salivary-gland chromosome (below). The region is the end portion of the right limb of the second chromosome of *Drosophila melanogaster.* (*After Bridges*)

genes are wholly missing) are, with very few exceptions, lethal. Demerec showed that homozygous deficiencies are usually lethal even if they arise in small groups of cells surrounded by normal tissues in which all the genes are present. This suggests that most genes are indispensable, at least in single

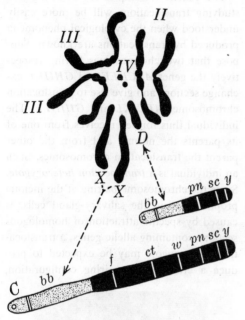

Fig. 15.6. A duplication for a section of the X chromosome of *Drosophila melanogaster.* The duplication (D) contains its own centromere and therefore appears as a separate extra chromosome. X, II, III, and IV are the X, second, third, and fourth chromosomes, respectively. Below is a schematic representation of the duplication and of a normal X chromosome; the heterochromatic parts are shown stippled, and the euchromatic parts are black; *bb, f, ct, w, pn, sc,* and *y* are the locations of some genes in the X chromosome; *C* is the centromere.

dose, for the development of a viable organism. In polyploid organisms, such as soft wheats (p. 301), each gene is present several times. Therefore, two of these can sometimes be lost (in nullisomics) with impunity.

DUPLICATION

Bridges (1919) observed that some individuals of *D. melanogaster* which should have been homozygous for certain recessive genes failed to manifest the effects of these genes in the phenotype. An analysis showed that dominant alleles of the genes in question were present in addition to, and at a different point in the chromosome from, the recessive ones. The flies evidently contained an extra piece of a chromosome, in addition to a complete diploid chromosome complement. Since, as a rule, one dominant allele of a gene is sufficient to suppress the effects of two recessives, the exceptional individuals with an extra piece of chromosome showed the effects of the dominant alleles in the phenotype. Cytologically, a duplication may produce the same kind of configuration in a chromosome as a deficiency does. Thus, in salivary-gland cells, one chromosome homologue is longer than the other and forms a buckle in pairing (Fig. 15.4).

If a duplicating fragment of a chromosome includes the centromere, it may be present as a small extra chromosome added to a normal chromosome complement (Fig. 15.6). Which genes are and which are not represented in the fragment can be determined genetically by observing the suppression or nonsuppression of recessive genes present in double dose in the normal chromosomes. Observations and measurements of the fragments under a microscope show, then, the size of the chromosome sections containing known gene loci.

The effects of duplications on viability are generally less deleterious than those of deficiencies, so that relatively long duplications survive. Individuals carrying duplications show, nevertheless, various abnormalities in bodily characters, and when these abnormalities are known, they may be used to identify the carriers of the corresponding duplications.

A careful study of the salivary-gland chromosomes in *D. melanogaster* led Bridges

(1935) to conclude that some blocks of genes are present more than once in the haploid chromosome complement. Such repeated sections, or *repeats*, have presumably arisen in the evolution of the chromosome complement of Drosophila by means of a process of duplication. The occurrence of repeats results in certain genes being present two or more times in the chromosome set. This creates a situation resembling that which obtains in polypoloids; it is possible that the exceptional cases of viable deficiencies are connected with the existence of repeats, or duplications of the same genes.

TRANSLOCATION

Deficiencies and duplications involve losses or additions of genes to the normal gene

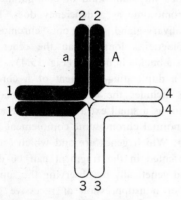

Fig. 15.7. Above, a diagram of chromosome pairing at meiosis in a translocation heterozygote. At right, a photomicrograph of chromosome pairing at meiosis in a reciprocal translocation between chromosome 8 and chromosome 10 in corn. (*Courtesy of M. M. Rhoades*)

complement; hence the carriers of these chromosomal aberrations are as a rule distinguishable from normal representatives of the species to which they belong by their appearance. Translocations and inversions change only the arrangement of the genes in the chromosomes, not the quality or quantity of the genes. For this reason they are sometimes referred to as *chromosomal re-*

arrangements. Individuals carrying such rearrangements should be phenotypically entirely normal unless the relations of a gene or genes to adjacent genes affect the phenotypic expression (cf. "position effect," p. 379). The first translocation was discovered by Bridges (1923) in *D. melanogaster*.

The genetic techniques for detecting and studying translocations will be more easily understood when the cytological phenomena produced by translocations are known. Suppose that two chromosomes having respectively the genes *ABCDEF* and *GHIJKL* exchange sections and give rise to translocation chromosomes *ABCJKL* and *GHIDEF*. The individual thus formed receives from one of its parents the normal and from the other parent the translocation chromosomes. Such an individual is a *translocation heterozygote*. Since the chromosome pairing at the meiotic prophase, or in the salivary-gland cells, is caused by specific attraction of homologous sections containing allelic genes, a translocation heterozygote may be expected to produce a cross-shaped pairing configuration,

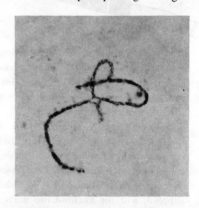

represented schematically in Figure 15.7. Such configurations have actually been observed in pachytene chromosomes of translocation heterozygotes in maize (Fig. 15.7) and in salivary chromosomes of Drosophila translocation heterozygotes. It is a rather simple matter to identify cytologically the points at which these chromosomes had broken to produce the translocation.

In organisms in which neither salivary-gland chromosomes nor pachytene chromosomes are favorable for study, translocations can be detected by means of observation of the chromosome configurations at the first

chromosomes—there will be formed a *quadrivalent,* a group of four associated chromosomes, each member of the group being partially homologous to two other chromosomes in the group. The quadrivalent will appear

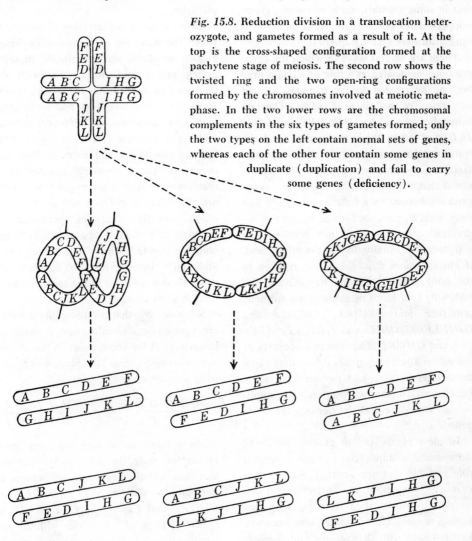

Fig. 15.8. Reduction division in a translocation heterozygote, and gametes formed as a result of it. At the top is the cross-shaped configuration formed at the pachytene stage of meiosis. The second row shows the twisted ring and the two open-ring configurations formed by the chromosomes involved at meiotic metaphase. In the two lower rows are the chromosomal complements in the six types of gametes formed; only the two types on the left contain normal sets of genes, whereas each of the other four contain some genes in duplicate (duplication) and fail to carry some genes (deficiency).

meiotic division. Consider again the cross-shaped arrangement of the chromosomes formed at the pachytene stage of meiosis in translocation heterozygotes (Fig. 15.7). Occurrence of crossing over in each of the four arms of the cross will result in formation of chiasmata in each arm. Instead of bivalents —that is, pairs of synapsed homologous

at diakinesis and at metaphase of the first meiotic division as a ring, or circle, of four chromosomes, which may be either twisted as shown in Figure 15.8, left, or open as in the center drawing of the same figure. If chiasmata fail to be formed in one arm of the pachytene cross, the ring is transformed into an open chain of four chromosomes.

Such rings or chains of chromosomes were observed and correctly interpreted by Belling at meiosis in the Jimson weed (Datura) and were thereafter found in maize, peas, wheat, spiderwort (Tradescantia), and other plants and in some animals, such as certain grasshoppers. They occur regularly in many evening primroses (see Chap. 19).

There are several ways in which the chromosomes associated in a ring or a chain may become distributed to the gametes formed as a result of meiosis (Fig. 15.8). The two original chromosomes, *ABCDEF* and *GHIJKL*, may go to the same gamete, and the translocation chromosomes, *ABCJKL* and *GHIDEF*, to another gamete. It may be noted that in each of these gametes, every gene symbolized by a letter occurs once and only once, as gametes formed by normal individuals, that is, those not containing a translocation, usually do. On the other hand, if chromosomes adjacent in the ring go to the same pole at the meiotic division, the following four kinds of gametes are formed: *ABCDEF* and *ABCJKL; ABCDEF* and *GHIDEF; GHIJKL* and *GHIDEF; ABCJKL* and *GHIJKL*. The common property of these four kinds of gametes is that they carry certain genes twice and do not have some genes at all. In other words, they carry duplications for some and deficiencies for other genes.

In most plants, pollen grains containing deficiencies or duplications are as a general rule inviable and are aborted. Such pollen grains appear empty and shriveled and can be clearly distinguished from pollen grains having normal chromosomal complements. Embryo sacs with deficiencies and duplications may also abort. Consequently, plants heterozygous for translocations may produce fewer seeds than normal, and such plants appear *semisterile*. The semisterility of translocation heterozygotes furnishes one of the simplest and most practical ways of detecting translocations in maize. It must be kept in mind, however, that semisterility may be produced by lethal genes as well as by translocations and that in some plants—for example, some evening primroses—translocation heterozygotes may give rise to gametes almost all of which have normal gene complements.

There is a very interesting difference between the behavior of translocation heterozygotes in plants and in animals. In maize, pollen grains and megaspores with deficiencies and duplications for blocks of genes abort; in Drosophila, eggs and spermatozoa with such abnormalities function normally and form zygotes (fertilized eggs) which lack certain genes and carry certain genes in excess. These abnormal zygotes die, so that translocation heterozygotes in animals are effectively semisterile, just as they are in plants. But the ability of spermatozoa to function despite gross abnormalities in gene contents has led Muller and Settles (1927) and other investigators to conclude that *genes do not function* in the spermatozoa, at least in some animals.

Suppose now that a Drosophila male heterozygous for a translocation is made also heterozygous for some genes in the chromosomes involved, thus (the black line symbolizing a chromosome):

$$\frac{A\ B\ C\ D\ E\ F}{A'\ B'\ C'\ J'\ K'\ L'} \qquad \frac{G\ H\ I\ J\ K\ L}{G'\ H'\ I'\ D'\ E'\ F'}$$

Since there is no crossing over in the Drosophila male, the only two kinds of gametes that will be free from deficiencies and duplications will be (1) *ABCDEF* and *GHIJKL* and (2) *A' B' C' J' K' L'* and *G' H' I' D' E' F'*. Gametes with all other combinations of chromosomes will give rise to inviable zygotes, as shown above. This amounts to saying that all the genes symbolized by the letters without primes and all the genes symbolized by the letters with primes will be *completely linked, despite the fact that they are carried in two different chromosomes. This apparent linkage* of genes known to belong normally to different linkage groups offers a method for detecting translocations in genetic experiments without the aid of a microscope. For example, in a certain experiment, 121 *Drosophila melanogaster* males heterozygous for the dominant genes Dichaete (*D*, certain bristles absent, wings spread) and Bristle (*Bl*, bristles short and stubby) were test-crossed individually to wild-type females. Since Dichaete belongs to the third and Bristle to the second linkage groups, the progeny of these crosses was expected to consist of four classes of flies in about equal numbers, namely, (1) wild type, (2) Dichaete, (3) Bristle, and (4) Dichaete Bristle. This is, indeed, what was observed in 117 out of the 121 test crosses. But in 4 test crosses, classes (2) and (3) proved to be absent, as the following numbers of flies obtained in one of these test crosses show:

wild	Dichaete	Bristle	Bristle Dichaete
106	—	—	82

The genes Dichaete and Bristle are completely linked, as though they were located in the same chromosome. The four cultures that showed this apparent linkage were studied further both genetically and cytologically, and they proved to contain translocations involving the second and the third chromosomes.

If a translocation heterozygote is a Drosophila female, crossing over will occur between homologous parts of the chromosomes. The linkage between the genes carried in these chromosomes will no longer be absolute but only partial. It will be strongest, however, between the genes that lie close to the points in the chromosomes at which it had been broken in the process of formation of the translocation (*C, D, I, J, C', J', I',* and *D'* in the scheme on p. 203) and will be the weakest between the genes remote from these points (*A, F, G, L, A', L', G', F'* in the scheme). The intensity of linkage, and the frequency of recombination, between the

Fig. 15.9. A chromosomal complement in an individual heterozygous for a translocation between the third and fourth chromosomes in *Drosophila melanogaster.* Note a single, dotlike, normal fourth chromosome, a hook-shaped fragment of the third chromosome which has lost a section, and a small rodlike chromosome that is the result of the union of a section of the third chromosome with the dotlike fourth.

genes in translocation heterozygotes permit, therefore, localization of the points of chromosome breakage in terms of the linkage maps of the chromosomes. Cytological examination of the same translocation heterozygotes enables one to correlate the genetically observed changes in the linkage relationships with the state of the chromosomes as observed under a microscope.

For example, in a strain of *D. melanogaster* linkage was observed between genes belonging normally to the third and the fourth linkage groups, indicating a translocation between these chromosomes. A study of recombination disclosed that the third chromosome had been broken between the loci of the genes pink and curled (*p* and *cu*, Fig. 14.1). The chromosomes of females heterozygous for this translocation appear as shown in Figure 15.9. One of the large V-shaped chromosomes has one of its limbs much shortened; there is only one free, dotlike fourth chromosome; and there is a single rodlike chromosome not present in the normal chromosome complement. The interpretation of these cytological findings is as follows: The shortened V-shaped chromosome is the third chromosome, which has lost the section corresponding to the *cu-Mg* interval of the linkage map (Fig. 14.1); this section is attached to a part of the fourth chromosome, giving rise to the "new" rod-like chromosome. This type of analysis has been carried out for a number of transloca-tions in *D. melanogaster,* in maize, and in a few other species.

INVERSION

Soon after the discovery of linkage and re-combination in *D. melanogaster,* it was no-ticed that some strains of this fly contain what were described as "C factors," which reduce or suppress the recombination of genes in a certain chromosome or a part of a chromosome in females heterozygous for such C factors. Sturtevant (1926) found that one of the C factors, which acted as a suppressor of recombination in the right limb of the third chromosome—that is, from the centromere to the right end, specifically, from the loci of the genes *Dfd* and *p* to *ca*

It may be noted that not only inversions but also heterozygous translocations and large duplications and deficiencies reduce the frequency of crossing over in the chro-mosomes involved. This is apparently caused by the difficulties the chromosomes encoun-ter in establishing the meiotic pairing be-tween the leptotene and the pachytene stages. Consider, for example, the situation in a nucleus of a translocation heterozy-gote, which has the chromosomes *ABCDEF, GHIJKL, ABCJKL, GHIDEF.* Every one of these four chromosomes contains parts that are homologous to parts of two other chromosomes in the same nucleus. At the onset of meiosis, when homologous loci be-gin to attract each other and establish the synaptic association, mechanical pulls and stresses may arise which will delay or pre-vent the pairing of all homologous chromo-

Fig. 15.10. Inversions in salivary chromosome B¹ of *Drosophila azteca* as revealed by loop formation. Left and right, two single inversions; center, a double inversion which is the combination of the two single ones. (*From Dobzhansky and Sokoloff*)

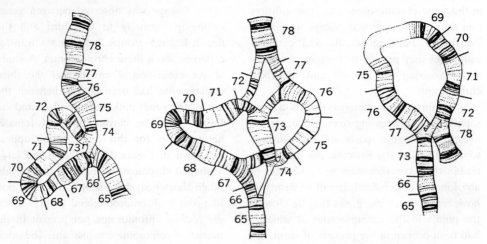

and *Mg* (Fig. 14.1)—was an inversion of a section of this chromosome. The reason why recombination is suppressed in inversion het-erozygotes will become clear when the cy-tological effects of inversions are considered.

some parts, especially of those adjacent to the points of change of linear homology. Disturbance of pairing interferes with the es-tablishment of chiasmata and crossing over

Suppose that an individual is heterozygous for an inversion, that is, has a chromosome carrying the genes *ABCDEFG* and a chromosome *AEDCBFG*. Since homologous loci are paired at meiosis as well as in the salivary-gland chromosomes, inversion heterozygotes will show, in the cells in which a complete pairing is attained, configurations like those represented in Figures 15.10 and 15.11. Such configurations have been observed at the pachytene stage in chromosomes of maize and in the salivary-gland chromosomes of inversion heterozygotes in several species of Drosophila. Since a chromosome once changed by an inversion may undergo another change by another inversion, even more complex pairing configurations may be observed. An example of a relatively complex one is shown in Figure 15.10.

Chiasmata may become established in the paired inverted segments as shown in Figure 15.11. The subsequent fate of the crossover chromatids will be different depending upon whether the centromere lies within or outside the inverted section. If the inversion does not include the centromere (*paracentric inversion*), the meiotic anaphase will contain a chromatid connecting the two centromeres, called a *chromatid bridge,* and a chromatid lacking a centromere altogether, called an *acentric fragment,* as shown in Figure 15.11, III. The formation of chromatid bridges and acentric fragments at the

meiotic divisions has been observed by McClintock in maize and by Darlington, Stebbins, and others in a series of other plants. The presence of such bridges and fragments furnishes a cytological method of detection of inversions which is used in organisms in which pachytene chromosomes

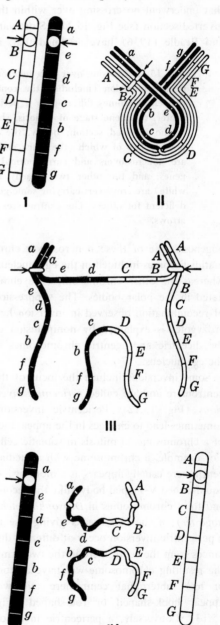

Fig. 15.11. Crossing over in a heterozygote for a paracentric inversion (not including the centromere). I, two chromosomes differing in a paracentric inversion; II, diplotene stage of meiosis showing a chiasma inside the inverted section; III, anaphase of the first meiotic division, showing a chromatid bridge and an acentric fragment; IV, the outcome of meiosis: two noncrossover chromosomes with normal gene complements, and (in the middle) chromatids with two centromeres and with no centromere (inviable). The centromeres are indicated by arrows.

or salivary-gland chromosomes are either absent or unfavorable for investigation. Now, neither the chromatid bridges nor the acentric fragments behave normally in cell divisions, and both are eventually lost. The only viable products of meiosis in paracentric inversion heterozygotes are the chromatids that underwent no crossing over within the inverted section (see Fig. 15.11). Sturtevant and Beadle (1936) have assumed that, in

may transform it into a V-shaped one with more or less equal arms. Such changes in the shape of chromosomes have been observed in laboratory cultures of Drosophila, and they are known to occur in nature as well.

Crossing over in a pericentric inversion does not result in production of chromatid bridges and acentric fragments at the *first* metaphase of meiosis. It does result, however, in formation of chromosomes having

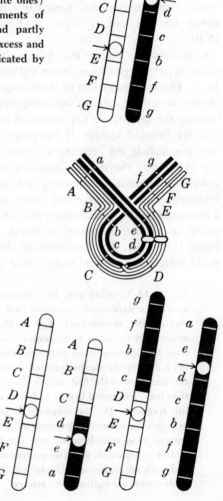

Fig. 15.12. Crossing over in a heterozygote for a pericentric inversion (including the centromere). Above, two chromosomes differing in a pericentric inversion; center, diplotene stage of meiosis, showing a chiasma in the inverted section; below, the four products of meiosis, two of which (the black and the white ones) are noncrossovers and carry normal complements of genes, and the other two (partly black and partly white) are crossovers carrying some genes in excess and deficient for others. The centromeres are indicated by arrows.

oögenesis, one of these noncrossover chromatids becomes included in the egg nucleus, whereas the other chromosomes are eliminated in the polar bodies. The suppression of recombination observed in inversion heterozygotes is explained by noninclusion of the dicentric and acentric chromosomes in the egg nucleus.

Some inversions include the locus of the centromere and are called *pericentric inversions* (Fig. 15.12). Pericentric inversions sometimes lead to changes in the appearance of a chromosome at mitosis in somatic cells. For example, a chromosome with a median centromere usually appears as a more or less equal-armed V-shaped body (like the second and third chromosomes in *Drosophila melanogaster*); if the two breaks giving rise to a pericentric inversion occur at different distances from the centromere in the two arms, the resulting chromosome will have a more or less subterminal centromere and will appear hook-shaped or rod-shaped (Fig. 15.13). Conversely, a pericentric inversion in a hook-shaped or rod-shaped chromosome

duplications for some genes and deficiencies for others (Fig. 15.12). Gametes that receive such chromosomes do not as a rule form viable zygotes. Recombination is therefore lowered in heterozygotes for pericentric inversions.

PERMANENCE OF THE CENTROMERE

Studies on chromosomal aberrations have emphasized the importance of the centromere, or the place where the chromosome is attached to the spindle in the meiotic and mitotic divisions. Drosophila, maize, and most other organisms important in genetic research have one and only one centromere per chromosome. The acentric fragments,

mosomes with two centromeres, are also inviable because they are frequently ruptured during mitosis. Such chromosomes have been seen in irradiated cells, and dicentric chromatids occur at meiosis in paracentric inversion. Among numerous translocations obtained in Drosophila and in maize the altered chromosomes invariably have one and only one centromere each, although translocations forming dicentric and acentric chromosomes doubtless arise and are eliminated.

The position of the centromere among the gene loci on linkage maps of chromosomes

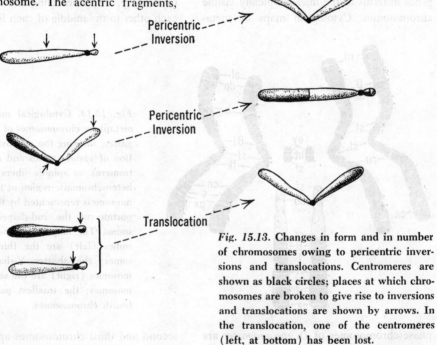

Fig. 15.13. Changes in form and in number of chromosomes owing to pericentric inversions and translocations. Centromeres are shown as black circles; places at which chromosomes are broken to give rise to inversions and translocations are shown by arrows. In the translocation, one of the centromeres (left, at bottom) has been lost.

that is, those chromosomes lacking a centromere formed as a result of crossing over in paracentric inversions, do not behave normally in cell division, are usually left out of the nucleus in the cytoplasm, and eventually die. A similar fate of acentric fragments is observed also in cells in which chromosomes are fragmented by X rays or other means. Dicentric chromosomes, that is, chro-

of *D. melanogaster* (*sp-a*, Fig. 14.1) was inferred, even before studies on chromosomal aberrations permitted it to be established beyond reasonable doubt, from observations on interference and crossing over in different chromosomes. We know that the occurrence of crossing over at some point in a chromosome diminishes the likelihood of another crossover taking place in the neighborhood of this point. There is, however, no interference across the centromeres in the V-shaped second and third chromosomes, for the two limbs of V-shaped chromosomes behave quite independently in crossing over. Similarly, heterozygosity for a paracentric inversion in one limb of such a chromosome does not suppress recombination in the other.

CYTOLOGICAL MAPS

Correlated genetic and cytological studies on chromosomal aberrations have permitted construction of *cytological maps* of chromosomes, which show the location of various genes in terms of the microscopically visible chromosomes. Cytological maps of meta-

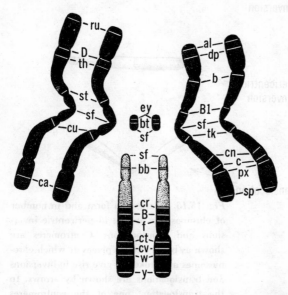

phase chromosomes of *D. melanogaster* are shown in Figure 15.14. The positions of some of the genes in this fly have also been determined in the chromosomes as seen in the salivary-gland cells (Fig. 15.5). Rough cytological maps of the chromosomes of *D. pseudoobscura* have been made by Tan. E. G. Anderson and others have succeeded in making such maps for some chromosomes in maize.

The linear orders of the genes shown by

cytological maps and by the linkage (genetic) maps are invariably the same (Fig. 15.15). *The work on cytological maps has therefore wholly confirmed the theory of linear arrangement of genes in chromosomes originally put forward on the basis of studies on recombination of traits in crosses.*

The relative distances between the genes on cytological and linkage maps do not always correspond (Fig. 15.15). The discrepancies are greatest in the vicinity of the centromeres (marked *sp-a* in Fig. 14.1), where one crossover unit corresponds to a relatively much greater distance on the physical chromosome than in other regions. Conversely, the genes lying rather close to each other in the middle of each limb of the

Fig. 15.14. Cytological maps of the metaphase chromosomes of *D. melanogaster*, showing the approximate location of various genes and of the centromeres, or spindle fibers (sf). The heterochromatic region of the X chromosome is represented by the stippled portion of the rod-shaped chromosomes. The longer V-shaped chromosomes (left) are the third chromosomes; the shorter V-shaped chromosomes (right) are the second chromosomes; the smallest pair are the fourth chromosomes.

second and third chromosomes appear relatively much farther apart on the linkage maps. Taken as a whole, the linkage maps represent the physical distances between genes in a chromosome as though seen in an uneven mirror; some parts of chromosomes are relatively compressed, while other parts are overextended.

The origin of these discrepancies in the spacing of genes on cytological and on linkage maps is not far to seek. It should be recalled that the "distances" between the genes on linkage maps are measured by the frequencies of recombination, in per cent, observed in hybridization experiments involving these genes. Hence, if in some parts of a chromosome—for example, in the vicinity of the centromere—crossing over takes place relatively rarely, this part will appear foreshortened on the linkage map. Conversely,

scribed below, is more uniform than it is on linkage maps.

EUCHROMATIN AND HETEROCHROMATIN
The most striking discrepancy between the cytological and the linkage maps in *D. melanogaster* (Fig. 15.15) is that approximately one-third of the length of the X chromosome contains only a single known gene,

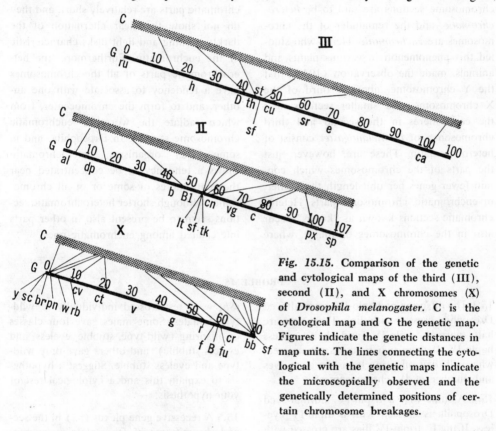

Fig. 15.15. Comparison of the genetic and cytological maps of the third (III), second (II), and X chromosomes (X) of *Drosophila melanogaster*. C is the cytological map and G the genetic map. Figures indicate the genetic distances in map units. The lines connecting the cytological with the genetic maps indicate the microscopically observed and the genetically determined positions of certain chromosome breakages.

crossing over is evidently frequent in the part of the chromosome lying about midway between the centromere and the free end, and genes lying in this part appear far apart on the linkage map. A glance at the linkage maps of *D. melanogaster* will show that some parts of the "chromosomes" are crowded with known genes, whereas others appear rather devoid of genes. The distribution of the known genes on the cytological maps, with the important exceptions described

bobbed, whereas more than 100 other genes lie in the remaining two-thirds. Now, bobbed is the only gene in the X chromosome which has an allele also in the Y chromosome. The Y chromosome, although it is larger than the X in dividing cells, is known to contain, apart from bobbed, only some factors that are necessary for the fertility of males. It appears, then, that about one-third of the X chromosome and the whole of the Y chromosome consist of a material different from that composing the remainder of the chromosomes.

Even before these facts were discovered, cytologists had found that in their preparations, some chromosomes and chromosome parts remain darkly staining in interphase nuclei or begin to stain in the prophase, whereas other chromosomes stain only faintly or not at all. The precociously staining chromosome sections are said to be *heterochromatic*, and the remainder of the chromosomes are *euchromatic*. Heitz, who studied this phenomenon in various plants and animals, made the observation (1934) that the Y chromosome, about a third of the X chromosome, and smaller sections near the centromeres in the second and third chromosomes of *D. melanogaster* consist of heterochromatin. These are, however, just the parts of the chromosomes which contain fewer genes per unit length than other, or euchromatic, chromosome parts. Heterochromatic sections known as "knobs" occur also in the chromosomes of maize, where

they appear to be devoid of known gene loci.

In Drosophila, the euchromatic and heterochromatic sections behave very differently in the salivary-gland chromosomes. The giant size of the chromosomes in the salivary-gland cells is due very largely to enormous expansion of the euchromatic chromosome parts, compared with their sizes in chromosomes of other cells. The heterochromatic parts are relatively short, and they do not show the clear alternation of the darkly staining and light disks characteristic of the euchromatin. Furthermore, the heterochromatic parts of all the chromosomes have a tendency to associate with one another, and to form the chromocenter, from which radiate the wormlike euchromatic chromosome strands. In Drosophila, and in some other organisms, heterochromatin shows a tendency to be concentrated near the centromeres of some or of all chromosomes, although shorter heterochromatic sections seem to be present also in other parts intercalated among euchromatic ones.

PROBLEMS

15.1 The offspring of haplo-IV, normal-eyed Drosophila crossed with diplo-IV eyeless are half normal diplo-IV and half eyeless haplo-IV. If these two F_1 types are crossed, what will their offspring look like as to eyes and number of IV chromosomes?

15.2 Assume that a triplo-IV, normal-eyed Drosophila is crossed with a diplo-IV eyeless. If the F_1 triplo-IV flies are crossed with the F_1 diplo-IV ones, what will be the eye character and IV-chromosome constitution of their offspring?

15.3 Notch female, red-eyed, crossed with wild-type (normal-winged), white-eyed male gives white-eyed Notch and red-eyed normal offspring. If a white-eyed, Notch offspring is mated with a red-eyed male, what will be the appearance of the offspring?

15.4 In Drosophila, male flies heterozygous for eyeless dominant (Ey^D) and stubble

(Sb) were test-crossed individually to wild-type females. Some males gave four classes of offspring (wild-type, stubble, eyeless, and eyeless stubble), and others gave only wild-type and eyeless stubble. Suggest a hypothesis to explain this and a cytological test of your hypothesis.

15.5 A recessive gene plexus (px) in the second chromosome of *Drosophila melanogaster* always shows pseudodominance when combined with the dominant mutant Minute 1 (Ml) but not with Ml^2, which behaves as an allele of Ml. Suggest an interpretation of this, together with breeding experiments and other observations by which your hypothesis could be tested.

15.6 In maize, assume that strain 1, which is homozygous for the recessive endosperm characters a, b, c, d, e, f, g, and h, is pollinated by pollen from strain 2, which is homozygous for the dominant alleles *A*, *B*, *C*, *D*, *E*, *F*, *G*, and *H*, but that the pollen has been subjected to irradiation before being placed on the styles of strain 1. If one of the resulting kernels is phenotypically *AbcdEFGH*, how would you explain this result?

15.7 Strain 1, with genes *A*, *B*, *C*, *D*, and *E* in the same chromosome known to be arranged in that order, is crossed with strain 2, homozygous for the recessive alleles of all these genes. The F_1 crossed back on *abcde* is found to produce only four types of gametes: *ABCDE*, *ABCDe*, *abcdE*, and *abcde*. Explain these facts.

15.8 Strain 1, with genes *A*, *B*, *C*, *D*, *E*, *F*, *G*, *H*, and *I* in the same chromosome and known to be arranged in that order, is crossed with strain 2, which is known to possess all the recessive alleles of these genes. Backcrosses show that in the F_1 there is crossing over between *A–B*, *G–H*, and *H–I* but never between *B–C*, *C–D*, *D–E*, *E–F*, or *F–G*. Explain these facts and map the chromosome for these genes as it occurs in strains 1 and 2.

15.9 In the case of semisterile maize (see Fig. 15.7), all the genes in each complete set of chromosomes (1 · 2 and 3 · 4, for example) are, of course, linked, just as though they were in one chromosome. Rhoades studied cases of double crossing over in such a system, where one crossover was in one arm and the other in the opposite one (as in arms 2 and 3 in Fig. 15.7), and found that there was no interference, coincidence being 1.0. Explain this difference from the usual behavior of double crossovers.

15.10 In maize, strain I and strain II differ by a single segmental interchange. I is genetically *aa* and II is *AA*. The F_1 from a cross between them is semisterile and *Aa*. When this is crossed back on strain I, the following offspring are produced: 35 per cent normal, *a;* 35 per cent semisterile, *A;* 15 per cent normal, *A;* 15 per cent semisterile, *a.* Where, with reference to locus *a*, is the translocation point?

15.11 Strain I, above, is also homozygous for gene *bb* and strain II for *BB*, so that the

semisterile hybrid is *Bb*. When this, as before, is crossed back to strain I, the following offspring are produced: 45 per cent normal, *b;* 45 per cent semisterile, *B;* 5 per cent normal, *B;* 5 per cent semisterile, *b.* It is known that, in strain I, *a* and *b* are in the same chromosome and not less than 30 units apart. For strain I, map the chromosome in which *a* and *b* occur, showing the position of these genes and of the translocation point.

15.12 In strain I, genes *c* and *d* are in the chromosome that later undergoes segmental interchange with that containing *a* and *b*, thus forming strain II. In strain II, *d* is now found to be linked with *b*, and *c* with *a*. By use of data similar to that presented in the two preceding problems, it can be shown that *c* gives 10 per cent crossing over with the translocation point and *d* gives 5 per cent. Make a diagram of the four chromosomes involved in the translocation between strains I and II as they appear at synapsis in the semisterile hybrid between these strains, showing the location of the four genes and the two translocation points.

15.13 The testes of several male mice were X-rayed. Five weeks later each was bred to several normal females that were known to produce litters of normal size. From these matings 20 sons were tested by mating to normal females. The litters from 12 of these males were of normal size, averaging 7 to 9. Eight males consistently gave small litters, averaging 2 to 3. About half the sons of these consistently repeated the fathers' performance. Suggest a hypothesis to account for these results and indicate what genetic, cytological, and embryological observations you would make to test the hypothesis.

15.14 In maize, pollen with n + 1 chromosomes is nonfunctional, but n + 1 ovules are functional. Trisomic plants *Rrr* form gametes in the ratio 2 *Rr* : 1 *R* : 2 *r* : 1 *rr*. If *R* produces red aleurone (e.g., *Rrr* is red), predict the outcome of the following crosses (*rr* is colorless; cf. p. 88):

♀ *Rrr* × ♂ *rr;* ♀ *RRr* × ♂ *rr;* ♀ *rr* × ♂ *Rrr;* ♀ *rr* × ♂ *RRr;* ♀ *RRr* × ♂ *Rr;* and ♀ *Rrr* × ♂ *Rrr*.

16 $\Join$ SPONTANEOUS MUTATION

IT IS OFTEN said that the genotype of an individual remains constant from fertilization to birth and to death, although his phenotype changes continuously. Strictly speaking, this statement is inaccurate. An adult person does not have the same genes he had as an infant or a fetus; rather, he has copies of these genes. Likewise, children do not have the genes of their parents but copies of parental genes. Whenever a chromosome divides, it gives rise to two daughter chromosomes with similar genes; all the genes of which the chromosome was composed must have reproduced themselves. Genes arise only from genes, although the materials for their synthesis must come from the outside, ultimately from food. Heredity is due, in the last analysis, to accurate gene reproduction.

Exact though the process of gene reproduction is, occasionally it goes wrong; a copy of a gene differs from the original, and the modified gene goes on reproducing its changed structure just as the original gene had earlier reproduced its structure. This is

gene mutation. By the same token, a chromosome usually divides or reproduces itself accurately; but from time to time a chromosome may be altered by the loss of some of its component genes, by reduplication, translocation, or inversion. Such *chromosomal mutations,* or *chromosomal aberrations,* were reviewed in Chapter 15.

Acceptance of Darwin's theory of evolution naturally made the problem of the origin of hereditary changes very important, for without such changes evolution would scarcely progress very far. Darwin knew of instances of sudden appearances of new hereditary types recorded by plant and animal breeders and referred to them as "sports." These sports, most of which are, in modern terminology, mutations, have often been points of departure for the creation of new varieties or breeds. Thus in the latter part of the eighteenth century, there appeared in the flock of Seth Wright, a New England farmer, a male lamb with short, bowed legs. Wright reared this lamb and bred from it, thereby

214

originating the Ancon breed of sheep, so short-legged that they could not jump over an ordinary stone fence. This breed became extinct about eighty years ago, but some fifty years later another short-legged lamb appeared in the flock of a Norwegian farmer, representing probably a new occurrence of the same mutation. From this, a new strain of short-legged sheep has been bred (Fig. 16.1). In the same way, hornless individuals have appeared in breeds of horned cattle. Pacing horses, double-toed cats, "mule-footed" swine, albino rats, and other new and distinct types have appeared as

stances the mutant character was found to be confined to a single branch. Such a branch, when artificially propagated, remains true to its new type. Many horticultural varieties, especially those with variegated foliage, have arisen from such *somatic* mutations, or "bud sports."

CONTINUOUS AND DISCONTINUOUS VARIABILITY

Darwin ascribed to sports a very minor role in evolution, because he regarded them as apt to produce monstrosities instead of viable new types. He supposed that natural

Fig. 16.1. The Ancon (short-legged) mutation in sheep (ewe in center, ram at right) compared with a normal ewe at left. (*Photograph from* Life Magazine, *courtesy of Storrs Agricultural Experiment Station*)

mutations. A mutation in man is shown in Figures 5.3 and 5.4.

The Shirley poppy, the dwarf "Cupid" sweet pea, and dwarf, cut-leaved, double-flowered, and white-flowered varieties of many plants have descended each from a single mutant individual that appeared under cultivation. Most of these mutations in plants arose from seed, but in some in-

selection favors survival and spread of the best-adapted products of *fluctuating variability,* a term applied to the ubiquitous small differences in size, color, shape, and other traits found among individuals in any population of any species. It was only in the first quarter of the present century, long after Darwin's death, that fluctuating variability, in so far as it is hereditary at all, was shown

Fig. 16.2. *Oenothera lamarckiana*, the evening primrose, and three of the mutants that arose from it: (left to right) *O. gigas*, the giant form; *O. lata*, the broad-leafed form; *O. lamarckiana*, the normal form; *O. nanella*, the dwarf form. (*Courtesy of Prof. O. Renner*)

to be due to the segregation of genes with very slight effects. Such polygenes, discussed in Chapter 8, are basically similar to other genes whose changes give rise to "sports."

The opposite view, that large, discontinuous variations are the chief sources of evolutionary change, was, however, advocated by Bateson (1894), Korjinsky (1899), and especially by de Vries, who, in his "mutation theory" (1901–1903) introduced the term *mutation* for large, discrete changes in the genotype. De Vries supported his views by extensive observations on mutations in the evening primrose, *Oenothera lamarckiana*.

De Vries' insistence that sudden and drastic changes, mutations, are basically different from Darwin's small or fluctuating variations proved to be unfounded. The studies of Morgan and his school on mutations in Drosophila, begun in 1909, showed that there are mutations of all magnitudes. The differences between a mutant and the parental form may sometimes be large, but they may also be so minute that refined methods are needed to detect the occurrence of the mutation at all. Mutations of every conceivable intermediate extent also occur. The mutation process supplies the raw materials from which evolutionary changes can be built.

MUTATIONS IN OENOTHERA

Lamarck's evening primrose, *Oenothera lamarckiana*, is a native of America, but de Vries found it growing as a weed in Holland and was struck by its unusual variability. In de Vries' garden it produced a number of striking mutants (Fig. 16.2). A mutant called *gigas* differed from the parental form in its large size; another, *nanella,* was a dwarf; still others differed in color, size, or shape of various parts. Much later it was discovered that what de Vries had described as mutations are actually changes of several quite different kinds. Thus, the mutant *gigas* proved to have 28 chromosomes instead of the 14 present in the parental form. It is a tetraploid, and its origin was the doubling

up of the entire chromosome complement. Some of the mutants were *trisomics* (cf. p. 197); they carried 15 chromosomes because a single chromosome of the normal complement was present three times. Perhaps only two of de Vries' mutants represented gene mutations. Others, including *nanella,* arose by a process that can be understood only in the light of the peculiar genetic properties of *O. lamarckiana* described on pages 266–267. Thus the species on which were based the observations that led to the mutation theory has since been proved to be a very peculiar organism and its "mutations" a mixture of different types of hereditary changes.

MUTATIONS IN DROSOPHILA AND OTHER ORGANISMS

In 1909 a single male with white eyes appeared in one of T. H. Morgan's cultures of a normal, red-eyed strain of *Drosophila melanogaster*. The white eye color proved to be inherited as a sex-linked recessive (Figs. 12.3 and 12.4), and a true-breeding white-eyed strain was easily established. Soon thereafter other mutants were observed in the same species of fly by Morgan and his collaborators. Since then, many hundreds of mutations have been observed among, perhaps, some 10 to 20 million specimens of Drosophila examined by competent observers. Mutations never arise gradually, becoming more and more apparent in several consecutive generations. A full-fledged mutant appears suddenly, usually as a single individual, and transmits its characters to its progeny as effectively as the parental normal type does. Apart from Oenothera and Drosophila, mutations have been observed in corn, snapdragon, mice, bread molds, man, and many other plant and animal species. The surest way to find mutants is to examine large numbers of individuals of a given species in the laboratory or in field cultures. In recent years microorganisms have proved to be unusually favorable for studies of mutation; mutants are found among bacteria, bacteriophages, and animal and plant viruses. There is every reason to think that mutants appear in all species of organisms. The traits of the pea varieties studied by Mendel doubtless had arisen through gene mutation. In fact, mutation is the only known method by which different alleles of a gene can arise.

PHENOTYPIC TRAITS CHANGED BY MUTATION
Mutants may differ from the parental strain in all kinds of traits, external or internal, morphological, physiological, or biochemical. Drosophila mutants differ in coloration or form of the eyes and the body, wings, bristles, legs, size of the body and its parts, sexual characters, fertility, longevity, serological properties, and behavior (reactions to light and gravity, courtship and mating habits). Some mutations produce *homeosis,* that is, transformation of one organ into another. Thus mutations are known that transform the antennae of Drosophila into legs, balancers into a second pair of wings, or sucking mouth parts into parts resembling those of some lower insects. In the bread mold Neurospora, mutations change the food requirements of the fungus and block certain biochemical reactions fundamental in cellular metabolism (p. 335). Bacterial mutants may lose virulence or acquire it, become resistant or susceptible to antibiotics such as penicillin or sulfa drugs and to attacks by bacteriophages, acquire or lose the ability to grow on food media with or without certain nutritive constituents. Mutations may also affect the appearance of the colonies of the bacteria grown on agar plates.

Mutations are usually named according to the traits that appear most striking to the observer. Thus, the mutants "white" and "yellow" in Drosophila differ from normal flies by having, respectively, white instead of red eyes and a yellow instead of brown body. This convention of naming mutants should not be taken to indicate that a mutant differs from the ancestral form always in one character only or even less that the gene white is a gene "for eye color" and without any other effects.

To de Vries, "mutation" meant a striking alteration of the phenotype. Some mutations are indeed drastic enough to upset the fundamental processes of embryonic or postembryonic development and thus to act as lethals. The mutations which are most useful in genetic experiments demonstrating Mendelian segregation, linkage, crossing over, and related phenomena, and which are for this reason mentioned most frequently in textbooks, produce changes sufficiently conspicuous to be recognized at sight. But some mutations are so slight that they can be detected only by the most competent and well-trained observers. Timoféeff-Ressovsky and Kerkis showed by means of specially devised experiments that such small mutations constitute, in fact, a majority of all the mutations that occur. Of course, small and large mutations are not different categories, since mutations form an uninterrupted spectrum, beginning with the most drastic ones and ending with those that are at the limit of detectability. All mutants, whether from small or large mutations, always belong to the same biological species to which the ancestral form belongs. This is true as well for those mutants in which alterations have occurred in traits that distinguish species, genera, and even higher taxonomic categories. For example, an order of insects, Diptera (flies), differs from other insect orders in, among other things, the possession of only one pair of wings. The mutant bithorax (tetraptera), in which the balancers became a second pair of wings, is still not only a fly but a member of the genus Drosophila and the species *melanogaster.*

STAGES AT WHICH MUTATIONS OCCUR
Mutation may occur at any stage in the development of the organism. If a mutation takes place in one of the mature gametes,

a single individual in the progeny will be a mutant. A mutation in one of the two daughter chromosomes formed at the first division in the fertilized egg will give an individual about half of whose body is normal whereas the other half carries the mutation. If the mutation is dominant, such an individual will be a *mosaic,* or a *fractional mutant.* Mosaics are formed also if a mutation takes place during development, the fraction of the body which shows the mutant traits being smaller the later the mutation has occurred. A mutation may affect only a single somatic cell, which, as in color variation in the endosperm of maize or in the epidermis of flowers or leaves, shows a specific difference from surrounding cells. In the larkspur, Delphinium, Demerec has found that somatic mutation in flower color occurs at rather early stages and at late stages of the development of the flower with higher frequency than in intervening stages (Fig. 16.3). Mutations in cells ancestral to the gametes, such as spermatogonia, may affect several or many gametes, resulting in the appearance of clusters of mutant individuals in the progeny.

When a group of cells is genotypically different from other cells in the same individual, a *somatic mutation* may be suspected. Therefore, one of the working hypotheses of the origin of malignant tumors is that they arise by somatic mutation. A cancer-producing mutation, on this hypothesis, changes the properties of cells in such a way that their growth and multiplication are no longer under control.

QUANTITATIVE STUDIES OF MUTATIONS

In the 1920s, Muller developed techniques for estimating the frequency of mutations. Without such techniques the detection of mutations involves a "personal equation," since some observers overlook many of the lesser mutations that attract the notice of other observers. Furthermore, since mutations arise in one gene at a time, a dominant

mutation may be detected at once, whereas a recessive may be present in heterozygous condition in a strain for many generations before it happens to become homozygous and thus apparent to the eye (see Chap. 19).

The detection of mutations obviously depends very much on the kind of observation applied. By using a microscope we have the opportunity to detect many more differences than the unaided eye can distinguish. If we confine our attention to lethal mutations, however, then we have only to detect the presence or absence of a whole category, such as males or females, among the

Fig. 16.3. Flowers of Delphinium, showing somatic mutations from rose to purple. Large areas result from early mutation, small ones from later mutation. (*From M. Demerec*)

descendants of a parent in whom the occurrence of mutation is being tested. Muller's success in measuring mutation frequency was due to his invention of an accurate method for detecting sex-linked recessive lethal mutations in Drosophila.

Fig. 16.4. The *ClB* method for detecting lethal mutations in the X chromosome in *Drosophila melanogaster.*

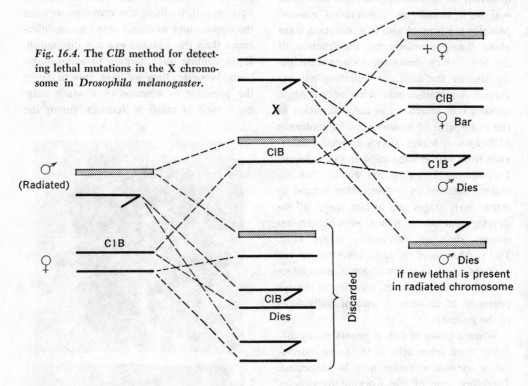

DETECTION OF SEX-LINKED MUTATIONS

Muller's *"ClB"* method makes use of an X chromosome of *Drosophila melanogaster* which contains the dominant gene Bar (*B*, narrow eyes), a recessive lethal (*l*, no expression in heterozygotes), and an inversion (*C*) which eliminates crossing over. A female carrying a *ClB* chromosome has Bar eyes. A male getting this chromosome dies on account of the lethal gene. Now, suppose that a *ClB* female is crossed to a normal male. As shown in Figure 16.4, half the male progeny will die, and the sex ratio will be about $2 \female : 1 \male$ among the survivors. Half the females will carry the *ClB* chromosome, and they can be recognized because of their Bar

eyes. If these females are tested singly, by crossing each of them to a male in a separate culture, the following results may be obtained: if the X chromosome of the original male, which was carried in the spermatozoon producing a given Bar-eyed female, was normal, the offspring will again consist of females and males in a ratio approaching 2 : 1. If, however, a spermatozoon contained an X chromosome in which a recessive lethal had arisen by mutation, the Bar-eyed female will carry a lethal in her *ClB* chromosome and another lethal in her second X, received from her father. In the offspring of such a female, half the males die because of the lethal in the *ClB* chromosome and the other half die because of the newly arisen lethal in the other X chromosome. The result is a progeny consisting only of daughters with no sons. Again, if the spermatozoon contains an X chromosome with a recessive mutant gene, the surviving sons of the particular *ClB* female that receives this spermatozoon will exhibit the phenotype of the mutation. If many *ClB* females are tested, one can determine the proportions of the spermatozoa of normal males, or of males treated with X rays, chemicals, or other agents (see Chap. 17), which contain newly arisen sex-linked mutants of various types. In recent years, another technique analogous to *ClB*, making use of the so-called "Muller-5" chromosome, has been used to measure the frequencies of mutations in the X chromosome of *Drosophila melanogaster*.

MEASUREMENT OF THE MUTATION RATES IN AUTOSOMES OF DROSOPHILA

The detection of mutants in chromosomes other than the X is more laborious but is based on the same principle. A series of crosses are made in which certain chromosomes are "tagged" by known mutant "marker" genes with easily visible external effects and by inversions that suppress crossing over. Unfortunately, such powerful tools for genetic analysis are thus far available only in some species of Drosophila. The technique used for the detection of muta-

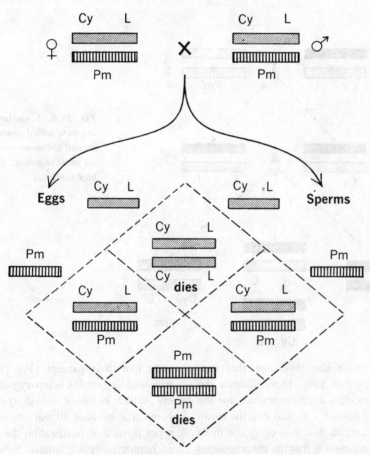

Fig. 16.5. A "balanced lethal system." Each chromosome carries a dominant marker and inversions that prevent recombination. Although half the progeny die, the strain breeds true because all the surviving offspring are like their parents.

tions in the second chromosome of *Drosophila melanogaster* is here considered as an example.

This technique makes use of a remarkable "balanced" strain of flies having the dominant mutant genes Curly (*Cy*, wings curled upwards) and Lobe (*L*, abnormal shape of the eyes) in one of their second chromosomes and Plum (*Pm*, a brownish eye color) in the other second chromosome. Both chro-

chromosomes. When *Cy L Pm* females and males are intercrossed (Fig. 16.5), three kinds of zygotes are formed. One-quarter of the zygotes have two *Cy L* chromosomes, and they are inviable because of the lethality of *Cy L*; one-quarter have two *Pm* chromosomes and they die because of the homozygosis for *Pm*; half the zygotes receive one *Cy L* and one *Pm* chromosome, and they produce viable *Cy L Pm* flies which are ex-

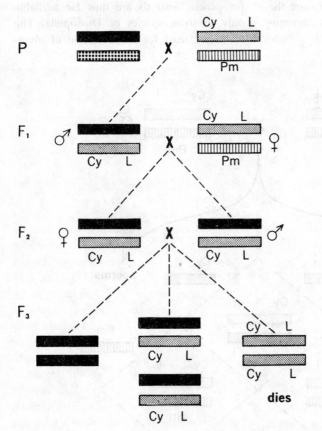

Fig. 16.6. A method of detecting new lethal mutations in the second chromosome of *Drosophila melanogaster.* (See text for explanation.)

mosomes contain also inversions that suppress crossing over (Fig. 16.5). Despite the fact that these flies are heterozygous for the three mutant genes *Cy*, *L*, and *Pm*, the strain breeds true and all flies in it carry the three mutants. The reason is that the chromosomes with *Cy L* and with *Pm* are lethal in double dose (in homozygous condition). The *Cy L Pm* flies form two kinds of gametes, half of them with *Cy L* and half with *Pm*

actly like their parents (Fig. 16.5). Such true-breeding strains heterozygous for lethals are called *balanced lethal systems.* They breed true because all but one of the genotypes formed at fertilization die on account of homozygosis for lethals. Balanced lethal systems are very useful as tools in many genetic experiments, and they occur in nature as a normal condition in some of the evening primroses, Oenothera, including

Oenothera lamarckiana, in which de Vries observed his mutations.

Suppose now that we desire to determine what proportion of the sex cells of *Drosophila melanogaster* contain newly arisen mutants in their second chromosome. The flies to be tested are crossed to the *Cy L Pm* strain (Fig. 16.6). In the F_1 progeny, every individual receives one *Cy L* (or *Pm*) second chromosome from one of its parents and a second chromosome to be tested for mutations from the other parent. Let us now take the *Cy L* flies from the F_1 progeny and cross them *singly*, each individual in a separate culture, to *Cy L Pm* flies from the original strain. In the next generation (F_2 in Fig. 16.6), there will appear *Cy L* flies that will necessarily carry the division products of *the same* second chromosome derived from a single gamete of the original parent. An F_3 generation is now obtained by intercrossing these *Cy L* flies from the same F_2 culture (Fig. 16.6). In this F_3, one-quarter of the zygotes will die on account of the homozygosis for *Cy L*. Among the surviving zygotes, two-thirds will carry the *Cy L* chromosome and the second chromosome under test, whereas one-third will be homozygous for the chromosome to be tested. If this chromosome transported any mutant gene that had arisen in the gamete of the original parent (generation P in Fig. 16.6), one-third of the F_3 flies must be homozygous for this mutant.

The method shown in Figure 16.6 can be used to detect various kinds of mutations which arise in the P generation (or which had been present in the population from which the P generation flies are taken). Suppose that the chromosome tested has acquired a recessive lethal mutation; the homozygotes in the F_3 generation will then die, and the test culture will contain only *Cy L* flies. A semilethal or subvital mutation (see p. 129) will kill a part of the homozygotes and will let others live, so that the test culture will contain more than two-thirds *Cy L* flies and fewer than one-third non-*Cy L* flies. Some mutations produce morphological or physiological changes, sterility, or behavior changes, all of which will be manifested in the non-*Cy L* flies in the F_3 generation. Similar methods have been worked out for other chromosomes of other species of Drosophila.

TOTAL MUTATION RATE IN DROSOPHILA

Mutations, or "sports," are said to be rare, but this is true only in the sense that mutation in any one gene is, as a rule, a rare event. However, most organisms have many genes, and the total frequency of mutation in all genes is substantial. The data are most abundant for sex-linked lethals in *Drosophila melanogaster*. Using the *ClB* method described above, it has been determined that on the average, about 15 per 10,000 spermatozoa bearing an X chromosome contain a newly arisen sex-linked lethal; this is a mutation rate of 0.0015, or 0.15 per cent per generation (Dubinin).

Mutations in chromosomes other than the X (autosomes) are more frequent. According to Ives, Wallace, and others who have used the *Cy L Pm* method, about 0.5 per cent of the second chromosomes of *D. melanogaster* acquire a recessive lethal mutation in every generation. The same mutation rate is probably found also in the third chromosome. Therefore, about 1.2 per cent of the gametes produced by a normal Drosophila fly carry a newly arisen lethal mutant. But, as stated above, geneticists have devoted so much attention to studying lethal mutations only because they are easiest to record accurately. Less drastic mutations, though most of them produce slight but still-perceptible deleterious changes in the organism (subvital mutations), arise more often than do lethals. Special efforts to detect these slight mutations have been made by Timoféeff-Ressovsky and by Kerkis. Slightly deleterious mutations were at least three to five times more common than lethal ones. It is, then, a rather conservative estimate that as many as 5 per cent of all gametes of Drosophila contain one or more newly arisen mutants of various kinds in each generation.

FREQUENCY OF MUTATION IN INDIVIDUAL GENES

Different genes are not equally mutable. In Drosophila, mutations to white and to vermilion eyes have appeared many times,

TABLE 16.1

Rates of spontaneous mutation in certain genes (*After Wagner and Mitchell*)

Organism and investigator	Gene	Number of gametes tested	Mutation frequency per 10,000 gametes
Corn (maize)	wx	1,503,744	0
(Stadler)	pr	647,102	0.11
	sh	2,469,285	0.012
	su	1,678,731	0.024
	i	265,391	1.06
	rr	43,416	18.2
Drosophila melanogaster	y	70,000	0.29
(Ives)	w	70,000	0.29
	lz	70,000	0.29
(Muller, Valencia, and Valencia)	ct	60,000	1.5
	v	60,000	0.3
	f	60,000	0.3

whereas many other mutants have been seen to arise only once. Corn (maize) is a very convenient material in which to detect mutations that change the visible characters of seeds on the cob. Stadler has made a study of this sort, and a summary of some of his data is shown in Table 16.1. It can be seen that the gene *r* (for color) is relatively mutable, whereas the genes for waxy (*wx*) and shrunken (*sh*) endosperm are relatively stable.

Despite the existence of such variations, it is interesting to estimate the average frequency of mutation per gene. In the giant chromosomes in the salivary glands of Drosophila (p. 190), about 7,000 stainable disks have been counted, and others have

doubtless been overlooked. On the assumption that each disk corresponds to a gene, the number of genes in a sex cell of Drosophila may be of the order of 10,000. The average mutation rate giving rise to lethal mutants is, then, about 0.00001, or 10^{-5}, per gene per generation (Dobzhansky and Spassky). It is interesting that the few human genes for which the mutation rates have been estimated mutate only slightly more often per generation than do Drosophila genes, despite the much longer generation length in man.

BIOCHEMICAL MUTANTS IN NEUROSPORA

The bread mold *Neurospora crassa* has become, together with Drosophila, one of the most extensively used materials for genetic study. It is particularly suitable for investigation of problems on the borderland of genetics and biochemistry. Beadle and Tatum (1945) invented a simple and ingenious method for detecting mutations that make the mold require the presence in its nutrient medium of chemical substances not required by the "normal" mold found in nature. Westergaard and his colleagues later worked out a method to detect reverse mutations, or changes back to the "normal" condition. The Beadle-Tatum method, described in greater detail on page 333, consists essentially in identifying strains of the mold which fail to grow unless some specific substance, such as an amino acid or a vitamin, is added to the culture medium. One mutant strain, for example, requires adenine for growth. This "adenineless" strain is maintained on a nutrient medium to which adenine has been added. Asexual spores (conidia) of this strain are then sown in large numbers (tens or hundreds of millions) on a nutrient medium *without* adenine. Such spores can give rise to successful fungus growths only if the "adenineless" gene allele has mutated back to the normal condition, thus restoring the power of the mold to grow without adenine. Counting the number of spores that grow successfully on the medium without adenine yields an estimate of the number of the mutations of the "adenineless" allele back to the normal allele of this gene. In a number of experiments the frequencies of such mutations ranged from 3 to 8 per hundred million conidia (3×10^{-8} to 8×10^{-8}).

MUTATIONS IN BACTERIA

The small size and rapid reproduction of bacteria, viruses, and other microorganisms permit the growth of millions and even billions of individuals in a single culture. This makes these lower forms of life exceptionally favorable for studies of mutation, since such studies with higher organisms are frequently handicapped by the necessity to raise prohibitively large numbers of experimental plants or animals. Bacteriologists knew for a long time that genetic changes occur in bacterial cultures. For example, bacteria cultured on certain media may be "trained" to grow on other media that were originally unsuitable for them. But the very ease and regularity with which such changes were obtained made it uncertain whether genotypic changes or merely phenotypic modifications were involved, and many bacteriologists felt inclined to interpret their observations according to Lamarckian ideas. The work of Luria and Delbruck (1943) and of Demerec and Fano (1945) placed the problem of mutation in bacteria on a new basis.

One of the commonest bacteria living in the intestinal contents of man and higher animals is the colon bacterium, *Escherichia coli*. In the same habitats bacteriophages occur which prey upon and destroy the colon bacteria. If a suspension of bacteriophage is added to a culture of the bacteria, bacteriophage particles (which are too small to be seen in an ordinary microscope but can be photographed by the electron microscope) multiply in the bacterial cells and cause their death. But an occasional bacterium survives despite the presence of many particles of phage, and from such a survivor a new strain of bacteria may be obtained which is now completely resistant to the phage. Such a strain resistant to a certain phage may remain nevertheless fully susceptible to other phage lines. However, bacteria resistant to any one line of the phage may usually be obtained by exposing susceptible bacterial cultures to the proper phage and picking up the few surviving bacteria (Fig. 16.7). Similarly, a bacterial strain that has become resistant to one phage line may acquire resistance to one or more other lines by exposure to the phages and isolation of the resistant survivors.

Off hand, these facts may be interpreted in one of two ways. First, one may suppose that mutations resistant to various kinds of bacteriophage occur in a bacterial strain from time to time regardless of whether or not this strain is exposed to the phages. In the absence of bacteriophages, such resistant mutants have no advantage over the ancestral susceptible form or have even a slight disadvantage compared to it. When exposed to bacteriophage, however, all susceptible cells succumb, and only the few available mutants resistant to the phage survive and give rise to resistant strains. Second, one might suppose that resistance is somehow induced in a few bacterial individuals by contact with bacteriophage. It is possible to test the validity of these two interpretations by a simple statistical method. If mutation to resistance takes place regardless of exposure to bacteriophage, the number of resistant mutants per culture will vary greatly depending upon when the mutation happens to occur. Their number will be large if a mutant appears early during the multiplication of the bacteria and produces many mutant cells by division but small if the mutation takes place shortly before the bacteriophage is applied. It can be shown mathematically that if the first interpretation is true, the variance (cf. p. 408) of the number of resistant cells in different cultures will be much larger than the mean number of these per culture. On the other hand, if the resistant bacteria appear only when the bacterial culture is exposed to the bacteriophage, the number of resistant cells in different cultures raised under uniform environmental conditions will be subject only to the variation due to sampling errors. As a result, the variance will be mathematically about as large as the mean number of resistant cells per culture. Tests have shown that the variance in most experiments is much greater than the mean.

It may, therefore, be concluded that resistance to bacteriophages is produced by mutations that occur in the bacteria regardless of exposure to the phages. Luria and Delbruck estimated that in their experiments the mutants occurred at a rate of about 2.45×10^{-8} per bacterium per generation.

When a large number of phage particles are added to a culture of bacteria resistant to the particular phage line, a few particles may prove to be able to attack the bacteria, and from them a new phage line may be isolated which overcomes the bacteria resistant to the original line. Luria has demonstrated that

what is involved in the appearance of new bacteriophage lines is mutation in the phage, which, again, occurs regardless of whether the bacteria are or are not resistant to the original phage line. A similar demonstration has been given by Demerec for the development of resistance in certain bacteria to streptomycin and penicillin, by Luria for resistance to sulfa drugs, and by Witkin for resistance to the killing action of ultraviolet light and X rays. The penicillin resistance is interesting, particularly because it has been found that a bacterial strain originally killed by relatively small concentrations of penicillin in the culture medium acquires resistance gradually in many generations, being able to withstand greater and greater concentrations of penicillin in the media to which it is transferred. The gradualness of this process, which appeared to be difficult to reconcile with the mutation theory, proved to be due to the fact that highly resistant bacteria strains arise by summation of several successive mutations, each of which taken separately induces only slight gains in the degree of resistance.

MUTATION IN MAN

It is no easy matter to estimate the rates of mutation for most genes in man. None of the genetic tools worked out for Drosophila or Neurospora are applicable, and recourse must be had to rather roundabout methods. The evidence comes mainly from mutants that produce hereditary diseases or abnormalities.

The sex-linked recessive disease hemophilia (see p. 148) occurs only in males and most persons afflicted with it die before reaching sexual maturity. On the average, hemophiliacs have less than a quarter as many children as their normal brothers. Haldane pointed out that, since the hemophilia genes are carried in the X chromosome, about one-third of these genes are at any given time in men and two-thirds in women in the population (since women, having two X chromosomes, are about as numerous in the population as men with their single X). Now, the hemophilia gene in men produces the disease and is consequently exposed to the risk of extinction by death; in women it is concealed by being a recessive suppressed by its dominant normal allele. Therefore, almost one-third of the hemophilic genes in the population will become

they depend on the environment. Moreover, both the total mutation rates and the rates for individual genes vary from strain to strain and are controlled by the genotype of these strains. Demerec, Neel, Ives, and others found strains of Drosophila which showed appreciably higher mutation rates than most "normal" strains, and Timoféeff-Ressovsky described two strains that dif-

TABLE 16.2
Approximate rates of mutation per million gametes of some genes in man (*After Neel and Schull*)

	Disease or abnormality	Rate
Autosomal dominants	Epiloia	10
	Achondroplasia	42
	Pelger's anomaly	80
	Aniridia	5
	Retinoblastoma	23
Autosomal recessives	Microphthalmos	15
	Albinism	28
	Color blindness (total)	28
	Infantile amaurotic idiocy	11
	Ichthyosis	11
Sex-linked recessives	Hemophilia	32

extinct in every generation. Since the frequency of cases of hemophilia does not change much with time, the supply of the hemophilic genes in the population must be kept up by new mutation. Knowing the frequency of hemophiliac males in the population, one can estimate the number of mutations needed for the replacement. Haldane's estimate is between 1 and 5 per 100,000 X chromosomes per generation (mutation frequency between 1×10^{-5} and 5×10^{-5}). For data on which other estimates are based, see page 248. A summary of some of these estimates is shown in Table 16.2.

GENETIC MODIFIERS OF MUTABILITY
The mutation rates are not permanent or constant. As will be shown in Chapter 17,

fered in the rates of production of the white-eyed mutants. More recently (1952) Giles showed that different strains of Neurospora show quite diverse mutation rates of the gene whose different alleles cause the mold to require or not to require inositol in its nutrient medium. Mutants are commoner in some strains than in others.

A most spectacular case has been studied in corn by Rhoades. The dominant allele of a gene, A_1, gives rise to a purple coloration in various parts of the plant, whereas the recessive allele, a_1, gives green plants. Under normal conditions both alleles mutate very infrequently. But in plants that carry the dominant gene Dt (Dotted, located in a different linkage group from that which carries the locus A_1-a_1), the gene a_1 mutates to A_1

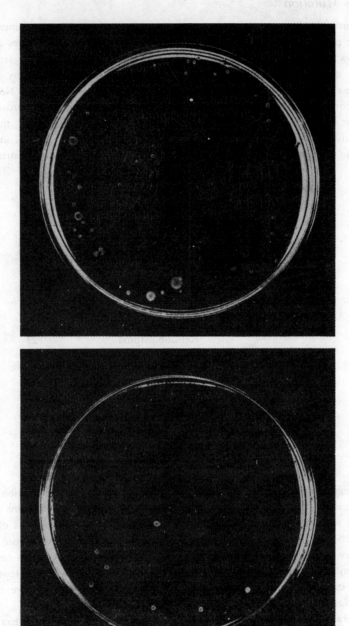

Fig. 16.7. Mutant colonies of *Escherichia coli;* below, large and small colonies; above, large and tiny colonies. The bacteria are growing on petri dishes coated with one strain of bacteriophage. Each colony type is characteristic of one clone of phage-resistant bacteria arising by mutation. (*From M. Demerec*)

so frequently that the plant has green leaves streaked with purple and seeds speckled with purple dots. The gene *Dt* has no other known effects apart from modifying the mutability of the gene a_1. The mutability of the allele A_1 is not affected by *Dt*. Dotted or streaked color patterns of some flowers have been shown by Demerec to be produced by similar unstable genes.

REVERSIBILITY OF MUTATION

The process of mutation is, in general, reversible. If a gene *A* mutates to *a*, the allele *a* may mutate back to *A*. The colon bacteria mentioned above are easily killed by the antibiotic streptomycin. However, some mutant cells survive, and from them strains may be obtained which not only grow well on streptomycin-containing media but, in fact, are unable to grow without streptomycin. Demerec and others have shown that such streptomycin "dependent" mutants may undergo reverse mutation, which makes them able to grow again on streptomycin-free nutrient media. The reverse mutation can be brought to light by placing very large numbers (hundreds of millions) of streptomycin-dependent cells on a medium without streptomycin. The few cells which multiply and form colonies (which look like those shown in Fig. 16.7) are reverse mutants to streptomycin independence.

Mutational reversion of some mutants in Drosophila has also been observed by many investigators, particularly by Timoféeff-Ressovsky. These studies also disclosed, however, a source of error which must be guarded against. One of the relatively common mutants in Drosophila changes the normal dark-red eye color to a bright vermilion red. In vermilion cultures, mutants have been observed which again have normal red eyes. However, some of these mutants did not change the vermilion allele (*v*, a sex-linked gene) back to its original state. Instead, the mutation occurred in another gene, in an autosome, the effect of which is to suppress the action of the vermilion allele. Such *suppressor* genes, the phenotypic effect of which is to cancel that of another gene, are not uncommon both in Drosophila and in Neurospora. Nevertheless, authentic reverse mutations have doubtless been observed.

PROBLEMS

16.1 How would you determine whether a variegated plant in the progeny of normal parents was due to a somatic mutation or to segregation of a gene for variegation?

16.2 Outline a scheme for utilizing an attached-X stock of Drosophila homozygous for a sex-linked recessive such as yellow body, for measuring the rate of mutation to alleles with visible effects in the X chromosome.

16.3 In the *ClB* method of determining the appearance of a new lethal mutation in the sex chromosome, why is it that the presence of a new lethal in the chromosome from the irradiated male parent does not prove lethal to this female, since she already possesses one lethal in the other chromosome?

16.4 In a balanced-lethal Beaded stock of Drosophila (p. 221), a few rare, exceptional flies with pink eyes were found. Pink proved to be due to a mutant gene in the third chromosome. Indicate how the following two hypotheses could be distinguished:

a. That a new mutation to pink has occurred.

b. That pink is due to recombination.

16.5 The average mutation rate for the 11 human genes in Table 16.2 is 26 per million. What is the probability that any person will receive in a gamete from one parent a newly mutated gene at one or more of these loci?

16.6 In a culture of Drosophila homozygous for eosin, an allele of white eye (cf. p. 114), a single fly with wild-type eye color is found.

How would you test the hypothesis that this was due to a reverse mutation? What other explanations would you consider worth testing?

16.7 In a black male mouse known to be heterozygous for the chinchilla allele of albinism, Cc^{ch}, some spots of tan color are noted. When tested by albino females ($c^a c^a$), the following progeny are observed:

black intense color   50
tan   60
albino   10

When tested by mating with albinos of the same strain, the F_1 animals give the results:

F_1 black × albino: 240 black, 230 albino
F_1 tan × albino: 303 tan, 292 albino
F_1 albino × albino: 82 albino

Suggest an explanation for these facts.

16.8 In Problem 16.7, test the agreement of the data with your proposed explanation by the chi-square method.

16.9 In testing the effect of the dominant gene Dt (cf. p. 227) on mutations from colorless, a_1, to colored A_1 aleurone, Rhoades

(Genetics, 23, p. 380) found fully colored dots of A_1 tissue with the following relative frequencies on seeds of the genotypes shown:

Genotypes	Ratio of numbers of dots
$a_1 a_1 \, Dt$	3
$a_1 a_1 a^p \, Dt$	2
$a_1 a^p a^p \, Dt$	1

What conclusions can be drawn about relative effects of Dt on mutability of a_1 and the pale allele a^p? How do you interpret the ratio of numbers of mutant spots on the three genotypes?

16.10 From pair matings of F_2 Cy L flies, each pair derived from a different P_1 as in Figure 16.6, the following flies per culture were counted:

Culture	Cy L	Wild type
1	281	142
2	210	112
3	180	0
4	199	18
5	211	105

What can you say about the second chromosomes of the 5 P_1 males?

PROBLEMS

16.4 In a balanced-lethal Beaded stock of Drosophila (p. 221), a few rare, exceptional flies with pink eyes were found. Pink proved to be due to a mutant gene in the third chromosome. Indicate how the following two hypotheses could be distinguished:

a. That a new mutation to pink has occurred.

b. That pink is due to recombination.

16.5 The average mutation rate for the 11 human genes in Table 16.2 is 26 per million. What is the probability that any person will receive in a gamete from one parent a newly mutated gene at one or more of these loci?

16.6 In a culture of Drosophila homozygous for eosin, an allele of white eye (cf. p. 114), a single fly with wild-type eye color is found.

17   INDUCED MUTATION

THE MUTATIONS observed by de Vries, Morgan, and other pioneers of genetics arose "spontaneously" in animals or plants not known to have been exposed to any *mutagen* —that is, a treatment known or suspected of being able to induce mutations. Saying that a natural event is "spontaneous" amounts, however, to admission of ignorance of its causes. For almost three decades, all attempts to induce mutations artificially were unavailing, and this was the more disconcerting since it had been recognized that the process of mutation is the fountainhead of evolution. In 1927, Muller announced that mutations are more frequent in the progeny of Drosophila treated with X rays than without such treatments. This was confirmed by Stadler in barley, and soon extended to a variety of animals, plants, and microorganisms.

The release and utilization of atomic energies in the early forties enormously enhanced the practical importance of the fact that X rays and related "penetrating," "high

energy," or "ionizing" radiations are powerful mutagens. Large numbers of people now risk being exposed to high-energy radiations used both for constructive and for destructive ends. Since a great majority of mutations are harmful to the organism (see p. 247), such exposures are liable to result, if proper precautions are not taken, in grave and even irreparable harm to the genetic endowment of mankind. In recent years a considerable amount of research has been devoted to study of the genetic effects of high-energy radiations, but many critical points still remain to be elucidated, especially the fate of the radiation-induced mutations in living populations. In the meanwhile, mutagens other than ionizing radiations have also been discovered.

MULLER'S EXPERIMENT
A summary of the results of Muller's classical experiment (1927) is given in Table 17.1. Muller treated Drosophila males with X rays, and, using the *ClB* method, tested

1,448 treated X chromosomes in the progeny of the X-rayed males for sex-linked lethal, semilethal, and visible mutations. A total of 154 lethals and semilethals appeared in the treated chromosomes; in the control experiments, 198 X chromosomes of untreated males were free of lethals and semilethals. The difference between the treated and the control chromosomes is statistically clearly significant.

ing radiations on human and other populations. It means that, as far as the genetic effects are concerned, there can be no "safe dose"; any exposure to radiation is likely to produce its share of mutations in proportion to the r units delivered.

However, mutations are induced only in the cells exposed to radiation, and not in other cells of the same body. Kerkis (1935) showed that if the body of a fly is irradiated

TABLE 17.1

Muller's experiment in induction of mutations by X-ray treatments in X chromosomes of *Drosophila melanogaster*

The t_4 dose is twice as large as the t_2 dose.

Experiment	Chromosomes tested	Mutations observed		
		Lethals	Semilethals	Visibles
Control	198	0	0	0
X rays (t_2)	676	49	4	1
X rays (t_4)	772	89	12	3

TIME-INTENSITY RULE

Careful studies have been made by Oliver, Timoféeff-Ressovsky, and others on the relation between the number of gene mutations induced and the amount of X-ray treatment given. The frequency of mutation proved to be simply proportional to the amount of X rays expressed in r units (Fig. 17.1). These are units of a physical measurement used to assess the amount of ionization produced by the passage of X rays through tissue. The same amount of X rays may, however, be given in a few seconds or minutes if the organism treated is placed close to a powerful source of radiation, or in days, weeks, and even years if the intensity of the radiation is low. The number of gene mutations produced is constant and independent both of the time and of the intensity of treatment, provided that the total r units delivered remain the same.

This rule is very important for evaluation of the dangers of the genetic effects of ioniz-

while its abdomen, which contains the sex cells, is shielded from radiation by a plate of lead, the frequency of mutation in the sex cells is no higher than in nonirradiated control flies. Conversely, if the abdomen is irradiated and the rest of the body protected, the frequency of mutation in the sex cells is as high as when the whole fly is treated. The danger of the genetic effects of radiations on human populations would be much reduced if persons who have to be exposed to such radiations had their gonads protected by cloth opaque to the radiations. Some radiation, however, is even then deflected from other parts of the body to the gonads (the "scattering" effect). Further discussion of the genetic effects of radiations on living populations will be found in Chapter 19.

EQUIVALENCE OF DIFFERENT RADIATIONS

The ionizing radiations are a part of the radiation spectrum extending from "soft" X rays (wave lengths of the order of 2 angstroms; 1 angstrom = 0.000,000,1 mm) to "hard" X rays, gamma rays of radium (wave length less than 0.01 angstroms), and to the very high energy and very short-wave-length cosmic rays. Timoféeff-Ressovsky and others have shown that all the radiations in this range which are available for experimentation are effective in inducing mutations. Moreover, they are equivalent in the sense that equal treatments measured in r units give the same output of mutations regardless of the wave length or the source

NATURAL RADIATIONS AND SPONTANEOUS MUTABILITY

Although powerful sources of ionizing radiations are mostly man-made, small amounts of such radiations are ubiquitous in nature. There are cosmic rays and traces of radio-active isotopes present in both living and nonliving matter. It is natural to ask whether these radiations may be responsible for the mutations that arise "spontaneously." Muller and Mott-Smith, as well as Timoféeff-Ressovsky, came to the conclusion that this

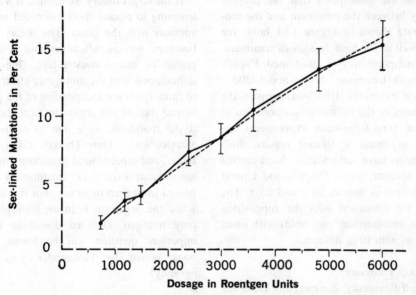

Fig. 17.1. The proportionality between the frequency of sex-linked mutations and the radiation dosages applied, in *Drosophila melanogaster.* (*After Timoféeff-Ressovsky*)

of the radiation (Fig. 17.1). The only exceptions are treatments with neutrons. Neutrons are electrically neutral particles and are not part of the radiation spectrum, but ionizations are produced in the tissue bombarded by a stream of these particles. Timoféeff-Ressovsky, Zimmer, and others have shown that neutron treatments yield only about two-thirds as many mutations as equivalent amounts of X rays in r units. The mutagenic action of neutrons needs, however, more study.

question must be answered in the negative.

Approximately 15 per 10,000 X chromosomes of *Drosophila melanogaster* acquire "spontaneously" a lethal or semilethal mutation per generation (see p. 129). Using the straight-line relationship between the mutations induced and the amount of treatment (Fig. 17.1), it can be calculated that a fly must receive about 60 r units of radiation to account for the frequency of mutations observed. Physical measurements show, however, that in nature a fly will get at most

0.045 r units during four weeks, which is a generous estimate of the average length of a fly generation. This is only about 0.075 per cent of the amount required to account for the spontaneous mutation rate. Although in man and in other long-lived organisms the proportion of mutations induced by natural radiation may be higher, a majority of mutations are produced by causes other than radiation. The origin of most spontaneous mutations remains an unsolved problem.

Of course, the foregoing computations are based on the assumption that the proportionality between the treatment and the mutation rate shown in Figure 17.1 holds for low as well as for high dosages of treatment. This assumption may be questioned. Experiments with treatments below about 200 r units are extremely laborious because the frequencies of the mutations induced are so low that very large-scale experiments are needed to obtain significant results. Such experiments have, nevertheless, been carried out by Spencer, Stern, Caspari, and Uphoff with dosages as low as 50 r and 25 r. The results are consistent with the supposition that the time-intensity rule holds with small as well as with large dosages.

THE TARGET THEORY

Timoféeff-Ressovsky, Zimmer, and Delbruck (1935), Lea (1936), Catcheside (1948), and others have proposed the so-called "target" theory of induction of gene mutations by high-energy radiations. This theory assumes that mutation is caused by a single ionization or atomic excitation within a certain volume of matter called the *target* or *sensitive* volume. The chief basis of this view is the time-intensity rule and the equivalence of different high-energy radiations. Since equal mutational effects are produced by equal amounts of ionization, it is assumed that a single radiation "hit" anywhere in the sensitive volume will always produce a given kind of mutation. If so, the dimensions of the sensitive volume may be calculated from the known frequency of a given kind of mutation per r unit (m) and the chance of ionization of an atom in the organic material (i). Thus the number of atoms a in the sensitive volume is simply $a = m/i$. This number, a, may be converted to approximate volume on the basis of physical considerations. Sensitive volumes of certain genes in Drosophila have been estimated by this method to have diameters ranging from 1 to 8 mμ. This is within the range of dimensions of organic molecules.

If the target theory were valid, it would be tempting to equate these estimated sensitive volumes with the genes. The theory meets, however, serious difficulties and is not accepted by many investigators. One of the difficulties is that the mutagenic effectiveness of radiation is not independent of the physiological state of the organism, as it should be if the mutations were due to single intra-atomic "hits." Thus Thoday, Giles, Riley, Baker, and others found that more mutations are induced if the X-ray treatment is administered in oxygen or in air than if it is given while the organism is in an atmosphere of pure nitrogen. Detailed discussion of this important question will be found in the book edited by Hollaender (see Bibliography).

INDUCTION OF CHROMOSOMAL ABERRATIONS

Gene mutations are changes localized at definite points in chromosomes, presumably in individual genes. As early as 1927, Muller showed that, apart from gene mutations, X rays produce changes of a cruder mechanical nature, namely breakages of the chromosomes. Chromosome breakages then lead to losses of chromosomes or to deficiencies, duplications, translocations, or inversions of chromosome sections (Figs. 15.1, 17.2). The mechanisms of formation of chromosomal aberrations are highly complex and remain insufficiently understood despite much work done in recent years on chromosomes of

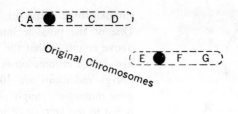

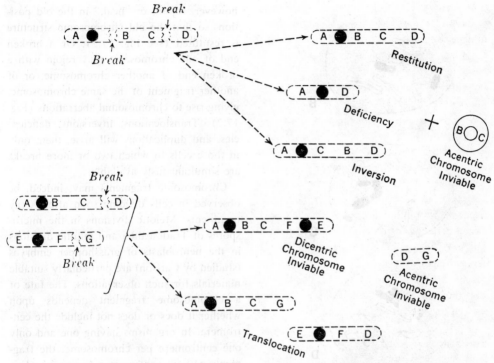

Fig. 17.2. Origin of chromosomal aberrations through chromosome breakage. The centromeres are shown as black circles.

Drosophila, of spiderwort (Tradescantia), and of other animals and plants.

Chromosomal aberrations are distinctly more frequent in the offspring of X-rayed Drosophila males than in the untreated controls. However, in contrast to gene mutations, the frequency of these chromosomal aberrations is not directly proportional to the amount of radiation measured in r units. Bauer, Demerec, and Kaufman found this frequency to grow rather as the 1½ power

or the square of the number of r units. In other words, stronger treatments produce disproportionally more chromosomal aberrations than weaker ones. Moreover, as shown particularly clearly by Sax and others in Tradescantia, short but intense treatments produce, for the same number of r units, more aberrations than do long but slow ones, and continuous treatments produce more chromosomal changes than those interrupted by periods of rest.

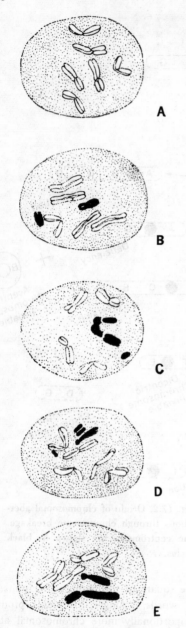

CHROMOSOME BREAKAGE AND REUNION

One of the possible interpretations of the above results is that the numbers of breakages in the chromosomes produced by high-energy radiations are, like the numbers of gene mutations, simply and directly proportional to the amount of treatment in r units. The broken ends of a chromosome may, however, rejoin, or "heal," in the old position, so that the old chromosome structure is restituted (see Fig. 17.2). Or a broken end of one chromosome may rejoin with a broken end of another chromosome, or of another fragment of the same chromosome, giving rise to chromosomal aberrations (Fig. 17.2). Translocations, inversions, deficiencies, and duplications will arise, then, only in those cells in which two or more breaks are simultaneously available.

Chromosome fragments may, indeed, be observed in cells dividing soon after X-ray treatments. Meiotic divisions in the microspores of Tradescantia and mitotic divisions in the neuroblasts of grasshopper embryos (studied by Carlson) are particularly suitable materials for such observations. The fate of a chromosome fragment depends upon whether it does or does not include the centromere. In organisms having one and only one centromere per chromosome, the fragments without centromeres (acentric) (Fig. 17.3) are unable to move properly on the mitotic spindle and are usually lost outside the daughter nuclei. When two fragments, each having a centromere, unite, the resulting dicentric chromosome may be pulled at the same time toward the opposite poles of the mitotic spindle and may be ruptured and

Fig. 17.3 Chromosomal aberrations induced by X rays in microspores of the spiderwort (Tradescantia). (A) Normal chromosomes; (B) a chromosome broken into two fragments; (C) a translocation producing a chromosome with two centromeres and a fragment without a centromere; (D) a chromosome broken in three fragments, only one of which retains a centromere; (E) a translocation involving an interchange of sections between two chromosomes, each retaining a centromere. In (B) to (E) the altered chromosomes are shown in black. (After Sax)

lost. Even more peculiar is the behavior of a fragment that includes a centromere but in which the broken end fails to rejoin with any other broken chromosome ends. Such a fragment may split into two daughter halves, and the broken ends of these halves may fuse together, giving rise to a single dicentric chromosome that may be pulled toward the opposite ends of the spindle and form a "bridge" between the daughter nuclei (Fig. 17.3). A rupture of this bridge results in two new fragments with "unhealed" broken ends, a new fusion, a new bridge formation at the next division, etc., until the chromosome is lost. This fusion-bridge-fusion cycle was first observed by McClintock in maize chromosomes.

As a result of these complex processes, a majority of cells with chromosome fragments induced by radiations are inviable. The mating of an irradiated Drosophila male to an untreated female causes the death of many eggs fertilized by his sperms. These *dominant lethals* are mostly due to inviable chromosomes introduced by the sperm. More generally, the injurious effects of X and gamma rays are most pronounced in those tissues in which many cell divisions occur and in which inviable chromosomes and fragments become lost or divide abnormally. This is the main reason for the sensitivity to radiations of cells of malignant tumors, and also the reason why an adult Drosophila becomes sterile but is not otherwise visibly injured by doses of radiation much greater than those lethal to man or other higher animals. In the body of the adult insect, cell divisions occur chiefly in the gonad.

COMPARISON OF SPONTANEOUS AND INDUCED MUTATIONS

One of the outstanding characteristics of the mutation process is its seeming irregularity: mutations occur from time to time with certain frequencies, but it is impossible to predict just what mutation, if any, will appear in a given individual at a given time. Mutations just happen. A single individual with a single gene altered by mutation appears in the offspring of a normal parent among numerous normal sibs. The cause of the mutation must be localized in a single chromosome of a single nucleus, since it did not produce similar changes in hundreds or thousands of presumably similar genes in similar nuclei in the same individual. This is one of the reasons why Timoféeff-Ressovsky and others conjectured that gene mutations stem ultimately from intra-atomic disturbances.

The mutations induced by X rays seem, in Drosophila, to represent the same assortment of changes that arise spontaneously. Such mutations as white eyes, yellow body, and cut wings have been observed repeatedly in untreated cultures, and they are also common following X-ray treatments. To be sure, chromosomal aberrations such as translocations and inversions arise, relative to mutations producing visible changes, more frequently in cultures treated with X rays than in untreated ones. In maize, Stadler and his collaborators found that X ray–induced mutations tend to be more extreme than spontaneous gene mutations, the induced ones possibly representing deficiencies of very small chromosome segments or even of single genes. One of the arguments in favor of this view is that the X ray–induced mutations are mostly irreversible; that is, they do not mutate back to the original type, as many spontaneous mutations do (see Chap. 16). The data on induced mutations in Drosophila are contradictory: Timoféeff-Ressovsky claimed to have observed reversals of X ray–induced mutations, but more recently Lefevre was unable to confirm this claim. This is one of the problems that need more study.

MUTAGENIC EFFECTS OF ULTRAVIOLET RAYS

Soon after the discovery of the mutagenic effects of X rays, Altenburg showed that ultraviolet also produces mutations in Drosophila. He irradiated Drosophila eggs instead of adult flies; this is necessary because, in contrast to X rays, the penetrating powers of the ultraviolet are so low that in adult flies the rays are mostly absorbed in the skin (integument) and fail to reach the gonads and the sex cells. This makes Drosophila rather unsuitable as experimental material, and most of the subsequent work on ultraviolet mutagenesis has been done on smaller objects, such as the pollen of the corn plant and various microorganisms. Ultraviolet is quite incapable of penetrating to the sex cells of higher animals and man, and presumably has no part in causing mutations in these organisms.

Ultraviolet radiations have much longer wave lengths than X rays (of the order of thousands of angstrom units) and carry much lower energies. The mechanics of their mutagenic action is also distinct. In contrast to X rays, ultraviolet rays of different wave lengths have quite different mutation-inducing potencies. The work of Noethling and Stubbe on irradiated pollen grains of snapdragon (Antirrhinum), of Knapp on spermatozoa of the little liverwort Sphaerocarpos, and of Stadler and Uber on corn pollen has shown that the mutagenic potency of the ultraviolet spectrum parallels the degree of absorption of the respective wave lengths in a certain class of chemical substances, namely, in nucleic acids—the greater the absorption, the higher the potency. Nucleic acids are, of course, one of the main constituents of chromosomes and presumably of genes.

The relation between the quality of ultraviolet and the number of mutations produced is complex and not well understood; the frequency of mutations rises at low dosages more or less in proportion to the amount of treatment, then rises more slowly, and may even decline with high dosages. Muller has speculated that this may be related to the phenomenon of "reactivation"

discovered by Kelner, Dulbecco, and Novick and Szilard. This phenomenon consists in partial cancellation of the effects of ultraviolet treatments by subsequent treatments with visible light or with long-wave ultraviolet. Like X rays, ultraviolet produces both gene mutations and chromosomal aberrations. However, Stadler has shown that, with doses that induce equal numbers of gene mutations, X-ray treatments produce many more chromosomal aberrations than do ultraviolet treatments. He has also shown that the ultraviolet-induced gene mutants resemble, at least in corn, the spontaneous mutants more than they do X ray–induced mutants.

This should not be taken to mean that gene mutations can be rigorously distinguished from chromosomal aberrations. Indeed, deficiencies and duplications that are too short to be seen under the microscope may be inherited as gene mutations and may be mistaken for them. Some mutations in Drosophila and in maize which were at first taken for gene mutations were later shown to be small chromosomal changes. Goldschmidt even contends that all mutations represent small chromosomal aberrations. Whether or not this is true, it is probable that what we call gene mutations are actually a residue left after the elimination of all changes for which a cytologically visible basis can be found. Now, how small the smallest chromosomal alterations are which can be identified under a microscope depends upon the organism concerned (since some forms have large and others small chromosomes), as well as upon the powers of observation of the investigator. The term "mutation" is used, then, in two senses. In the broader sense, it covers any change in the genotype, no matter how produced (that is, by a gene change or by a chromosomal aberration). In the narrower sense, a mutation is a change in the properties of a single gene.

CHEMICAL MUTAGENS

Although visible light itself is not mutagenic, Döring, Stubbe, and Kaplan observed increased mutation rates in the fungus Neurospora, in the pollen of snapdragon, and in bacteria impregnated with fluorescent substances (eosin, erythrosine, fluorescein) and then treated with visible light. Stone, Wyss, and Haas reported that mutations in bacteria may be induced by ultraviolet treatments not only of the bacteria themselves but also of the nutrient medium on which they grow. This curious effect was later shown to be due to the formation of organic peroxides in the medium under the influence of ultraviolet. Mutation induction here depends upon the action of a mutagenic chemical substance. Dickey, Cleland, and Lotz observed induction of mutations in Neurospora without irradiation by addition of several kinds of organic peroxides to the medium on which the fungus grows.

The most powerful chemical mutagens yet discovered (by Auerbach and Robson) are mustard gas, $(Cl \cdot CH_2 \cdot CH_2)_2 S$, and related compounds. In Drosophila, this substance induces both gene mutations and chromosomal aberrations, and the frequencies of the gene mutations obtained with the strongest treatments may be as high as with the strongest practicable X-ray treatments. Mustard compounds are mutagenic also in organisms other than Drosophila (Neurospora, bacteria, etc.). The list of chemical substances shown to be mutagenic becomes longer with every passing year. Perhaps the most interesting among them are ethyl urethane, the mutagenic action of which was discovered in Drosophila by Rapoport and by Vogt, formaldehyde (Rapoport, Kaplan), and ferrous and manganous salts found to be highly mutagenic in bacteria by Demerec and his colleagues. Several experimenters tested for mutagenicity substances known to be carcinogenic, that is, able to induce malignant growths; the results are,

thus far, inconclusive. The modes of action of these substances are not understood; for example, formaldehyde is mutagenic when given to Drosophila with food but nonmutagenic when injected into the fly's vagina to treat the sperm delivered at copulation (Herskowitz, Auerbach). The problems of chemical mutagenesis and the related problem of biological modifiers of mutability require further research.

DIRECTED MUTATION

Both spontaneous and induced mutations are predictable in the sense that one can determine the probability of a given kind of mutation or chromosomal change arising in a given environment. In this sense mutation is a random event, perhaps dependent on a chance encounter between an energetic particle or a free radical and a gene, the result of which is to interfere with the copying process by which the daughter gene is produced. But mutation remains unpredictable in so far as we cannot tell just what mutation, if any, will occur in a given individual, or what gene will be changed. This is a challenge for further study, and some promising leads have been discovered. We have already seen that Giles found diverse rates of certain biochemical mutations in different strains of Neurospora. He also found that these mutations were speeded up to different extents by X ray and by ultraviolet treatments. Some strains with relatively high or low spontaneous mutations became relatively more or less mutable when treated with different mutagens. Demerec and his colleagues also found that different mutagens are particularly efficient in causing certain mutations in colon bacteria.

The most striking case of directed mutation was discovered by Avery, MacLeod, and McCarthy in pneumococci, bacteria responsible for most cases of pneumonia in man. These bacteria occur in a variety of "types" differing in the composition of the gelatinous capsule surrounding the bacterial cell. The types are most easily diagnosed by exposing them to antibodies in the immune sera produced by injection of cells of a given type into a rabbit or other suitable laboratory animal; these antibodies are type-specific and kill only the bacteria of the type that induced them. "Type" is a heritable character, and a culture of a given type breeds true unless a mutation intervenes. Such mutations occur spontaneously, but they may also be induced under certain circumstances if living bacteria are kept in a medium containing an extract (vaccine) from the bodies of bacteria with capsules of different type. The remarkable thing is that the mutation occurs toward the type that furnished the extract. From such extracts a "transforming principle" has been isolated in a chemically nearly pure form that is responsible for the directed mutation. This "principle" appears to be a nucleic acid, DNA (cf. p. 375). Now, this nucleic acid is continuously produced in the body of a given type of pneumococcus, and it is able under certain conditions to become established in cells derived from other types and subsequently to go on producing more of itself.

PROBLEMS

17.1 Spencer and Stern (Genetics, 33, p. 55) report the following data for X chromosomes of *Drosophila melanogaster* tested (by a method similar to the *ClB* method in Fig. 16.4) for the frequency of lethals:

Dose	Number of chromosomes tested	Number of chromosomes with lethals
Control	73,901	72
25 r	51,907	88
50 r	31,560	77
150 r	23,195	74
500 r	6,634	87
1000 r	6,977	147
2000 r	2,755	130
3000 r	2,029	132
4000 r	1,843	182

Compute the lethal mutation frequencies and show graphically the relation between X-ray dosage and mutation rate.

17.2 Sax (Genetics, 23, p. 506) observed the following results after exposing flower buds of Tradescantia to X rays and examining the microspores for chromosomal aberrations from which the number of breaks were calculated:

Dosage	Number of chromosomes observed	Number of breaks
100 r	2538	40
150 r	1896	48
200 r	1476	70
300 r	1626	120
400 r	3384	332
600 r	1446	275
800 r	2214	796
1200 r	1086	644

Show graphically the relation between X-ray dosage and proportion of breaks. Compare the results with the graph from Problem 17.1 and suggest an interpretation of similarities and differences between the two sets of data.

18 GENES IN POPULATIONS

UP TO THIS POINT we have been concerned with the behavior of genes in individuals and in families. The rules of the transmission of heredity discovered by Mendel, Morgan, and others permit prediction of the characteristics of the progeny of some marriages and crosses. In well-studied organisms, such as Drosophila, corn, or Neurospora molds, strains with desired characteristics can be made to order. Even in man, a species quite inadequately studied as far as genetics is concerned, the probable distribution of blood groups and of certain other traits among the children can be foreseen if the characters of the mother and the father are known.

Problems of a new kind arise when we consider heredity not in families but in populations. One may ask, for example, what effects mutants induced by exposure to radiations will have on the welfare of a particular community in various generations. Or one may wish to know the frequencies of various blood groups among the inhabitants of New York, or of Peking, or of the United States, or of China, or of the world. One may ask whether the mutants induced by radiations or the blood-group genes will become more or less frequent with time or will retain their frequencies unchanged; or one may wish to devise methods of freeing a population of harmful genes or of increasing the frequencies of useful ones. Such problems belong to the field of *population genetics*. Since organic evolution is, basically, change in the genetic composition of populations, population genetics strives to elucidate also the mechanisms of evolution.

In a broad sense, a population is any assemblage of living beings. Thus we may speak of the tree population of a forest or of the fish population of a lake, meaning all the trees or fishes, regardless of species, which live in a certain place. Genetics, however, is interested more particularly in Mendelian populations of sexually reproducing and cross-fertilizing organisms. *A Mendelian population is a community of interbreeding individuals.* The most extensive Mendelian population is the species, for this sets the usual limits within which matings occur. Mendelian populations consist, then, of potential mates or of individuals connected by bonds of marriage, parentage, or common descent.

Mankind is a large Mendelian population divided into subordinate Mendelian populations, or races (see Chap. 20), which are divided further into linguistic, national, religious, economic, and other groupings within which intermarriage is more frequent than marriages between them. Note, however, that people having blood group A, or those having blue eyes, or criminals, or fat or lean people do not constitute Mendelian populations because they do not form mating groups. Organisms that reproduce exclusively by asexual means or by self-fertilization do not form Mendelian populations. Thus, there are diverse clones of bacteria and diverse pure lines of wheats or oats.

THE HARDY-WEINBERG LAW

Population genetics is founded on a principle demonstrated in 1908 independently by Hardy in England and Weinberg in Germany. This principle is concerned with frequencies of genes and of homozygous and heterozygous genotypes in Mendelian populations. As pointed out in Chapter 3, it is by no means always true that dominant genes make their carriers strong and recessives make them weak, or that dominants are frequent and recessives rare, or that dominants and recessives should appear in populations in a ratio 3 : 1 or in any other specific ratio. Hardy and Weinberg showed that in the absence of forces that change gene frequencies, populations may have any proportions of dominant and recessive traits, and *the relative frequencies of each gene allele tend to remain constant from generation to generation.* This is a law so important that its derivation must be thoroughly understood.

We know that in human populations persons who carry the gene T find weak solu-

tions of phenyl-thio-carbamide (PTC) bitter, whereas to homozygous tt persons such solutions are tasteless. Suppose that some isolated town or island is populated initially by an equal number of homozygous tasters, TT, and of nontasters, tt. Since people are usually unaware of their reaction to PTC, nobody selects his mate according to whether he or she can or cannot taste this substance. Thus marriages take place at random, and the population is *panmictic* with respect to this trait. The possible marriages are, of course, $TT \times TT$, $TT \times tt$, and $tt \times tt$. These marriages and the progenies from them may be represented by the following table:

TABLE 18.1

Fathers	Mothers	
	0.5 TT	0.5 tt
0.5 TT	0.25 TT	0.25 tT
0.5 tt	0.25 Tt	0.25 tt

The first generation will consist, therefore, of 25 per cent homozygous tasters, TT, 50 per cent heterozygous tasters, Tt, and 25 per cent nontasters, tt; since homozygous and heterozygous tasters are phenotypically alike, the population will be 75 per cent tasters and 25 per cent nontasters. The same result is obtained more simply if we consider not marriages of individuals but simply unions of gametes at fertilization. The original population evidently produces sex cells with T and t in equal numbers, a "pool" of genes in the proportion 0.5 T and 0.5 t. If the gametes combine at random, we have:

TABLE 18.2

Sperm	Eggs	
	0.5 T	0.5 t
0.5 T	0.25 TT	0.25 tT
0.5 t	0.25 Tt	0.25 tt

But what will this population be like in the next generation? Let us again consider the frequencies of gametes in the gene pool. Suppose that every individual produces equal numbers of functioning gametes. The homozygotes, *TT* and *tt,* will produce only *T* and *t* gametes, respectively; the heterozygotes, *Tt,* produce, according to the first law of Mendel, equal numbers of gametes with *T* and with *t*. The frequencies of the genes *T* and *t* in the gene pool will consequently be

T = 0.25 (from the homozygotes, *TT*)
  + 0.25 (from the heterozygotes, *Tt*) = 0.5
t = 0.25 (from the homozygotes, *tt*)
  + 0.25 (from the heterozygotes, *Tt*) = 0.5

Thus, the frequencies of *T* and *t* among the gametes giving rise to the second generation will be the same as in the preceding generation, and our population will consist in the first, second, and all following generations of

0.25 *TT* (tasters) + 0.50 *Tt* (tasters)
  + 0.25 *tt* (nontasters)

Now suppose that the tasters and the nontasters were not equally frequent among the original population of our territory but, for example, that the nontasters outnumbered the tasters in the ratio 4 *tt* : 1 *TT*. The frequencies of the alleles in the gene pool will, accordingly, be 20 per cent *T* and 80 per cent *t*, or 0.20 *T* : 0.80 *t*. The next generation will be as follows:

TABLE 18.3

Sperm	Eggs	
	0.2 *T*	0.8 *t*
0.2 *T*	0.04 *TT*	0.16 *tT*
0.8 *t*	0.16 *Tt*	0.64 *tt*

In other words, 4 per cent of the individuals will be homozygous tasters, 32 per cent will be heterozygous tasters (or a total of 36 per cent tasters), and 64 per cent will be

nontasters. The gametes from which the next generation will arise will be as follows:

$$T = 0.04 \text{ (from } TT) + 0.16 \text{ (from } Tt)$$
$$= 0.20$$
$$t = 0.64 \text{ (from } tt) + 0.16 \text{ (from } Tt)$$
$$= 0.80$$

The gene frequencies 0.2 *T* : 0.8 *t* and the phenotype frequencies 36 tasters : 64 nontasters will thus recur in every generation.

These results can be generalized as follows: let q be the fraction of *T* gametes, and 1 − q be the fraction of *t* gametes in the gene pool. Then the distribution of phenotypes in the next generation will be:

TABLE 18.4

Sperm	Eggs	
	q*T*	(1 − q)*t*
q*T*	q^2TT	$q(1-q)Tt$
(1 − q)*t*	$q(1-q)Tt$	$(1-q)^2tt$

That is, $q^2\,TT : 2q(1-q)Tt : (1-q)^2tt$.

This expression is known as the *Hardy-Weinberg* formula. Provided that we are dealing with a population (1) which is numerically so large that accidents of sampling may be ignored, (2) in which mates are chosen at random, (3) in which the mutation from *T* to *t* or from *t* to *T* is infrequent, and (4) in which the carriers of the genotypes *TT, Tt,* and *tt* are equal in survival and reproduction rates, then the frequencies of the genes *T* and *t* among the gametes will be as follows:

$$T = q^2 \text{ [from } TT] + q(1-q) \text{ [from } Tt]$$
$$= q$$
$$t = (1-q)^2 \text{ [from } tt] + q(1-q)$$
$$\text{[from } Tt] = 1 - q$$

The proportions of the gametes with *T* and *t* and the proportions of the zygotes *TT, Tt,* and *tt* in the population will be constant from generation to generation.

GENE FREQUENCY AND PHENOTYPE FREQUENCY

It is only rarely that one can determine directly the frequency of gametes that carry this or that gene (see p. 56). However, the frequency of a gene in the gene pool of a Mendelian population can be deduced from the observed frequencies of certain phenotypes. If the frequency of the homozygous recessive class in a population is known (as is the frequency of nontasters of PTC in a human population), the frequency of the recessive gene may be calculated. In the American white population, approximately 70 per cent of persons are tasters and 30 per cent nontasters. The frequency of the homozygous recessive phenotype is then

$$tt = (1 - q)^2 = 0.30$$

Therefore

$$i = (1 - q) = \sqrt{0.30} = 0.55$$

Since this gene has only two known alleles, the frequency of the dominant allele is:

$$T = q = 1 - 0.55 = 0.45$$

The frequency of homozygous tasters, *TT*, in the population should then be

$$q^2 = 0.45^2 = 0.2025, \text{ or about 20 per cent}$$

And the frequency of heterozygous tasters, whom we cannot distinguish from the homozygous tasters by their phenotype, should be

$$2q(1 - q) = 2 \times 0.45 \times 0.55 = 0.4950, \text{ or 49.5 per cent}$$

We can now make a more critical analysis of the data in Table 5.1, showing the proportions of taster and nontaster children in various types of marriages, than we could without making use of the Hardy-Weinberg law.

The marriages in which one of the parents is a taster and the other a nontaster are expected to produce different results depending upon whether the taster parent is a homozygote, *TT*, or a heterozygote, *Tt*. All the children from a marriage $TT \times tt$ will be tasters, whereas half the children from a $Tt \times tt$ marriage will be tasters and half nontasters. We have just calculated that the relative frequencies of *TT* and *Tt* tasters in the American population should be as 20 : 49.5. Therefore, the proportions of tasters and nontasters among the children of taster × nontaster marriages should be

> Tasters: $20 + (0.5 \times 49.5) = 44.7$, or 64.4 per cent of the children
> Nontasters: $0.5 \times 0.495 = 24.7$, or 35.6 per cent of the children

Table 5.1 records 761 children observed from such marriages, 483 of whom were tasters and 278 nontasters. The expected numbers are $761 \times 0.644 = 490$ tasters and $761 \times 0.356 = 271$ nontasters. The agreement between the observed and the expected numbers is quite good. The expected numbers of taster and nontaster children from taster × taster marriages can also be calculated and compared with the observed numbers given in Table 5.1.

A gene may be represented in a population by several alleles, $A, A^B, a \ldots$, the frequencies of which in the gene pool are as $p + q + r + \ldots = 1$. Assume that the population is panmictic with respect to this gene, that is, that marriages occur at random among the carriers of its different alleles (see above). The Hardy-Weinberg equilibrium assumes then the form

$$p^2 AA + q^2 A^B A^B + r^2 aa + \ldots 2pq AA^B + 2pr Aa + 2qr A^B a \ldots = 1$$

This expression is applicable, for example, to the composition of human populations with respect to the alleles of the genes giving rise to the O–A–B or to the Rh blood groups (see pp. 116 and 118).

FACTORS OF EVOLUTION

According to the pre-Mendelian conception of heredity held by Darwin and everyone else until the study of genetics elucidated this problem, the heredity of a child is a mixture, an alloy, of the heredities of his parents. If this conception were valid, a panmictic Mendelian population would become more and more genotypically uniform with time.

Consider, for example, a population in which some individuals are genotypically tall, others intermediate, and still others short. Suppose that matings occur at random, so that there is no preference or tendency for tall (or for short) individuals to mate with tall, or with intermediate, or with short ones. In such a population, whenever a tall individual mates with an intermediate or with a short one, the progeny would, according to the pre-Mendelian view, be both genotypically and phenotypically intermediate; intermediate progeny would be produced also in matings of short with intermediate and tall and in matings between intermediate individuals. After several generations, tall and short variants would disappear, and eventually the whole population would become intermediate and uniform in genotype, that is, it would become a "pure race." But Mendel's discovery showed that sexual reproduction does not lead to disappearance of the hereditary variability present in a population. In our example, the population will always contain tall, intermediate, and short individuals, because the gene combinations that give rise to individuals of different stature are equally likely to arise in all generations. Pure races cannot be formed in sexually reproducing organisms. The Hardy-Weinberg theorem demonstrates that the relative frequencies of various gene alleles in a Mendelian population tend to remain constant indefinitely. The genotypic variability present in a population is perpetuated from generation to generation.

Note, however, that we have defined evolution as change in the genetic composition of populations. If the frequencies of all genes in all populations always remained constant, evolution obviously could not occur. The Hardy-Weinberg law describes only the statics of Mendelian populations. We must also consider the dynamics of populations. There exist genetic forces that disturb the genetic equilibrium and modify the gene frequencies in populations. These forces are:

1. Mutation
2. Selection
3. Random genetic drift in small populations
4. Differential migration

In deriving the Hardy-Weinberg law, we made a number of implicit assumptions. We assumed that the genes reproduce themselves accurately. However, if a gene A_1 changes by mutation to an allele A_2, the population will be losing some A_1 and gaining A_2. This is *mutation pressure*. We also assumed that the carriers of different genotypes transmit their genes to the succeeding generations at uniform rates. But the carriers of the gene A_1 may survive more often and/or produce more progeny than the carriers of A_2. The frequencies of A_1 will then increase, and those of A_2 will decrease. Differential perpetuation of genes from generation to generation constitutes *selection*. With *artificial selection*, the differential survival or reproduction or both are caused by human choice, as in domestic animals and plants in which some individuals are chosen for reproduction or some seeds are chosen for planting. In *natural selection* the differential survival or reproduction or both are caused by different degrees of adaptedness of various genotypes to the environments in which they live.

Again, in deriving the Hardy-Weinberg law we implicitly assumed that the population is infinitely large; in populations that consist of small numbers of breeding individuals, the gene frequencies are subject to *random genetic drift*, that is, to accidental fluctuations from generation to generation. Finally, we assumed that the population is isolated, and there is no immigration or emigration of carriers of some genotypes in preference to others. *Migration,* interchange of individuals, and hybridization with genetically different populations may also increase or decrease the frequencies of some gene alleles in the gene pool.

MUTANTS IN POPULATIONS

It has been shown in the two foregoing chapters that most or all genes are exposed to greater or lesser risk of undergoing mutation. A mass of newly arisen mutants is, therefore, introduced into the populations of most living species in every generation. The problem is: what happens to these mutants after they enter the gene pool of a population? The answer is that this depends upon how fit the mutants are to survive and to reproduce in the environments in which the Mendelian population in question normally lives.

Mendelian populations are genetically so variable that no two individuals (excepting identical twins) are likely to have the same genotype. In human populations, some persons have brown eyes and others blue, some are of O and others of A or B blood type, some are inclined to be slim and others fat, some are afflicted with hereditary diseases and others free of them. This genetic variability is due to many genes being unfixed, that is, represented in the gene pool of a population by two or more alleles. The existence of a variety of alleles is ultimately due to mutation, since mutation is the only known source of the diversity of genetic materials. This does not mean, of course, that the allele for brown or for blue eyes has just arisen by mutation. Some mutants neither harm nor appreciably improve the survival ability of the carriers; in other words they are approximately neutral with respect to adaptedness to the environment. Such mutants may persist in the gene pool of the population for many generations after their origin, even indefinitely, as the Hardy-Weinberg theorem shows. The fact that no two persons and no two dogs or cats or flies are genetically alike is, then, a consequence of the accumulation of mutants in the gene pools of Mendelian populations.

Suppose that a gene A_1 mutates to an allele A_2 at a rate u per generation (for example, one newly arisen A_2 is carried in every 100,000 gametes, or u = 0.00001). The frequency, q, of A_1 will then decrease, and the frequency of A_2 will increase in every succeeding generation. If A_1 and A_2 are equally fit to survive, A_1 will eventually mutate itself out of existence and A_2 will become fixed. It is likely, however, that the mutation is reversible and that A_2 sometimes changes back to A_1, say at a rate v per generation. With mutation being reversible, both alleles A_1 and A_2 will persist in the population. Their relative frequencies will eventually reach an equilibrium when the number of A_1 changed to A_2 per generation will be just the same as the number of the genes A_2 changed back to A_1. It can be shown by simple algebra that this equilibrium will be established when $q = v/(u + v)$. Suppose, for example, that u = 0.00001, and the back mutation is v = 0.00002. The frequency of A_1 will then be 0.00002 : 0.00003, or 0.67; in other words, A_1 will be twice as frequent as A_2. It is one of the possibilities that the genetic variability of many human traits, such as the blood groups, taste blindness to PTC, and others, is maintained in the populations by this equilibrium of opposing mutation rates.

NATURAL SELECTION

Most mutants that arise in natural or artificial populations are decidedly harmful to the organism; in fact, some are complete lethals. The mutation process, nevertheless, unrelentingly generates a supply of these harmful mutants and introduces them into the gene pools of populations. The accumulation of harmful mutants, of hereditary diseases, is opposed by selection.

Darwin's theory of *natural selection* is based on the obvious fact that only a part, and often a very small part, of the progeny of any species survive and become parents of the next generation, and that different parents produce different numbers of surviving offspring. The population of a species may, however, include genetic variants, some of which are more and others less well adapted to survive in a given environment. The better-adapted variants will, then, constitute a greater proportion of the survivals than the less well adapted ones. The incidence of the former will increase, and of the latter decrease, in the succeeding generations. *Artificial selection* is a process similar to natural selection, except that the variants that leave the greater progeny are chosen by man rather than by the general environment.

The theory of selection may be restated very simply in terms of population genetics. In the demonstration of the Hardy-Weinberg theorem we assumed that the genotypes TT, Tt, and tt are equally efficient in the transmission of their genes to the next generation —in other words, that their carriers survive and reproduce at similar rates. But suppose that the recessive, tt, produces only 99 surviving offspring for every 100 produced by the dominants, TT and Tt. The frequency of the allele T will then increase, and of t decrease, with every generation. We may say that the *adaptive value* (also called *selective value* or *Darwinian fitness*) of the TT and Tt genotypes is 1.00, whereas that of tt is 0.99, or else that the genotype tt is opposed by a *selection coefficient,* s $= 0.01$. The selection coefficient is zero when the genotypes concerned survive and reproduce equally well. When a genotype is completely lethal or causes complete sterility, the selection coefficient s $= 1$ and the adaptive value w $= 1 - s = 0$.

GENETIC DEATH

To most of the nineteenth-century evolutionists, natural selection meant the "survival of the fittest" in the "struggle for existence." These emotionally loaded phrases have been often misused for political propaganda purposes. A less spectacular but more accurate statement is that carriers of different genotypes transmit their genes to the succeeding generations at different rates. There may occur a differential mortality of different genotypes (which is the same as saying that the carriers of these genotypes have differential viabilities), or they may cause greater or lesser fecundity or differences of other types at any of the various stages of the life cycle. The "fittest" is nothing more remarkable than the producer of the greatest number of children and grandchildren. The "struggle" is usually nothing like physical combat; rather, it is doing one's best to avoid combat and making the best provisions for the welfare of one's progeny.

A deleterious mutant is said to be opposed by natural selection; this means that the mutant allele is perpetuated from generation to generation less efficiently than the normal allele of the same gene. It is obvious that a deleterious mutant will be able to persist in the population for a smaller number of generations than a neutral mutant. Muller said that a deleterious mutant will sooner or later be eliminated by "genetic death." This may also sound more drastic than the situation warrants, for a genetic death often produces no cadaver. A mutant suffers genetic death if it is transmitted to one child fewer than its normal allele. But, with this reservation, it is perfectly true that a deleterious mutant gene introduced into the gene pool of a population will, sooner or later, have to be taken out—by "genetic death."

Moreover, and this may seem a paradox, an only mildly deleterious mutation, a subvital one that weakens its carriers only slightly, will produce a genetic death just as surely as a complete lethal, say a fatal hereditary disease. A subvital mutant will persist in the gene pool of the population for, on the average, a greater number of generations than will a lethal mutant, but it will be removed sooner or later.

EQUILIBRIUM BETWEEN MUTATION AND OPPOSING SELECTION

Natural selection opposes the spread in populations of deleterious mutants. Nevertheless, a certain number of deleterious mutants of various kinds are introduced into the gene pool of a population in every generation. A certain number of such mutants are also eliminated in every generation by genetic death. What will be the result of the joint action of these opposing processes? So long as more mutants are produced than eliminated, the frequency of the mutant genes will evidently increase; if elimination is greater than mutation, the mutants will become less frequent; when the numbers produced just balance the numbers eliminated, there will be established an *equilibrium*. The population will at all times carry a "load" of deleterious mutants; the magnitude of this load will be determined by the equilibrium frequencies of these mutants.

Suppose that a dominant allele arises by mutation at a rate u per generation and is opposed by selection at a rate s. The equilibrium frequency of the mutant, q, will be simply u/s. If the dominant is lethal (s = 1) and shows full penetrance, the number of cases of the disease will equal the number of the mutants produced, q = u. This is approached by retinoblastoma, the lethal disease mentioned on page 129. Another interesting example is achondroplastic dwarfism in man (see p. 227). Although the health of the dwarfs is not much affected, the data collected by Mørch in Denmark show that the dwarfs have only 9.8 per cent as many children as do their nondwarf brothers and sisters. The selection coefficient opposing this form of dwarfism is, then, s = 1 − 0.098 = 0.902. The rate of mutation which produces this form of dwarfism can be deduced from the fact that, again in Denmark, 8 achondroplastic babies were born among 94,075 babies from normal— that is, nonachondroplastic—parents. This makes u = 8/(2 × 94,075) = 0.000042, with

a large observational error. If we nevertheless substitute these values in the above formula, we get u/s = 0.000,047, or approximately 5 genes for dwarfism per 100,000 gametes. This means about 10 dwarfs per 100,000 persons, which is about the right frequency. No exact statistical data for this type of dwarfism seem to be available.

The situation is different with recessive mutants. When recessive mutants do not incapacitate the heterozygous carriers to any appreciable extent, they will accumulate in the population until enough homozygotes are produced and then suffer genetic death. The equilibrium value for a harmful recessive will, accordingly, be $(1 - q) = \sqrt{u/s}$. For a recessive lethal (s = 1) with complete penetrance, this value reduces simply to the square root of the mutation rate, $\sqrt{u}$. Note, then, that with similar mutation rates, deleterious recessives will have higher equilibrium values than deleterious dominants. In other words, a population will carry a much greater load of recessive than of dominant mutants giving rise to various diseases and malformations.

DELETERIOUS GENES IN NATURAL POPULATIONS OF DROSOPHILA

If one collects a sample of some dozens or hundreds of individuals of a species of Drosophila in their natural habitats, the flies do not appear particularly variable; in fact, they seem much less so than would an equal number of men or cats or dogs, at least to our eyes. Clear-cut mutants such as are used in the genetic experiments described in this book are exceedingly rare among flies in the state of nature. At one time some sceptics contended on this basis that mutants are purely laboratory products. Chetverikov pointed out in 1926, however, that it is not enough merely to look at flies, even under a microscope, to detect the mutants among them. Heterozygotes for recessive mutants may appear normal. Experiments must, then, be so arranged that flies are obtained which carry in double dose genes and chromosomes that were present only in heterozygous condition in wild flies.

The technique described in Chapter 17 for the detection of newly arisen mutants can be used as well to detect recessive mutants concealed in a natural population. Flies collected in nature are crossed to laboratory flies with suitable gene "markers," and further crosses are made as shown in Figure 16.6 to obtain flies carrying in duplicate, or homozygous for, certain chromosomes present in the original flies only in heterozygous condition. Natural populations of several species of Drosophila have been so analyzed by Dubinin and his collaborators in Russia, Spencer, Ives, Dobzhansky, and others in the United States, Pavan and others in Brazil, and still others. In every case a remarkable situation is revealed. Natural populations are replete with deleterious recessive mutants concealed in the wild flies in heterozygous condition with their normal alleles. Table 18.5 shows the percentages of the chromosomes in two closely related species of Drosophila which carry various kinds of mutant genes.

Normal, healthy, vigorous Drosophila flies were collected from their natural habitats. And yet, Table 18.5 shows that between a third and a fourth of each kind of chromosome in their gene pool carry genes that kill the flies if they become homozygous. Between 41 and 98 per cent of the chromosomes that are not lethal or semilethal are perceptibly deleterious (subvital) when homozygous, and a good many chromosomes make the homozygotes sterile as females, as males, or (more rarely) in both sexes.

Consider that every individual carries a pair of second, of third, and of fourth chromosomes. The frequencies of various kinds of recessive mutants being as shown in Table 18.5, it is quite certain that a great majority of Drosophila flies in nature harbor one or more recessive lethal, semilethal, subvital, or sterility genes in their genotypes. And these are "normal" flies, well-adapted for the "struggle for existence"! Note that individuals that carry two lethal-containing chromosomes will usually survive, because in most instances the two lethals will be non-allelic, the effects of each suppressed by that of its dominant allele, making the fly viable.

DELETERIOUS GENES IN POPULATIONS OTHER THAN DROSOPHILA

Table 18.6 shows the percentages of individuals in some varieties of corn which are heterozygous for various kinds of recessive defects, many of them lethal in homozygotes. For example, if an individual is heterozy-

---

TABLE 18.5

Percentages of the chromosomes in natural populations of *Drosophila pseudoobscura* and *Drosophila persimilis* which contain recessive genes for various kinds of abnormalities (*After Dobzhansky and Spassky*)

Species	Chromosome	Lethal or semilethal	Subvital	Female sterility	Male sterility
Pseudoobscura	Second	33	93	11	8
	Third	25	41	14	11
	Fourth	26	95	4	12
Persimilis	Second	25	84	18	13
	Third	23	74	14	16
	Fourth	28	98	18	8

TABLE 18.6

Percentages of individuals heterozygous for various recessive defects encountered in some varieties of maize (*Data of M. M. Rhoades*)

Variety	White seed-lings	Vi-res-cent seed-lings	Yel-low seed-lings	Glossy seed-lings	Pale green seed-lings	Dwarf seed-lings	Striped seed-lings	De-fec-tive endo-sperm	Lig-ule-less	Mis-cel-lane-ous
Hays Golden	12	46	3	3	5	2	3	23	1	3
Reid Yellow Dent	14	66	9	1	2	—	1	5	—	2
Pride of Saline	28	39	6	2	—	2	2	11	—	9
Golden Glory	15	40	1	4	17	—	1	20	—	3
Woodburn Dent	4	34	—	4	2	—	—	8	10	34
Midland Yellow Dent	5	62	—	2	3	—	2	9	—	10
Silver King	11	64	3	2	5	—	—	11	—	5

gous for a recessive gene producing white seedlings, about one-fourth of the seedlings in its progeny obtained by self-pollination are white. Some of the genes found (white and yellow seedlings, defective endosperm, and germless seeds) are lethal when homozygous, whereas others (virescent, pale-green, and dwarf seedlings) may be classified as semilethals.

Although no exact data on the incidence of deleterious recessive genes are available for human populations and for populations of other organisms, it is certain that the commonness of concealed harmful genes found in Drosophila and in corn is a general phenomenon in cross-fertilizing animals and plants. Evidence of this in man is provided by the fact, among others, that the incidence of various recessive defects and diseases is higher in the progeny of marriages between cousins and other close relatives than in the general population. Animal and plant breeders are also familiar with "freaks," "rogues," and "monstrosities" appearing in progenies of matings between close relatives (this problem is discussed further in Chap. 19).

SELECTION AGAINST DOMINANT DEFECTS

It is natural and proper to inquire whether anything can be done to diminish the load of mutations which human populations carry. Plant and animal breeders have used selection as a powerful tool to alter the characteristics of agricultural and other domesticated species in conformity with man's needs and desires. *Eugenics* is a movement which aims to improve the genetic endowment of human populations by scientifically directed selection. Thus the purpose of negative eugenical measures would be to diminish the incidence of undesirable traits by discouraging the procreation of carriers of certain genes; and positive eugenics would encourage the carriers of desirable genotypes to assume the burdens of parenthood. Let us, then, consider how selection might act upon harmful mutant genes in human and other populations.

An undesirable and fully penetrant dominant gene may, theoretically, be eliminated from a population in one generation if all persons who carry this gene abstain from having children. If, for example, all achondroplastic dwarfs were sterilized by a surgical operation or otherwise debarred from parenthood, the next generation would be free of this malformation, except for the new achondroplastic mutants that might arise. However, as we have seen, the reproductive efficiency of these dwarfs is, anyway, only about one-tenth of that of normal people; therefore, sterilization of all achondroplastics would produce only a very small decrease in the frequency of this form of dwarfism in the population. Dominant mutants which kill or sterilize their carriers destroy themselves automatically. Unfortunately, this does not mean that they are about to disappear from the world, because new crops of them continuously arise by mutation.

Selection against dominant defects will succeed in diminishing their incidence chiefly if the proportion of newly arisen mutants among the carriers of the defect is low. This will be the case with relatively mild defects or with grave ones that manifest themselves in middle or old age. We have already discussed Huntington's chorea in man, a very serious disease that often appears after its carriers have become parents (Table 10.2). There are two possible ways to make Huntington's chorea rare. First, methods may conceivably be discovered to diagnose the presence of the gene responsible for the disease in young carriers before its symptoms have appeared. These carriers might, then, refrain from parenthood. Secondly, although only half the children of a parent heterozygous for Huntington's chorea inherit the mutant gene, all these children may abstain from the risk of transmitting the defect to future generations.

SELECTION AGAINST RECESSIVE DEFECTS

In Drosophila, the mutants that arise are more often recessive than dominant to the original or "normal" condition. Most likely this is true also in man, although actually more dominant than recessive traits are recorded in medical and genetic literature.

This may be due to the greater facility of discovering the hereditary basis of a dominant than of a recessive trait. A fully penetrant dominant trait never "skips" a generation in a pedigree, whereas a recessive may appear so sporadically that the trait may not be recognized as conditioned by heredity at all.

Let us, then, consider a recessive human trait such as albinism. Although this trait is only mildly deleterious, it is interesting to see what effects selection against such a trait might have. In the English population, about 1 person in every 20,000 is a homozygous albino. The frequency of albinos is, thus, 0.00005. According to the Hardy-Weinberg formula, the frequency of a homozygote in a panmictic population equals the square of the gene frequency. Therefore, $(1 - q)^2 = 0.00005$, and $1 - q = \sqrt{0.00005} = 0.007$. In the gene pool of the English population, the gene for albinism has a frequency of about 0.7 per cent and its normal allele about 99.3 per cent ($q = 0.993$). At equilibrium, the heterozygotes in the English population will have the frequency $2q(1 - q) = 2(0.007 \times 0.993) = 0.0138$, or 1.38 per cent. The heterozygotes, who are themselves normally pigmented, are thus 276 times more frequent than the homozygous albinos ($0.0138 : 0.00005 = 276$).

In general, the less frequent a recessive gene in a population, the more strongly are the homozygotes outnumbered by heterozygotes. Since heterozygous carriers are more numerous than recessive homozygotes, selection against a recessive trait is less effective than that against a dominant trait. Suppose that recessive homozygotes are destroyed or sterilized generation after generation ($s = 1.00$, complete selection). If the frequency of the recessive gene in the gene pool of a population is initially $1 - q = 0.5$, the population will consist, according to the Hardy-Weinberg formula, of 25 per cent AA, 25 per cent aa, and 50 per cent Aa. The heterozygotes are, then, twice as numerous

TABLE 18.7

Effects of complete selection against a recessive trait

Generations	Gene frequency (1 − q)	Recessive homozygotes %	Heterozygotes %	Dominant homozygotes %
1	0.500	25.00	50.00	25.00
2	0.333	11.11	44.44	44.44
3	0.250	6.25	37.50	56.25
4	0.200	4.00	32.00	64.00
5	0.167	2.78	27.78	69.44
9	0.100	1.00	18.00	81.00
10	0.091	0.83	16.53	82.64
20	0.048	0.23	9.07	90.70
30	0.032	0.10	6.24	93.65
40	0.024	0.06	4.76	95.18
50	0.020	0.04	3.84	96.12
100	0.010	0.01	1.96	98.03

as the homozygotes (Table 18.7). If all recessive homozygotes are prevented from reproduction, the recessive genes carried in the heterozygotes are still passed on to the next generation. As shown in Table 18.7, the frequency of the recessive gene in the gene pool of the next generation will be 0.33, and the frequency of recessive homozygotes will have dropped from 25 per cent to 11.11 per cent.

This is good progress. But notice that the heterozygotes are now already four times as frequent as the homozygous recessives. After 7 more generations of total selection against the recessive trait, the gene frequency drops to $1 - q = 0.1$, and the frequency of recessive homozygotes to just 1 per cent of the population, the heterozygotes being 18 times

more frequent (Table 18.7). To depress the frequency of recessive homozygotes to 0.01 per cent (twice the frequency of albinism in the English population), 90 more generations are needed.

The selection against a recessive trait may, however, be only partially effective, because the gene is not lethal when homozygous (in natural selection), because only some of the recessive homozygotes show the phenotypic trait by which they may be identified, or, finally, because some homozygous individuals escape sterilization. Table 18.8 shows the effects of various degrees of selection in a population that initially contains 1 per cent of homozygous recessive individuals (that is, the initial gene frequency being 0.1). With complete selection (s = 1.0), 10 generations

TABLE 18.8

Effects of partial selection against a recessive trait on the frequency in per cent of individuals homozygous for the recessive gene

Generations	s = 1.0.	s = 0.50	s = 0.10	s = 0.01
1	1.00	1.00	1.00	1.00
10	0.25	0.46	0.84	0.98
20	0.11	0.26	0.71	0.97

are needed to cut the frequency to one-quarter of its former value and 20 generations to reduce it to 0.11 per cent. If the gene is semilethal, or if selection misses half the homozygotes (s = 0.5), 20 generations are needed to reduce the frequency of homozygous recessives to about one-quarter of its former value. With selection s = 0.01, 20 generations bring a reduction only from 1 per cent to 0.97 per cent. Many hereditary diseases and defects in man are due to recessive genes each of which, taken separately, is rare, although they may be very frequent in the aggregate. Reducing the frequency of these afflictions in the population by means of sterilization or similar measures directed against rare homozygotes would be a very slow process.

PROBLEMS

18.1 The frequencies in per cent of the blood-group alleles in a Scottish population were computed to be I^A, 20.62; I^B, 7.56; i, 71.83. What are the expected phenotype frequencies in this population, on the assumption of random mating?

18.2 In Problem 18.1, the phenotype frequencies actually found were: 1337 O; 894 A; 309 B; 70 AB. Test the agreement of these frequencies with those expected, using the chi-square method. Is the assumption of random mating justified?

NOTE: Three independent values, N, frequency of I^A, and frequency of I^B, are obtained from the four observed values (the frequency of i is 100 per cent − I^A − I^B). Hence χ^2 has 4 − 3 = 1 degrees of freedom.

18.3 In a Chinese population, 99 per cent of all persons tested were Rh-positive (D+, cf. p. 118). What are the frequencies of the three genotypes *DD, Dd,* and *dd* expected on the assumption of random mating? What proportion of matings in this population would be subject to the risk of having a baby with erythroblastosis due to *D* incompatibility?

18.4 Carry out the same computations as in Problems 18.3 for the white population of New York City (85 per cent Rh+) and for Spanish Basques (75 per cent Rh+).

18.5 What would you expect to be the direction of change in frequency, with time, of the alleles *D* and *d* in the three populations in Problems 18.3 and 18.4? Consider only the effects of erythroblastosis foetalis.

18.6 From the data in Table 16.2, compute the equilibrium frequency of the gene for infantile amaurotic idiocy, a complete lethal, in a large random-mating population.

18.7 In Drosophila, if a single white-eyed female is crossed with a red-eyed male and the F_2 is allowed to interbreed freely in large numbers, what will be the appearance of the F_3 as to eye color, assuming equal viability and fertility of all genotypes?

18.8 Repeat the computation of Problem 18.7 for an F_3 population descended from a single white-eyed male crossed with a homozygous red-eyed female.

18.9 If mating is at random and red-green color blindness does not affect survival or fertility, what should be the proportion of color-blind women in a population at equilibrium in which 8 per cent of the men are color-blind?

18.10 Assuming an initial frequency of 0.5 per cent of hemophilia among males at birth, and assuming that no male with hemophilia lives to transmit the gene, what should be the frequency of hemophilia in males at each generation after 1, 2, . . ., 5 generations of random mating?

19 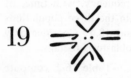 CROSSING, SELFING, INBREEDING, AND HETEROSIS

REPRODUCTION IS by far the most important biological function that any living species has to perform. The only alternative to adequate performance of this function is extinction. No wonder, therefore, that a great variety of reproductive mechanisms have developed and become perfected in the process of evolution. Most widespread, apparently because it is most successful, is sexual reproduction. The success of this type of reproduction is probably due to the fact that it results in gene recombination, and gene recombination furnishes the raw materials among which natural selection picks out the adaptively most suitable genotypes (see Chap. 20). In turn, sexual reproduction appears in a great variety of forms—separation of sexual functions in males and females or hermaphroditism, sex determination by special chromosomes or by females being diploid and males being haploid, crossing of individuals not closely related, inbreeding, or self-fertilization (see Chap. 22). Some organisms, however, reproduce asexually, by simple fission of the body of the parent, or

254

by buds, roots, runners, tubers, or spores. In some plants and animals evidently descended from sexually reproducing ancestors, the sexual process has degenerated and has been replaced by parthenogenesis or apogamy. Finally, two or more of these reproductive mechanisms may coexist in the same organism and may be used alternately or under different circumstances.

The reproductive biology of every living species has been shaped in the process of evolution, and, as a general rule, deviations from the historically established method of reproduction are likely to be harmful. Particularly interesting and important among such deviations is inbreeding in normally cross-fertilizing species.

EARLY WORK ON INBREEDING

Most human societies prohibit incest. This prohibition is biologically sound, although there is some doubt as to whether it arose from a knowledge of the undesirable consequences of inbreeding (mating of close relatives). Many of the pharaohs of Egypt married their sisters, and history does not record any harmful effects of this practice. Cousin marriage is still very common in many countries. Breeders of domestic animals and plants were aware for a long time that inbreeding often leads to degeneration of the progeny. Nevertheless, a valuable stallion or bull may be mated to his own sisters or which can also be self-pollinated. Darwin, as well as several American plant breeders (Beal, 1880, Sanborn, 1890, McClure, 1892, and others), noted that selfed progenies of corn produce low yields of seeds and do not grow tall, whereas crossing of inbred lines leads to restoration of normal vigor. This was amply confirmed in the experiments of

Fig. 19.1. Heterosis in maize followed by decline in height after inbreeding. Representative plants of the two parent strains at left, followed by average plants from the F_1, F_2, . . ., F_3 generations of inbreeding toward the right. (*From Jones*)

daughters; pedigrees of race horses and cattle show a high degree of consanguinity (descent from parents that are relatives).

Koelreuter (1766), Knight (1799), Naudin (1865), and other pioneer experimenters noted that hybrids between races and species of plants are often "luxuriant," that is, larger than either parent. One of the last works of Darwin (1876) was an experimental study of the influence of inbreeding and crossbreeding on vigor. He concluded that "cross-fertilization is generally beneficial and self-fertilization injurious," but he also recorded many exceptions to this rule.

INBREEDING AND HETEROSIS IN CORN

Corn, *Zea mays,* is one of the plants which are normally cross-pollinated in the field but

G. H. Shull and East, begun independently in 1905. The very first generation coming from selfing is inferior to the parental crossbred variety both in the size of the plants and in the yield (Table 19.1 and Fig. 19.1). Subsequently, with further selfing, the deterioration continues for several generations. Many inbred lines become so weak that they are difficult to propagate and are lost or discarded. With the remainder, a point is reached when inbreeding has no further deleterious effects. However, intercrossing the inbred lines restores the vigor in the very next generation following the cross. Shull proposed the word *heterosis* to describe this restoration of the normal crossbred, hybrid vigor in the progeny of crosses between inbred strains.

HYBRID CORN

The idea of exploitation of heterosis by planting F_1 hybrid seeds obtained by crossing inbred lines was propounded by Shull in 1910. The difficulty in practice was that most inbred lines are so infertile that obtaining from them enough seeds for commercial plantings was prohibitively expensive. Jones (1917) overcame this by the double-cross method (Fig. 19.2). Four inbred lines, A, B, C, and D, are intercrossed in pairs: A × B and C × D. The resulting hybrids are vigorous and fertile; when interplanted in alternate rows, one of the hybrids is "detasseled" by removal of the male inflorescence; its seeds are then quadruple hybrids, ABCD.

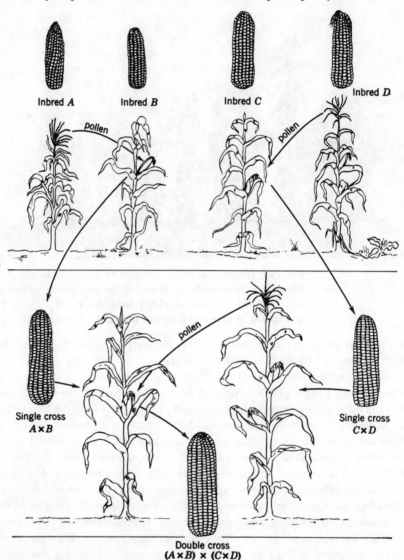

Inbred A   Inbred B   Inbred C   Inbred D

pollen   pollen

pollen

Single cross A × B   Single cross C × D

Double cross (A × B) × (C × D)

Fig. 19.2. The double-cross method of utilizing heterosis for the improvement of yield in corn. (*Reprinted by permission from Dobzhansky, "Genetics, Evolution, and Man," John Wiley & Sons, Inc., New York, 1955*)

The average yield of intercrosses between many inbred lines is about as high as that of the crossbred parental varieties from which these lines were isolated. But the hybrids between some of the inbreds are exceptionally high-yielding, and they are the ones utilized. The inbred lines that produce high-yielding hybrids are said to possess a good *combining ability*. Large-scale plantings of hybrid corn were started in the United States particularly after 1935, and at present almost the whole corn acreage in the Corn Belt is planted

TABLE 19.1
Yield, in bushels per acre, in three inbred lines isolated from the same cross-pollinated variety and propagated by selfing for thirty generations (*After Jones*)

The parental variety yields about eighty-one bushels per acre.

Generations	Line 1–6	Line 1–7	Line 1–9
0	81	81	81
1–5	64	51	41
6–10	45	36	34
11–15	38	34	26
16–20	22	24	14
21–25	20	21	13
26–30	24	18	9

in hybrid corn. The improvement of the yield has been spectacular, amounting to 30, 40, and even as much as 50 per cent. Hybrid-corn programs have been started in most corn-producing countries of the world; that carried out by Wellhausen and his colleagues in Mexico with support from the Rockefeller Foundation appears to be particularly successful.

MUTATIONAL HETEROSIS

Although hybrid corn represents the most important practical application of genetics to date, the genetic mechanisms that bring about heterosis are by no means completely understood. Bruce (1910), Jones (1917),

and others realized that the restoration of vigor in hybrids between inbred lines would follow if these inbreds were homozygous for *different*, nonallelic, deleterious recessive genes. In the hybrids, the deleterious effects of these recessives are concealed by their favorable dominant alleles.

In terms of population genetics, this hypothesis can be stated more meaningfully as follows. The mutation process constantly generates mutants most of which are deleterious to their carriers. As shown in Chapter 18, dominant and semidominant mutants are eliminated relatively rapidly from the population by natural selection. On the contrary, recessive mutants are temporarily sheltered from elimination by their concealment in heterozygotes. Therefore, normally cross-fertilizing populations carry great loads of concealed deleterious recessives (see Tables 18.5 and 18.6).

The effect of inbreeding is to increase the proportion of homozygotes in the population above that expected according to the Hardy-Weinberg formula in a panmictic population. Suppose that we have an F_2 generation of a cross between two varieties of corn differing in one gene, *A-a*. The Mendelian segregation gives plants in a ratio approaching $25\ AA : 50\ Aa : 25\ aa$, in other words, 50 per cent of homozygotes and 50 per cent of heterozygotes. Suppose now that all these plants are selfed. The entire progeny of the homozygotes remain homozygous, but half the progeny of the heterozygotes are still heterozygous and the other half homozygous. Therefore, the first inbred generation will consist of the genotypes in a ratio of about $37.5\ AA : 25\ Aa : 37.5\ aa$. Another generation of selfing will give $43.75\ AA : 12.5\ Aa : 43.75\ aa$, the next $46.87\ AA : 6.25\ Aa : 46.87\ aa$, etc. In other words, selfing cuts the proportion of heterozygotes to one-half of what this proportion was in the preceding generation. This effect of continued self-fertilization had already been clearly recognized by Mendel (cf. Appendix, p. 427).

Selfing is, of course, the most extreme form of inbreeding and is possible only in some hermaphrodites. Milder forms of inbreeding, mating between brothers and sisters, first cousins, second cousins, etc., also lead to progressive homozygosis, though much more slowly than self-fertilization (Fig. 19.3).

The great load of deleterious recessive mutants present in a normally crossbred pop-

as shown on page 251, more efficient in controlling the fitness of the dominant than of the recessive gene alleles present in a population.

An apparent objection to his hypothesis of the origin of heterosis is that inbreeding should be at least as likely to lead to homozygosis for vigorous dominant alleles as for the weak recessive ones present in the initial

Fig. 19.3. Changes in the per cent of homozygous offspring from continuous matings with different degrees of inbreeding. (*After Wright*)

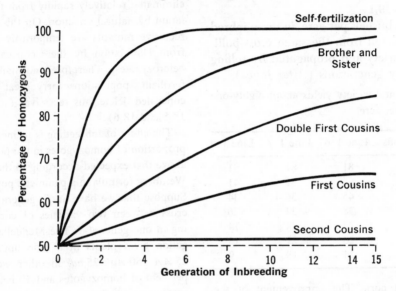

ulation is, as we know, mostly concealed in vigorous heterozygotes. This load is felt more and more upon inbreeding, because inbred lines become more and more homozygous. Different inbred lines are, however, likely to become homozygous for *different* deleterious recessives harbored in the original crossbred population. Suppose, for example, that one inbred line has the genes *aaBB* and the other *AAbb*. Crossing the inbred lines restores the heterozygous condition, *AaBb*, and restores the normal vigor. It is not that dominant genes are inherently good and recessives bad; the origin of hybrid vigor lies rather in that natural selection is,

crossbred population. Jones (1917) took care of this objection by supposing that every individual in crossbred populations of such species as corn carries several deleterious recessives linked in the same chromosome. For example, assume that one chromosome of a pair carries the alleles *AbCdEf* and the other *aBcDeF*, the small letters standing for the deleterious recessives and capitals for the dominants. To get a chromosome with the dominants *ABCDEF* would require the occurrence of crossing over in just the right places in the chromosome, and this makes the obtaining of a fully vigorous inbred line very improbable.

BALANCED POLYMORPHISM AND BALANCED HETEROSIS

When a heterozygote, A_1A_2, resembles in phenotype one of the homozygotes, A_1A_1 or A_2A_2, the allele A_1 is said to be dominant, or recessive, to A_2. When A_1A_2 is intermediate between A_1A_1 and A_2A_2, the dominance is incomplete; and when the heterozygote is exactly midway between the homozygotes the dominance is absent. It may happen, however, that the heterozygote A_1A_2 is more extreme—for example, larger—than either homozygote A_1A_1 or A_2A_2. This is *overdominance*. Overdominance leads to particularly interesting consequences if the character involved is heterosis; in other words, if the adaptive value of the heterozygote is higher than that of either homozygote. Taking the adaptive value of the heterozygote to be unity and the selective disadvantages (selection coefficients) of the two homozygotes to be, respectively, s_1 and s_2 (see p. 247), we have

Genotype	A_1A_1	A_2A_1	A_2A_2
Adaptive value	$1 - s_1$	1	$1 - s_2$

How will the gene alleles A_1 and A_2 fare in a population under selection? If the adaptive value of the heterozygote is equal to that of one of the homozygotes or intermediate between them (in other words, if $A_1A_1 \geqslant A_1A_2 \geqslant A_2A_2$), natural selection will, given enough time, eliminate entirely the less well adapted allele (A_2) and make the population uniformly homozygous for the better adapted one, A_1 (this, of course, ignores the possibility of mutation and other influences on gene frequencies). Something quite different will come to pass with heterosis—in other words, if the heterozygote is superior to both homozygotes ($A_1A_2 > \geqslant A_1A_1$, A_2A_2). Selection will now result in an equilibrium, and both alleles, A_1 and A_2, will continue to occur in the population indefinitely. It can be shown mathematically that equilibrium will be attained when the frequencies of the alleles in the gene pool are equal to

$$s_2/(s_1 + s_2) \text{ of } A_1 \quad \text{and} \quad s_1/(s_1 + s_2) \text{ of } A_2$$

Biologically, this heterosis leads to a most interesting situation known as *balanced polymorphism*. The population will always be composed of heterozygous and homozygous individuals A_1A_2, A_1A_1, and A_2A_2. Seemingly the strangest thing is that natural selection will maintain the balanced polymorphism even if one or both homozygotes have low fitness and even if they are lethal (s_1 and s_2 close to or equal to 1). But, it may be asked, how can natural selection maintain in the population genes that produce serious hereditary diseases when homozygous? The answer is that this will happen if the heterozygote is heterotic, that is, at least slightly superior to the best homozygote. This is, after all, not as strange as it seems; it can be shown that the average adaptive value of an individual in a Mendelian population with balanced polymorphism is highest when the equilibrium proportions of the alleles A_1 and A_2 have been reached. In other words, natural selection maximizes the adaptedness of a Mendelian population as a whole, even at the price of producing some ill-adapted homozygotes in every generation.

Balanced Polymorphism in Natural and Experimental Populations of Drosophila. In recent years, evidence has been accumulating that balanced polymorphism is quite frequent and important in natural populations. Ford has described some particularly spectacular cases in butterflies and moths, when two or more classes of individuals sharply distinct in coloration or other traits coexist in the same population. In populations of many species of Drosophila, balanced polymorphism involves what may seem a very recondite trait—inverted sections in the chromosomes (see pp. 276–278). Two or several variant structures of the same chromosome, differing in the gene arrangement, occur in many populations. Flies with different chromosomes interbreed freely, so that both homozygotes (individuals having the two chromosomes of a pair with the same gene arrangement) and heterozygotes (having the two chromosomes of a pair with different gene arrangements) are formed.

L'Heritier and Teissier constructed population cages in which experimental populations of Drosophila can be maintained in the laboratory (Fig. 19.4). A mixture of flies

obscura in which two types of chromosomes, called "ST" (Standard) and "CH," were present. The most remarkable thing about these changes is that, about ten generations from the start of the experiment, the population reaches a stable equilibrium at a level

Fig. 19.4. A population cage in which experimental populations of Drosophila are maintained in the laboratory. Jars with culture medium can be seen through the glass top of the cage. (*Photo courtesy of V. M. Pavlovsky*)

with known proportions of different chromosomes is introduced in such a cage; fresh food is given at intervals and the used-up medium is removed; the population breeds freely for as many generations as desired;

of about 80 per cent ST and 20 per cent CH. From the rate of changes of the frequencies of these kinds of chromosomes per generation it is possible to compute the following estimates of the adaptive values:

	Homozygote	*Heterozygote*	*Homozygote*
	ST /ST	ST /CH	CH /CH
Adaptive value	0.895	1	0.413
Selection coefficient	$s_1 = 0.105$	0	$s_2 = 0.587$

from time to time a sample of the flies or their larvae or eggs is taken, and the proportions of individuals with different chromosomes determined by inspection under a microscope of the larval salivary-gland cells (Fig. 15.10).

Figure 19.5 shows the changes observed in a population cage with *Drosophila pseudo-*

The heterozygote, having the two chromosomes with the ST and CH gene arrangements, is heterotic. One of the homozygotes, ST/ST, has an appreciably lower adaptive value, about nine-tenths that of the heterozygote. But the other homozygote, CH/CH, has less than half the adaptive value of the heterozygote. It is effectively semilethal. And yet, natural selection maintains the situation when such poorly fit homozygotes continue to occur generation after generation.

HOW WIDESPREAD IS BALANCED HETEROSIS? Balanced heterosis certainly occurs without inversions or other microscopically visible changes in the chromosomes. Lerner's anal-

and brings about loss of productivity and vigor and often various abnormalities that Lerner has called *phenodeviants*. One of the phenodeviant characters in poultry is crooked toes (Fig. 19.6), observed in many inbred lines. When two inbred lines with crooked toes are intercrossed, the F_1 hybrids are free of this defect. Koref and Brncic

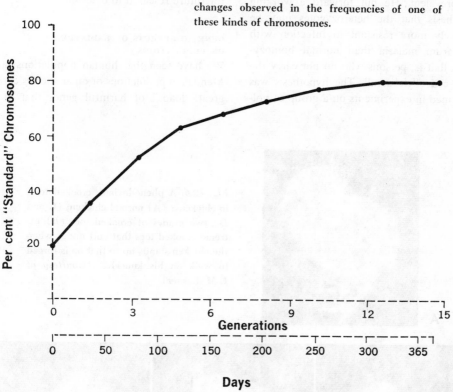

Fig. 19.5. The effect of natural selection in an experimental population of *Drosophila pseudo-obscura*. The population contains a mixture of two kinds of chromosomes; the curve shows the changes observed in the frequencies of one of these kinds of chromosomes.

ysis of genetic experiments and of the work of practical breeders of poultry and other domestic animals suggests that the highest yields in at least some breeds are attained through maintenance of a high level of heterozygosis for different alleles of many genes with individually small effects (polygenes). Inbreeding lowers the level of heterozygosity

believe that one of the phenodeviants that arise in inbred Drosophila strains are melanotic tumors in larvae and adults. Crow has argued that balanced heterosis may be responsible for about 95 per cent, and mutational heterosis for only 5 per cent, of the improved yields in hybrid corn. If confirmed, this would mean that balanced heterosis is the chief source of the most spectacular achievement of applied genetics.

In man, evidence strongly suggestive of balanced polymorphism has been found by Allison for the sickle-cell gene. As stated on page 127, the recessive allele of this gene is a lethal, since the homozygotes die of a fatal anemia. Heterozygotes are normal or only slightly anemic persons. Allison noted that the recessive allele is particularly common among the inhabitants of malarial districts in parts of central Africa and less frequent in adjacent districts where malaria is less prevalent. He put forward a working hypothesis that the heterozygotes may be relatively more resistant to infection with falciparum malaria than normal homozygotes, that is, persons who do not carry the sickle-cell allele at all. The hypothesis was confirmed in experiments on a group of vol-

unteers artificially infected with the malarial parasite, some of whom were heterozygotes and others homozygous normals. Most of the normals became infected with this form of malaria, and most of the heterozygotes did not. The heterozygotes are, then, heterotic in environments in which malaria is prevalent but possess no adaptive advantage over the normals where malaria is rare or absent. The recessive homozygote is lethal in most environments. How important balanced heterosis may be in the maintenance of other hereditary defects in human populations is for future research to determine.

GENETIC EFFECTS OF RADIATIONS ON POPULATIONS

We have seen that human populations and Mendelian populations of other species carry great "loads" of harmful genes that may

Fig. 19.6. A phenodeviant, crooked toes, in chickens: (A) normal chicken; (C and D) two grades of crooked toe; (B) extreme crooked toes that curl under when the chicken stands up so that he is forced to walk on his knuckles. (Courtesy of I. M. Lerner)

A

B   C   D

produce hereditary diseases, weaknesses, and malformations. In these "loads," three components may be distinguished (although situations intermediate between the three classes of components also occur). First, there exist harmful dominant, semidominant, and incompletely recessive genes, which weaken the organism both when homozygous and when heterozygous. Second, there are more or less completely recessive deleterious genes. Third, genes which give rise to hybrid vigor when heterozygous may produce poorly viable homozygotes. The first and the second class of genetic defects is constantly replenished, owing to the occurrence of new mutant genes, and constantly eliminated by "genetic death." However, natural selection does not eliminate the harmful mutants as soon as they are produced, and therefore such mutants may persist in the population for several or even for many generations. The third class of genetic defects, those that are vigorous in heterozygotes although weak when homozygous, are perpetuated by natural selection as long as the heterozygotes show hybrid vigor under the environmental conditions in which the population lives.

A conceivable way to diminish the load of harmful mutants would then be to decrease the rates of the mutations that produce them. Unfortunately, man has thus far learned how to increase but not how to decrease mutation rates (see Chap. 17). High-energy radiations are powerful mutagens, and the use and misuse of X rays in medical practice, as well as the use and the threatening misuse of atomic energy, may play havoc with the genetic endowment of mankind. Very properly, this problem has begun to claim increasing attention in recent years.

The basic fact to be remembered is that the numbers of gene mutations induced by high-energy radiations is simply proportional to the amount of the radiation received by the gametes. Therefore, as far as the genetic effects of radiation are concerned, there is no such thing as a "safe" dose. Genetic effects of radiations are even more insidious than their physiological effects, and one must distinguish them clearly. Physiological effects induced by exposures to radiations—radiation "burns," wounds, or tumors—may or may not be curable, but in any case they die with the persons exposed. Not so with the genetic effects. The induced mutants begin to appear in the progeny of exposed persons, and they may persist in the gene pool of the population for several or for many generations. Only the fully penetrant, dominant lethal diseases will be eliminated in the first generation after the exposure. The incompletely dominant, recessive, and not fully penetrant defects, which are much more numerous, will linger on, some of them for a long time—centuries or millennia in a slowly breeding species such as man. Since the "genetic deaths" will thus be spread over long periods, it may be hard to discriminate between the "genetic deaths" resulting from induced and from spontaneous mutations. An exceedingly painstaking study by Neel and his collaborators on the progeny of persons exposed to atomic-bomb blasts in Japan has failed to give any evidence of enhanced mortality or morbidity in these people. But this does not mean that no harmful mutants were induced or that they will not yield, slowly but unrelentingly, their crop of "genetic deaths."

There is no doubt that uncontrolled increase of mutation rates in human populations might produce very serious deterioration of public health for generations to come. It is obvious that all possible precautions should be taken at least to minimize the genetic harm that exposure to radiations of masses of people might cause.

EXPERIMENTS ON IRRADIATED POPULATIONS
Experimental studies on the effects of high-energy radiations have been made by Wallace and his collaborators on populations of *Drosophila melanogaster* living in population cages of the type discussed on pages

260–261. Several populations were started with flies known to be free of recessive lethal and semilethal mutant genes in their second chromosomes. Some of these populations lived for as many as 149 generations under continuous radiation, receiving about 2,000 r units of gamma rays of radium per generation. This is considerably above the dose of radiation that is lethal when applied to man. One population (number 1) received a heavy

pool became lethal when homozygous. Eventually the frequency of chromosomes carrying recessive lethals became stabilized between 25 and 30 per cent of all chromosomes. This was evidently due to an accumulation of spontaneously arising recessive lethal mutations; attainment of an equilibrium here means that the numbers of recessive lethals newly arising by mutation in every generation are balanced by their elimi-

Fig. 19.7. Accumulation of recessive lethal mutants in the experimental populations of *Drosophila melanogaster* not exposed to gamma rays of radium (No. 3), exposed to a strong gamma-ray treatment at the beginning of the experiment (No. 1), and exposed to a continuous treatment for 126 generations (No. 6). (*After B. Wallace*)

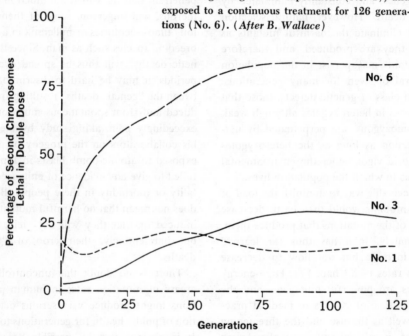

initial radiation treatment (7,000 r units to males, 1,000 r units to females) and no radiation thereafter. There was, of course, also a control population, number 3, which received no treatment.

Some of the results of these experiments are shown in Figure 19.7. Consider first the control population. Although it was originally free of lethals, gradually more and more of the second chromosomes in its gene

nation by genetic death. Natural populations of most plants, animals, and men probably approach such equilibrium states. The population (number 6) that received continuous irradiation accumulated recessive lethals much faster than the control population. It eventually also reached an equilibrium, but at a level much higher than the control population—when about 80 per cent of the second chromosomes contained recessive lethals. With more lethal genes to eliminate because of a higher mutation rate, the equilibrium is higher than it is when mutation is relatively infrequent. Finally, population 1 showed a high frequency of lethal chromosomes in the first generation after the irradiation; this was followed by a drop, by another rise, and by establishment of an equilibrium that was even lower than in the control population. The drop is explained by a rapid elimination of deleterious mutants that were partly dominant and the rise by subsequent accumulation of spontaneously arising mutants. The reasons for a lower equilibrium value are unknown. Populations 6 and 1 are models of what might be expected to happen in human populations exposed to mutagenic radiations. Harmful mutants induced in such populations would have to be eliminated by "genetic deaths."

Wallace has pointed out, however, that some of the heterozygotes for recessive lethal mutants in his experimental populations are quite normally viable. In fact, the average fitness of an individual in his continuously irradiated population (number 6) is only slightly below that in the nonirradiated control population (98 per cent if one takes the control to have a fitness of 100). The average fitness of an individual in population 1 is even higher than in the control (103 compared to 100). The most probable explanation of this unexpected discovery is that the intense natural selection to which these experimental populations have been exposed has resulted in formation of some balanced polymorphisms with heterotic heterozygotes (see above). There is certainly no reason to suppose that irradiation of human populations would result in much heterosis; one would hesitate to recommend that human populations be subjected to forms of selection as drastic as those applied to fly populations. Wallace's results show rather how insufficient is our present understanding of the dynamics of living populations and how

necessary it is that further research be done in this field.

WEAKNESS OF HETEROSIS IN SELF-FERTILIZING FORMS

Some of the most important agricultural plants—wheat, rice, barley, oats, tomatoes, tobacco, some cottons, garden peas, soy bean, peanuts, flax, coffee, and others—reproduce chiefly by self-pollination. The same is true in some wild plants, and there exist forms in which the flowers are so constructed that selfing occurs before the flowers open (cleistogamous flowers). Now, as pointed out above, self-fertilization is the closest possible form of inbreeding, and inbreeding leads to homozygotes becoming frequent and heterozygotes rare. Natural selection will, then, eliminate recessive and incompletely dominant deleterious mutants almost as rapidly and efficiently as the dominant ones.

Close inbreeding being a normal method of reproduction in these organisms, they may be expected to have become adapted to it in the process of evolution. It is not surprising, then, that artificial hybridization of the normally selfed strains leads to no striking heterosis in the hybrids and inbreeding to no appreciable deterioration. Whether or not there is any heterosis at all in normally self-pollinated plants is an open problem. Powers intercrossed ten varieties of tomatoes and recorded higher average yields of fruits in F_1 hybrids than in the parents. The same has been claimed for flax, for eggplants, and, by Müntzing and Hagberg in Sweden, also for the normally self-pollinated weed Galeopsis. It is possible that some of the cultivated plants that are normally selfed are descended from cross-pollinated wild ancestors and have not yet become completely adapted to selfing. According to Rick, the tomatoes growing wild in Peru are cross-fertilized, and they are the probable ancestors of the garden tomato. However, Haldane, Lerner, and others conjecture that heterozygosis, the presence in the genotype of a variety of gene alleles, might produce a greater biochemical versatility of the organism and hence a greater vigor.

PERMANENT HETEROZYGOTES IN OENOTHERA

As pointed out above, under balanced polymorphism the highly fit heterozygotes A_1A_2 exist in the population with the less fit homozygotes A_1A_1 and A_2A_2. It would obviously be an advantage to the species if all individuals in the populations were the heterotic A_1A_2 and if the relative weaklings A_1A_1 and A_2A_2 were to disappear. But this seems incompatible with sexual reproduction; a population consisting entirely of heterozygotes A_1A_2 in one generation will produce 50 per cent of homozygotes in the next generation. And yet, some varieties of the evening primrose, Oenothera, accomplished just this genetic feat of making not merely sexual reproduction but predominant self-pollination compatible with having the population consist entirely of heterozygotes for many genes. This is attained by a very remarkable genetic mechanism which exists, among others, in the varieties of Oenothera that furnished de Vries with the material for his study of mutation (Chap. 16).

Except for throwing occasional mutants (see p. 217), *Oenothera lamarckiana* breeds true. If, however, two different varieties of Oenothera are intercrossed with each other, more than a single type of hybrid appears in the F₁ generation. The different types of hybrids appearing in F₁ are referred to as "twin hybrids."

The appearance of twin hybrids and other facts led Renner to the hypothesis that *Oenothera lamarckiana* and its relatives are actually "permanent hybrids," or "permanent heterozygotes," each producing two types of gametes. These types differ not in a single gene but in many linked genes; in *gene complexes*. The complexes are so different in the gene combinations they contain that they are easily recognized, and Renner

gave a name to each. According to this hypothesis, each species contains two gene complexes that are clearly different, and at meiosis each separates from the other as a single entity. *Lamarckiana* is composed of gene complexes called *gaudens*, which contain the genes for green buds, nonpunctate stems, white nerves, broad leaves, and red flecks on the rosette leaves, and *velans*, which contain genes for red-striped buds, punctate stems, narrow leaves, white nerves, and no red flecks on the rosette leaves. *Lamarckiana* may thus be described as *gaudens-velans*. Half its pollen grains and half its eggs contain the gene complex *gaudens* and the other half the gene complex *velans*.

Three types of offspring should arise from self-fertilization in this species: *gaudens-gaudens* (¼), *gaudens-velans* (½), and *velans-velans* (¼). The first and the last apparently do not survive, an assumption which is supported by the fact that about half the ovules fail to produce seed. Thus only heterozygous *gaudens-velans* (which is *lamarckiana*) survives, and the species appears to breed true. The death of the two homozygous combinations is readily explained on the hypothesis of balanced lethal factors (p. 221). One complex contains one lethal (l_1, let us say) and the other another (l_2), and each has the dominant allele of the other's lethal. The heterozygous types L_1l_1 and L_2l_2 thus survive, but the homozygotes l_1l_1 and l_2l_2 die.

It has been possible in this way to determine the genetic constitution of other forms of Oenothera. Thus *Oenothera biennis* is *albicans-rubens*, and *O. muricata* is *rigens-curvans*. Some species, notably *O. hookeri*, differ from the rest in being entirely homozygous and displaying normal Mendelian breeding behavior. The chromosomal basis of these remarkable phenomena has been worked out by Cleland, Darlington, and others. Some (though not all) varieties of evening primroses have at meiosis four or

Fig. 19.8. Chromosomes of *Oenothera lamarckiana* at meiosis, showing a ring of 12 and one pair. (*After Cleland*)

more of their chromosomes attached end to end to form rings of chromosomes. Thus, *Oenothera lamarckiana* has at meiosis a ring of 12 chromosomes and only a single bivalent (Fig. 19.8). Some forms have all the 14 chromosomes present in the evening primroses united in a single ring. Now, the presence of rings of chromosomes at meiosis is characteristic of translocation heterozygotes (p. 203). If two chromosomes exchange parts, as shown in Figure 15.7, a cross-shaped pairing configuration will result at the pachytene stage and a ring of four chromosomes at metaphase and anaphase of the first meiotic division (Fig. 15.8). If another translocation occurs between one of

the chromosomes involved in the first translocation and a previously independent chromosome, the new translocation heterozygote will form at metaphase a ring of six chromosomes. More translocations involving new chromosomes might eventually tie together all the chromosomes in a ring at the meiotic metaphase.

If at the meiotic division the alternate chromosomes in the ring go to the same pole and chromosomes adjacent in the ring go to the opposite pole, then the resulting cells will have sets of chromosomes containing the full complement of genes. The genes located in all the chromosomes of a set will be inherited together, exhibiting the phenomenon of apparent linkage, which, as shown on page 203, is characteristic of translocation heterozygotes. If all the chromosomes that an individual has are involved in a system of translocations that give a ring at meiosis, there will be, in effect, only a single linkage group of genes, as though this individual had all its genes in a single pair of chromosomes. In conjunction with the lethals, this will give the gene complexes that are actually observed in Oenothera. In Oenothera, as in the balanced lethal systems observed in Drosophila (p. 221), an occasional crossover between chromosomes belonging to different "complexes" may give rise to gene recombinations that may stimulate mutations. Some of the "mutants" observed by de Vries (p. 217) were probably of this origin. However, normally the entire progeny of a selfed individual will consist of heterozygotes for the genes carried in the "complexes." This permits the species to enjoy the advantages of heterosis, without paying the price of producing also the ill-adapted homozygotes.

PARTHENOGENESIS, APOGAMY, AND ASEXUAL REPRODUCTION

Some organisms, chiefly plants, have obtained the advantages of heterosis without production of poorly fit homozygotes by methods even more radical than that found in Oenothera. Preserving the external appearance of sexual reproduction (flowers with often normal appearing female and male parts, pollination), they allowed the processes of fertilization and meiosis, which constitute the essence of sexuality, to degenerate or to be lost entirely. Meiosis, with its chromosome pairing and disjunction, may be suppressed, and diploid cells may give rise without fertilization to individuals of the next generation. This is one of several known forms of *apogamy* or *apomixis*. It occurs in many species of plants and in a few animals. Finally, *asexual reproduction* by fission (buds, bulbs, tubers, or runners) dispenses altogether with specialized sex cells and sex organs. Potatoes, sugar cane, bananas, strawberries, and pineapples are examples of cultivated plants propagated chiefly or exclusively asexually. Unless mutation occurs, offspring produced apogamically or asexually carry the same genes that were present in the parent. If the parent was a heterozygote, so is the offspring.

In oranges, lemons, and other citrus fruits, pollination of the flowers stimulates the development of seeds and fruits, but the seeds are produced mostly by apogamy. Individual citrus plants are highly heterozygous. Fertilization occasionally takes place, but the plants that grow from sexually produced seeds often differ greatly from the parental trees because of the occurrence of complex gene segregations. Similar high heterozygosis is characteristic of most cultivated apples. Accordingly, apples are propagated in practice almost entirely asexually, by grafting, rather than by being grown from seeds. Among the varieties of the genus Rubus, to which belong blackberries, raspberries, and related types, many apogamic forms are known, although some sexual species also exist. The cultivated types of these plants are propagated asexually. Apogamy is also common in some grasses. Strains of the bluegrass, *Poa alpina,* may carry 26, 31, 33, 35, 37, 38, and higher numbers of chromosomes in their somatic cells, and the apogamically produced progeny retain the parental chromosome numbers. This variation of chromosome numbers arose doubtless by polyploidy and aneuploidy through the occurrence of trisomics and monosomics (cf. p. 197). Aneuploids do not breed true when reproducing sexually, but they can be perpetuated by apogamy. Strains of *Poa alpina* and related forms can occasionally be crossed, and the sexually produced F_1 plants are highly variable on account of segregation. But the F_2 progenies obtained apogamically from the F_1 segregants show no further segregation, thus inverting the usual behavior of hybrids.

Relatively few organisms reproduce exclusively parthenogenetically, apogamically, or asexually. More often these aberrant methods of reproduction alternate at more or less regular intervals with the usual sexual one. Such alternation permits the species to exploit the advantages both of sexuality and of asexual reproduction. Sexual reproduction engenders numerous gene and chromosome combinations, some of which prove advantageous to the organism. These advantageous combinations are then perpetuated by asexual reproduction for a time in a state that protects them from being shattered by more recombination.

PROBLEMS

19.1 What should be the proportion of heterozygous individuals among the descendants of a single *Aa* plant after 5, 10, 15, 20, 50, and 100 generations of selfing? Graph the results.

19.2 Following Bonnier (1947) (cf. Bibliography), find the consequences of mating in each generation between a single brother-sister pair in a population in which the alleles *A* and *a* are initially equally frequent.

19.3 What is the chance that a child of a marriage between first cousins will be homozygous for gene *a*, for which only one of the common grandparents was heterozygous, *Aa*, whereas all other parents were *AA*?

19.4 Why may selection for vigor in inbred lines delay the attainment of homozygosity?

19.5 Why may persistent inbreeding in a number of lines, later followed by crosses between them, result in more vigorous individuals than are produced by crosses between members of lines that have not been inbred?

19.6 In corn, assume that a plant has the following arrangement of genes in one chromosome pair $\dfrac{AbC}{aBc}$ with crossover values of 2 per cent between the successive gene loci and no double crossing over in this stretch of the map. Indicate the steps to be taken in obtaining, by selfing, an inbred line homozygous for all the incompletely dominant alleles. Estimate the number of generations required.

19.7 In corn, assume that a plant is heterozygous for six pairs of alleles *Mm, Nn, Oo, Pp, Qq, Rr*, each on a different chromosome. Indicate the steps to be taken in obtaining by selfing an inbred line homozygous for all the dominant alleles. Estimate the numbers of generations required and the numbers of plants to be raised, with .98 confidence coefficient for the latter at each generation.

19.8 Wright (1929) reported that in the first nine years (12 generations) of brother-sister matings, five strains of guinea pigs had declined below an outbred control stock in weight, fecundity, and vitality and had become markedly different from each other, whereas during the second nine-year period of inbreeding no further changes occurred in these respects. Give your explanation of these facts.

19.9 Samples of three large populations of Drosophila mating at random in population cages were found to have the following genotypes, different cages being scored for different characters:

Population 1	57 *AA*	169 *Aa*	29 *aa*
Population 2	92 *BB*	199 *Bb*	77 *bb*
Population 3	21 *CC*	183 *Cc*	50 *cc*

Compare each of these distributions with that expected on Hardy-Weinberg assumptions and account for any differences.

19.10 A population of *Drosophila tropicalis* collected in El Salvador and raised under optimal conditions gave the following frequencies of gene arrangements in chromosome II: homozygotes *AA* 14, heterozygotes *Aa* 111, homozygotes *aa* 0. Assuming the population to be in equilibrium, compute the values for selection coefficients and adaptive values of the three genotypes.

19.11 The following data were obtained from three populations:

Proportion of children dying at early age

		Parents first cousins	Parents unrelated
U.S.A.	1858	692 /2936	134 /837
U.S.A.	1908	113 /672	370 /3184
France	1953	165 /1417	306 /5382

Suggest an explanation of the differences in mortality between offspring of cousins and of unrelated parents.

19.12 In Problems 19.11 let f_c be the proportion of deaths in the combined cousin matings for all three sets of data and f_u the proportion in the unrelated matings. Give 95 per cent confidence intervals for f_c and f_u. An approximate confidence interval for the difference $f_c - f_u$ can be obtained from the approximate standard error

$$\sqrt{\frac{f_c(1 - f_c)}{n_c} + \frac{f_u(1 - f_u)}{n_u}}$$

where n_c and n_u are the total number of children of the two types. Give this confidence interval.

19.13 In Problem 19.11, calculate χ^2 and **P** for the test of homogeneity of the three sets of cousin matings and for the three sets of unrelated matings. How might these results affect the answer to Problem 19.12?

20 ✕ GENETICS OF RACE FORMATION

MUTATIONS of genes and chromosomes occur from time to time in all organisms. Mutation thus supplies the raw materials from which—and, as far as we know, only from which—evolution may arise. But mutation alone is not enough to bring about evolution. Just as a supply of raw materials in a factory is a necessary but not a sufficient condition to insure that a finished product will be manufactured, so in organic evolution the mutants must be sorted out and combined and recombined in various patterns to yield adaptively competent genotypes. The sorting out is done by natural selection. The result is formation of races and species adapted to the many different environments that the world has to offer.

MUTATION AND ADAPTEDNESS

It has been pointed out repeatedly in the foregoing chapters that most mutations have deleterious effects. How can this fact be reconciled with the theory that the process of mutation is the fountainhead of evolution? Although it may seem strange at first,

270

the deleterious character of most mutations is really what one should expect. Indeed, the mutants that arise today have probably appeared repeatedly in the long past. Therefore, any mutation that improves the chance of survival of its carriers in the normal environment in which the species lives has had the opportunity of becoming established as the "normal," or prevailing, condition. The normal, or "wild-type," genotype of a species incorporates most of the useful mutants that have arisen in its evolution. New mutations that occur are, therefore, more likely to be deleterious than beneficial.

A mutation deleterious in one environment may, however, be neutral or beneficial in other environments. Thus, the mutants of the colon bacteria which are resistant to bacteriophage attacks (see p. 225) are neutral or even deleterious in cultures that are free of bacteriophages, but only the mutants survive in the presence of bacteriophages.

Table 20.1 shows the viability at different temperatures of individuals homozygous for certain second chromosomes found in natural populations of *Drosophila pseudo-obscura*. The chromosomes are designated arbitrarily as A, B, C, etc., and viability is given in percentages of the average, or "normal," viability of flies of the same species in the same environments.

TABLE 20.1
Viability at different temperatures of individuals homozygous for certain chromosomes found in natural populations of *Drosophila pseudoobscura* (*After Dobzhansky and Spassky*)

Chromosomes	Temperature, °C		
	25½	21	16½
A	99	98	100
B	95	89	87
C	92	109	109
D	0	43	89
E	28	73	106
F	3	39	0

The viability of individuals homozygous for chromosomes A and B is normal or subnormal at all temperatures. C has a superior viability at lower temperatures and is subnormal at the higher one. D is slightly below normal at 16½°, semilethal at 21°, and completely lethal at 25½° C. E is superior to normal at 16½°, subnormal at 21°, and semilethal at 25½° C. F survives best at the intermediate temperature.

A mutant gene that produces deleterious effects in combinations with some genes may not be deleterious in combinations with other genes. For example, Timoféeff-Ressovsky found that the mutant bobbed (bristles) in *Drosophila funebris* reduces the viability of the flies to 85 per cent of normal and that the mutant miniature (wings) reduces it to 69 per cent of normal. The combination bobbed-miniature, however, has a viability about 97 per cent normal.

The better known the properties of different genetic variants of a species, the greater the possibilities of creating environments in which each genotype might produce its optimal phenotype. A Neurospora mutant unable to synthesize an essential vitamin may be successfully reared in an environment in which this vitamin is supplied.

This does not mean that every mutant should be favorable in some environment. A majority of mutations are disadvantageous in all environments. For example, one could imagine an environment in which the dominant mutation for brachydactyly in man (absence of the middle phalanx in the fingers, making them short and stubby) might conceivably be useful. But such an environment is hardly imaginable for the dominant mutation for brittle bones, for the sex-linked recessive mutation for hemophilia, or for the numerous lethal mutations in Drosophila. Mutational changes arise regardless of whether they may prove useful or not. Uncontrolled mutation would lead to decay of the genotype, since most mutations are harmful, being in the nature of hereditary diseases. A species in which mutation had ceased to occur would, therefore, gain a temporary advantage because of the nonproduction of genetically defective types. Yet in a changing environment such a species would lose in competition with more mutable rivals, which would be able to become adapted to new environmental conditions. Indeed, the mutation process supplies the raw materials by means of which biological adaptations occur in the course of evolution. Evolutionary plasticity can be maintained only if mutations take place. Deleterious mutations are eliminated, but those that are advantageous in some of the environments accessible to the species are multiplied by natural selection and eventually supplant the ancestral type.

ADAPTIVE CHANGES IN EXPERIMENTS
Adaptive changes can be observed directly in organisms that multiply rapidly and can be bred under observation in large numbers.

These requirements are most easily satisfied in microorganisms; hence the emergence
of strains of viruses, bacteria, and lower
fungi adapted to various culture conditions
has been known in microbiology for some
time. The formation of strains of bacteria
resistant to bacteriophages and to penicillin
have been discussed above (pp. 225–226).
Adaptive changes can, however, be observed
in more complex organisms as well.

We have seen (p. 249) that in *Drosophila
pseudoobscura* and other species a large proportion of chromosomes in wild flies contain
recessive mutants that act as lethals, semilethals, or deleterious modifiers of viability
when homozygous. Seven strains homozygous for such deleterious genes were chosen
and bred for 50 consecutive generations in
laboratory cultures. By placing some four
dozen parents in each culture, the cultures
were deliberately overcrowded with larvae,
which accordingly developed under conditions of severe competition. Each of the

seven strains was subdivided into two parallel lines; in one line the parents were treated
with X rays in every generation, and in the
other lines the parents were left untreated.
It was expected that any mutants that might
appear with favorable effects on the viability
of the flies or their larvae would be multiplied by natural selection and could become
established in the strains. Since the strains
had a low initial viability on account of the
abnormal genetic constitution (homozygous
for deleterious recessive mutants), it seemed
reasonable that mutants might arise, bringing
the viability back to normal.

The outcome of the experiment is shown
in Figure 20.1. In this diagram, the height
of the black columns shows the initial viability of the seven strains expressed in percentages of the average viability of normal (heterozygous) flies of the same species. The
white columns show the viability of the same
strains after 50 generations of strong selection, and the hatched columns show the

Fig. 20.1. Results of fifty generations of natural selection for
viability in seven strains of *Drosophila pseudoobscura.* Ordinates, per cent of normal viability; black, viability of the
strain at beginning of the experiment; white, viability after
50 generations, untreated; crosshatched, viability after 50
generations of exposure to low doses of X radiation. (*From
Dobzhansky and Spassky*)

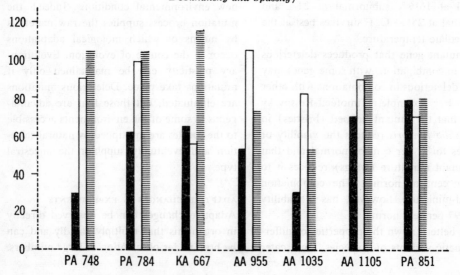

viability of the same strains after 50 generations of treatment with X rays combined with selection. It can be seen that six out of the seven X-rayed and five out of the seven untreated strains showed substantial, and in some cases striking, improvements in survival ability. Many more deleterious mutations than beneficial ones must have arisen in these strains, particularly in the X-rayed lines. The deleterious mutants have, however, been eliminated, and the beneficial ones increased and established by the natural selection that took place during the 50 generations of breeding. Evolutionary changes giving rise to improved adaptation of some strains to their environments have, thus, taken place.

ARTIFICIAL SELECTION IN SELF-FERTILIZING FORMS

As pointed out by Darwin, the varieties of domesticated animals and plants now in existence have been developed from their wild ancestors by selection directed by man. It is enough to compare, for example, wild boars with modern breeds of pigs or wild apples with an improved variety to appreciate how great may be the changes induced by selection in a very short time, geologically speaking. In some cases authorities disagree as to just which wild species gave rise to the modern domesticated one, so extensive have been the changes under domestication.

In cultivated plants that reproduce mainly asexually or by self-pollination, a commercial "variety" grown in the field is usually a collection of genotypically uniform clones or pure lines that exchange genes only rarely, as a result of occasional crossing. As shown by Johannsen in his classical studies with beans (1909), selection is ineffective in a homozygous pure line. For example, the offspring of large and of small beans of the same pure line have the same range of sizes. This is as it should be, since individuals within a pure line or a clone have the same genotype and belong to the same "pure race," and the phenotypic differences among them are of purely environmental origin. The concepts of genotype and phenotype were, in fact, formulated by Johannsen on the basis of these experiments. Applied to a mixture of pure lines or clones in a commercial variety, selection merely chooses the most desirable line or lines from the mixture. Once isolated, a pure line remains constant, unless mutation or hybridization intervenes.

The simplest method of improving asexual or self-fertilizing crops consists, then, in picking out, after adequate testing in field environments, of clones or pure lines that produce superior yields in these environments. Both "local" varieties and those introduced from foreign countries may be the source of such superior genotypes. However, since the success of the work depends upon the availability of a variety of genotypes among which to select, one of the powerful breeding methods is hybridization. Recombination of genes contributed by the varieties crossed often produces superior genotypes in the F_2 and later generations of the hybrids. Suppose, for example, that one line of wheat gives good yields, another is resistant to rust fungi, a third excels in winter hardiness, drought resistance, or straw strength; then bringing together the genes for all these desirable properties is obviously advantageous. Indeed, many varieties now cultivated on a very large scale were obtained by selection from hybrid progenies. A classical example is Thatcher wheat, obtained by hybridization of three varieties (Iumillo, Marquis, and Kanred, belonging to two different wheat species), introduced in commercial planting in 1934 and later grown on millions of acres in the wheat belt of the United States and Canada.

ARTIFICIAL SELECTION IN CROSS-FERTILIZING SPECIES

In sexual, cross-fertilizing species, two or more alleles of many genes are present in most populations. So great are the numbers of gene combinations generated continuously by Mendelian recombination in the progeny of heterozygotes that no genotype is likely to be repeated exactly in more than a single individual (see p. 80). Selection may, then, continue to bring progressive improvement of the animals or plants in the direction desired for many generations without exhausting the genetic variability already present in the original populations, and new variability may be added by mutation. In contrast to asexual and self-fertilizing species, selection in cross-fertilizing populations often produces improved varieties with genotypes different from and superior to any that had been present in the population with which the selection has started. The progress of selection for high and low protein content in corn seeds is shown in Figure 20.2. The selection was started in 1896, and was still continuing even after 50 generations, when the protein content in the high line was already considerably greater than in the low line. In other experiments the progress is fastest

in the early generations, becomes slower and slower, and finally reaches a plateau where further improvement can come only from new mutations or from outcrossing.

The simplest technique used by breeders is *mass selection,* which consists in systematically choosing the part of the population in which the desired qualities are most strongly developed and using the individuals chosen to become parents of the next generation. The rate of progress of selection will, of course, depend upon the ability of the breeder to pick out individuals that are not only phenotypically but also genotypically superior in size, high yield of grain or of milk, high speed on the race track, or whatever other characteristics are considered most desirable. However, the phenotype depends upon the genotype as well as upon the environment; for example, the milk yield in cattle depends upon the genotype as well as upon nutrition and the general health of the cows. A high-yielding cow may carry

Fig. 20.2. Progress of artificial selection for high and low protein content in seeds of corn (maize). (*After Woodworth, Lang, and Jugenheimer*)

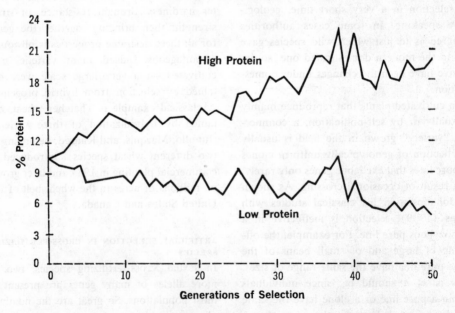

a genotype less favorable for milk production than another cow that gives a lower yield. *Progeny testing* is a method of making selection faster and more efficient. If the progeny of a given cow has given a higher average milk yield than the progeny of another cow in a similar environment, then the former probably carried a superior genotype.

HERITABILITY AND SELECTION

A breeder of domestic animals or cultivated plants faces a problem analogous to the nature-nurture problem in man (Chap. 11). He wants to know how much of the observed variation of the phenotypes in the population with which he is working is due to genotypic and how much to environmental diversity. The breeder has a double advantage over the student of man, since his materials can be experimented with and since the environment of animals and plants can be controlled and made uniform more easily than human environments. Mathematical geneticists and breeders have expended considerable effort in recent years to develop methods of estimation of *heritability*. Heritability is the percentage ratio of the hereditary, or genotypic, variance (σ_H^2) to the total observed variance (σ_O^2) in the trait concerned. For methods of computing variance, see Chapter 29. A knowledge of heritability might permit prediction of the rate of progress to be expected in the selection for a given trait or quality.

The greater the heritability, the greater the average resemblance between the parents and the progeny. The greater the environmental component of the observed phenotypic variation, the less the correlation between the traits of parents and children. Researchers have developed some ingenious and elaborate mathematical techniques of progeny testing and of the so-called "analysis of variance observed" in field trials or laboratory experiments. The following estimates of the heritability of certain characters in corn have been obtained by Robinson, Comstock, and Harvey (1949):

Plant height	70.1	Ear number	23.6
Ear height	55.4	Yield	20.1
Husk extension	49.5	Ear length	17.3
Husk score	35.9	Ear diameter	14.1

The relative importance of "nature" is highest in the variation of plant height, whereas in ear diameter "nurture" is of greater importance. Such estimates of heritability are most serviceable in the analysis of the selection process in those characters determined by additive effects of many genes with individually small effects (*polygenes*, Chap. 8). Dominance, interaction of gene effects, and epistasis and hypostasis complicate the situation, and fully satisfactory methods of estimation of the heritability of characters in which these complications are involved have yet to be invented.

A prime concern of a scientific breeder is, thus, to have available a supply of genes from which the new and superior genotypes can be constructed. As pointed out particularly by Vavilov, this makes imperative the collection, study, and preservation of varieties of cultivated plants and animals that occur anywhere in the world. Even varieties which, by themselves, are inferior to others may contain desirable genes that can be used to create the superior varieties of the future. Another method, thus far little explored, of getting new genes for breeding work is induction of mutations by X rays, ultraviolet, and other mutagens. Interesting pioneer work in this direction has been done in Sweden by Gustafsson on strains of barley.

ADAPTIVE CHANGES IN NATURAL POPULATIONS OF DROSOPHILA

Neither Darwin nor other classical evolutionists claimed to have actually observed evolutionary changes taking place in nature under the influence of natural selection. Changes wrought by artificial selection under domestication furnish only an instructive model of the evolutionary process as it occurs in nature. Evolution theories have been accepted not because observers have witnessed evolution, but because countless facts of biology make sense on the assumption that evolution has happened and is happening, and these facts make no sense otherwise. Evolutionary changes in nature are mostly too slow to be observable within a human lifetime. Of course, hereditary diseases and malformations are kept in check in natural populations by strong selection, and the maintenance of balanced polymorphism may also involve powerful selection pressure (see p. 260). However, the role of natural selection in bringing about the "genetic death" of organisms with hereditary diseases is purely negative rather than constructive or creative, and in the maintenance of balanced polymorphism selection mostly acts to preserve an equilibrium rather than to bring about changes in it.

Nevertheless, observations on polymorphic populations disclose some interesting changes, apparently unconnected with man-induced modifications of nature. As we saw in Chapter 19, natural populations of many species of Drosophila are mixtures of heterozygotes and homozygotes for chromosomes differing in inversions of blocks of genes. Each type of chromosome has a definite frequency in the gene pool of the population, and these frequencies are characteristic for each population. If, however, the same population is sampled repeatedly, in different months, the relative frequencies of chromosomes of different types may be observed to change from season to season and sometimes from year to year. These changes are mostly cyclic; in other words, the changes during the summer are reversed during the winter or some other season, so that the population may have a similar composition in a specific season in different years. Nevertheless, here we observe genetic changes in the composition of a population, hence evolutionary changes occurring in nature.

Figure 20.3 shows the percentages of chromosomes of three types, designated ST, AR, and CH, during different months in the populations of *Drosophila pseudoobscura* in a certain locality in California. It can be seen that ST chromosomes (the black columns) decrease in frequency from March to June and increase from June to October. Chromosomes of type CH, shown by the hatched columns in Figure 20.3, become more frequent from March to June and less frequent from June to October. Finally, the frequency of type AR (the white columns in Fig. 20.3) is relatively constant. A working hypothesis that would explain these changes is that flies that carry ST chromosomes are for some reason more successful in survival and reproduction in summer environments than flies with other kinds of chromosomes, whereas carriers of CH chromosomes are similarly favored in spring environments. In this way, natural selection augments the frequencies of ST chromosomes in summer and produces the same effect on CH chromosomes in spring.

The validity of this hypothesis has been tested in several ways. In some of the tests, artificial populations of *Drosophila pseudoobscura* were set up in population cages (see p. 260). The initial population of the cage may have any desired proportions of different chromosomal types; from time to time samples of the population are taken, and the frequencies of the chromosomal types in them are determined by analysis of the chromosomes in the cells of the salivary glands. It has been shown by this method that, at the temperature of $25°$ C ($77°$ F), flies homozygous for ST chromosomes have higher adaptive values than AR homozygotes, and these latter have a higher adaptive value than CH homozygotes. Thus, if the initial population of a cage contains few ST but many AR or CH chromosomes, the proportions of ST rapidly rise and those of AR and CH drop, generation after generation.

But at 15° C (59° F) the adaptive values of the carriers of all chromosome types are equal; hence the proportions present in the population with which the experiment is started persist indefinitely. Finally, as shown by Birch, when the population is not crowded, so that the larvae and the adult flies have unlimited food, the CH homozygotes are superior to the ST homozygotes. Thus the

GEOGRAPHIC CHROMOSOMAL RACES IN DROSOPHILA

As we have seen, natural populations of *Drosophila pseudoobscura* which occur in different localities may be described in terms of the relative proportions in them of the different chromosomal types discussed above in connection with the seasonal adaptive changes and with experimental populations.

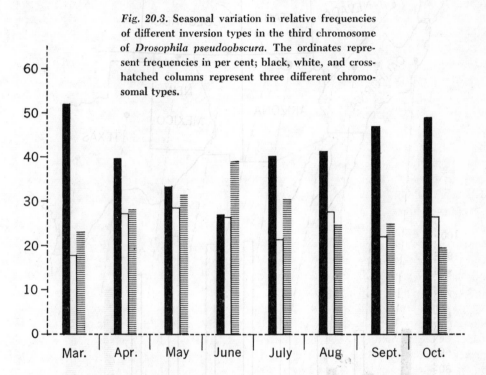

Fig. 20.3. Seasonal variation in relative frequencies of different inversion types in the third chromosome of *Drosophila pseudoobscura*. The ordinates represent frequencies in per cent; black, white, and cross-hatched columns represent three different chromosomal types.

changes produced by natural selection in a wild population can, in this case, be reproduced experimentally. Indeed, as Figure 20.3 shows, ST chromosomes wax and CH wane in frequency in nature during the hot summer and the same thing happens in crowded population cages at 25° C. In the spring, when the natural population is expanding because of abundance of food, CH chromosomes become more and ST less frequent; the same happens in experimental populations without crowding. In winter no changes occur, just as none occur in the laboratory at 15° C.

The proportions may vary greatly in different localities. For example, ST chromosomes (shown in the black columns in Fig. 20.4) occur frequently in populations of California, but they dwindle in frequency as one moves eastward. AR chromosomes (the white columns in Fig. 20.4) are commonest in Arizona and New Mexico and become less frequent both westward and eastward from there. PP chromosomes (the hatched columns in Fig. 20.4) are commonest in Texas and rapidly become less frequent westward (the species does not occur east of Texas). CH chromosomes (mentioned above

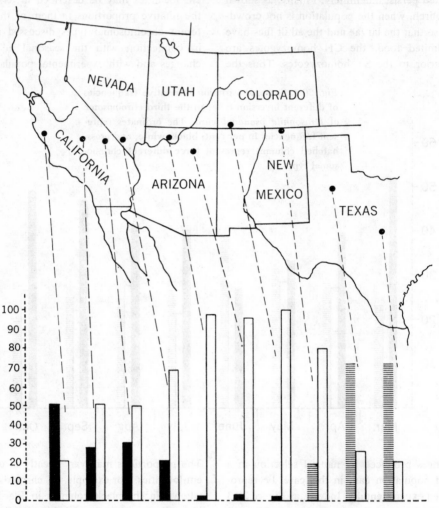

Fig. 20.4. Relative frequencies of three chromosomal types in geographic races of *Drosophila pseudoobscura* in the southwestern United States. The heights of the black, white, and hatched columns represent the frequencies (in per cent) of the three types.

but not shown in Fig. 20.4) are more frequent in populations of northern Mexico and become less frequent as the distance from that region increases.

It can be seen, then, that the differences between populations of different geographic regions are essentially quantitative rather than qualitative; they are differences in relative frequencies of the chromosomal types, although some types may be wholly absent in some localities. Moreover, the differences between populations are compounded from the same elements in which individuals within a population often differ, in this case the gene arrangement in the chromosomes.

Populations of *Drosophila pseudoobscura* which inhabit different territories and which differ in relative frequencies of the chromo-

TABLE 20.2

Frequencies in different populations of the alleles i, I^A, and I^B, giving rise to the blood groups O, A, B, and AB (*Data from Boyd and from Mourant*)

Population	Number of persons tested	i	I^A	I^B
Americans (white)	20,000	0.67	0.26	0.07
Icelanders	800	0.75	0.19	0.06
Irish	399	0.74	0.19	0.07
Scots	2,610	0.72	0.21	0.07
English	4,032	0.71	0.24	0.06
Swedes	600	0.64	0.28	0.07
French	10,433	0.64	0.30	0.06
Basques	400	0.76	0.24	0.00
Swiss	275,644	0.65	0.29	0.06
Croats	2,060	0.59	0.28	0.13
Serbians	6,863	0.57	0.29	0.14
Hungarians	1,500	0.54	0.29	0.17
Russians (Moscow)	489	0.57	0.25	0.19
Hindus	2,357	0.55	0.18	0.26
Buriats (N. Irkutsk)	1,320	0.57	0.15	0.28
Chinese (Huang Ho)	2,127	0.59	0.22	0.20
Japanese	29,799	0.55	0.28	0.17
Eskimos	484	0.64	0.33	0.03
American Indians (Navajo)	359	0.87	0.13	0.00
American Indians (Blackfeet)	115	0.49	0.51	0.00
W. Australians (aborigines)	243	0.69	0.31	0.00
African Pygmies	1,032	0.55	0.23	0.22
Hottentots	506	0.59	0.20	0.19

somal types may be described as different *races*. Races are, then, *populations that differ in the relative frequencies of gene alleles or of chromosome structures*.

GEOGRAPHIC DISTRIBUTION OF BLOOD GROUPS

Human populations native to different parts of the world show racial differences in the incidence of genes for various bodily traits. Owing to the collective efforts of many investigators in different countries, a very considerable amount of data has accumulated on the incidence in human populations of the classical (O–A–B–AB) blood groups, making this the best-studied genetic trait in our species. As we have seen, three alleles of a single gene, I^A, I^B, and i, account for the inheritance of the classical blood groups. Table 20.2 shows the frequencies of these alleles in some populations.

It can be seen that, with the exception of some American Indian tribes, populations of all countries contain all three alleles, although with different frequencies. The frequency of I^B (Figs. 20.6 and 20.7) is low in Western Europe, increases as one proceeds eastward, reaches a maximum in central Asia and India, and declines again on the shores of the Pacific. Australian aborigines have little I^B but considerable I^A. Most American Indians show a predominance of i amounting in some tribes to exclusion of other alleles, but Blackfeet and related tribes

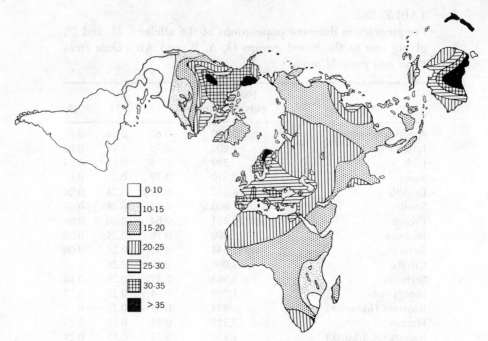

Fig. 20.5. The frequencies of blood-group gene A in different parts of the world. (*After Mourant*)

0·10
10·15
15·20
20·25
25·30
30·35
> 35

in the northern United States and Canada have very high frequencies of I^A. The distribution of these alleles (Figs. 20.5 and 20.6) is shown in aboriginal populations of these areas.

Differences of a similarly quantitative nature occur also with other antigens of human blood. The rhesus blood types (cf. p. 118) are particularly interesting, since racial differences in the distribution of some alleles (D, d), as in Table 20.3, may be accompanied by differences in the frequency of hemolytic disease of the newborn (see p. 117) and thus be due in part to selection. The Rh-negative r(cde) allele is rare or absent in most human races except European whites, where it reaches frequencies of 0.30–0.45, corresponding to the frequencies of 10 to 20 per cent of the recessive cde phenotype. Among the Basques the cde phenotype is still more frequent, 30 to 40 per cent, corresponding to about 0.6 of the r(cde)

allele. The Basques, living in the Pyrenees Mountains in Spain and France, are descended from an ancient population of Europe which has been largely displaced elsewhere on that continent by later immigrants. Boyd has supposed that, as a race, these early Europeans were characterized by still higher frequencies of cde than the Basques now living. The antigen pattern cDe, due to the allele $R°(cDe)$, has a frequency of 40 per cent and higher in African Negroes and in populations in part descended from them (such as American Negroes and many Puerto Ricans), but this allele is rare or absent elsewhere.

EXTERNALLY VISIBLE RACE DIFFERENCES
The genes that determine the blood antigens are certainly not the only ones that vary in frequency in human races. Skin, hair, and eye colors, stature, hair form, conformation of nose and lips, and shape of the head are

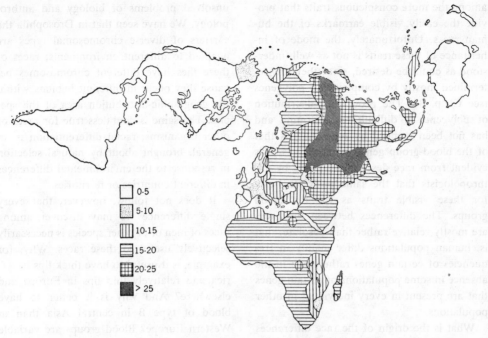

0.5
5-10
10-15
15-20
20-25
> 25

Fig. 20.6. The frequencies of blood-group gene *B* in different parts of the world. (*After Mourant*)

TABLE 20.3

Phenotype frequencies in per cent of the commoner rhesus blood types (*Data from Boyd, 1954*)

Population	Rh-negative	Rh-positive				Rarer types
	cde	Rh 1 (*CDe*)	Rh 2 (*cDE*)	Rh 1 Rh 2 (*cDE/CDe*)	Rh 0 (*cDe*)	
Basques	28.8	55.1	7.8	6.0	0.6	1.8
French	17.0	51.7	13.6	13.0	3.6	1.2
English	15.3	54.8	14.7	11.6	2.3	1.3
White, U.S.A.	14.7	53.5	15.0	12.9	2.2	1.7
Arabs (Baghdad)	10.3	50.3	13.7	15.7	8.3	1.7
Puerto Ricans	10.1	39.1	19.6	14.0	15.1	2.2
Negroes, U.S.A.	7.4	23.7	16.3	4.4	45.9	2.2
Bantu (S. Africa)	5.3	27.0	0.0	2.3	64.3	1.0
Chinese	1.5	60.6	3.0	34.1	0.9	0.0
Japanese	0.6	51.7	8.3	39.4	0.0	0.0
American Indian (Ramah, N.M.)	0.0	28.5	20.0	41.0	0.7	9.9
American Indian (Brazil)	0.0	22.7	19.3	53.2	0.0	4.8
Indonesians	0.0	74.0	2.5	22.5	0.5	0.5
Siamese	0.0	74.7	3.3	21.1	0.5	3.3
Australian aborigines	0.0	58.2	8.5	30.4	1.3	1.7

among the more conspicuous traits that provide the easily visible earmarks of the human races. Unfortunately, the mode of inheritance of these traits is not as well understood as could be desired, since they are determined mostly by complexes of polygenes (see Chap. 8). The geographic distribution of polygenes is difficult to determine and has not been mapped as accurately as that of the blood-group genes. Nevertheless, it is evident from race descriptions made by anthropologists that the same principle holds for these visible traits as for the blood groups. The differences between the races are mostly relative rather than absolute; that is, human populations differ mainly in frequencies of certain genes rather than in the absence in some populations of certain genes that are present in every individual in other populations.

What is the origin of the race differences among men? What causes have brought about the differentiation of mankind into populations with different frequencies of certain genes? This is one of the outstanding

unsolved problems of biology and anthropology. We have seen that in Drosophila the carriers of diverse chromosomal types are adapted to different environments; races of these flies have different chromosomes because they occur in different habitats within the geographic-distribution area of the species. The same is doubtless true for races of other organisms; racial differentiation is, in general, brought about by natural selection in response to the environmental differences in different countries or territories.

It does not follow, however, that every single difference we may discover among races of men or of other species is necessarily selectively useful to these races. Why, for example, is it useful to have thick lips in Africa and relatively thin lips in Europe and elsewhere? And why is it better to have blood of type B in central Asia than in Western Europe? Blood groups are variable

Fig. 20.7. The frequencies of blood-group gene B in different populations of Europe. (After Mourant)

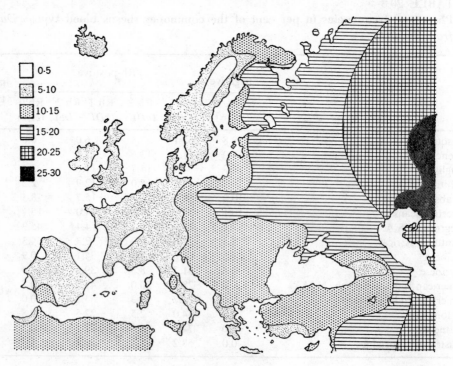

in other species than man, for individuals with O and A bloods occur also among chimpanzees, whereas orangutans are of types A, B, and AB. The variability of the blood groups was probably present in the remote common ancestor of man and apes. We do not need to suppose that these traits are absolutely neutral; in fact, several investigators have found indications that persons with O blood are perceptibly more common among patients with duodenal ulcers than those with A or B blood. But there is no evidence that duodenal ulcers are less dangerous in Europe than in Asia. We must explore the possibility that factors other than natural selection may bring about differentiation of gene frequencies in populations. One such factor is random genetic drift.

GENETIC DRIFT

Hardy and Weinberg demonstrated that, in the absence of mutation, selection, and differential migration, the gene frequencies in Mendelian populations will remain constant from generation to generation. This will be strictly true, however, only in ideal populations consisting of an infinite number of breeding individuals. In reality populations are finite. Consider, then, two populations, one of 500,000 and the other of 50 individuals. Suppose that in both populations a gene is represented by two alleles, A and a, which are at the outset equally frequent in the gene pool, so that $q = (1 - q) = 0.5$. The larger population has thus arisen from 1 million gametes and the smaller one from only 100 gametes. When a sample of 1 million genes is taken from the gene pool, which contains equal numbers of alleles A and a, the numbers of A and a will not necessarily be exactly equal; there may be slightly more than 500,000 A and slightly fewer a alleles, or vice versa. The numbers of A and a alleles in a sample of 1 million gametes, with the standard error of the number (cf. p. 414), will be

$$500,000 \pm \sqrt{\frac{500,000 \times 500,000}{1,000,000}} = 500,000 \pm 500$$

Similarly, in the small population, the expected numbers of A and a alleles in a sample of 100 gametes will be

$$50 \pm \sqrt{\frac{50 \times 50}{100}} = 50 \pm 5$$

The standard error for the large population is 500 and for the small one only 5. However, for the large population the standard error constitutes only 0.1 per cent of the number of gametes, whereas in the small population it constitutes as much as 10 per cent of the number of gametes. It is easy to see that the proportions of the alleles A and a in the gene pool will remain rather constant from generation to generation in the large population but will be much more variable in the small population. Variations in gene frequencies which arise because of sampling errors in finite populations are known as *genetic drift*. Sewall Wright has shown by mathematical analysis that if several small populations have at some time identical gene frequencies, these gene frequencies may, because of genetic drift, become different with time. Similarly, in any one population the gene frequencies may change with time if the population is small. Kerr and Wright have demonstrated experimentally that this is what actually happens in Drosophila populations.

The smaller the population, the greater will be the importance of genetic drift (the "bottleneck" effect); in very large populations its influence will be negligible. Whether or not the differences in the incidence of the blood-group genes among human populations can be accounted for by genetic drift alone is a problem that cannot be settled at present. This depends on whether or not human populations were sufficiently small to permit the requisite amount of genetic drift to occur during the early stages of human evolution, when the human species was becoming distributed over the face of the earth. Random genetic drift is, of course, not a force which excludes selection. It is indeed probable that the development of human races involved interaction of natural selection with genetic drift, selection being relatively more important for some traits and drift for others.

RACES AND INDIVIDUALS

In organisms that reproduce sexually and by cross-fertilization, races are Mendelian populations that differ in the relative frequencies of genes or chromosomal structures. They are neither individuals nor arbitrarily chosen groups of individuals but Mendelian populations (see p. 241). Suppose that we designated everyone having blood of Group O as belonging to an "O race," everyone with blood of group A as belonging to an "A race," etc. The race to which any individual belongs would then be determinable simply by testing his blood. Such a "racial" classification would lead to absurd consequences, because brothers and sisters often have bloods that differ from one another or from those of the parents. Furthermore, a "race" classification based on the O–A–B–AB blood grouping would not coincide with that based on the rhesus alleles, and such characters as eye colors, skin colors, and head shapes are again distributed to some extent independently of the blood groups and of each other. A "race" classification that would unite in a single race individuals with identical genotypes might be applicable to organisms that reproduce asexually or by self-fertilization, in which exist clones and pure lines, the members of which are genotypically identical. In cross-fertilizing organisms such a classification would be absurd, because virtually every sexual individual has a genotype not found in any other individual, so that a "race" would consist of a single individual.

Since, in crossbreeding species, members of a race have different genotypes, it may happen that an individual of one race population will, with respect to some genes, resemble members of another population more than it resembles other individuals of its own race. For example, a "white" person who has blood of *cDe* type resembles, *to that extent,* many members of the Negro race (see p. 281); and an individual of *Drosophila pseudoobscura* from Arizona carrying an ST chromosome is, in that respect, more like a representative of the California population than most other individuals native to Arizona (Fig. 20.4). Because races are populations and not individuals, it may be difficult or impossible to classify some individuals as belonging to any one race. A specimen of *D. pseudoobscura* with PP chromosomes is more likely from Texas than from California, but a specimen with AR chromosomes may occur anywhere from Texas to California (Fig. 20.4). It is easy to distinguish members of human populations native to northern Europe from members of the population of central Africa, but it is often difficult to distinguish members of northern European and central European populations.

RACE DIVERGENCE

Race differences vary in magnitude. Neighboring populations may contain the same genes with only slightly different frequencies, but between populations of remote countries frequencies may be distinct enough to identify most individuals as belonging to one or the other population. In systematic zoology and botany, only populations that are distinct enough so that at least 80 per cent of the individuals in them are classifiable as belonging to one or the other population are referred to as races and are given scientific names in Latin (Mayr). But geneticists and evolutionists are inclined to emphasize the fact that races may have any degree of distinctness. They are dynamic rather than static entities; they become more and more distinct in the course of evolution and finally cease to be races, turning into separate species. This is an essential part of Darwin's theory of evolution. Populations in countries with different environments become adapted to these environments and accumulate numerous genetic differences, for races may differ in many genes, just as species do.

Races of sexually reproducing species occur mostly in different territories, so that in no one territory will more than a single race of any one species be found. In other words, most races are *geographic races* or *subspecies*. This is understandable, for if more than one sexual population lived in the same territory, these populations would cross, and the gene exchange between the populations would fuse them into a single population. There are, however, exceptions to the rule of geographic separation of races of a species. One of these exceptions occurs in the human species. The development of culture has permitted human races, which in the past were restricted to different territories, to exist side by side in the same geographic region without immediate fusion. This is possible because intermarriage of members of differ-

ent human populations, or *isolates,* as they are sometimes called, is often prevented not only by geographical but also by social, religious, economic, and other cultural causes. Nevertheless, as time goes on, the genetic differences between human populations are decreasing rather than increasing. Isolates tend gradually to break down and eventually to fuse into larger, more variable populations.

Varieties and "breeds" of domesticated animals and plants are also races in the genetic sense, some of which occur in the same territory without fusion. Several breeds of dogs, and, of course, that variable animal called the mongrel, occur in every American town. However, the separate existence of the breeds is possible only so long as mating between them is prevented by man, who accomplishes for the breeds of dogs what geographic isolation does for races of wild animals and plants. The situation is quite different in asexually reproducing or self-pollinated forms, for in them relatively simple precautions suffice to prevent crossing of the different populations.

GENETICS OF SPECIES FORMATION

SPECIES ARE FUNDAMENTAL biological units which, before the advent of evolution theories, were supposed to represent separate acts of creation. How great an importance was attached by Darwin to the demonstration that species arise by divergence of races of previously existing species can be seen from the title of his classical work, "The Origin of Species by Means of Natural Selection or the Preservation of Favored Races in the Struggle for Life." Genetics has made significant contributions toward a better understanding of the nature of species.

REPRODUCTIVE ISOLATION AND SPECIATION

We have seen in the preceding chapter that races of sexually reproducing species are, as a rule, *allopatric,* that is, geographically isolated and living in different territories. Geographic isolation permits races not only to maintain their distinctness as populations but also to diverge further, that is, to accumulate more and more genetic differences. Increas-

ing genetic divergence of races may lead to formation of reproductively isolated populations, or *species.* Owing to reproductive isolation, related species may, and often do, become *sympatric,* that is, live side by side in the same territory. The most important change that transforms races into species is, then, the development of reproductive isolating mechanisms between the diverging populations. A *reproductive isolating mechanism* is any genetically determined agency that restricts or prevents the interbreeding of Mendelian populations. Several kinds of reproductive isolating mechanisms are known. The following are probably most important in the maintenance of species in nature.

Populations of different species may be confined to different habitats in the same geographic region because of their preferences for different soils or different amounts of moisture or because of dependence upon different hosts or different kinds of food. Such *habitat isolation* may give members of the isolated populations little or no opportunity to meet and mate. For example, the spiderwort species *Tradescantia canaliculata* and *T. subaspera* grow, respectively, on sunny exposures at the tops of cliffs and in the forest shade at the bottom of cliffs (Fig. 21.1). In the Sierra Nevada of California, the related species *Drosophila pseudoobscura* and *D. persimilis* prefer to live, respectively, at low and at high elevations.

If representatives of different species reach sexual maturity or flowering times at different seasons of the year, they are called *seasonally isolated*. According to Blair, the toad

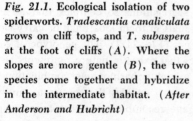

Fig. 21.1. Ecological isolation of two spiderworts. *Tradescantia canaliculata* grows on cliff tops, and *T. subaspera* at the foot of cliffs (*A*). Where the slopes are more gentle (*B*), the two species come together and hybridize in the intermediate habitat. (*After Anderson and Hubricht*)

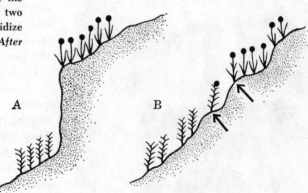

talia of one species are mechanically incompatible with the genitalia of the opposite sex of another species (*mechanical isolation*). In plants, differences in flower structure often make cross-pollination by the same insect difficult.

Spermatozoa of one species may not be attracted to eggs of another or may be poorly viable in the sexual ducts of females of foreign species (*gametic isolation*). According to Patterson and Stone, spermatozoa of *Drosophila virilis* survive for only about a day in the sperm receptacles of *D. americana*

Bufo americanus breeds earlier in the spring than the related species *B. fowleri*. The breeding seasons of the species overlap to some extent, and some interspecific hybrids are produced.

When females and males of different species come together, matings may occur mainly or exclusively between representatives of the same species. This is *sexual isolation*. For example, if a mixture of females of *Drosophila persimilis* and *D. pseudoobscura* are exposed to males of one of these species, the proportion of conspecific females inseminated is greater than that of foreign females. Selective mating occurs because courtship and mating habits often differ in different species. It may occur also because the geni-

females, whereas spermatozoa of *D. americana* males remain alive much longer. In plants, the pollen tubes of one species may grow slowly, or may burst, in the styles of other species, as shown in species of the Jimson weed (Datura) by Blakeslee, Buchholz, and their collaborators.

If F_1-generation hybrids between species are produced, gene exchange between the populations of these species may nevertheless fail to occur because of *hybrid inviability* or *hybrid sterility*. Hybrid zygotes may die at any stage, from the time immediately following fertilization to reproductive maturity. For example, the two species of flax, *Linum austriacum* and *L. perenne*, can be crossed, but the hybrid seeds fail to germinate. Laibach showed, however, that if the embryos are dissected from these seeds and grown on nutrient media they eventually give rise to seedlings, which then develop into

Fig. 21.2. Hybrids between different species of tobacco illustrated by typical corollas. Upper row: left, *Nicotiana langsdorffii;* right, *N. san-derae;* center, F$_1$ hybrid *N. langsdorffii* × *san-derae.* Remaining four rows: corollas of F$_2$ segregants from this cross. (*Courtesy of Harold H. Smith*)

normal, fertile plants. In other species crosses, the hybrids not only survive but may be fully as vigorous as the parental species; yet they may be partly or completely sterile. The classical example of hybrid sterility is the mule, the outcome of hybridization of the horse and the ass. The degeneration of

the sex cells in mules contrasts strongly with their general hardiness and the normality of their sexual instincts. Female mules are alleged to be occasionally fertile. Fertility of one sex in species hybrids frequently goes together with partial or complete sterility of the other sex. Thus, *Drosophila pseudoobscura* and *D. persimilis* produce completely sterile male hybrids, whereas hybrid females deposit about as many eggs as do females of pure species when crossed back to males of either of the latter.

Since species usually differ in many genes, progenies of fertile, interspecific hybrids may show segregations so complex that no two individuals in them look alike or carry similar genes (Fig. 21.2). The genotype of each species that exists in nature represents an at least tolerably harmonious combination of genes which enables the species to survive. The gene recombinations that arise in species hybrids are, on the contrary, often disharmonious to such an extent that the F$_2$ of species crosses may consist largely of ill-adapted individuals. Such a *hybrid breakdown* has been observed, for example, in hybrids between different species of cotton (Gossypium) by Harland, Stephens, and other investigators.

Partial and Complete Isolation. Reproductive isolating mechanisms may be either complete or partial. Thus, sexual isolation may amount merely to a slight preference for mating with representatives of the same species. It may be strong enough so that mating of females of one species with males of another occurs only as an exception. Or the aversion to interspecies mating may be absolute. Hybrid inviability may involve only a constitutional weakness, or the hybrids may seldom or never survive.

Furthermore, the exchange of genes between related species is usually prevented not by a single isolating mechanism but by cooperation of several mechanisms that reinforce one another. For example, although *Drosophila pseudoobscura* and *D. persimilis* show some ecological isolation, both species occur side by side in many localities; sexual isolation is quite pronounced, yet if females of one species are confined with males of the other, some cross-inseminations occur; male hybrids are invariably and completely sterile, but hybrid females are fertile if crossed back to males of the parental species; the backcross offspring are weak, but some individuals survive. In laboratory experiments, genes and chromosome sections of either species may, by appropriate crosses, be "transferred" to the other species. Nevertheless, almost no hybrids between these species have been found in nature, even in localities where they occur together.

The combined actions of several reproductive isolating mechanisms may add up to a complete suppression or to only partial inhibition of hybridization and of the consequent gene exchange between species populations. Interspecific hybrids are known to occur in nature as more or less exceptional individuals. Thus, Blair, Volpe and others found that hybrids between the toad species *Bufo americanus* and *B. fowleri* occur rather regularly whenever these two species inhabit the same territory.

The Process of Speciation. Many attempts have been made to define species as forms that produce no hybrids or completely sterile hybrids. All such attempts break down. There exist species that are completely isolated reproductively, so that no hybrids occur in nature, and yet they can be crossed and produce fertile hybrids in experiments (for example, the mallard and pintail ducks, *Anas platyrhynchos* and *Dafila acuta*). Furthermore, since species arise by gradual divergence of races, there is bound to be a stage in this divergence process when some reproductive isolation has appeared but when it is not yet strong enough to suppress the gene exchange to an extent sufficient to maintain the species populations as separate entities. In other words, there exist borderline cases between races and species. Pat-

terson and Stone regarded *Drosophila americana, D. texana,* and *D. novamexicana* as distinct species, but finding hybrids between them in nature, they now prefer to consider them races of a single species. The existence of such borderline cases is troublesome to taxonomists who would like to have races and species absolutely fixed categories, but such cases are most interesting and valuable to a geneticist, since they furnish one of the best proofs of the reality of the evolutionary process.

The attainment of the species status, that is, the advent of reproductive isolation between populations, is, biologically considered, an event of fundamental importance. This is because the evolutionary divergence becomes irreversible at this stage. So long as diverging races are not yet reproductively isolated, they are potentially able to hybridize and to merge back into a single population. Human races are an excellent example of such a merging process. Even before the dawn of civilization, *Homo sapiens* had become split up into races which, if the genetic divergence had continued, might have reached the status of separate species. But with progressively increasing mobility of human populations, the races of man now show an unmistakable trend toward hybridization and fusion into a single highly variable population. In contrast, horse and ass are species that have attained complete or nearly complete reproductive isolation. A genetic barrier between them is maintained despite the mass production of sterile, man-made hybrids.

INTROGRESSIVE HYBRIDIZATION

Interesting results come from occasional hybridization of incompletely isolated species. In nature, highly variable populations that consist of segregating progenies of species hybrids (*hybrid swarms*) may occur at geographic boundaries that separate the distribution regions of related species, especially in plants. Thus, the ecologically isolated species *Tradescantia canaliculata* and *T. sub-aspera* intercross in places where their habitats merge into each other.

Teosinte (*Zea mexicana*), a grass species found in some parts of Mexico and Guatemala, is, botanically speaking, the nearest relative of cultivated maize, *Zea mays*,

Fig. 21.3. A plant of teosinte (*Zea mexicana*). (*From Mangelsdorf and Reeves*)

which grows in a wild state (Fig. 21.3). It was a plausible guess that teosinte is the wild progenitor from which maize arose in cultivation. Mangelsdorf and Reeves have, however, put forward an alternative hypothesis. Teosinte, far from being the ancestor of cultivated maize, is itself the result of hybridization of maize with still another grass, namely Tripsacum (Fig. 21.4). The chromosomes of teosinte are similar to those of maize except for four different blocks of genes presumably derived from Tripsacum. Maize arose, according to this view, from an unknown plant that grew wild somewhere in Central or South America and became ex-

Fig. 21.4. Representatives of maize (left) and of Tripsacum (right). (*Courtesy of P. C. Mangelsdorf*)

tinct in the meanwhile. In Central America the primitive maize encountered Tripsacum, and from hybridization of the two there arose, on the one hand, teosinte and, on the other, the varieties of maize now cultivated in North America. Hybridization that introduces some genes of one species into the genotype of another species has been called by Anderson *introgressive hybridization*.

MORPHOLOGICAL AND GENETIC DIFFERENCES
BETWEEN SPECIES

Races of a species and species of a genus carry different assortments of genes. The genes of these races and species make them adapted to live in different environments or to exploit the same environment in different ways. Since their genes are different, species often differ from each other in color, size, and the properties of various body parts. These external manifestations of the genotypic differences permit recognition of the species, and sometimes of the race, to which an individual belongs. Systematic zoologists and botanists distinguish species and races by their visible external characteristics. The genetic divergence need not, however, be strictly proportional to the externally visible divergence. Some species are reproductively completely isolated but are similar or identical in appearance, whereas races of a species may be strikingly different to our eyes. An example of species that are morphologically almost indistinguishable are *Drosophila pseudoobscura* and *D. persimilis*. They differ in geographical distribution and in habitat preferences; they show many physiological differences; and reproductive isolation between them is strong enough so that no hybrids are found in nature. They differ also in the arrangement of the genes in some of their chromosomes. Yet except for very slight and broadly overlapping differences in the proportions of the wings and the thorax and slight differences in the shape of the male genitalia, the two species are externally identical. Such morphologically similar species are called *sibling species*. Conversely, geographic races within certain species of pheasants, birds of paradise, and of some insects show external differences that are more striking than those that distinguish many species.

ORIGIN OF REPRODUCTIVE ISOLATION

The essential feature of the process of species formation, or *speciation,* as it is sometimes called, consists in the development of reproductive isolation between the genetically diverging Mendelian populations. An example of how reproductive isolation may arise and become strengthened may be seen in the work of Koopman on the sibling species *Drosophila pseudoobscura* and *D. persimilis.* As we have seen, these species show a considerable sexual isolation, so that in mixed populations the matings between females and males of the same species are more frequent than interspecific matings. This sexual isolation is, however, weaker at lower than at higher temperatures, at least when the flies live in laboratory environments. Koopman set up at a low temperature experimental populations consisting of equal numbers of individuals of the two species in population cages (Fig. 19.4). The two species were each made homozygous for different recessive mutant genes, so that the hybrid flies were easily recognizable. In every generation, the hybrid flies were removed and the populations restarted with the pure species. Generation after generation, the proportion of the hybrid flies diminished until the sexual isolation at the low temperature became about as strong as at higher temperatures. This result is due to the selection in the experimental populations of flies genetically conditioned to mate with partners of their own species in preference to interspecific matings. Indeed, the "promiscuous" flies that mated with the species other than their own produced hybrid progenies, and these were removed from the population; the progenies of the matings within a species served as parents of the next generations. Such a selective process would be expected to favor the development of reproductive isolation in nature as well when the gene exchange between different races leads to formation of poorly viable, sterile, or otherwise adaptively inferior hybrids.

CHROMOSOME DIFFERENCES
BETWEEN SPECIES

Species of a genus or a family may have either similar or different numbers of chromosomes. Thus, most of the numerous species of several subfamilies of short-horned grasshoppers (Acrididae) have 12 pairs of chromosomes. Mosquitoes have 3 pairs of chromosomes. On the other hand, species of Drosophila may have 3, 4, 5, or 6 chromosomes, and closely related species often have different numbers. The Old World species of Crepis (plants of the family Compositae) have 3, 4, 5, 6, or 7 chromosomes, whereas American species have 11 or more chromosomes. A special case of variation in chromosome numbers occurs in *polyploid series,* the members of which have chromosome numbers that are multiples of some basic number. For example, species of wheat and related grasses have 7, 14, or 21 chromosomes. Polyploid series are common in some genera of plants but rare in animals.

Except for polyploidy (p. 299), changes of chromosome numbers arise by translocations. Suppose, for example, that two of the chromosomes in a haploid set of a certain species have subterminal centromeres (Fig. 15.13). The translocation shown in the diagram results in the formation of a V-shaped chromosome (with a median centromere) and a small fragment with another centromere. If this fragment is subsequently lost, the chromosome number becomes one less than it originally was, and yet few or no genes are lost, since the part of the chromosome adjacent to the centromere is often heterochromatic and contains few indispensable genes. Increase of the chromosome number usually requires a duplication by nondisjunction of a chromosome or a chromosome fragment to furnish an extra centromere. A translocation of a part of one of the other chromosomes onto the duplication then gives a chromosome group (*karyotype*) with one chromosome more than was originally present (Fig. 15.6). Dubinin has succeeded in proving that these theoretical schemes actually work in practice; he obtained in experiments a strain of *Drosophila melanogaster* with *three* instead of the original *four* pairs of chromosomes. Less direct evidence has been obtained by Tobgy for *Crepis fuliginosa,* with three pairs of chromosomes, and *C. neglecta,* with four pairs of chromosomes (Fig. 21.5).

These changes in the numbers of chromosomes are made possible by the fact that in a majority of plants and animals, each chromosome has a specialized organelle, the centromere, which controls the anaphase movements of the chromosomes. Chromosomes that lack a centromere undergo irregular disjunction at mitosis, fail to be included in the daughter nuclei, and ultimately are lost. In some plants at least, the centromeres are capable of being fractured, and it is a remarkable fact that each portion of the original centromere is still able to function normally and thus to provide one additional

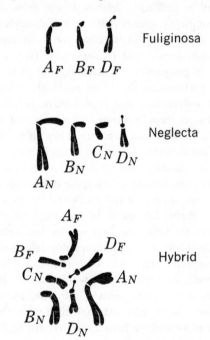

Fig. 21.5. Haploid sets of chromosomes of *Crepis fuliginosa* and *C. neglecta,* and a diploid chromosome group in a hybrid of these species. (*After Tobgy*)

centromere. The divisibility of the centromeres has made it possible for Rhoades to synthesize a strain of maize with 11 rather than 10 pairs of chromosomes. It is possible that increases in chromosome number in the course of evolution have occurred in a similar fashion.

A convincing demonstration of evolutionary changes in karyotype brought about by translocations has emerged from compara-

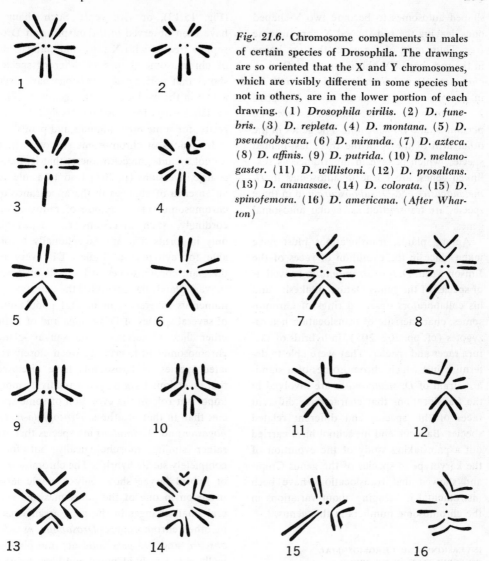

Fig. 21.6. Chromosome complements in males of certain species of Drosophila. The drawings are so oriented that the X and Y chromosomes, which are visibly different in some species but not in others, are in the lower portion of each drawing. (1) *Drosophila virilis*. (2) *D. funebris*. (3) *D. repleta*. (4) *D. montana*. (5) *D. pseudoobscura*. (6) *D. miranda*. (7) *D. azteca*. (8) *D. affinis*. (9) *D. putrida*. (10) *D. melanogaster*. (11) *D. willistoni*. (12) *D. prosaltans*. (13) *D. ananassae*. (14) *D. colorata*. (15) *D. spinofemora*. (16) *D. americana*. (After Wharton)

tive cytogenetic studies on species of Drosophila. The simplest, and perhaps ancestral, chromosome complement present in species of various sections of the genus Drosophila consists of five pairs of rod-shaped and one pair of dotlike chromosomes (*Drosophila subobscura, D. virilis,* and others, Fig. 21.6). One of the rod-shaped chromosomes is the X chromosome. Translocation between the X chromosome and one of the autosomes gives rise to the chromosome complement found

in *D. pseudoobscura* and *D. persimilis*: a pair of V-shaped X chromosomes and three pairs of rodlike and a pair of dotlike autosomes. Two more translocations combine two of the autosomal rods into another V-shaped autosome with a median centromere and cause the dot to join the remaining rod, thus giving rise to the karyotype of *D. willistoni* (Fig. 21.6). The karyotype of *D. melanogaster* is derived from the presumed ancestral one by two translocations that tie together four rod-shaped autosomes to become two V-shaped ones, leaving the rod-shaped X chromosome free. Thus, most of the genes that are borne in the rod-shaped X chromosome of *D. melanogaster, D. subobscura,* and *D. virilis* lie in just one of the two arms of the V-shaped X chromosome in *D. pseudoobscura, D. persimilis,* and *D. willistoni.* The genes in the other arm of the X in the three last-named species, which behave in inheritance as sex-linked genes, are borne in autosomes in *D. melanogaster* and *D. subobscura* and in these species are transmitted as regular autosomal genes.

Among plants, translocations must have taken place in the evolution of races of the Jimson weed, *Datura stramonium,* as well as of species of the genus Datura. Blakeslee and his collaborators observed rings of chromosomes, characteristic of translocation heterozygotes (cf. pp. 202–205), in hybrids of Datura races and species. They were able to determine just which chromosomes of a stand-ard strain of *D. stramonium* are involved in the translocations that characterize different races of this species and different related species. Babcock and his school have carried out a painstaking study of the evolution of the karyotype in species of the genus Crepis and showed that translocations have been instrumental in bringing about variations in the chromosome numbers in this genus.

INVERSIONS AND CHROMOSOMAL
DIFFERENTIATION OF SPECIES

Inversions of blocks of genes play an important role in the evolution of chromosomes. However, changes of the gene arrangement produced by inversions only rarely lead to visible alterations of the chromosome shape, when in some pericentric inversions (see p. 208) a shift in the position of the centromere occurs with respect to the ends of the chromosome. An originally V-shaped chromosome (with a median centromere) may then become hook-shaped or rod-shaped (with a subterminal centromere)

(Fig. 15.13), or vice versa. Such changes have been observed in the offspring of Drosophila treated with X rays, and comparison of chromosome shapes in different species shows that pericentric inversions have been active in the evolution of this genus. Similar evidence exists for grasshoppers and, less directly, for some other animals and plants.

Inversions of chromosome sections which do not include the centromere, that is, paracentric inversions (p. 207) lead, as a rule, to an absence of changes in the appearance of chromosomes at metaphase of mitosis. Accordingly, such inversions are detectable only in forms that are exceptionally favorable for cytogenetic studies. Discovery of the giant chromosomes in the cells of larval salivary glands has permitted the detection of numerous inversions in natural populations of several species of Drosophila and of some other flies. Observations on salivary-gland chromosomes in hybrids between closely related species of Drosophila have disclosed that inversions have played a relatively more important role in the evolution of some species than in that of others. *Drosophila melanogaster* and *D. simulans* are species that are rather similar morphologically but form completely sterile hybrids. The chromosomes of hybrid larvae show only a single large inversion in one of the autosomes and several small changes in the gene arrangement in other chromosomes. *Drosophila pseudoobscura* and *D. persimilis* are morphologically very nearly identical and form hybrids that are sterile in the male sex but fertile in the female. Their chromosomes differ usually in four large inversions.[1] The incipient species or races *D. americana, D. texana,* and *D. novamexicana* and their close relative, *D. virilis,* show slight morphological differences and give semifertile hybrids. Ac-

[1] Since, as shown above, inversions occur not only between species but also within a species, the number of inversions in interspecific hybrids depends somewhat on which strains of the parental species are used to produce hybrids.

cording to Patterson and Hsu, these forms differ in up to eight inverted sections in several chromosomes. Finally, *D. pseudo-obscura* and *D. miranda* differ morphologically to about the same extent as *D. melanogaster* and *D. simulans* and also give completely sterile hybrids. The gene arrangements in their chromosomes have been modified by repeated inversions to such an extent that the homology is no longer recognizable in many chromosome sections, and very complex pairing configurations are formed by the chromosomes in the salivary-gland cells of hybrid larvae (Figs. 21.7 and 21.8).

Thus the degree of morphological divergence, of hybrid sterility, and of the differentiation of the chromosome structure do not necessarily go hand in hand in evolution.

GENIC AND CHROMOSOMAL STERILITY

In 1913, while studying spermatogenesis in the semisterile hybrids between species of the moth genus Pygaera, Federley made the fundamental discovery that their sterility is connected with the failure of the chromosomes of the parental species to pair at meiosis. In the testes of the hybrid males, the behavior of the cells is normal up to the stage when the chromosomes should undergo pairing. Only a few of the chromosomes pair, whereupon most of the prospective gametes degenerate and make the hybrid very nearly sterile. Failure of the meiotic pairing of chromosomes has been observed since 1913 in many other semisterile and sterile species hybrids both in plants and in animals. This naturally leads to the surmise that the failure of chromosome pairing is a cause of hybrid sterility.

As was shown above (p. 204), individuals heterozygous for translocations produce spores or gametes some of which contain certain genes in excess and are deficient for certain other genes. In plants, spores with such duplications and deficiencies usually abort. In animals, gametes with abnormal complements of genes function, but the zygotes they form usually die. In either case, translocation heterozygotes are semisterile. Since translocations occur in the evolution of species, species hybrids are often translocation heterozygotes. This probably accounts for the sterility of some hybrids. Furthermore, we know that chromosomes are changed in evolution by inversions and other chromosomal aberrations. Chromosomes of different species may, then, contain the same gene loci but arranged in quite different orders. When such chromosomes meet in the cells of an interspecific hybrid, they may be unable to accomplish meiotic pairing for purely mechanical reasons. Indeed, meiotic pairing depends upon attraction between homologous genes rather than between chromosomes as wholes. Chromosomes that contain genes differently arranged will hence be subjected at meiosis to conflicting attraction forces. Failure of the meiotic pairing and failure to establish chiasmata between homologous chromosomes interfere with the normal course of meiosis and may tend to make the hybrid sterile. Hybrid sterility produced by differences in the gene arrangements in the chromosomes of the parental species is termed *chromosomal sterility*.

The sterility of some hybrids cannot, however, be ascribed to difficulties in the meiotic pairing alone. For example, in the testes of male mules the degeneration of the prospective gametes begins before the stage at which the meiotic pairing of chromosomes would normally take place. Conversely, in hybrids between some strains of *Drosophila pseudoobscura* and *D. persimilis*, chromosomes seem to pair normally, but in spite of this, degenerative changes occur. *D. melanogaster* and *D. simulans* produce completely sterile hybrids, although their gene arrangements are more similar than among some races within a species which produce quite fertile hybrids. This suggests that the sterility of these hybrids is not caused by differences in gene arrangement between the parental species. An alternative explanation of the sterility is that the parents contribute genes that interact in the hybrid in such a manner as to disturb the normal course of meiosis and of sex-cell formation. Hybrid sterility caused by the genic constitution of

many chromosomes as the ancestral cells do. Formation of such polyploid cells occurs spontaneously and may be induced artificially. Among polyploids, *tetraploids* have the diploid chromosome complement doubled, *triploids* have each chromosome in trip-

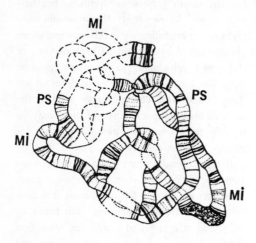

the hybrids rather than by differences in the gene arrangements in the parental chromosomes is called *genic sterility*. A good example is found in the amphidiploid hybrid of *Nicotiana sylvestris* × *N. tomentosa,* which showed female sterility. Greenleaf found that this was due to the complementary action of genes from the parent species in causing abortion of embryo sacs. It is, of course, quite possible that the sterility of some hybrids is caused by a combination of chromosomal and genic sterility. One of the possible methods of testing whether the sterility of a given hybrid is chromosomal or genic is examination of the behavior of the chromosomes in individuals in which the chromosomal complement has been doubled by polyploidy.

AUTOPOLYPLOIDS

Chromosome division followed by failure of division of the nucleus and of the cell results in the production of cells in which every chromosome in the original cell is present in duplicate; therefore these cells have twice as

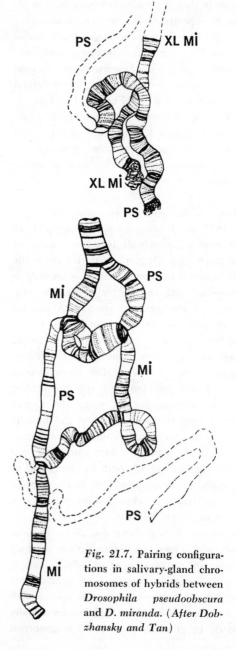

Fig. 21.7. Pairing configurations in salivary-gland chromosomes of hybrids between *Drosophila pseudoobscura* and *D. miranda.* (*After Dobzhansky and Tan*)

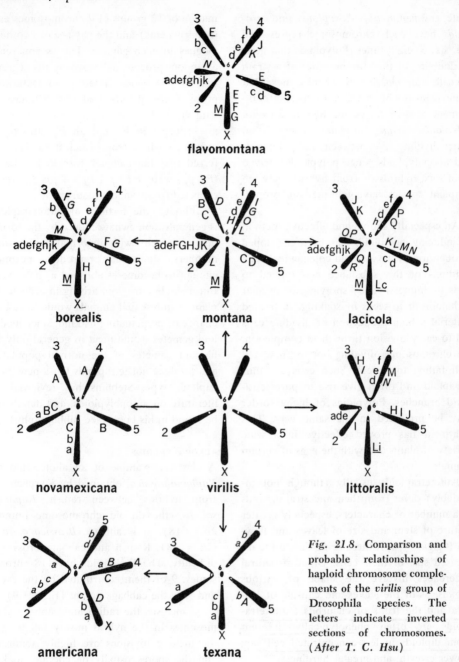

Fig. 21.8. Comparison and probable relationships of haploid chromosome complements of the *virilis* group of Drosophila species. The letters indicate inverted sections of chromosomes. (*After T. C. Hsu*)

licate, and *pentaploids, hexaploids,* and *octoploids* have each chromosome represented five, six, or eight times. Polyploids that arise by doubling of the chromosomes of a strain are called *autopolyploids,* whereas those that come from doubling the chromosome complement of an interspecific hybrid are *allopolyploids,* or *amphidiploids.* There is no sharp dividing line between autopolyploids and allopolyploids, since polyploids derived from race hybrids or from hybrids between incipient species have intermediate properties.

An especially simple and effective method of inducing polyploids has been developed through use of the alkaloid colchicine. Weak solutions of this substance are applied to buds by immersion, by spraying, or in agar or lanolin or to seeds by soaking. In treated material a high proportion of dividing cells fail to carry division through to completion, the chromosomes dividing but the new cell wall failing to appear. Such cells are thus tetraploid and often give rise to pure tetraploid branches. Polyploids of higher order may be produced in the same way. This treatment has proved effective in a wide variety of plants and with the eggs of certain animals.

Autotetraploids usually (though not invariably) differ from their ancestral diploids in a number of characters, especially greater stature of stem and size of leaves and flowers ("gigas" type), these being due to the increased size of their cells. Other structural differences involve the shape of various organs, as of the leaves and capsule of Datura and the fruits of cucurbits. Autotetraploids are often phenotypically different from diploids in less-concentrated cell sap, slower growth, and greater hardiness.

The reproduction of autotetraploids may be almost normal. The tetraploid Datura produces viable gametes with 2n chromosomes (24) and a few with irregular numbers. These regular gametes result from the reduction of the 48 chromosomes by the formation of 12 groups of 4 chromosomes each (quadrivalents) and the passage of two homologues to each gamete. This is apparently a random process, as shown by the segregation of two genes in tetraploid Datura. A purple-flowered tetraploid (*PP PP*) crossed with a white-flowered tetraploid (*pp pp*) gives purple in F_1 and an F_2 ratio of 35 purple : 1 white, from which it has been inferred that the gametes formed by the F_1 (*PP pp*) were 1 *PP* : 4 *Pp* : 1 *pp,* the result expected from random assortment.

Although the fertility of autotetraploids is generally somewhat reduced by the formation of gametes with abnormal chromosome numbers, some may reproduce normally enough to become established as new types. But a single tetraploid arising in a dioecious plant or in bisexual animals would have little chance of perpetuating its kind, since its diploid gametes would meet in general only the haploid gametes of the normal population and produce not tetraploids but a new 3n or triploid, type. Stebbins has reviewed the literature on autopolyploids, and details will be found in his book (see Bibliography).

ALLOPOLYPLOIDS

A classical example of an allotetraploid is *Raphanobrassica,* obtained by Karpechenko from hybrids between radish, *Raphanus sativus* (the diploid chromosome number, 2n = 18), and cabbage, *Brassica oleracea* (2n = 18). Radish and cabbage cross with difficulty. The F_1 hybrids have 18 chromosomes, 9 of them contributed by the radish and 9 by the cabbage parent (Fig. 21.9).

At meiosis, the radish and cabbage chromosomes in the hybrid mostly fail to pair, the meiotic divisions are highly abnormal, and the spores usually degenerate, making the hybrid very nearly sterile—a typical case of sterility of an interspecific hybrid. However, in some cells the chromosome complement undergoes a doubling, and this leads to formation of a few seeds, from which some second-generation hybrids can be obtained.

Most of these have 36 chromosomes, the sum of the chromosome numbers of the two parent species (9 *pairs* of radish and 9 *pairs* of cabbage chromosomes). Such tetraploid hybrids are remarkable for their giant size and even more so for their almost complete fertility and true breeding; since their morphological characters are intermediate between radish and cabbage, although they are infertile with both parent species, the name

and in no segregation of characters of the parental species.

The contrast between the abnormal chromosome behavior at meiosis in the diploid radish × cabbage hybrid and the normal meiosis in the tetraploid Raphanobrassica is striking. No less striking is the contrast between the sterility of the diploid and the fertility of the tetraploid hybrid. The failure of bivalent formation in the diploid hybrids

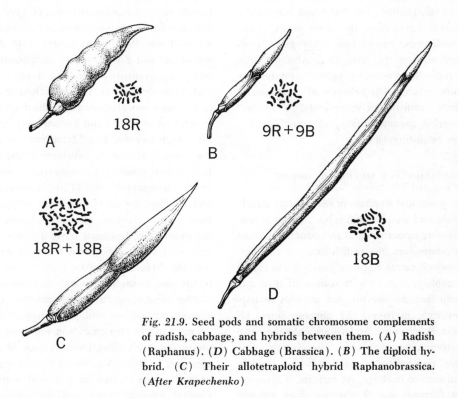

Fig. 21.9. Seed pods and somatic chromosome complements of radish, cabbage, and hybrids between them. (*A*) Radish (Raphanus). (*D*) Cabbage (Brassica). (*B*) The diploid hybrid. (*C*) Their allotetraploid hybrid Raphanobrassica. (*After Krapechenko*)

Raphanobrassica has been given to them (Fig. 21.9).

The chromosome behavior at meiosis in diploid Raphanobrassica is entirely normal. The plant's 36 chromosomes form 18 bivalents, and the embryo sacs and pollen grains carry 18 chromosomes, 9 of them representing the full radish complement and the other 9 the full cabbage complement. Fertilization results in new plants with 36 chromosomes

is here caused by dissimilarities in the gene arrangements in the radish and cabbage chromosomes. This is a case of *chromosomal sterility*. At meiosis, radish chromosomes do not find normal mates among the cabbage chromosomes, and vice versa. On the other hand, the tetraploid carries every radish and cabbage chromosome in duplicate, and consequently every chromosome has a mate with a precisely similar gene arrangement, as the formation of the 18 bivalents clearly shows.

Allotetraploid hybrids are, however, by no means always fertile, nor do they always have normal meiosis. For example, tetraploid cells are frequently formed in the testes of the sterile male hybrids between *Drosophila pseudoobscura* and *D. persimilis,* but meiosis in such cells is just as abnormal as in the diploid ones, and no functional gametes are formed. The sterility of these hybrids is evidently genic, caused by their genetic constitution. The tetraploid cells in the hybrids carry, then, the same genes as the diploid ones, except that every gene is reduplicated in the tetraploid. Abnormalities in meiosis accordingly persist, and fertility is not restored. The behavior of the allotetraploids furnishes, consequently, a method whereby chromosomal and genic sterility may be distinguished.

POLYPLOIDY AS A METHOD OF ORIGIN
OF SPECIES

The tetraploid Raphanobrassica is not merely fertile and true-breeding, but it is to a considerable extent isolated reproductively from its progenitors, the radish and the cabbage. Crosses between Raphanobrassica and radish or cabbage succeed with some difficulty, and when they do, the progeny consists of triploid hybrids having 27 chromosomes. Of these, 9 are radish and 18 are cabbage chromosomes, or vice versa, depending upon whether Raphanobrassica is backcrossed to radish or to cabbage. At meiosis, 9 bivalents are formed, and 9 chromosomes are left without mates and remain univalent. The bivalents result evidently from pairing among the two sets of 9 chromosomes derived from one species, and the univalents are the chromosomes of the other species. At the meiotic divisions, the bivalents divide normally, sending a set of 9 chromosomes to each pole of the division spindle; but the univalents are distributed at random to the daughter cells so that the spores have varying chromosome numbers, from 9 to 18.

Most of these spores degenerate, and the triploid hybrids are largely sterile.

Raphanobrassica is, then, effectively a new species produced in an experiment. It is important that species formation by allopolyploidy, by a method exemplified by Raphanobrassica, has taken place in nature in many plant genera. Furthermore, in at least one case an existing polyploid species has been resynthesized experimentally. Müntzing crossed two species of the mint family, *Galeopsis pubescens* and *G. speciosa,* both having 16 chromosomes in diploid condition. From the diploid hybrid, with 8 *G. pubescens* and 8 *G. speciosa* chromosomes, Müntzing eventually obtained a tetraploid with 32 chromosomes. This tetraploid proved to resemble morphologically a third species, also found in nature and known as *G. tetrahit,* which likewise has 32 chromosomes in the body cells and 16 bivalents at meiosis. It is probable that *G. tetrahit* arose in nature as an allotetraploid hybrid of *G. pubescens* and *G. speciosa* or species very similar to them. The "artificial tetrahit" obtained in the experiment has been crossed to the natural *G. tetrahit.* The cross succeeds easily, and the hybrid resembles both parents, is fertile, and forms 16 bivalents at meiosis.

The American cultivated cottons, *Gossypium barbadense* and *G. hirsutum,* have 26 pairs of chromosomes and represent amphidiploid derivatives from crosses of species with 13 pairs. A group of diploid species with 13 pairs occurs in the wild state in Central America, Peru, and the Galapagos Islands; another group occurs in the Old World (tropical Asia, Africa, and Australia). The American tetraploid cottons contain 13 pairs of chromosomes similar to those found in the American diploids and 13 pairs similar to those in the Old World diploids. The chromosomes of the Old World diploids do not resemble those of the American diploids. The tetraploid species probably arose from hybrids between the American and the Old World diploid species, by doubling of the chromosomal complement. An intriguing but unsolved problem is just where and when the American and the Old World diploid species met and crossed. Their present geographic distributions are separated by thousands of miles of tropical oceans, and wild cottons are so definitely tropical and subtropical plants that it is difficult to conceive any of them migrating overland, through the arctic territories in the region of Bering Strait, which seems to furnish the only possible land connection between America and Asia. As a solution to this difficulty, Harland proposed the hypothesis that the formation of the tetraploid cotton species took place very long ago, in early Tertiary or even in Cretaceous times, when the climate of the world was much warmer than it is now. Conversely, Hutchison, Silow, and Stephens suppose that seeds of Old World diploid cottons were transported from Asia across the Pacific Ocean to the west coast of South America by Polynesian mariners. These introduced species then crossed spontaneously with the native American diploids, probably with *Gossypium raymondii* growing wild on the coast of Peru. Doubling of the chromosome complement then gave rise, only some centuries ago, to the American tetraploid cottons.

Species of wheat fall into three groups: diploid einkorn wheats with 14 chromosomes (7 pairs), tetraploid emmer, or hard, wheats with 28 chromosomes (14 pairs), and hexaploid *vulgare,* or soft, wheats with 42 chromosomes (21 pairs). The work of Sax, Kihara, and others showed that the chromosome complement of emmer wheats contains a set of 7 chromosomes similar to those of einkorn wheat and a set of 7 other chromosomes derived from some other plant. *Vulgare* wheats contain 14 pairs of chromosomes similar to the emmers and 7 pairs similar to those found in some species of the grass genus Aegilops. The emmer wheats must, then, have arisen as allotetraploid hybrids. The *vulgare* wheats are allohexaploid

hybrids derived from emmerlike and Aegilopslike ancestors.

ANIMAL POLYPLOIDS

The facts presented on the foregoing pages show that two fundamentally distinct methods of species formation may be distinguished. In probably all groups of organisms that reproduce sexually and by cross-fertilization, species arise by gradual accumulation of genetic differences and divergence of geographic races. On the other hand, in many plant genera, species arise through polyploidy, chiefly through allopolyploidy. By comparison with the slow emergence of species from races, species formation by polyploidy may be said to be an instantaneous process. This instantaneous method of species formation occurs but rarely in the animal kingdom. Chromosome numbers in species of many plant genera and families form series of multiples of a basic number, thus giving indirect evidence of the occurrence of polyploidy in evolution. Such multiples are rare among animals. Although orders and classes of animals may have rather different chromosome numbers (for example, marsupials have 6 to 13 chromosome pairs, whereas placental mammals have 7 to 39 pairs), there is no good reason to think that such differences could not have evolved by translocation (see p. 209) rather than polyploidy.

Spontaneous chromosome doubling leading to formation of polyploid cells and polyploid individuals is not rare in animals, as shown particularly by Fankhauser and his students in salamanders. Yet polyploid races and species have been found, mainly in the aberrant groups that multiply by parthenogenesis rather than by cross-fertilization. Such is the case in the shrimp Artemia, according to Artom, the sow bug Trichoniscus, according to Vandel, and the moth Solenobia, according to Seiler.

Among the species of weevils of the family Curculionidae, Suomalainen has found that all bisexual species have the same chromosome number ($2n = 22$) and sex determination of the Drosophila type (XY males). All the related species that are parthenogenetic are polyploid with 33, 44, or 55 chromosomes. The establishment of bisexual polyploid races in natural populations of an animal species with male heterogamety would, of course, encounter difficulties because of the appearance of sterile intersexes among the triploids as in Drosophila. This would tend to restrict the origin of polyploid races to species with facultative parthenogenesis, and this would be rather rare.

22   DETERMINATION OF SEX

ONE OF THE most conspicuous and interesting kinds of hereditary differences observed among individuals of the same species is surely sex. What determines whether an offspring will be a male or a female? Biologists and nonbiologists alike were puzzled by this riddle for centuries. Literally hundreds of mistaken hypotheses and wild guesses were proposed before 1900 in vain attempts to find a solution to this problem. A valid solution became possible only with the development of genetics in the early years of the twentieth century.

Before the concepts of the genotype and the phenotype were formulated (see Chap. 2), heredity was thought to determine merely the similarities between parents and offspring, and the heredity of a child was supposed to be a compromise between the heredities of the parents. On such a basis, it was difficult to understand how sex could be controlled by heredity. After all, every child had a mother and a father, but some children are females and others males.

THE CHROMOSOMAL THEORY OF SEX DETERMINATION

Two lines of discovery converged in the years after 1900 to clear up the situation. First, it was shown (see Chap. 12) that in some insects the males have an odd number of chromosomes and the females an even number; or in the males one of the pairs of chromosomes consists of unequal partners (XY), whereas in the females this pair is formed by similar chromosomes (XX). In either case, two kinds of spermatozoa are formed in approximately equal numbers, contrasting with only a single kind of egg. Second, Mendelian segregation in backcrosses in which one of the parents is heterozygous for a single pair of alleles was found to produce two types of offspring in nearly equal numbers (see Chap. 3). The male sex is, thus, heterozygous, or *heterogametic*. The sex of an individual is, accordingly, determined at fertilization. The union of an egg with an X-carrying spermatozoon gives a zygote with two X chromosomes, which develops into a female; a spermatozoon containing no X chromosome gives a zygote with a single X, which becomes a male. Females and males obviously differ in their chromosomes and hence in their genotypes. But when they mate, their progeny contains individuals of both genotypes, females and males.

Although the principle is much the same, the chromosomal mechanism of sex determination was found to vary in different organisms. Some of these variations are presented in Table 22.1. In man, in other mammals, and in most insects, including Drosophila, males have an X and a Y chro-

tions of sex-linked inheritance (see Chap. 12) showed that many sex-linked genes are carried in the X, whereas the Y behaved as though it were "empty" of genes. The critical evidence was supplied by Bridges in 1916 (see p. 152). Drosophila males were discovered which lack a Y chromosome (XO males). Such males are sterile but otherwise normal in appearance and in behavior. Females may carry a Y chromosome (XXY females) and, even so, be normal and fertile. This seemed to show that, at least in Drosophila, the presence of one X chromosome makes a male and of two X's a female. The Y chromosome is sexually "neutral."

TABLE 22.1
Varieties of chromosomal sex determination

Organism	Heterozygous sex	Gametes		Zygotes	
		Sperm	Eggs	Females	Males
Drosophila, man, etc.	Male	X and Y	All X	2X = ♀	XY = ♂
Protenor (bug), grasshoppers	Male	X and O	All X	2X = ♀	X = ♂
Birds, moths	Female	All X	X and Y	XY = ♀	2X = ♂
Fumea (a moth)	Female	All X	X and O	X = ♀	2X = ♂

mosome and females have two X's. But some insects, particularly species of short-horned grasshoppers, have no Y chromosomes. In birds, in at least some reptiles and amphibians, in butterflies, moths, and certain other insects, females are XY and males XX. The rarest type is XO condition in females and XX in males.

THE SEXUAL FUNCTION OF X AND Y
CHROMOSOMES
These facts concerning sex determination were discovered early in the current century by Wilson, Sutton, Stevens, Montgomery, and others. Many questions were, however, left unsettled. One of the most obvious is: What are the functions of the X and Y chromosomes in determining the sex of Drosophila? Is the presence of a Y chromosome essential in the male? Morgan's investiga-

GYNANDROMORPHS
Morgan and Bridges (1919) used the chromosomal theory of sex determination to explain the origin of gynandromorphs, which are usually female on one side of the body and male on the other. Gynandromorphs occur occasionally in many organisms that normally produce females and males. In Drosophila, gynandromorphs arise from zygotes that have originally two X chromosomes and hence should develop into females. Misdivisions of chromosomes may, however, occur, and one of the X chromosomes may be lost in some of the cells during the cleavage of the fertilized egg. The body parts formed by the descendants of the cells that have a single X left are male, whereas the cells that keep their two X's give rise to female parts of the gynandromorph. Gynandromorphs that arise in crosses involving

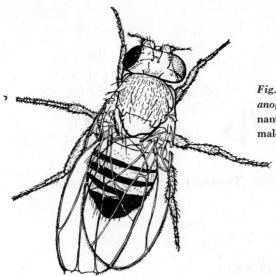

Fig. 22.1. A gynandromorph of *Drosophila melanogaster*. The left side of the body is predominantly female and the right side predominantly male. (*After Bridges*)

sex-linked mutant genes may be particularly spectacular in appearance (Fig. 22.1). The male portions of the body may have eye and body colors, bristles, and other characters that differ sharply from those in the female portion.

A different mechanism that gives rise to gynandromorphs was discovered in the silkworm moth by Goldschmidt and Katsuki. Some eggs come to possess two nuclei instead of the normal one, and both nuclei may be fertilized by different spermatozoa. If one of the nuclei contains an X and the other a Y chromosome, the body that develops will have some parts female and others male.

INTERSEXES AND SUPERSEXES IN DROSOPHILA
An important development of the theory of sex determination took place in 1922. Bridges found some females of *Drosophila melanogaster* that had every chromosome, including the X chromosome, in triplicate. Such *triploid* females are much like the normal diploid ones in appearance and are fertile. They can be mated to diploid males, and they produce progenies in which several interesting types of individuals are found. The eight sexually distinct kinds are the following: (1) triploid females, with three X chromosomes and three sets of autosomes (a "set" of autosomes consists of a second and a third chromosome; the small fourth chromosome may be present in single dose or in duplicate); (2) normal diploid females, with two X's and two sets of autosomes; (3) diploid XXY females with two X's, one Y, and two sets of autosomes; (4) intersexes with two X chromosomes and three sets of autosomes; (5) intersexes not distinguishable from the foregoing class except in having two X chromosomes, one Y chromosome, and three sets of autosomes; (6) normal males with one X, one Y, and two sets of autosomes; (7) superfemales with three X's and two sets of autosomes; (8) supermales with one X, one Y and three sets of autosomes (Fig. 22.2).

Intersexes are sterile individuals intermediate between females and males. They should not be confused with gynandromorphs, which are individuals having some parts of the body pure female and others male. Superfemales and supermales are also sterile individuals that show some relatively

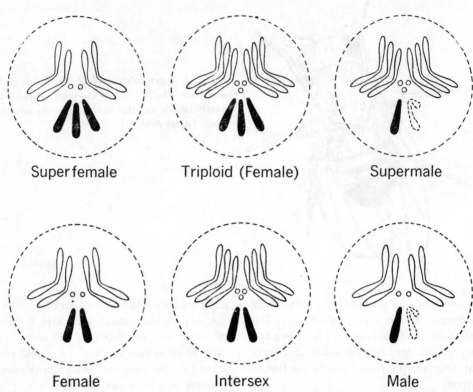

| Superfemale | Triploid (Female) | Supermale |

| Female | Intersex | Male |

Fig. 22.2. Effect on sex of the balance between X chromosomes (solid) and autosomes (outlined) in *Drosophila melanogaster.*

minor differences from ordinary females and males. Bridges gave the following interpretation to his findings:

"The intersexes and 3n (triploid) types lead to the conclusion that sex in *Drosophila melanogaster* is determined by the autosomes as well as by the X chromosomes, the ratio of autosomes to X's being the significant relation. The old formulation of 2 X = ♀ is at once seen to be inadequate; for here we have individuals with two X chromosomes, and yet [they] are not females. They are shifted out of the female class by the presence of an extra set of autosomes, and thereby the autosomes are proved to play a positive role in the production of sex. Since the intersexes differ from females by the as-

sumption of certain male characters, this effect of the autosomes is due to an internal preponderance of 'male-tendency' genes. We may now reformulate the sex relation as follows: Both sexes are due to the simultaneous action of two opposed sets of genes, one set tending to produce the characters called female and the other to produce the characters called male. These two sets of genes are not equally effective, for in the (chromosome) complement as a whole the female-tendency genes outweigh the male and the diploid (or triploid) form is female. The male-tendency genes in the autosomes are more numerous or more effective than those in the X chromosome, while the net effect of genes in the X chromosome is a tendency to the production of female characters. When in a diploid zygote the relative effectiveness of the female-tendency genes is lowered by the absence of one X, the male-tendency genes outweigh the female, and the result is the normal male. When the two sets of genes are acting in a ratio between these two extremes, as in the case in the ratio of 2 X : 3 sets of autosomes (2 X : 3 A), the result is a sex intermediate—the intersex."

GENIC BALANCE AND DETERMINATION OF SEX
The foregoing quotation from Bridges' classical work states the theory of sex determination by means of genic balance. Every individual has in his genotype both female and male potentialities. Which sex actually develops is decided by the balance, that is, by the preponderance of the female-tendency or of the male-tendency genes. The "sex chromosomes" and other chromosomes are merely vehicles of genes. It happens that in Drosophila the X carries more genes that incline the development of the individual toward femaleness, and the autosomes more that incline it toward maleness. The deciding factor is the ratio between the number of X chromosomes and of sets of autosomes in the fertilized egg.

As shown in Table 22.2, genic balance is, in turn, governed by the ratio of the number of X chromosomes to the number of sets of autosomes in the zygote at fertilization. This ratio is 1.0 in any individual that is to develop into a female but 0.5 in a male. If the ratio is intermediate between 1.0 and 0.5, the resulting individual is neither a female nor a male but an intermediate, an intersex (0.67). Superfemales have a ratio of 1.5, which is higher than that in normal females, and supermales 0.33, which is lower than in normal males.

INTERSEXES AND ENVIRONMENT
A careful study of the intersexes in Drosophila has revealed a very interesting fact. As shown by Bridges, these intersexes all have two X chromosomes and three sets of autosomes. Yet the sexual characters of intersexes vary all the way from a condition resembling normal males (male-type intersexes) through various intermediate situations to a condition approaching normal females (female-type intersexes) (Fig. 22.3). If sex is determined by the ratio of X chromosomes to autosomes, what causes this wide variation among the intersexes?

Triploid females were allowed to produce offspring at different temperatures, and the

TABLE 22.2
Sexual types in *Drosophila melanogaster* (*After Bridges*)

Sex		X chromosomes	Sets of autosomes (A)	Sex index (ratio X/A)
Superfemale		3	2	1.5
Normal female	tetraploid	4	4	1.0
	triploid	3	3	1.0
	diploid	2	2	1.0
	haploid *	1	1	1.0
Intersex		2	3	0.67
Normal male		1	2	0.50
Supermale		1	3	0.33

* A whole individual of this type has not been obtained, but patches of tissue with one X and one of each autosome have been found in diploid flies. These patches show female characters.

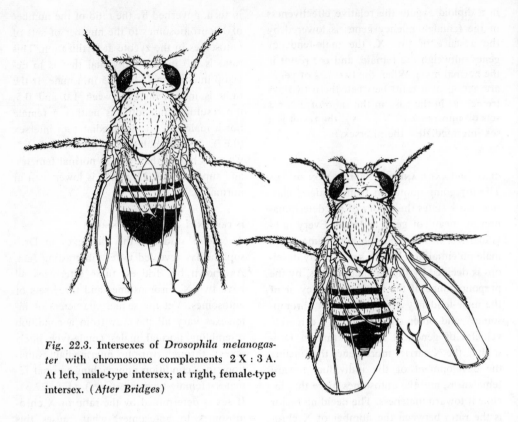

Fig. 22.3. Intersexes of *Drosophila melanogaster* with chromosome complements 2 X : 3 A. At left, male-type intersex; at right, female-type intersex. (*After Bridges*)

sexual characteristics of the intersexes that appeared in their offspring were compared. The average sex type in the intersexes developed at high temperatures was shifted in the female direction, and at low temperatures in the male direction. High temperature has a feminizing and low temperature a masculinizing effect in Drosophila.

Some triploid females produce intersexes that, in a given environment, are on the average more feminine or more masculine than others. By selecting females that produce the most feminine or most masculine intersexes in several generations, it is possible to obtain triploid strains that produce only female-type or only male-type intersexes. All these intersexes have the same chromosomes, namely two X chromosomes and three sets of autosomes, but some of them have more feminizing and others more

masculinizing genes. The chromosomal mechanism interacts with different genetic "environments" or "modifiers."

FACTOR OF SAFETY

We have seen that the sexual state of triploid intersexes in Drosophila can easily be altered by external influences, such as temperature, as well as by modifying genes. The remarkable and significant fact is that the same influences have no noticeable effects on the sex of normal males and females. Females and males grown at temperatures as high and as low as Drosophila can withstand show no trace of intersexuality. Neither is there evidence of intersexuality in females and males that contain the same modifying genes that strongly alter the sexual traits of intersexes.

How does it come about that the sex of

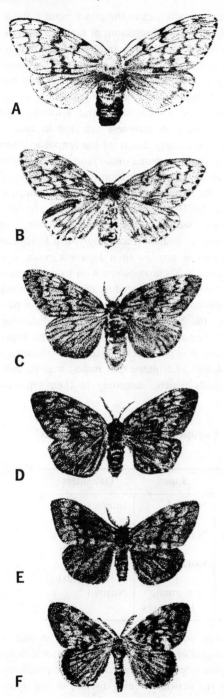

A

B

C

D

E

F

Fig. 22.4. Intersexes in *Lymantria dispar.* (*A*) Normal female. (*B*, *C*, *D*, and *E*) Intersexes with increasing grades of maleness. (*F*) Male. (*After Goldschmidt*)

diploid females and males is determined far more rigidly than that of intersexes? The explanation of this fact must be looked for in the characteristics of the evolutionary process. It stands to reason that proper functioning of the sex mechanism on which reproduction depends is vitally important for the preservation of the species. Now, intersexes are sterile or at least less efficient than the normal sexes. Therefore, natural selection can be expected to purge the species of the genotypes that allow the determination of sex to be easily upset by environmental agents that the species meets in nature, such as temperature variations. Conversely, natural selection will favor genotypes that buffer the sexual balance of females and males against disturbance by environmental and genetic modifiers. The result is that the sexual balance is protected by a factor of safety—the femaleness of females and the maleness of males are so strong that they are not easily upset by environmental or genetic variations. No such factor of safety can be expected to develop in intersexes, since they are rare in nature and, when they do appear, are useless to the species.

Sex is, after all, a phenotypic trait; and like all phenotypic traits, it is determined by interaction of the genotype with the environment. The chromosomal mechanism of sex determination directs the development of the individual either along the path of femaleness or along that of maleness; the sexual phenotypes that develop in the environments in which the species normally lives are reproductively competent females or males, not intersexes. But the factor of safety may be broken down by unusual genetic and environmental influences. Addition of a set of autosomes to the chromosome complement of a normal female turns the latter into a triploid intersex. From time to time, mutations also arise which have effects drastic enough to upset the sexual balance and transform diploid females into phenotypic intersexes. Such mutants have been observed in at least four different species of Drosophila. These intersexes have, of course, two X chromosomes and two sets of autosomes. Their intersexual condition is caused not by an abnormal X chromosome : autosome ratio (as in triploid intersexes) but by qualitative changes in their genes. They are known as *diploid intersexes*. Such intersexes occur also in man, though rarely.

DIPLOID INTERSEXES IN THE GYPSY MOTH

The classic work of Goldschmidt on diploid intersexes in the gypsy moth, *Lymantria dispar*, has made an important contribution to the understanding of the mechanisms of sex determination. This moth (Fig. 22.4) is remarkable for its striking *sexual dimorphism* (external differences between females and males); it occurs naturally in Europe, northern Africa, and northern Asia. It has been introduced and has become a serious pest in New England. The offspring of matings between females and males from any one geo-

supposes that sex in the gypsy moth is determined by the interaction of factors for maleness carried in the X and factors for femaleness carried in the Y or in the cytoplasm. These factors vary in "strength." In any one race, the strengths of these factors are so adjusted by prolonged natural selection that two doses of maleness (carried in two X chromosomes) dominate the femaleness and produce a normal male and one dose of maleness (one X chromosome) is dominated by the femaleness and gives rise to a normal female. However, the sex factors are relatively "weak" in European and "strong" in Japanese strains. Accordingly, if a European female is crossed to a Japanese male, one Japanese X chromosome with its maleness is not entirely dominated by the relatively weak femaleness inherited from the European parent; the XY individuals that should develop into females become intersexes. In the gypsy moth, it is possible to distinguish intersexual females and intersexual males, that is, individuals which, according to their chromo-

TABLE 22.3

Sexual types resulting from crosses of European and Japanese strains of the gypsy moth

Cross	Parents	Sons	Daughters
1	European "weak" ♀ × Japanese "strong" ♂	Normal	Intersexual
2	Japanese "strong" ♀ × European "weak" ♂	Normal	Normal
3	F_2 from cross 1	Normal	½ normal, ½ intersexual
4	F_2 from cross 2	½ normal, ½ intersex	Normal

graphic locality consist of females and males only, but if strains of European origin are crossed with those from Japan or if strains from northern and southern Japan are intercrossed, the progenies contain some intersexes, as shown in Table 22.3 and Figure 22.4.

To account for these results, Goldschmidt

somal constitution (XY or XX), should be females or males, respectively, but which become intersexes on account of the unbalance of the sex-determining factors in the different races.

Goldschmidt has also shown that all intermediates between strong and weak sex factors can be found in different races. The "weakest" race of the gypsy moth lives on the northern island of Japan (Hokkaido), and the "strongest" race occurs at the northern extremity of the main Japanese island (Honshu). Crosses of these races result not in intersexuality but in sexual transformation (sex reversal); that is, some of the XY individuals develop into "transformed," or sex-reversed, males and XX individuals into "transformed" females. Thus the sex phenotype may be the opposite of the one chromosomally established. As one proceeds southward from the northern tip of Honshu, "strong" races are met with less and less, until in southern Japan and Korea the strength of the sex factors is not very different from that encountered in typical European populations.

Goldschmidt and his coworkers have also proposed a mechanism by which the sex factors influence the development of the sex phenotype. The essential assumption is that intersexes begin their development as females (or as males) and develop as such up to a certain critical point, the so-called "turning point," after which their development is of the opposite sexual type. The mixture of female and male traits found in intersexes is thus explained as due to the switching from the female developmental course to the male course, or vice versa, occurring earlier or later in development. A similar mechanism may operate also in the triploid intersexes in Drosophila, where the intersexes seem to start their development as males but complete it as females. The hypothesis of the turning point has, however, met with many objections and cannot be regarded as established.

HOW MANY GENES DETERMINE SEX?

We have seen above that sex in diploid Drosophila is generally decided simply by the number of X chromosomes present in a fertilized egg, one X making a male and two X's a female. However, the studies of Bridges and others on Drosophila and of Gold-schmidt on the gypsy moth disclosed that it is not really the chromosome number but the balance of the genes contained in the chromosomes which determines sex. It is now logical to inquire how many genes in the X chromosomes and in the autosomes are concerned with sex determination. Two possibilities may be considered. First, the X chromosome may contain a single gene or a group of closely linked genes which determines femaleness (the "female sex differentiator"), and one of the autosomes may carry a gene or a small section that determines maleness (the "male sex differentiator"). Second, many or even all the genes in all parts of the X chromosome may be female-determining, and many or all the genes in the autosomes may be male-determining. Any one of these genes taken separately may have a small effect on sex, but their aggregate effect may be powerful.

To discriminate between these possibilities, triploid females were outcrossed to diploid males that carried duplications for some sections of the X chromosome or of other chromosomes. In the progeny of these crosses, intersexes were obtained which carried two X chromosomes and three sets of autosomes and some of which had, in addition, a fragment of a third X chromosome or autosomal fragment. Now, if a given section of the chromosome represented in the fragment contains genes that modify the development toward femaleness, the intersexes that carry the duplicating fragment should be more femalelike than the intersexes without the duplication. Conversely, if the duplication contains genes that tend toward maleness, the duplication-carrying intersexes should be more malelike than those without the duplication. Just which parts of a chromosome are contained in a duplication can be determined genetically as well as cytologically, as explained in Chapter 15. The experiments showed that intersexes that carry duplications for any section of the X chromosome (except for the heterochromatic part, which includes the centromere) are always more femalelike than intersexes without duplications. The longer the duplication —in other words, the more female-tendency genes are added to an intersex—the more femalelike it becomes. Intersexes that carry duplications for about one-third of the euchromatic part of the X chromosome (that is, carrying about 2⅓ X chromosomes) not only resemble females morphologically but deposit fertile eggs and are, therefore, functional females. On the other hand, no single gene or short section of the X chromosome by itself can transform intersexes into females. It can be concluded that the X chromosome of *Drosophila melanogaster* has no single female sex differentiator but that it contains many female-determining genes scattered throughout its euchromatic length, the combined effects of which make the chromosome female-determining. The situation of the autosomes is as yet not clear, since at least some duplications for sections of autosomes are neither male- nor female-determining.

SEX CHROMOSOMES IN DIFFERENT ORGANISMS
The X chromosome of Drosophila contains many genes for femaleness, none of which is particularly strong by itself but the combined effects of which are decisive in sex determination. It certainly does not follow from this that the sex-determining genes are as numerous in all organisms as they are in Drosophila.

In many organisms the sex chromosomes (X and Y) are quite different in size and shape; the Y is usually smaller than the X, and in extreme cases (as in short-horned grasshoppers) the Y may even be absent. On the other hand, in some other organisms the X and Y are very much alike, or at least not distinguishable under the microscope. The midges of the genus Chironomus are particularly interesting in this respect, since the salivary glands of their larvae contain giant chromosomes that are even larger and more

easily studied than those in Drosophila. Now, in Drosophila the Y chromosome is heterochromatic and is reduced in the salivary-gland cells to a tiny lump in the chromocenter; the X is largely euchromatic (see Figs. 14.6 and 15.14). In Chironomus the X and Y chromosomes appear to be quite similar in the salivary-gland cells, both chromosomes being chiefly euchromatic. Beerman has recently (1955) produced good evidence that the sexual difference between the X and the Y in Chironomus is contained in only small parts of these chromosomes, possibly in a single gene that may have a decisive effect on sex determination.

It is probable that the determination of sex by a single sex-differentiator gene is a situation more primitive in the evolutionary sense than is possession of X and Y chromosomes strongly different in their contents. Starting with a situation like that in Chironomus, it is easy to visualize that more and more genes in the X and Y chromosomes will become involved in sex determination. As pointed out particularly by Muller and by Darlington, crossing over between X and Y becomes restricted to only part of the length of these chromosomes (the *pairing segment*), whereas other parts that carry the sex-differentiating genes undergo no crossing over (the *differential segment*). The genes borne in the differential segment of the Y chromosome, provided they play no important part in sex determination, gradually degenerate by mutation or become lost. This is because the Y chromosome is transmitted only from father to son (or from mother to daughter) and never becomes homozygous in any individual. Recessive lethal mutations or gene deficiencies that are eliminated in chromosomes other than the Y in homozygous individuals are sheltered from natural selection when they occur in the Y chromosome. Such losses of genes lead to the situation exemplified by the Y chromosome of Drosophila, which is genetically nearly inactive, or "empty." Or the Y chromosome may be lost altogether, as in some grasshoppers and other insects. At the same time, the single sex differentiator in the X chromosome is gradually replaced by numerous cooperating sex genes, as in Drosophila. The process ends in a complete loss of the Y chromosome.

SEX CHROMOSOMES IN MAN

It may be noted that the X and Y chromosomes in man are, in a way, intermediate between the more extreme situations exemplified by Chironomus and by Drosophila. It was observed by Koller and Darlington that chiasmata are formed between the X and Y chromosomes in man. This indicates that parts of these chromosomes are rather similar in their genetic contents. It then occurred to Haldane that the presence of similar "pairing segments" in the X and Y chromosomes must lead to interesting genetic consequences. The genes in the X chromosome will generally show sex-linked inheritance, like those in Drosophila's X (Chap. 12). However, where crossing over had occurred between the X and the Y, such genes may be transferred to the Y chromosome and may then be transmitted from father to son. The frequency of such exceptions will be a measure of the frequency of crossing over between the gene in question and the part of the chromosome (differential segment) which contains the sex-determining genes (Fig. 14.3). However, the existence of a pairing segment in man has recently been questioned on statistical grounds.

The pedigree in Problem 14.7 illustrates the method of detection of incompletely sex-linked genes. The first male in the third generation got the gene from his mother, hence in the X, and passed it on to four daughters but not to three sons. On the assumption of incomplete sex linkage, these would be the noncrossovers. However, one son got the gene from his father, hence in the Y, and two daughters failed to get it in the paternal X chromosome. These must have been cross-

overs. The analysis of such pedigrees led to an estimate of about 32.6 per cent of crossing over between this gene and the differential part of the X. A modification of the method permitted detection of additional incompletely sex-linked recessives and led to the construction of a map like that in Figure 14.2. This map is not so accurate as those for Drosophila species and maize, which are based on large numbers of experimentally controlled observations, but it is a useful approximation. Since the most reliable sex-linked mutant genes are rare, it is unlikely that two will often be found in the same pedigree; hence the construction of a map of the differential segment of the X is probably a matter for the distant future.

THE EFFECTS OF HORMONES

The general theory of sex as the result of a balance between opposed tendencies has been successfully applied to the conditions found in many animals. In the higher animals, and especially in vertebrates, the secondary products of the sex glands—the sex hormones—may very considerably alter the final characters. In the fowl, for example, early removal of the ovary from a "genetic" female may reverse some of the normal processes and result in the development of a male comb and male plumage and behavior and even in the appearance of a testis. An extreme case of sex reversal of this sort has been reported by Crew. A hen said to have laid fertile eggs ceased laying, developed a male comb and plumage, crowed, and finally functioned as a male and became the father of two chickens. Its ovary had apparently been destroyed by disease and replaced by a testis. A similar case has been reported in pigeons, and such reversals of sex are known to occur normally in certain amphibia, fish, and lower forms.

The effect of early hormonal influence on sexual characters in cattle has been studied by Lillie and others, who have shown that, where twins of opposite sex are born, one is a normal male and the other usually a sterile female with many malelike traits—the so-called "freemartin." The evidence from early development shows that, through the fusion of blood vessels, the blood of one embryo, with its hormones, may enter the blood stream of the other. In this case the male hormones seem to influence the development of the female embryo in a male direction.

In plants, also, the development of the sex organs may be altered by influences from the environment which operate through channels like those of the animal hormones. In the dioecious hemp plant, for example, changing the length of day to which the plant is normally exposed may result in production of male flowers on female plants, and vice versa.

Such cases remind us that sexual differences, like other phenotypic differences, depend upon the reaction of a genotype to the conditions it encounters during development. Where the sex-chromosome mechanism is well established, as in most animals, sex is *determined* at fertilization, in the sense that the preponderance of genes producing development toward one sex type is decisive, although, as we have seen from instances of sex reversal and of intersexuality, the preponderance may be overcome by genes of the opposed type or by environmental factors. The means by which the sex genes influence the development of sexual characters, that is, the problem of sex differentiation, is thus a part of the more general problem of how genes influence development. In the demonstration of the interaction of many genes, some tending to influence a character or reaction in one direction, whereas others tend in an opposite direction, the balance theory of sex-determination reveals a more general mechanism, known as genic balance, by which the genes influence the adult characters. Some of the evidence and ideas concerned with the developmental origins of phenotypes (phenogenetics) are reviewed in Chapter 25.

23 VARIETIES OF SEXUAL REPRODUCTION

REPRODUCTION, which is perhaps the most basic function of all life, is accomplished in a variety of ways. In asexual reproduction, a single individual undergoes fission into equal parts or produces buds, bulbs, tubers, or spores. The essential feature of sexual reproduction is a union of two gametes to form a zygote. In some lower organisms the gametes that unite are at least superficially alike. More often, female gametes, eggs, are much larger and less motile than male gametes, spermatozoa. Eggs and sperms are produced in the body of the same individual in *hermaphroditic* or *monoecious* organisms, whereas they arise in different individuals, females and males, in *bisexual* or *dioecious* organisms.

Regardless of whether the gametes are differentiated into eggs and sperms and whether they are produced by a hermaphrodite or by a bisexual organism, sexual reproduction performs the same basic biological function. It provides a greater variety of genotypes than could arise under asexual reproduction. As shown in Table 5.2, a heterozygote for n genes may give rise to 2^n kinds of gametes with different assortments of genes. With n of the order of 50–100, these may be enormous numbers, greater than the numbers of individuals of any species living. The importance of this tremendous power of sexual reproduction to engender a practically infinite variety of genotypes is that, by natural selection, the better adapted can be perpetuated and the less well-adapted weeded out. Evolutionary plasticity is much lower with asexual than with sexual reproduction. In an asexually reproducing clone, an adaptively valuable combination of genes can arise only if all the genes concerned undergo the proper mutations in the same line of descent. With sexual reproduction, these mutants may appear in different places and at different times, but they may eventually be brought together, if individuals carrying them meet and mate. Because of this, sexual reproduction facilitates evolution.

In most cases, sexual reproduction is served by elaborate but precise mechanisms that bring about sexual union, fertilization, meiosis, sex determination, hormonal control of physical and behavioral characteristics of sexually mature individuals, etc. These complex mechanisms are often masterworks of nature which arose and were gradually perfected by a long process of evolutionary development. However, interesting variants and perhaps some primitive forms of these mechanisms continue to exist, especially among the lower organisms. Their study leads to better understanding of the biological function of sexual reproduction in all its diverse forms.

SEX IN BACTERIA

For many years bacteria were believed to be entirely asexual, reproducing by simple fission, which transforms a single mother cell into daughter cells. However, Tatum and Lederberg (1947) and Lederberg (1947) demonstrated that at least some bacteria may undergo a sexual process. Since, in most experiments, sexual union occurs millions of times less frequently than simple fission, it has been observed directly under a microscope only recently. A rather complex but extremely ingenious experimental technique had to be resorted to for an unambiguous proof.

Lederberg utilized mutants of the so-called K-12 strain of colon bacteria (*Escherichia coli*), which required for their growth certain substances in the nutrient medium which normal bacteria are able to make for themselves. These auxotrophic mutants are quite analogous to the mutants of the fungus Neurospora described on page 332. One of the lines of bacteria used by Lederberg required for growth a medium containing biotin and methionine, but it was able to make its own threonine and leucine and to ferment the sugar lactose, and it was resistant to attacks of a bacteriophage. The genetic constitution of this line may be represented as $B-$

$M-$ $T+$ $L+$ $Lac+$ Vr. The $+$ sign indicates ability to perform a given function and the $-$ sign indicates lack of ability to perform the function. Another line was able to make its own biotin and methionine, but required threonine and leucine, was unable to ferment lactose, and was susceptible to attacks of the bacteriophage. The genetic constitution of this second line may be written $B+$ $M+$ $T-$ $L-$ $Lac-$ Vs.

A mixture of many millions of bacteria of both lines was plated on a "minimal" medium lacking biotin, methionine, threonine, and leucine. Neither line of bacteria is able to grow on such a medium. Nevertheless, a few cells did survive and formed colonies of *prototrophs,* which, like normal bacteria, were capable of growing on a minimal medium. Such prototrophs carry a combination of the genes that were present separately in the two lines of the bacteria mixed together. Such a combination ($B+$ $M+$ $T+$ $L+$) is expected to arise if the bacteria had undergone sexual union and gene exchange. But how to exclude the alternative possibility, that the appearance of the prototrophic bacteria was due to simultaneous mutation of the genes $B-$ and $M-$ to $B+$ and $M+$ (or of the genes $T-$ $L-$ to $T+$ and $L+$)? Lederberg tested the prototrophic bacteria which he obtained for their ability to ferment lactose and for their susceptibility to attacks of bacteriophages. The growth of the bacteria on the minimal medium is independent of these particular characteristics. Nevertheless, during the process the respective genes underwent recombination, which gave rise to the prototrophs. Indeed, among 2,013 prototrophs tested, the following were observed:

Lactose fermenters, bacteriophage resistants ($Lac+$ Vr) 32.5%
Lactose negative, bacteriophage susceptible ($Lac-$ V_s) 42.7%
Lactose fermenters, bacteriophage susceptible ($Lac+$ V_s) 1.6%
Lactose negative, bacteriophage resistants ($Lac-$ V_r) 23.2%

Lederberg, Cavalli, and others carried out many hybridization experiments similar in principle to that described above. The genes in the colon bacteria proved to exhibit a linkage, as though they were borne in a single chromosome. A linkage map of this "chromosome" has been made. There is evidence that sexual union is occasionally interpolated

like the tails of the spermatozoa of certain animals, which are left outside the eggs at fertilization. The DNA somehow reproduces itself inside the bacterium; and some half an hour after infection with the bacteriophage, the bacterial cell bursts, releasing some hundreds of new bacteriophage particles capable of infecting other bacteria.

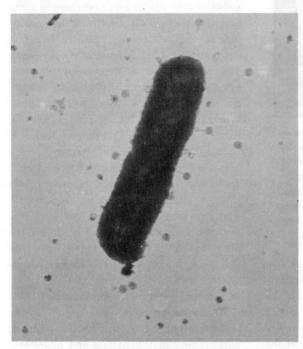

Fig. 23.1. Electron micrograph of a bacterium (*E. coli,* strain B) being attacked by particles of T-5 phage. The phage particles attach by the tail. (*Courtesy of Thomas F. Anderson*)

among asexual fissions in certain bacteria other than the K-12 strain of the colon bacteria, although many strains seem to have lost the sexual propensity altogether.

RECOMBINATION IN BACTERIOPHAGES

Not only bacteria but also bacteriophages (see Chap. 16) are capable of gene recombination suggesting a sexual process. A bacteriophage particle (Fig. 23.1) is only about one tenth of a micron (or 1,000 angstrom units) long; it consists of a protein "envelope" and a core composed of DNA (desoxyribonucleic acid). When a bacteriophage particle attacks a susceptible bacterial cell, the DNA passes into the body of the victim, while the envelope remains outside, rather

Treatments with ultraviolet light inactivate the bacteriophage; treated bacteriophage particles penetrate into bacterial cells but fail to reproduce there. Luria and Dulbecco found, however, that if two or more such inactivated particles happen to enter the same bacterium, then reproduction does take place and normal infective bacteriophage is released. It is as though the ultraviolet radiation had induced different lethal mutations in bacteriophage particles, but somehow a normal particle can be compounded from healthy constituents of two or more injured particles. Indeed, Hershey and Rotman proved that gene recombination takes place when two bacteriophage particles infect the same bacterium. These authors used two

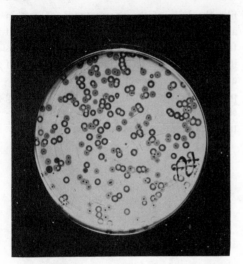

Fig. 23.2. Recombination in a bacteriophage, P-22, growing on Salmonella typhimurium. Parents: v_2 t, virulent (clear center) and turbid halo, respectively; + +, solid center and clear halo. Recombinants: v_2 +, clear center, clear halo; + t, solid center, turbid halo. (Courtesy of Norton D. Zinder)

strains of bacteriophages differing in two clear-cut characteristics, namely, the appearance of the "plaque" produced when the phage multiplies in bacteria grown on an agar medium (see Fig. 23.2) and the ability to infect different kinds of bacteria. Let the characteristics of the two strains of the bacteriophages be denoted as A_1B_1 and A_2B_2 respectively. When a single particle infects a bacterial cell, only A_1B_1 or A_2B_2 particles are released. The differences symbolized by A_1–A_2 and B_1–B_2 are, consequently, hereditary. However, when one bacterial cell is infected simultaneously by the A_1B_1 and A_2B_2 phages, then four kinds of phage particles may be produced: A_1B_1, A_1B_2, A_2B_1, and A_2B_2. Depending upon the characteristics used, the four kinds may appear with frequencies expected if the genes A and B are not linked. Or, else, the recombinations A_1B_2 and A_2B_1 may be less frequent than the original combinations A_1B_1 and A_2B_2, as expected if the genes lie in the same chromo-some and are recombined only by crossing over of linked genes. In either case, the process yields new combinations of genes which were present separately in different strains. This is, as we know, the fundamental biological function of sexuality.

Transduction. An even more extraordinary mechanism of gene exchange has been discovered by Zinder and Lederberg in some bacteria, particularly in the form responsible for mouse "typhoid," *Salmonella typhimurium.* These bacteria are often *lysogenic.* The phenomenon of lysogenicity, investigated particularly by Lwoff, consists in association of bacteria with bacteriophages. Whereas ordinary bacteriophages kill the bacteria in which they reproduce, lysogenic bacteria carry "temperate" phages, which grow and reproduce in the bacterial cells synchronously with the cells themselves, only a single phage particle living in each cell. This is evidently a case of friendly association of different organisms, or symbiosis; the phage multiplies inside the bacteria at about the same rate at which the bacteria themselves reproduce and presumably has no detrimental effect on the bacterial cell.

Under certain conditions, however, the temperate phage may be released from the bacteria and may penetrate and henceforth reproduce in other bacteria previously free of phages. Zinder and Lederberg found that the migrating temperate phage somehow takes with it from the donor bacterium some of the genetic materials of the latter and transfers them to the recipient bacterium. The precise mechanism whereby this transport of genes from one bacterial cell to another is accomplished is as yet obscure. Demerec and others found that what is transferred is often not single genes but groups of linked bacterial genes such as could be transferred if the temperate phage transported with it sections of the bacterial chromosome and these sections were sometimes incorporated into the chromosome of the recipient bacterium. However that may be, gene recombination in these bacteria is here accomplished not through sexual fusion of the bacterial cells themselves, but apparently through the intervention of a third party, a temperate bacteriophage.

BACTERIAL TRANSFORMATIONS

The important experiments on pneumococci —bacteria responsible for pneumonial infections in man—have already been considered in Chapter 17. In these experiments, some genetic traits of the bacteria are changed when living bacteria are placed on nutrient media which contain a "transforming principle" and certain other conditions favoring transformation. The transforming principle consists of pure or almost pure desoxyribonucleic acids extracted from killed bacteria of a known kind and chemically purified. Hotchkiss and his collaborators have shown that the transforming principles may transfer genetic factors from one strain of bacteria to another and that recombination of genes may take place in the process. By selection of resistant mutants (see Chap. 16), strains of pneumococci have been obtained which can grow in the presence of the antibiotics streptomycin or penicillin and which can ferment the carbohydrate mannitol. Normal pneumococci are streptomycin- and penicillin-sensitive and cannot utilize mannitol in the nutrient medium. Transforming principles have been extracted from killed bacteria of strains with various combinations of the above traits. Bacteria grown in the presence of such transforming principles may change their genetic characteristics and acquire the genetic characteristics of the bacteria from which a given "principle" was extracted. Now, if the donor bacteria (which yield the transforming principle) differ from the recipient bacteria (which are being transformed) in two different traits (streptomycin resistance as well as the ability to utilize mannitol), then these traits are transformed together more frequently than might be expected from their separate and independent

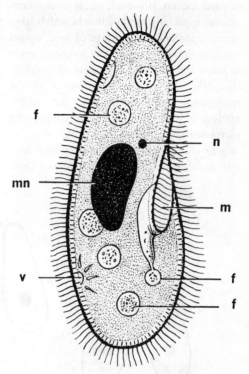

Fig. 23.3. A paramecium: m, mouth; n, nucleus; mn, macronucleus; f, food; v, contractile vacuole. (*After Sonneborn*)

transformation. This suggests an analogy with linkage of genes located in the same chromosome. It is not known how often such transformations may occur in bacteria multiplying in living hosts.

MATING TYPES AND MULTIPLE SEXUALITY IN INFUSORIA

Many infusoria, such as the common paramecium familiar to students of zoology, carry two kinds of nuclei, the larger of which are called *macronuclei* and the smaller *micronuclei* (Fig. 23.3). The paramecium reproduces mostly asexually, by fission of a single individual into two. Both macronuclei and micronuclei divide, and the division products pass into the daughter cells. Genotypically uniform clones may therefore be obtained from single isolated individuals of paramecium. However, under certain conditions, especially in old cultures which have begun to suffer from shortage of food, sexual reproduction intervenes. The infusoria unite in pairs and undergo a process of *conjugation* (Fig. 23.4). The macronuclei of the conjugating cells disintegrate; the micronucleus of each member of the conjugating pair undergoes meiosis (see Chap. 4), and two meiotic divisions give rise to four haploid micronuclei in each cell. Three of these

disintegrate, and the remaining nucleus divides in two by a simple mitosis; one of these two moves over into the body of the mate, while the other remains stationary; the nuclei then fuse in pairs, achieving mutual fertilization of the conjugating individuals. The fusion nucleus, now diploid, divides and gives rise to a new macronucleus and a new micronucleus. Conjugation is, then, a sexual process that yields, by gene recombination, a variety of genotypes. The significance of this

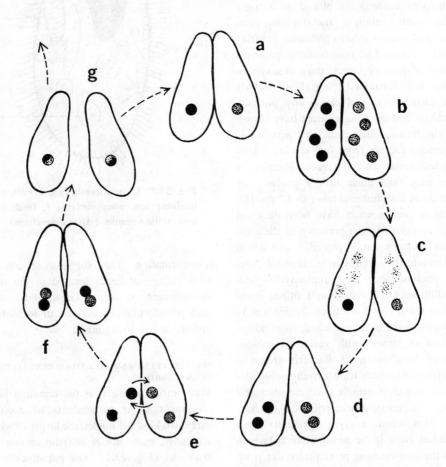

Fig. 23.4. Conjugation in paramecia. In *a* and *b* above, the single micronucleus in each conjugant divides twice, producing four haplonuclei, of which three disintegrate (*c*). In *d*, each remaining micronucleus divides in two. In *e*, the cells exchange one of their micronuclei. In *f*, the micronuclei in each individual fuse, and in *g* the two exconjugants. (*After Sonneborn*)

for adaptation to environmental changes is obvious: an opportunity is provided for the natural selection of the genotypes most suited to the new environments.

The work of Sonneborn and his school has disclosed that conjugation does not occur indiscriminately between any two paramecia. It occurs exclusively between members of different *mating types*. The mating types function like different sexes, although they are not recognizably different either in appearance or in behavior and cannot be designated as females and males. In addition, the infusoria known as *Paramecium aurelia* belong to about fifteen different "varieties," each consisting of two mating types. The varieties either do not cross at all, or, in the rare instances when they do, produce inviable hybrid progenies. The varieties are thus reproductively isolated biological species, rather like *Drosophila pseudoobscura* and *Drosophila persimilis,* which were discussed in Chapter 21.

When the sexes show no appreciable structural differences and no division of labor, a species may well consist of more than two sexes. This is what Jennings, Chen, and others found in *Paramecium bursaria.* This name applies to five different varieties, which act as distinct biological species. However, three of these species have not two but four mating types each, one species has as many as eight mating types, and only one species gets along with only two "sexes." In the species that has eight "sexes," individuals of each of the eight mate freely with individuals of any of the remaining seven, but not with individuals of their own mating type.

This phenomenon of *multiple sexuality* has been studied by Nanney, Elliott, and others also in another infusorium, *Tetrahymena pyriformis.* One of the species included under this name has as many as eleven different mating types or "sexes." Multiple sexuality is known also in certain fungi and algae. The biological function of multiple sexuality may be simply to increase the chances that individuals who mate will be genetically different and thus will produce a variety of genotypes in the progeny.

SEX IN FUNGI

The bread mold Neurospora and many other fungi are easily propagated asexually by placing a fragment of the threadlike hyphae of the mycelium of the fungus on a suitable culture medium. The hyphae, which contain nuclei with haploid sets of chromosomes, may, by simple mitotic divisions, form also chains of haploid asexual spores called *conidia* (Fig. 23.5). Sexual spores, or *ascospores,* are formed in a different way discovered by Dodge. Cells of the hyphae of different mycelia fuse, and the nuclei of these cells unite to form diploid zygotic nuclei. The zygotic nuclei exist only a short time; they undergo two meiotic divisions followed by a mitotic division, thus giving rise to eight haploid nuclei; these nuclei are arranged in a linear file and form the eight ascospores of a single ascus (see Figs. 13.9 and 23.5). The asexual spores contain the same genes which were present in the original mycelium; the sexual ascospores contain different combinations of the genes contributed by the parental mycelia, assorted in meiosis.

In Neurospora and other *heterothallic* fungi, it is possible to assign every individual to one of two mating types, arbitrarily designated "plus" and "minus." Ascospores are formed only when cells of the opposite mating types unite in sexual fusion. In some heterothallic fungi, as in the infusoria discussed above, three or more mating types occur. On the other hand, Blakeslee showed that in the bread mold Mucor and its relatives sexual spores may be produced also by the union of hyphae from the same mycelium. Such forms are called *homothallic.*

HETEROCARYONS AND PARASEXUALITY

Many so-called "imperfect" fungi have never been observed to form ascospores. They seem to reproduce exclusively asexually,

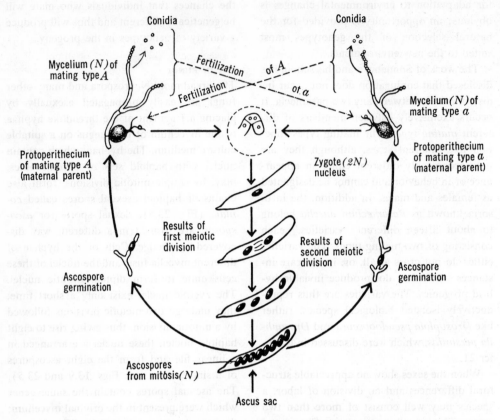

Conidia

Mycelium *(N)* of
mating type *A*

Fertilization

of *A*

Fertilization

or *a*

Conidia

Mycelium *(N)* of
mating type *a*

Protoperithecium
of mating type *A*
(maternal parent)

Protoperithecium
of mating type *a*
(maternal parent)

Zygote *(2N)*
nucleus

Results of
first meiotic
division

Results of
second meiotic
division

Ascospore
germination

Ascospore
germination

Ascospores
from mitosis*(N)*

Ascus sac

Fig. 23.5. The life cycle of bread mold, Neurospora. (Reprinted with permission from Wagner and Mitchell, "Genetics and Metabolism," John Wiley & Sons, Inc., 1955)

usually by conidia. Such seemingly completely asexual organisms may exist in nature in a variety of different haploid clones that do not exchange genes at all. Curiously enough, some of these forms of life have developed a sort of substitute for sexuality. One of these substitutes is the formation of *heterocaryons*. Heterocaryons are formed sometimes also in fungi that can produce sexual spores as well, for example, the bread mold Neurospora. Heterocaryons arise through fusion of the hyphal cells of different individuals growing in close proximity to each other. However, the nuclei of the fused hyphae do not unite, and the cells are formed with two or several separate nuclei carrying different sets of genes. Thus no fertilization takes place, but the heterocaryon cells give rise, by mitotic division of the haploid nuclei they contain, to new heterocaryotic mycelia.

Dodge, and later Beadle and Coonradt, have shown that heterocaryotic mycelial growths may display a kind of hybrid vigor or heterosis, which has been called heterocaryotic vigor. Suppose that one of the fungus mycelia that unite to form the heterocaryon contains a mutant gene that makes the mold unable to synthesize some essential vitamin, such as nicotinic acid. The other uniting mycelium can make its own nicotinic acid but is unable to synthesize some other essential substance, such as pantothenic acid.

Neither of the mycelia is capable of growing alone on the minimal medium, which lacks both nicotinic and pantothenic acids. The heterocaryon, however, will grow quite well on the minimal medium. This situation is explained quite simply. The two kinds of nuclei which are present together in the heterocaryon supply each what the other lacks. One of them has a gene that enables the fungus to make nicotinic acid, and the other has a gene needed to synthesize pantothenic acid. The heterocaryon has both of them. Emerson and Rendel have speculated that heterosis in sexually reproducing organisms (see Chap. 19) may depend on similar physiological complementary reactions.

Pontecorvo found that the separate haploid nuclei present in the multinucleate heterocaryon cells occasionally fuse together to form diploid nuclei. This happens in three species of mold fungi with which he worked —*Aspergillus nidulans, Aspergillus niger,* and *Penicillium chrysogenum*—and in some other species, although the first of these three has also the standard sexual cycle, whereas in the second and the third true sexual reproduction is unknown. The fusion of the haploid nuclei is usually a rare event—it takes place once in about ten million conidial spores. Moreover, the heterozygous diploid nuclei which result from the fusion are quite unstable. They undergo what Pontecorvo has called "haploidization," an irregular distribution of the chromosomes at a mitotic division which may lead to formation of viable haploid nuclei. There occurs also a peculiar process of crossing over between the homologous chromosomes in diploid cells not immediately followed by reduction division. All in all, the *parasexual* process just described achieves the recombination of genes and is to this extent a valid substitute for the full-fledged sexual process. It differs from the true sexual process in the absence of the regular time sequence—fertilization, meiosis, and reduction of the diploid to the haploid chromosome complement.

HERMAPHRODITISM AND BISEXUALITY

The diverse methods of gene recombination described in the present chapter may be viewed as attempts, some of them rather fumbling ones, of the evolutionary process to achieve an efficient mechanism of sexuality. Such a mechanism, which withstood the test of natural selection and was eventually established in most subdivisions of the living world, was obviously differentiation of the sex cells into female and male ones. Female cells sacrifice motility for storage of nutrients for the coming generation, whereas male cells pack the hereditary materials in a minimum of space and specialize in motility. Female and male cells may, however, be produced either in the same individual (hermaphroditism) or in different individuals, females and males (bisexuality). There is apparently no unconditional advantage in either of these, and both are abundantly represented among organisms now living as well as among fossils. Thus vertebrate animals are bisexual, whereas most higher plants are hermaphroditic. There is also evidence that hermaphroditism gave place to bisexuality, and vice versa, repeatedly in the course of the evolution of life.

It is interesting that in some organisms, even those belonging to groups quite predominantly bisexual, sex determination is still precariously poised. This is particularly true among the amphibians. Witschi has shown that some European species of frogs are sexually "undifferentiated," since the reproductive organs in young animals all resemble female organs and only later are some of the growing animals transformed into males. Males of some species of toads have rudimentary oviducts and so-called Bidder's organs, which resemble ovaries in histological structure. Castration of such males gives an impulse to the development of the ovaries and oviducts, and eventual transformation of the genotypic male into a functional female. Ponse succeeded in mating such a transformed male with an ordinary one and obtained an all-male progeny. This is as expected if the toads, like birds and probably like most reptiles, have XX males and XY females (see Chap. 22). A "transformed" male is phenotypically a female and acts as such, but his genotype, determined by his chromosomes, remains the same as it was before the transformation. Humphrey succeeded in making the reverse transformation in the Mexican axolotl (Ambystoma), converting a genetic female into a functional male. Such a "transformed" female crossed to a normal female gave a progeny consisting of about three-quarters females and one-quarter males. A cross XY × XY is expected, of course, to give a segregation in a ratio 1 XX : 2 XY : 1 YY, and it has to be supposed that, in these animals, YY individuals are viable and are females.

SEX IN HIGHER PLANTS

Most seed plants are hermaphrodites—the same individual (sporophyte) produces both female gametophytes (ovules) and male gametophytes (pollen). However, in some seed plants, ovules and pollen are borne not only in different flowers but on different plants. In such *dioecious* species, the two kinds of sporophytes are genetically different, as discovered already by Correns, one of the rediscoverers of Mendel's laws. In the genus Melandrium (a member of the pink family), the species *Melandrium dioicum* is dioecious, but it can be pollinated by the hermaphroditic *M. album*. The progeny consists of all female plants. The reciprocal cross, *album* × *dioicum*, gives progeny of which about half are males and half females. From this Correns inferred that male plants are heterozygous for sex (XY) and females are homozygous (XX).

The cytological basis for sex differences in dioecious plants has also been determined in many cases. Female plants of Melandrium, for example, have been shown to possess two large X chromosomes and male plants an X and a much smaller Y. A similar distribution of heterochromosomes has been found

in over 50 other species of dioecious plants, as in Elodea, Rumex, and Humulus. In many other dioecious forms there are no visible chromosome differences between the sexes.

Westergaard in Denmark and Warmke and Blakeslee in the United States independently studied sex inheritance in the polyploid *Melandrium album*. The diploid female plants have 24 chromosomes, of which 22 are autosomes and 2 are X chromosomes (22 + 2 X); diploid males have the same chromosome number, but they have one X and one Y chromosome (22 + XY). Tetraploid plants are of three types: 44 + 4 X females, 44 + 2 X + 2 Y males, and 44 + 3 X + 1 Y males. This shows that, in contrast to Drosophila, the Y chromosome of Melandrium is definitely sex determining and carries genes for maleness. One Y chromosome is sufficient, even in the presence of three X's, to make a tetraploid plant male. Triploid plants, obtained by crossing the tetraploids and diploids, are 33 + 3 X females and 33 + 2 X + 1 Y males. According to the Drosophila model of sex determination (see Chap. 22), the latter plants, having two X's and three sets of autosomes, should be intersexes. But in Melandrium, the genes for maleness are carried in the Y chromosome, and the presence of a single Y chromosome makes plants male. Intersexual (or, more precisely, hermaphroditic) Melandrium plants have been obtained by fragmentation of the Y chromosome.

SEX DETERMINATION BY MALE HAPLOIDY

A most peculiar but apparently quite efficient mechanism of genetic sex determination has been evolved in one of the large, and supposedly quite "advanced" phylogenetically, order of insects—Hymenoptera (bees, wasps, ants, parasitic wasps, etc.). In these insects, some of the eggs deposited by the female are fertilized by spermatozoa; these eggs usually develop into females. Other eggs are unfertilized, and they develop parthenogenetically into males. Females are, accordingly, diploid, whereas males receive only a haploid set of chromosomes from their single parent, the mother. All sperms from any one male are alike, no matter how heterozygous the mother from which he came.

We have seen that, in Drosophila, sex is decided by the balance of the genes for femaleness, carried in the X chromosome, and the genes for maleness, carried chiefly in the autosomes. Haploid individuals, having a single set of chromosomes in all their cells, are unknown in Drosophila; however, some mosaic individuals with partially haploid bodies have been seen, and the haploid parts were female. This is, indeed, as expected, since one X chromosome and one set of autosomes give, in Drosophila, a female sex-determining ratio (see Table 22.2). How, then, can a haploid bee or wasp be male?

Whiting has done much to solve the above puzzle by his work on the parasitic wasp *Habrobracon juglandis*. Since the males come from unfertilized eggs, the sex ratio in Habrobracon, as in most other hymenopterous insects, is not constant. An old mated female that has used up her supply of sperm will, like an unmated female, produce only haploid males. With a good supply of sperm, a progeny consists of diploid females and haploid males. However, if the parents are closely related, a few sons appear which, unlike their normal haploid brothers, have fathers. These biparental males have 20 chromosomes like their sisters instead of 10 like their haploid brothers. They tend to be inviable, and fraternities in which they occur have very low egg hatchability.

Analysis of this situation by Whiting and his students led to the following interpretation. Populations of Habrobracon contain a variety of sex alleles, which can be designated S^1, S^2, S^3, etc. The haploid males are, then, of as many kinds as there are S alleles in the population. A diploid zygote which contains any two *different* alleles (S^1S^2, S^1S^3, S^2S^3, etc.) develops into a normal female. But if both the father and the mother happen to contain the same allele, some zygotes homozygous for a given sex allele (S^1S^1, S^2S^2, etc.) are formed and then develop into the poorly viable biparental males. Such homozygotes are formed as a result of inbreeding, and accordingly they occur more frequently in laboratory experiments than in nature.

SEX IN BONELLIA

Perhaps the most outlandish mechanism of sex determination known is that in the marine echiuroid worm *Bonellia viridis*. This worm has an extreme sexual dimorphism. The female is about an inch long and possesses a fairly complex anatomical organization. Males are of the size of large infusoria and have rudimentary alimentary and other organs; they live as parasites in the uterus of the female. Baltzer and his collaborators have shown that the sex of a larva of Bonellia is determined by chemical stimuli emanating from the environment in which they live; larvae that settle on the proboscis of a female develop into males, whereas larvae that lead a free life develop into females. Intersexes can be obtained if larvae which have spent some time in contact with a proboscis are removed from it and forced to live away from their mother. It appears that the proboscis of a female contains a substance of the hormone type which strongly influences the sexual traits of larvae.

This peculiar situation has, however, an important lesson to teach. Normal females and males are individuals with female and male phenotypes respectively. Sexual phenotypes are, like any other phenotypic traits, the outcome of developmental processes directed by genes and enacted in certain environments. The chromosomes that determine sex must be viewed as merely convenient switch mechanisms evolved by natural selection as adaptations to fulfill an important biological function, that of producing two stable sexual states. It is interesting that other switch mechanisms, which evidently fulfill the same function in a satisfactory manner, occur in nature. Those in Bonellia and in hymenopterous insects are perhaps the most noteworthy ones.

24 PHYSIOLOGICAL GENETICS

THE PRINCIPLES of genetics have been derived chiefly from a study of genes and chromosomes at the time of meiosis and fertilization. However, since genes are known by their effects, the laws of their transmission are, in fact, inferences from the distribution of phenotypes, that is, from the appearance of the differentiating characters. In the higher plants and animals, most of these characters do not arise directly from genes but result from a chain of developmental processes, initiated by one or more genes, leading through interactions with events controlled by other genes and factors of the internal and external environment to the final phenotype. A recurrent question in genetics concerns the way in which the genotype is causally related to the developed character. Through what means do the thousands of individual genes of the fertilized egg cell produce the phenotype of the multicellular individual, with its complex organization of specific structures and functions and its behavior and individual peculiarities?

326

For convenience in discussion, two closely related aspects of this question may be distinguished. One concerns the mechanisms by which the hereditary characters achieve their final form. In seeking the principles governing the relationships of genes and characters, we are led to trace the differences between specific phenotypes, such as those associated with the genotypes *AA, Aa,* and *aa,* back toward their origins in ontogeny. This involves an analysis of the character during development, a type of study referred to, since Haecker first used the term in 1918, as *phenogenetics,* or developmental genetics. In practice, phenogenetics deals only with comparisons of structures, processes, or substances in individuals with known genetic differences. In general, only gene differences, not genes themselves, can be studied by such a method. The primary problem of developmental genetics is to elucidate the genic control of development.

The other aspect of this question concerns the mechanisms by which genes influence the reactions that give rise to specific substances. These reactions occur within the cell during metabolism; subsequently they influence the phenotype. In this chapter our primary problem is to elucidate the genic control of metabolism.

Both these problems lie in the domain of *physiological genetics.*

No sharp distinction can be drawn between attempts to study the genic control of

often morphological ones, presently available. In comparing the metabolic systems in two different genotypes, one would be more interested in identifying *reactions* by which particular compounds are synthesized or degraded and in discovering the energetics of the reactions as revealed by the behavior of enzymes. Although in general it is true that intracellular metabolic events precede

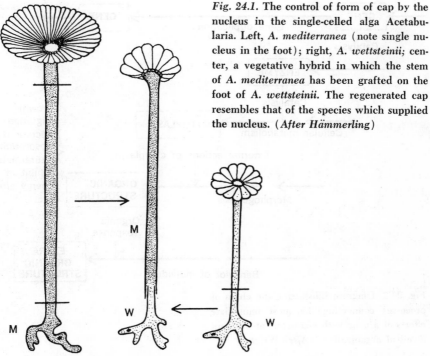

Fig. 24.1. The control of form of cap by the nucleus in the single-celled alga Acetabularia. Left, A. *mediterranea* (note single nucleus in the foot); right, A. *wettsteinii*; center, a vegetative hybrid in which the stem of A. *mediterranea* has been grafted on the foot of A. *wettsteinii*. The regenerated cap resembles that of the species which supplied the nucleus. (*After Hämmerling*)

metabolism and studies of the control of development. However, although both are concerned with ontogeny, they deal with it at different levels; therefore, different methods and materials must be employed in the two kinds of studies. In comparing developmental events in organisms with a specified difference in genotype, one can begin with the developed character difference, the phenotype, and work backward, following the difference to stages as near its origin as can be reached by means of the methods,

those that occur by interaction between cells, it is illusory to believe that for this reason metabolic studies reveal direct or immediate effects of the genes. This question will be discussed further in Chapter 28.

A single example will illustrate the general rule that genic control over metabolic and developmental processes is exercised by influences emanating from the nucleus and carried into effect by reactions in the cytoplasm. Acetabularia (Fig. 24.1), a large unicellular alga, is differentiated into three main parts: rhizome or holdfast, stalk, and cap or umbrella, resembling superficially the root, stem, and fruiting body of a multicellular plant. The single nucleus is in the rhizome. Hämmerling showed that when the stalk and cap are cut off, the nucleated part remaining can regenerate the whole with the type of cap characteristic of the species. He showed also that ability to form the cap depends on

actions in the cytoplasm. One could call the effective substances hormones in the broad sense, since they act at a distance from the point of origin, carrying into effect instructions received from the genes. In other cases to be discussed below, intermediate steps in this process involve enzyme activities specified by the genotype.

Using this as a general scheme extending

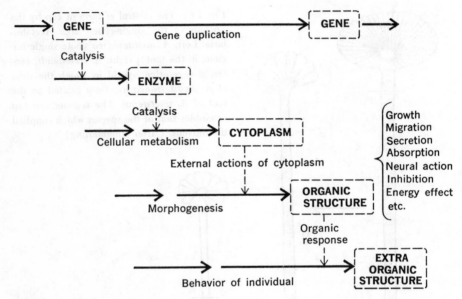

Fig. 24.2. Diagram illustrating the chain of processes connecting the most immediate effects of a gene with characters at different levels of organization. (*After Wright*)

the presence of substances coming from the nucleus and distributed in a gradient decreasing from the upper to the lower part of the stalk. When nucleated and nonnucleated parts of plants of different species, distinguished by the form of the cap, were combined by grafting, the specific form of the cap was found to be determined by the specific genome of the nucleus, even when the effective substances had to diffuse through cytoplasm of a different species. Here morphogenesis in a single cell is controlled by the nucleus acting through a system of re-

to relations in multicellular organisms as well results in a model such as that in Figure 24.2. Here the essential idea expressed is that of chainwise relations between a gene and its effects at different levels of organization. The first level, that of gene structure, duplication, and primary effects, is the subject of Chapter 27, since what we know about it is based largely on inferences from genetic analysis and from studies of subsequent levels; the third level, morphogenesis and development, will be discussed in Chapter 25. In the present chapter we shall examine the intermediate level, the genic control of metabolic processes.

GENIC CONTROL OF PIGMENTS IN FLOWERING PLANTS

If metabolic processes are genically controlled, we should expect to find this control expressed in differences in chemical end products associated with particular gene differences. The striking variations in flower colors in sweet peas, stocks, primroses, and other plants have long attracted the attention of geneticists, and a number of genes affecting flower color have been identified. Subsequently the pigments themselves were studied by chemists with the result that we now have a partial picture of the gene-influenced reactors responsible for such color variations.

or by the presence of H (in the flavones) or OH (in the flavonols) at position 3. All the anthocyanins are red in acid and blue in alkaline solution. They become bluer in combination with certain colorless anthoxanthins known as *copigments*.

Known genes for flower-color differences influence all the following components: presence of pigment and copigment, degree of oxidation or reduction, position of methyl groups, relative acidity or alkalinity, and local distribution of the pigments. In several species—for example, *Dahlia variabilis*—one gene is responsible for the presence of anthocyanin and another for the increased production of the pigment. In others, two or more complementary genes must be present before any anthocyanin appears, although anthoxanthin formation is independent of

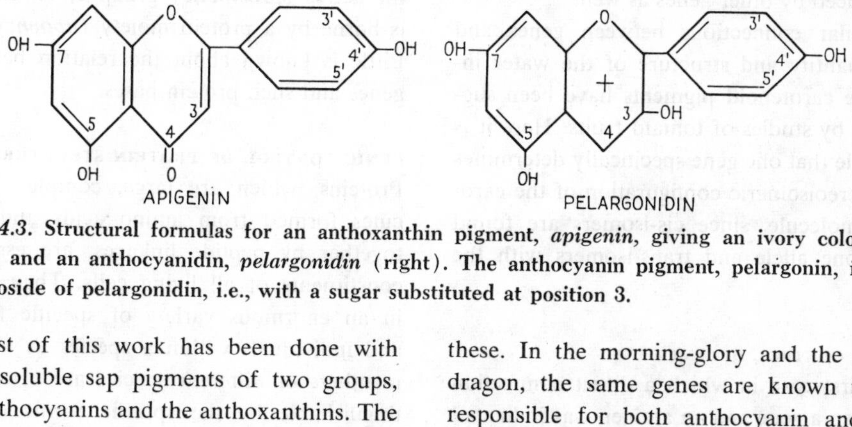

Fig. 24.3. Structural formulas for an anthoxanthin pigment, *apigenin*, giving an ivory color (left), and an anthocyanidin, *pelargonidin* (right). The anthocyanin pigment, pelargonin, is a glycoside of pelargonidin, i.e., with a sugar substituted at position 3.

Most of this work has been done with water-soluble sap pigments of two groups, the anthocyanins and the anthoxanthins. The former are responsible for the various shades or mixtures of red and blue (pinks, purples, magentas, lavenders), and yellow and ivory colors are due to the related group of anthoxanthins. The anthocyanins and anthoxanthins all contain similar ring structures (Fig. 24.3) derived from the condensation of sugars. Anthocyanins differ according to the number and position of the hydroxyl groups in the phenyl ring and the methylation of the hydroxyls at 3′, 5′, and 7. Anthoxanthins differ by having either one hydroxyl at 4′ (as in the ivory apigenin) or at both 3′ and 4′ (as in the yellow luteolin),

these. In the morning-glory and the snapdragon, the same genes are known to be responsible for both anthocyanin and anthoxanthin pigments, since a single recessive-gene mutation interferes with the production of any sap pigment, probably by blocking the production or conversion of some precursor substance from which both pigments are derived. When anthocyanin is present, other genes determine modifications in the molecular structure. Genes are known, for example, which control the degree of oxidation of the phenyl ring. Of these, the genes determining hydroxyl groups at 3′ and 5′ in addition to 4′ and producing delphinidin are dominant to alleles determining oxidation at 3′ and 4′ (cyanidin) or at 4′ only (pelargonidin). In sweet peas, genes *A* and *B* together or *A* alone (*AA bb*) produce delphinidin, *aa BB* cyanidin, *aa bb* pelargonidin. The more oxidized pigments turn out to be dominant to the less oxidized ones. One mutant change in flower color from rose pink to salmon pink in *Pelargonium zonale* was shown by Scott-Moncrieff to be due to a gene causing substitution of OH for H at position 3 in the anthocyanidin molecule.

Although the production of these pigments is clearly under the control of specific genes that determine the arrangement of elementary radicals or atoms in a molecule, the relation of gene to pigment character is indirect, probably through the modification of synthetic steps carried out by enzymes in compounds produced as part of the general metabolic processes of the plant and thus influenced by other genes as well.

Similar connections between genes and the quantity and structure of the water insoluble carotenoid pigments have been suggested by studies of tomato fruits. Here it is possible that one gene specifically determines the stereoisomeric configuration of the carotene molecule, since cis-isomers are found with one allele and trans-isomers with the other.

GENIC CONTROL OF ANTIGENS

The first case in which a direct connection between a gene and an antigen was indicated has already been pointed out in connection with the classical system (ABO) of blood-group antigens on the surface of human red blood cells (p. 116). In persons of blood group AB, both alleles, I^A and I^B, express themselves, each responsible for its own specific antigen. Similarly, in persons of blood type MN, two different antigens, each due to an allele of the same gene, can be demonstrated, as in heterozygotes for alleles at the Rh, Kell, Duffy, and other blood-factor loci. This indicates a one-to-one correspondence between genotype and phenotype. Molecular specificities, detected in these cases by immunological reactions rather than by chemical methods, may thus be determined by single allelic alterations of the same gene. Antigens, however, are complex substances, probably with many reactive sites that may be separately affected. The A blood-group substance is a polysaccharide that is probably widely distributed in other organisms, and the relation between its chemical constitution and its antigenic properties has not yet been fully elucidated. Instances of interactions between alleles in determining the degree of antigenicity (strength of reaction with an antibody) and even the specificity of antigens in hybrids suggest that the chemical milieu in which the antigen is formed plays a part in determining its character. Cellular antigens appear to be borne by proteins in somewhat the same way that the active (*prosthetic*) group of an enzyme is borne by a protein moiety (*apoenzyme*). Little is known about the relation between genes and such protein bases.

GENIC CONTROL OF PROTEIN STRUCTURE

Proteins, which are large, complex molecules formed from amino acids and held together by peptide linkages, are essential constituents of all living cells. They occur in an enormous variety of specific forms, and individuals within a species as well as members of different species are often distinguishable by the specific forms of the proteins they contain and are able to synthesize. This suggests that the behavior of specific proteins such as enzymes or hemoglobins is controlled by specific genes, but evidence for this has been indirect and inferential.

Recently, however, direct connections between specific chemical differences in protein molecules and allelic alterations in genes have been demonstrated. One such case was found in studying the difference between the normal and abnormal hemoglobins in persons who carry the gene for sickle-cell anemia. The steps in establishing this were as follows. Differences in the three pheno-types—normal, sickle-cell trait, and sickle-cell anemia—were found to be associated with the three genotypes *si/si, Si/si,* and *Si/Si,* respectively. Pauling and Itano then showed that the hemoglobins (in the re-duced form) from bloods of these three gen-otypes differed in the speeds with which they migrated when placed in an electric field (Fig. 24.4). The hemoglobin of normal per-sons moves as a negative ion, that of sickle-cell-anemia patients moves as a positive ion,

hemoglobins have now been found, differ-ing in electrophoretic mobility or in solubil-ity from the normal form or in both. One of these at least (hemoglobin C) is due to an allele of *Si,* and several others may also be alleles. It can therefore be said that this locus controls a specific step or steps in the formation of a specific protein.

Evidence of a difference in the form of an enzyme due to different alleles of one gene has been provided by Horowitz, who found in the bread mold Neurospora two forms of

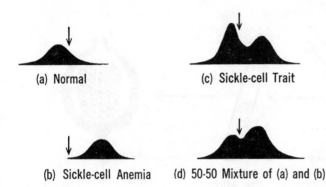

(a) Normal

(b) Sickle-cell Anemia

(c) Sickle-cell Trait

(d) 50-50 Mixture of (a) and (b)

Fig. 24.4. Differences in the electrophoretic mobility of he-moglobins of normal subjects, of persons with sickle-cell trait (heterozygotes), and of persons with sickle-cell anemia (homo-zygotes). Scanning diagrams show sickle-cell hemoglobin moving to the left more slowly than normal. (*After Pauling, Itano, Singer and Wells*)

and that of persons with the sickle-cell trait (the heterozygotes) contains two compo-nents, one positive and one negative, which therefore separate during electrophoresis. The difference was shown to be due to the globins, not to the hemes, and the difference in isoelectric points of the normal and ab-normal proteins indicated that the abnormal protein was more positively charged (by two or more charges) than the normal one. Re-cently Ingram succeeded in splitting these molecules with trypsin, which attacks spe-cific peptide linkages and releases amino acids. He identified one peptide that differs in the normal and abnormal proteins; it is positively charged in the abnormal but un-charged in the normal. The chemical effect of the mutation from *si* to *Si* is thus to change a peptide linkage in a small part of one of the polypeptide chains, resulting in an altered charge.

A number of other genetically abnormal

the same enzyme, tyrosinase, differing only in stability toward heat. The difference shows simple Mendelian inheritance.

GENIC CONTROL OF METABOLIC PATTERNS

We come now to the *processes* through which gene differences express themselves, resulting in differences in chemical constitu-tion, and in such chemical activities as syn-thesis of compounds, inhibitions of synthesis, and resolution of compounds into simpler substances. The sum total of these anabolic and catabolic activities is referred to as me-tabolism.

These processes, occurring as they do within cells, are interdependent, some sup-plying energy, substrates, oxygen, and other necessary elements to others, which in turn influence other reaction systems. In studying the parts played by the genes in such a com-plex network of interactions, we must obvi-ously simplify the problem by separating for analysis a limited series of steps or reaction sequences, not forgetting, however, that in the organism they are parts of a functioning whole.

BIOCHEMICAL SYNTHESIS

The most thoroughly explored of the gene-controlled metabolic processes are those concerned with the synthesis of amino acids, the purine and pyrimidine bases of nucleic acids and of some of the vitamins. The reason for this is that, among microorganisms, many

mutants have been found which are incapable of carrying out the synthesis of certain of the above compounds that are necessary for growth. Such mutants can grow only when supplied with a particular substance in the culture medium; these mutants are called "nutritional mutants" or are described as having a requirement for a substance—for example, "adenine-requiring." Study of the bread mold Neurospora has supplied many analyzed cases of nutritional mutants and may serve to illustrate the meth-

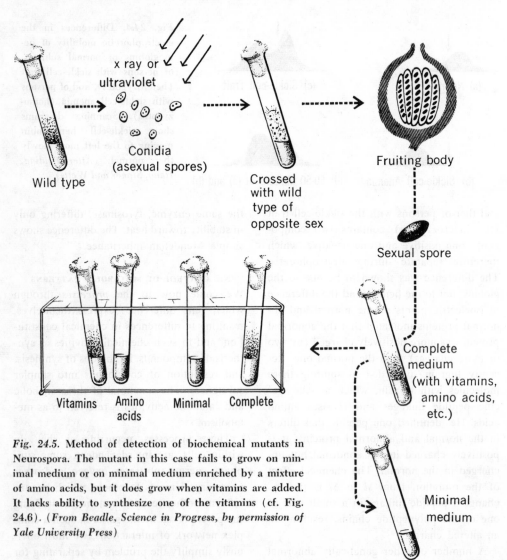

Fig. 24.5. Method of detection of biochemical mutants in Neurospora. The mutant in this case fails to grow on minimal medium or on minimal medium enriched by a mixture of amino acids, but it does grow when vitamins are added. It lacks ability to synthesize one of the vitamins (cf. Fig. 24.6). (*From Beadle, Science in Progress, by permission of Yale University Press*)

ods and results obtained generally in micro-organisms.

The life cycle of *Neurospora crassa* is shown in Figure 23.5. The mycelium of the fungus contains haploid nuclei, which multiply as the hyphae grow and parts of which may give rise to new colonies. Another form of asexual reproduction is by spores or conidia, one class of which contains a single nucleus, another class several nuclei. These germinate and reproduce the whole mycelium. Sexual reproduction is by fertilization of a nucleus of one mating type by a nucleus from the conidia or mycelium of the opposite mating type, resulting in a fusion (diploid) nucleus which then undergoes two meiotic and one mitotic division to form eight haploid ascospores. These spores occur two by two in the ascus and may be dissected out and tested separately as described on page 173. The original method of Beadle and Tatum for detecting biochemical mutants is illustrated in Figure 24.5, and the inheritance of the mutants can be tested as in Figure 24.6.

This fungus can be grown on a "minimal" culture medium, which consists of sugar, a nitrogen source such as ammonium nitrate

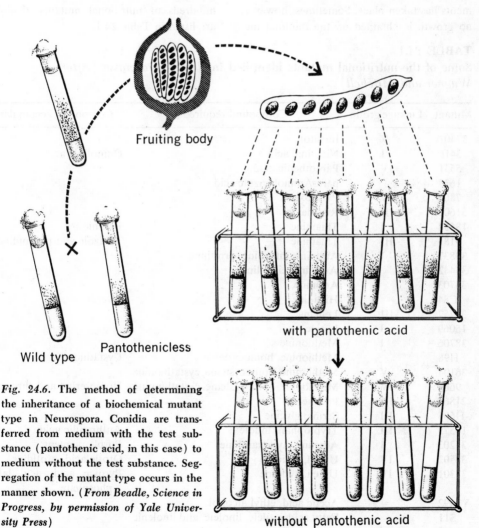

Fruiting body

Wild type Pantothenicless

with pantothenic acid

without pantothenic acid

Fig. 24.6. The method of determining the inheritance of a biochemical mutant type in Neurospora. Conidia are transferred from medium with the test substance (pantothenic acid, in this case) to medium without the test substance. Segregation of the mutant type occurs in the manner shown. (*From Beadle, Science in Progress, by permission of Yale University Press*)

and tartrate, some inorganic acids and salts, and a single vitamin, biotin. The standard, or "complete," medium on which the mold is cultured contains, however, many more organic compounds, vitamins, amino acids, and other substances. Ascospores from a Neurospora culture, untreated or treated by a physical or chemical agent, are placed singly in tubes containing a complete medium and allowed to produce mycelial growths. Then parts of the mold from each tube are transferred to tubes with the minimal medium. If growth continues normally, no change in the minimal nutritional requirements has taken place. Sometimes, however, no growth is obtained on the minimal medium; this indicates that a mutation blocking some physiological process essential for growth on this medium has occurred. Just what process is blocked in a given mutant can be determined by testing the mutant strain on minimal media to which various supplemental substances have been added. For example, if a mutant strain fails to grow on the minimal medium but does grow on a medium to which pantothenic acid has been added, the conclusion is that the mutation interferes with some reaction essential to the synthesis of this compound in the growing mold. Examples of some of the hundreds of nutritional mutants identified are listed in Table 24.1.

TABLE 24.1

Some of the nutritional mutants identified in *Neurospora crassa* (*After Wagner and Mitchell*)

Mutant	Linkage group	Compound required	Compound accumulated
37401	V	Inositol	
3416	I	Nicotinic acid	Quinolinic acid
5531	IV	Pantothenic acid	
1633		para-Aminobenzoic acid	
7803	IV	Pyridoxin	
51602	II	Riboflavin	
18558	I	Thiamine	Pyrimidine
9185	III	Thiamine	Thiazole and pyrimidine
30837	I	Arginine, citrulline, ornithine	
33442		Arginine, citrulline	
36703		Arginine	
C84		Histidine	Several
33757	III	Leucine	
15069	I	Lysine	
38706	I	Methionine	
H98		Methionine, homocysteine	Cystathionine
36104	V	Methionine, homocysteine, cystathionine	
9666	IV	Methionine, homocysteine, cystathionine	Homoserine and threonine
21863	III	Proline	
H605	III	Serine, glycine	
10575	III	Tryptophan, indole	Anthranilic acid
35203	I	Adenine, hypoxanthine	Purple pigment
38502	IV	Uracil, cytidine	Orotic acid, orotidine
37301	IV	Uracil, cytidine'	Pyruvic acid, acid labile phosphate
Y2492		Acetic acid, ethyl alcohol	
S11		Fatty acids: oleic, linoleic, and linolenic	

Seven linkage groups have been identified in this species, in which the haploid chromosome number is seven. Independently occurring mutants may affect the same nutritional requirements, and the genes responsible may not be alleles or even in the same linkage group. Examples are the two thiamine mutants in linkage groups I and III and the methionines in I, IV, and V. The two uracil-requiring mutants in group IV differ in other effects also. The ability to detect many differences in the effects of individual mutations on the synthesis or degradation of known chemical compounds gives to this microorganism and certain others their peculiar advantages for the study of the mechanisms by which genes control biochemical reactions.

Mutations detected by such means have a variety of effects. Nearly all reduce viability; many act as lethals when their specific nutritional requirements are not met; and many are unable to reproduce sexually. The common property of those that have been analyzed genetically is the ability of a single mutant to block a specific reaction. Often the reaction steps related in a sequence or chain leading to a synthesis can be identified merely by a study of nutritional requirements. Therefore, of the three arginine-requiring mutants in Table 24.1, the third can utilize only arginine, the second will grow if supplied with either arginine or citrulline, and the first will utilize arginine, citrulline, or ornithine for growth. One might guess, therefore, that the second one can produce arginine for itself if supplied with citrulline, whereas the third can also produce arginine from ornithine. The three compounds might thus be arranged in a reaction sequence as follows:

1, could be repaired by supplying ornithine (from which the organism could then make citrulline and arginine), citrulline, or arginine itself; if only step 2 were blocked by mutation, the organism could repair the deficiency if given either citrulline or arginine, whereas a block in step 3 could be repaired only by arginine itself. The principal assumption is that different mutants that use the same substance—arginine in this example—will often have blocks at *different* steps in one chain of reactions leading to the synthesis of that substance. This principle in its simplest form has proved useful not only in identifying gene-controlled reaction sequences in microorganisms but in other developmental sequences in higher organisms as well. Oftentimes it turns out that individual steps are themselves complex as revealed by different mutants that affect different parts of one conversion. More details of the ornithine cycle worked out by Srb and Horowitz are shown in Figure 24.7. (The gene-controlled steps in this figure have been numbered differently from those in our example.) This diagram illustrates also the cyclical character of many metabolic sequences, since when urea is split off from arginine, ornithine is again provided for the initiation of the cycle.

Another effect of some of the nutritional mutants shown in Table 24.1 results in the accumulation of substances due to a gene-controlled block which prevents their utilization in a synthesis. Thus of two different thiamine-requiring mutants, one accumulates pyrimidine, the other both thiazole and pyrimidine. Clues as to the substances related in a synthesis can be obtained in this way and steps controlled by different genes worked out.

$$\underset{\text{gene 1}}{-------\to \text{ornithine}} \underset{\text{gene 2}}{-------\to \text{citrulline}} \underset{\text{gene 3}}{-------\to \text{arginine}}$$

A block in the sequence prior to the synthesis of ornithine, by mutation only of gene

Gene-controlled reaction sequences have been identified in many other microorgan-

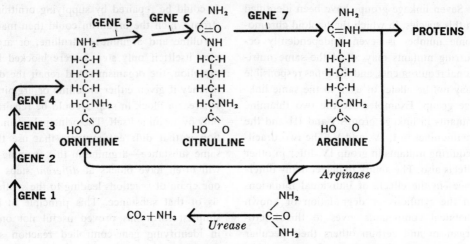

Fig. 24.7. The assumed effects of seven different mutant genes on the ornithine cycle in Neurospora. A mold in which gene 7 has mutated is unable to convert citrulline to arginine and can survive only if arginine is present in its food medium. Mutations in either gene 5 or gene 6 prevent conversion of ornithine to citrulline, whereas if gene 1, 2, 3, or 4 is defective, no ornithine is synthesized. (*From Beadle, after Srb and Horowitz*)

isms: the fungi Aspergillus, Penicillium, and Ophiostoma; bacteria such as the colon bacillus *Escherichia coli,* Pneumococci, the typhoid bacteria of the genus Salmonella; yeasts; and others. Our information on the genetic control of metabolism has been extended in several directions, some of which will be referred to in subsequent chapters. For a review of work in this field, see the book of Wagner and Mitchell. For human biochemical genetics, see Harris, and Haldane.

HUMAN BIOCHEMICAL GENETICS
Of special interest is the evidence concerning the effects of mutant genes on metabolic systems in man, for it was with observations on hereditary diseases in man that the whole field of biochemical genetics was initiated by the English physician A. E. Garrod. In 1902 he recognized alcaptonuria, the "black urine" anomaly, as due to a rare recessive gene. Affected persons fail to break down, as normal persons do, the substance known

as *alkapton,* or homogentisic acid, and it is excreted in the urine, being oxidized to an insoluble black substance on exposure to air. Garrod subsequently interpreted the action of this mutant gene as blocking a step in the normal conversion of alkapton to colorless substances. Later the German chemist Gross claimed that the blood of alcaptonurics was deficient in an enzyme which catalyzed this step.

Later work has revealed other abnormal genes in man which interfere with steps in normal metabolism, some of which are shown in Figure 24.8. Thus a type of imbecility known as *phenylpyruvic oligophrenia* (or Følling's disease, after its Norwegian discoverer) is due to a recessive gene. The frequency is about 1 to 40,000 in England. In such homozygotes, the conversion of phenylalinine to tyrosine is blocked, and phenylalanine accumulates, some of it being broken down and excreted as phenylpyruvic acid. It is not known whether the accumulation of phenylalanine or of its breakdown

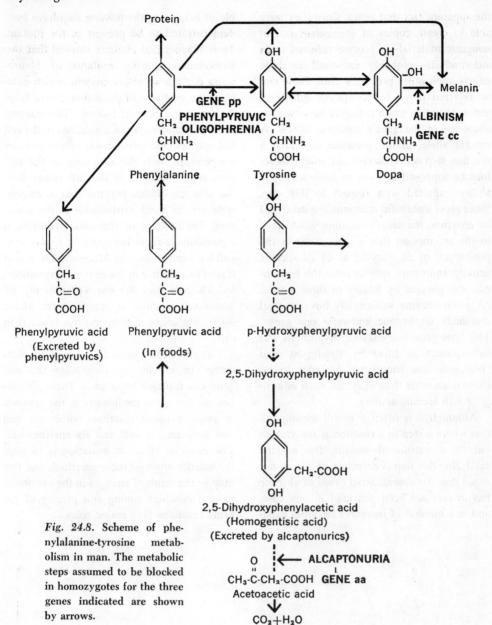

Fig. 24.8. Scheme of phenylalanine-tyrosine metabolism in man. The metabolic steps assumed to be blocked in homozygotes for the three genes indicated are shown by arrows.

Protein

OH

CH₂
CHNH₂
COOH

Phenylalanine

GENE pp
PHENYLPYRUVIC OLIGOPHRENIA

OH

CH₂
CHNH₂
COOH

Tyrosine

OH
OH

CH₂
CHNH₂
COOH

Dopa

Melanin

ALBINISM
GENE cc

CH₂
C=O
COOH

Phenylpyruvic acid
(Excreted by phenylpyruvics)

CH₂
C=O
COOH

Phenylpyruvic acid
(In foods)

CH₂
C=O
COOH

p-Hydroxyphenylpyruvic acid

2,5-Dihydroxyphenylpyruvic acid

OH

CH₂-COOH
OH

2,5-Dihydroxyphenylacetic acid
(Homogentisic acid)
(Excreted by alcaptonurics)

O
‖
CH₃-C-CH₂-COOH
Acetoacetic acid

ALCAPTONURIA
GENE aa

$CO_2 + H_2O$

products is the cause of the severe congenital mental impairment.

ENZYMES AS AGENTS OF GENIC CONTROL
Since similar systems of genetic control over metabolic processes exist throughout the plant and animal kingdoms, a question of general importance is: how do genes exercise this control? To put the question in a form in which experiment may throw light upon it: how do mutated genes block particular steps in biochemical reactions?

A general hypothesis suggested by several early students of genetics was based upon the apparent fact that genes, since they were able to create copies of themselves out of nongenic material—a process referred to as *autocatalysis*—probably exercised catalytic effects upon other processes also. These can be referred to as *heterocatalytic effects* of genes. Mutation could therefore be viewed as a change in the gene's catalytic effects. A mutant allele, in the presence of which a reaction step is not carried out, might therefore be supposed to have its heterocatalytic ability impaired with respect to this step. Since most metabolic reactions are catalyzed by enzymes, the same reasoning would lead to the assumption that a gene controls the production of an enzyme or of its specific activity. In its most specific form this hypothesis was phrased by Beadle in these words: "A given enzyme will usually have its final specificity set by one and only one gene." This "one gene–one enzyme" hypothesis was subsequently modified by Beadle to read "one gene–one function," in order to include units other than enzymes, such as antigens with specific activity.

Although it is often a useful assumption that where a step in a reaction is not carried out by a nutritional mutant, the enzyme catalyzing this step is defective, this does not mean that it is absent. Strict proof of absence has in fact not been provided in any case, and in a number of instances enzymes capable of catalyzing the missing step have been demonstrated to be present in the mutant. Thus Wagner and Haddox showed that two pantothenic-requiring mutants of Neurospora contain an active enzyme which catalyzes the synthesis of pantothenic acid from β-alanine and pantoyl lactone. This enzyme is inactive under certain conditions in the cell but may become active under aeration at low temperature. It is the alteration of the balance of interactions in the cell rather than the absence of this enzyme that is responsible for the block attributable to the mutation. The absence of the same synthesis in a pantothenic-requiring strain of *Escherichia coli* has been studied by Maas and Davis and traced to a change in the enzyme responsible, by which it had become (presumably by mutation) inactive at temperatures above 30° C but active at temperatures lower than this.

Cases like these point to the essential difficulties in proving or disproving the one gene–one function hypothesis. These difficulties are due to the complexity of the network of interdependent reactions within the cell and between the cell and its environment. The essential effect of mutation is to alter the balance amongst these reactions, and this may be the result of changes in the metabolic pattern in which timing and placing of enzyme reactions play major roles.

25   THE GENIC CONTROL
OF DEVELOPMENT

HOW DOES an organism, beginning as a single cell, reach its mature form, achieving division of function among many parts that nevertheless act as a whole? The causal analysis of this process constitutes the central problem of the study of development. *Epigenesis* is the descriptive term applied to the succession of changes by which the organism passes through stages, more or less distinct from each other, in which new parts appear which were not preformed. The gradual acquisition of the characteristic form and function of the individual is referred to as *morphogenesis*. During morphogenesis the phenotype changes radically, yet all these changes occur within a single cell lineage in which descendant cells are derived by mitosis from preceding cells. Are these changes to be accounted for by the same assumptions—namely, changes in the genetic constitution—by which phenotypic differences between individuals in the same environment are explained? Or are new assumptions about genes and their effects needed to explain the genic control of developmental processes?

Finding the answers to these basic questions constitutes the reason for studying developmental genetics. The purpose of this study is not only to explore the application of known genetic principles to the problems of development but also to discover new ideas about genes and their functions in a setting different from that in which the problems of classical or formal genetics are studied. In formal genetics, gene differences are detected by their effects on the phenotypic characters of higher animals and plants as these characters are observed during development. In developmental genetics, the differences observed arise within members of the same cell lineage and are traceable to the same set of genes in the fertilized egg.

GENIC CONTROL OF DEVELOPMENTAL PROCESSES

By and large, the genic control of development must be exercised first through the effects of genes on growth and metabolism. Since these effects must appear first within

339

the cell, it is pertinent to inquire whether the nuclei of all descendant cells retain the capacities of the single nucleus—that of the fertilized or activated egg—from which all the other cells of the organism arise. It has been commonly thought that since cells multiply by mitosis, in which all genes are replicated, all the nuclei derived from the first one should be equivalent to it, and differentiations arising between cells should involve only the cell parts outside the nucleus —that is, the cytoplasmic structures. An alternative view, first maintained by Weismann, was that elements in the nucleus underwent at mitosis a process of segregation by which the nuclear contents were divided qualitatively among different descendant cells. It is significant that this view fell from favor largely because mitoses appear to produce morphologically equivalent daughter nuclei. It was also refuted by studies of regeneration, which show that some differentiated cells from a plant can, if isolated under proper conditions, reconstitute an entire new plant with all its specific characters. Work on regeneration in animals leads to the same conclusion.

Nuclear differentiation. The question of the functional equivalence of nuclei was not subjected to direct critical examination until recently. Some experimental observations now partially answer the question whether nuclei of differentiated animal cells retain the capacity of the zygote and cleavage nuclei to regulate development. By removing nuclei from the egg of the frog before cleavage and replacing them with nuclei from blastula and gastrula stages, Briggs and King have shown that later nuclei from blastulae retain the capacity to direct development normally from the egg stage. Yet this *totipotency* is gradually lost, since when nuclei from certain regions of the neurula stage are substituted for zygote nuclei, they are unable to carry out all differentiations: they have become incomplete in this sense. Evidence for nuclear differentiation in different tissues has also been provided by chemical observations (Mirsky and coworkers), and visible differences in the chromosomes of diverse tissues of an insect have been demonstrated by Pavan and Breuer. In Paramecium, Sonneborn has shown that both morphological and physiological differentiations occur. Since they occur between nuclei derived from a common source by mitosis, it is not to be inferred that mutations cause the differences; rather genic activities depend upon the cellular environments in which they take place. The cytoplasms of cells of different tissues clearly become different; one has only to compare cells from neural, muscular, and blood systems in animals or from phloem, bast, and cambium in plants to observe this elementary fact. In these different environments the expression of the same genetic constitution takes different forms. The retention of nuclear equivalence after many cell divisions in the early development of an amphibian and the reacquisition of totipotency of the nuclei of some differentiated cells when cultivated under specified conditions indicate that different cytoplasmic environments may not produce irreversible changes in nuclei. The emphasis is clearly to be put upon the total reacting system of nucleus and cytoplasm rather than upon either one alone.

GENE AND CHARACTER

In seeking the origins in development of the phenotype differences that appear at later stages, it is necessary to retrace the pathway leading from gene to character but in the reverse direction, beginning with the observed phenotype. Here the customary finding is that many phenotypic differences can be traced to a single gene substitution, and this leads to the assumption that most, perhaps all, gene differences have widespread, manifold effects. Genes for which this has been demonstrated are said to have *pleiotropic* effects. Pleiotropy is to be expected from the general character of development, in which the parts are interdependent, so that gene effects on one part or process are likely also to influence other parts dependent upon the first. This is especially evident in processes with a widespread distribution, such as those determining colors. Albinism in animals, for example, results in the reduction or absence of pigmentation in eyes, skin, and hair; in plants it results in the absence of chlorophyll and other colored substances such as anthocyanins. The mutant change from black to red eyes in the flour moth, described on page 343, is accompanied by loss of dark pigment in many parts of the body, traceable to inability to synthesize the key substance, kynurenine. Pleiotropism in such cases is not a property of the gene but of its *effects* on different structures. We have already cited the yellow mutant in the mouse, in which viability, color, obesity, and the degree of extension of white spotting are affected. These are not related in any obvious way, and the question is raised whether the same mutation has affected several pathways more or less unrelated to each other. We shall not know whether the gene is pleiotropic in this sense until we prove that the different developmental effects trace to different primary effects of the gene. A primary effect of the gene is not known in any case because of the difficulty of isolating its action in the cell. The same difficulty is therefore encountered at lower levels of organization, in which a gene-determined enzyme reaction may be influenced by accumulation of blocked precursor, by inhibitor substances, by temperature, and by effects of other genes that give the gene effect the appearance of primary pleiotropy.

Often, perhaps usually, the effects of a gene on a character depend on the other genes affecting the metabolic system in which it acts, on the external milieu, and on many other factors. It has been frequently observed that specific genes do not always produce the same character effects in all the individuals in which they are present. Thus, of all members of a Drosophila population homozygous for the mutant gene "abnormal abdomen," only about 15 per cent show the kind of difference from the normal type for which the mutant is named. This mutant is said to have a penetrance in the population of 15 per cent. Similarly, the dominant mutant Lobe [5], when heterozygous, may show a penetrance of about 75 per cent under certain conditions, and this can be changed by changing the culture conditions. Often the penetrance of one gene is increased or decreased by other genes, which thus act as modifiers or suppressors. Whether or not a gene produces a detectable change in phenotype thus depends on the environment and the residual genotype as a whole, and penetrance merely describes the frequency with which overt expression is reached. Expressivity (p. 129) is the degree and type of expression of a gene in the individual. Like dominance, penetrance and expressivity appear to be due to the interaction during development between the gene and the system of which it is a part.

GENIC BALANCE

A general fact about the relations of genes and characters has been embodied in the concept of genic balance. Bridges, in attempting to explain the "exaggeration" effects of recessive mutant genes opposite a deleted or deficient piece of chromosome, assumed that, of the many genes influencing a character, some tend to accentuate and others to diminish the character, and the actual condition of the character thus represents the point of balance between the opposed tendencies. This view gained considerable support when applied in the balance theory of sex determination (p. 307) and is a necessary assumption in explaining the developmental effects of chromosomal aberrations such as heteroploidy, which differ from the normal type not by mutated genes but by the ratios or relative dosages of unchanged genes.

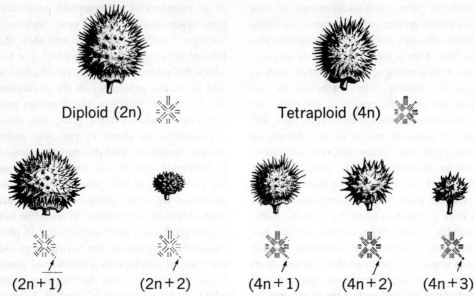

Diploid (2n)   Tetraploid (4n)

(2n+1)   (2n+2)   (4n+1)   (4n+2)   (4n+3)

Fig. 25.1. Chromosome mutants and chromosome balance in Datura, as shown by differences in capsule form. Above, at left, the normal diploid type, from a plant with twelve pairs
of chromosomes. Below (left), the mutant
globe, in which one set of chromosomes has
three members, thus upsetting the normal balance. The effect of this particular chromosome
set is evidently to flatten the capsule, for the
addition of an extra chromosome results in a
flatter capsule than the normal. The addition
of two extra chromosomes (as shown to the
right of this) has the effect of flattening the
capsule still further.

Thus, when one of the 12 chromosome
sets in a diploid Jimson weed, Datura, contains three instead of the normal two chromosomes (2n + 1), several plant characters
regularly differ from the normal type (Fig.
25.1). The differences produced are characteristic of the particular chromosome present in excess. The mutant "globe," for example, is trisomic (2n + 1) for a chromosome
that we may identify as Gl. This produces a
change in the shape of the seed capsule and
in other plant characters. If two extra Gl
chromosomes are present in the diploid
(2n + 2Gl), the mutant effect is greatly en-

Above, at right, a capsule from a tetraploid
plant, which has four chromosomes in each set
instead of the normal two. The balance between
the twelve sets is thus maintained, and there is
little variation from the normal in capsule form.
The results of the addition of one, two, and
three chromosomes to the globe set are shown
below. It is evident that the change produced
by each additional chromosome is less than it
is in a corresponding diploid plant, presumably
because the number of chromosomes is greater,
the contribution of a single chromosome is less
in proportion to the whole, and the balance is
therefore less upset. (*After Blakeslee*)

hanced, but the effect of one, two, or even
three extra Gl chromosomes in a tetraploid
(4n + 1Gl), etc., is proportionally much
less than in the diploid. The mutant "character" is evidently due to the ratio of the
extra chromosome to all the others. This
rule is borne out by similar data from other
mutants, showing that departure from the
wild type is due to the effect of a particular
chromosome relative to the others. The wild-
type condition of the characters represents
the stable equilibrium that is disturbed by
changes in the ratios of the genes.

This concept makes it possible to understand why a change in a single gene (a point mutation) may and often does produce a greater or more specific change in development than the addition or subtraction of a whole chromosome set. The change in ratio between a single locus that lost its normal or wild-type allele and the few other loci with similar but opposite effects is much greater than the change involved in adding one each of the whole series of unmutated loci in a normal chromosome set, in which the balance of plus and minus effects is at or near the equilibrium point. From this and many other similar cases we derive the rule that relations between genes and characters are indirect and depend on the state of the system as a whole. We should thus expect to find that the balance can be upset and "mutant" characters produced not only by failure of one or more genes to contribute their normal share of effect but by other alterations of the internal environment imposed by changes in nutrients, chemicals, and other agencies from the external environment.

Adaptation. The evidence from microorganisms, especially those consisting of single cells, is especially pertinent here. If the conditioning of the cytoplasm by the *genome*, or the gene complement, is important, the effect of the milieu is equally so. In Paramecium, for example, the surface antigens depend upon the genome, but which antigen is expressed depends upon the temperature, since an alteration in temperature can cause a change in antigenic type. Since it is reversible by temperature, this effect is not due to mutation. In yeast and bacteria, an enzyme activity not previously present can be induced when the organism is grown in a new substrate. Thus cells adapted to fermentation of glucose may adapt to galactose by producing without mutation an adaptive enzyme system capable of splitting galactose. These are *phenotypic adaptations*, which show that responses conditioned by the genome may appear when

required for the life of the cell under new conditions. This may be a model of the adaptive responses of tissue cells in multicellular organisms as development proceeds.

This interplay of the genome with its environment is shown also by the experimental production of phenocopies in higher animals —that is, of changes in the response of an unaltered genome which resemble the changes produced by mutation.

Our first examples of genetically controlled developmental sequences come from experimental studies of the development of pigments in insects, since these studies led to a general analytical method by which a total process may be broken up into a series of chemical steps controlled by identified mutants.

EYE COLOR IN EPHESTIA

In the European flour moth, Ephestia, Kühn found a recessive mutation, *a,* which alters the wild-type eye color from dark brown to red and also affects the size and chemical composition of the pigment granules formed in cells in other parts of the body (Table 25.1).

When Caspari transplanted testes from *AA* or *Aa* larvae to *aa* larvae, the grafts retained their dark color and caused the eyes of the host to develop the dark color. Testes transplanted from *aa* to *AA* larvae became colored like those of the host. It became apparent that the wild-type gene *A* was responsible for the production of a diffusible substance (known as A or a+ substance) which entered the blood stream and caused the production of the *A* characters in *aa* tissues. This substance was later identified as *kynurenine,* which is formed in the body from the amino acid tryptophane, a normal cell metabolite. Injection of kynurenine into *aa* larvae results in the production of wild-type pigment. It was therefore assumed and later demonstrated that the production of kynurenine from tryptophane was blocked in the *aa* mutant and that tryptophane should

TABLE 25.1

Comparison of the wild-type Ephestia with its mutant

Character affected	Color in wild-type *AA* or *Aa*	Color in mutant *aa*
Adult eyes	Black	Red
Adult brain	Dark brown	Pale red
Adult testes	Brown-violet	Colorless
Larval skin	Reddish	White
Larval eyes	Much pigment	Little pigment

therefore accumulate in these mutants. Thus the mutant requires kynurenine if dark pigment is to be produced. The failure of the oxidative step from tryptophane to kynurenine is not due to an enzyme deficiency, since *aa* tissues contain an enzyme that can catalyze this step. The effect of *aa* is rather to prevent the enzyme and the substrate tryptophane from reacting with each other. Here again, as we saw in Chapter 24, the character is affected not by the presence or absence of substances but by the setting in which particular reactions become possible or impossible.

EYE COLOR IN DROSOPHILA

Independently of these studies, a chain of reactions involving at least two different substances concerned in producing the wild-type eye color in Drosophila was demonstrated by Beadle and Ephrussi. In dipterous insects, many of the structures of the adult, or imago, such as the compound eyes, legs, and wings, develop from anlage formed in the late embryo or early larval stages. These are known as *imaginal disks*. In Drosophila, the imaginal disk of the compound eye can be transplanted from one larva to another and then can continue its development in the body cavity of the host. When the host has undergone metamorphosis and has emerged as an imago, the implanted eyes can be dissected out from the body cavity and their color characteristics observed. The colors of intact eyes are apparently not altered by the

operation itself or by development within the body cavity.

When eye disks are taken from larvae of strains with mutant eye colors (white, peach, pink, carmine, etc.) and implanted in wild-type larvae, or the reverse, the disks usually develop antonomously (Fig. 25.2); that is, they produce eyes with the color of their own genotype and are not affected by the genotype of the host. There are, however, two important exceptions. Eye disks from larvae with the mutant gene vermilion implanted into larvae of the wild type or of certain eye-color mutant types develop not vermilion but wild-type color. Similarly, eye disks from larvae with the mutant eye-color gene cinnabar (an eye color similar to vermilion) implanted into larvae of the wild type and of some mutant types develop wild-type pigmentation. In both cases something from the host has caused the implant to develop a phenotype that does not correspond to its own genotype. Beadle and Ephrussi assumed that the vermilion and cinnabar mutant flies each lack some substance that is an essential link in the chain of reactions leading to the formation of the wild-type eye pigment, that the eye disks remain sensitive to such substances, and that, in the cases just quoted, the essential substance has been supplied to the disk from the body fluids of the host.

It has been shown that the substance lacking in the vermilion eye is not the same as the substance lacking in the cinnabar eye. When eye disks from vermilion larvae are

Host

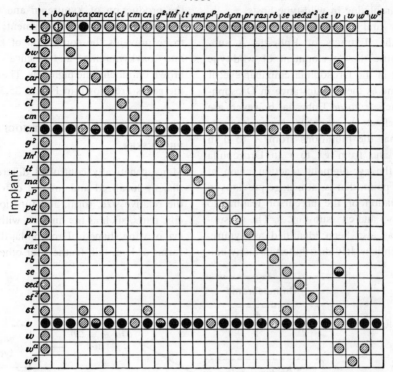

Fig. 25.2. Diagrammatic representation of the results of eye transplantation in Drosophila. Shaded circles indicate autonomous development; for example, brown (*bw*) disks transplanted into wild-type (+) larvae develop brown color. Black circles indicate nonautonomous development of pigmentation. Half-black and half-shaded circles indicate that the resulting implant is intermediate in color. (*From Beadle and Ephrussi*)

transplanted into cinnabar larvae, the implants develop wild-type pigmentation, showing that the cinnabar host supplies what is lacking in vermilion. However, when eye disks from cinnabar larvae are transplanted into vermilion larvae, the implants develop cinnabar pigmentation; vermilion does not supply what is lacking in cinnabar. It appears, then, that two substances known as cn+ and v+ are lacking in vermilion, that one of these, the cn+ substance, is lacking in cinnabar, and that both v+ and cn+ are present in the wild type. Other observations show that the second of the substances (the one that cinnabar

lacks) is produced only when the first is present; that is, one substance acts as a precursor of the other. Thus have been demonstrated two related links in a chain of reactions leading to the development of wild-type eye color, and this chain has apparently been broken at an earlier point by mutation to vermilion, at a later point by mutation to cinnabar. Now we can see why those eye disks that retained their own phenotype did not respond to the environment of the wild-type host. It is not the kynurenin-tryptophan system that is defective in these (they are known to have both v+ and cn+)

but other systems not reparable by the substances circulating in wild-type hosts.

The v+ and cn+ substances are not species-specific. Extracts of Ephestia A substance cause the development of wild-type eye color in the Drosophila cinnabar eye; it is the same as the v+ substance in Drosophila. Extracts from *aa* Ephestia, however, are without effect on cinnabar; hence it is assumed that the mutations from *A* to *a* in Ephestia and from *v+* to *v* in Drosophila blocked the eye-pigment reaction chain at the same point, that is, at a stage previous to the formation of the precursor leading to both the v+ and cn+ substances. The v+ substance has also been identified as kynurenin, which is widely distributed in many ani-

mals. Mutations of *v+* to *v* or *A* to *a* blocks the production of kynurenin and thus prevents formation of brown pigment; mutation to *cn* prevents the conversion of kynurenin into oxykynurenin and thence into the brown ommochrome pigments. The effects of the genes are shown in Figure 25.3.

GENIC CONTROL OF MORPHOGENETIC PROCESSES

Many genetically controlled differences are sharply localized and involve differences in the relative size, form, and function of specific parts, such as the mutants with changed eye or wing shape in Drosophila, the variant forms of legs, tail, feathers, or other parts in

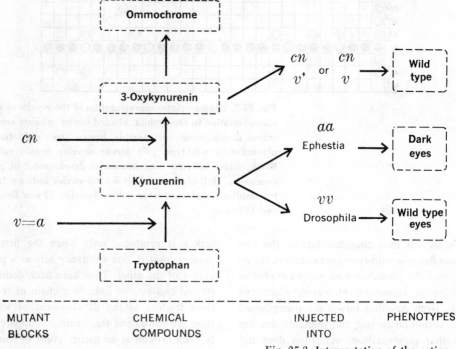

MUTANT
BLOCKS

CHEMICAL
COMPOUNDS

INJECTED
INTO

PHENOTYPES

Fig. 25.3. Interpretation of the action of the mutant genes vermilion and cinnabar in *Drosophila melanogaster* and *Ephestia kühniella.* The metabolic steps blocked in the mutants are indicated at the left and the effects in the two species at the right. (*After Kühn*)

birds and mammals, or the variations in the size and form of leaf, flower, or fruit in plants. Here the problem is to explain what seems to be a localized effect of a gene difference on one organ or part. Such cases can be studied by standard embryological methods and the difference traced to its first appearance. When this is done, it often turns out that the apparently localized effect is actually a secondary result of some more general change, such as (1) a modification of an over-all rate of growth or metabolism which finds one part of the organism in an especially sensitive or plastic state; (2) a changed dependence or "organizer" relationship that especially affects those parts whose fates are being determined; (3) changes in circulating substances such as hormones, which have local effects; or (4) changes in the movements or multiplication of particular groups of cells that affect the character of an organ or tissue. Some illustrative examples of each of these will be briefly described.

GENERAL METABOLIC EFFECTS

The Creeper fowl, whose legs are considerably shortened, differs from the normal by a dominant mutation that is lethal when homozygous. Landauer has shown that this mutation has many effects on the skeleton and other parts and that the several effects are consequences of a retardation of growth occurring in the early embryo. Embryos homozygous for this mutation die after about 72 hours of incubation (Fig. 25.4); but after only 36 hours they fall behind the normal in growth, and the anlage of the legs, which in the normal fowl grow rapidly at this time, fail to grow in the homozygotes. Rarely, one

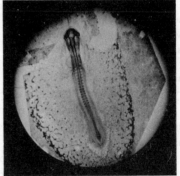
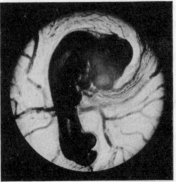
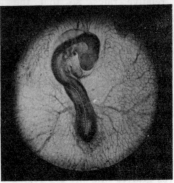

Fig. 25.4. Photographs of normal and homozygous Creeper chick embryos. From top to bottom: (1) normal embryo at 48 hours of incubation, (2) Creeper at 48 hours, (3) normal at 72 hours, (4) Creeper at 72 hours. (*From Landauer*)

Fig. 25.5. A homozygous Creeper embryo that has lived beyond the lethal period, showing marked changes in legs (only toes showing), wings (less reduced), head, and eyes. (From Landauer)

of these lethal embryos lives until a later embryonic period; such animals are smaller than the normal ones, have only rudiments of hind limbs, and have characteristic abnormalities of head, eyes, and other parts (Fig. 25.5). An embryological study of the parts reveals that they deviate from normal in the order of their normal growth potencies during the early period of retardation; that is to say, those that grow most rapidly at that time in the normal fowl are most retarded and abnormal in the homozygote.

In the heterozygotes ($Cp/+$) a similar relationship holds, the longer and more distal limb bones being most shortened. These differences in limb length and proportion are established in the early embryo, and thereafter the different bones grow at about the same relative rates, so that the altered growth pattern appears as a result of the retardation suffered in the earlier period.

Transplantation of presumptive limb buds from Creeper homozygotes into normal hosts shows that the effect of the Creeper gene on the limbs is autonomous from stages as early as 24 hours, for the grafts develop the Creeper characters. But the effects of this gene on the development of the eyes are nonautonomous: eye rudiments of Cp/Cp embryos grafted into the eye region of normal embryos ($+/+$) develop as normal

eyes, whereas eye rudiments of $+/+$ embryos grafted into Cp/Cp embryos show all the peculiarities of the eyes of homozygous Cp/Cp—microphthalmia, open embryonic fissure (*coloboma*), and absence of scleral cartilage layer.

The effects of the gene are thus not gene- or locus-specific but depend on developmental processes intervening between the first effects of the gene in the cells (which are unknown) and the final manifestations of the character; the succession of these processes differs in different regions of the embryo. The grafting experiments show also that the Creeper mutation is not a cell-lethal, since tissues taken from a homozygous embryo, normally destined to early death, are viable when transplanted. Lethality can be "cured" by the environment in which the tissues develop. Such tissues are nonautonomous, like the eye disks of the cinnabar and vermilion mutants of Drosophila and the red-eye mutant of Ephestia. The mutant defects are reparable, like those of the nutritional mutants of Neurospora and other microorganisms.

In fact, explantation and cultivation of Creeper embryonic tissues in vitro give results quite comparable to those from nutritional mutants grown in complete media. Most tissues of homozygotes have normal growth potencies in normal culture media, although heart tissue regularly grows less well; this suggests that defective functioning of the circulatory system may be concerned in the pleiotropic effects of the mutation. When limb rudiments from normal ($+/+$) embryos are grown in dilute culture media with low nutritive content, they show many of the characteristics of Creeper limbs, suggesting that this phenotype may be a result of general metabolic deficiency in early development. Similar abnormalities, or phenocopies, may be induced in developing embryos of normal genotype ($+/+$) by injecting into the yolk sac a variety of chemical compounds, such as boric acid and insulin, many of which interfere with carbohydrate metabolism, possibly by affecting enzyme or coenzyme systems.

The effects of the Creeper mutation on the long bones appear to be of a nonspecific character. The parts of the embryo seem to respond to the altered metabolism brought about by the mutation in accordance with differences in the needs imposed upon them by their differing growth rates and their positions in the developmental sequence. Thus a generalized early change may have specific or localized effects, such as that in the circulatory system; and these, in turn, may have general effects on structures developing later, which suffer in different degrees from deficiencies in metabolism.

EFFECTS OF GENES ON "ORGANIZER" RELATIONSHIPS

An important principle of development is embryonic induction, whereby one structure or tissue exerts a determining influence upon the differentiation of another. One of the best known examples of this is the ability of one tissue, the chordamesoderm, formed during gastrulation of vertebrate embryos, to induce another tissue, the overlying ecto-

Fig. 25.6. Inheritance and effects on development of the Brachyury mutation in the house mouse. Note, in the 11-day heterozygous embryo, the constriction that marks the end of the notochord. The tail beyond this point has been resorbed in the 16-day embryo.

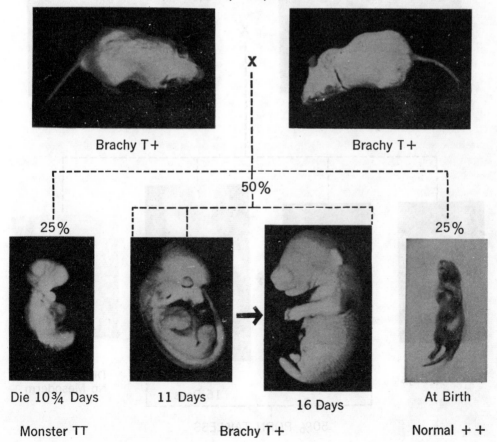

Brachy T +   X   Brachy T +

25%   50%   25%

Die 10¾ Days   11 Days   16 Days   At Birth

Monster TT   Brachy T +   Normal + +

derm, to form such axial structures as the brain and the medullary tube. Pieces of chordamesoderm, which Spemann first designated as the organization center or primary organizer, when implanted into the presumptive flank region of an amphibian gastrula, cause the flank ectoderm to form structures quite different from those that ordinarily arise from it. After the brain has been induced by a process of this kind, the optic vesicle evaginating from the brain acts upon the head ectoderm to induce formation of a crystalline lens, while the hindbrain induces an ear vescicle from undetermined ectoderm. These inducing areas may be called second-

ary organizers, and the gradual determination of specific differentiations during development may be looked upon as part of a continuous series of developmental interdependencies integrated by means of relations between inductors, or organizers, and the tissues that respond to the inductions.

There is now a good deal of evidence that such chains of inductions are controlled by genes. A case in point is provided by the effects of a series of mutant alleles in the house mouse which have been analyzed by genetic and embryologic methods. One mutation, T, produces in heterozygotes ($T/+$) a reduction in the length of the tail by inter-

Fig. 25.7. The breeding behavior of a balanced lethal line in the mouse (*Mus musculus*).

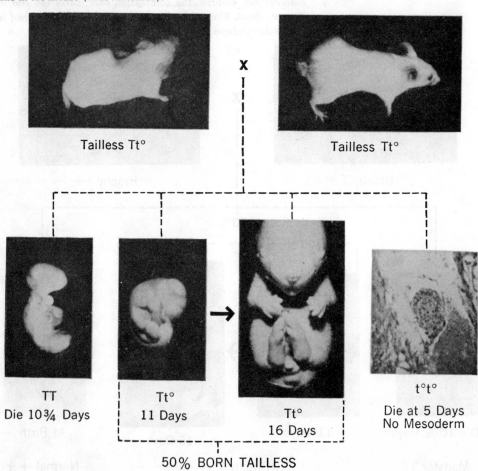

Tailless Tt°   X   Tailless Tt°

TT   Tt°   Tt°   t°t°
Die 10¾ Days   11 Days   16 Days   Die at 5 Days
                                                      No Mesoderm

50% BORN TAILLESS

fering with the development of the notochord in the distal part of the tail (Fig. 25.6). Somites and other structures in this region which depend upon a normal notochord undergo differentiation and then are resorbed before birth. Embryos homozygous for this mutation always die after 10 days of development; in them the notochord is entirely lacking, somites and neural tube are grossly abnormal, the posterior part of the body, including the tail and hind limbs, does not develop, and there is no functioning allantois or umbilical vessel; hence there are lethal defects in both the nutritional and the excretory functions.

Another series of mutations (t^0, t^1 . . . t^n), which show no recombination with T and hence behave as alleles at this locus, produce complete taillessness when combined with T and, when homozygous, kill the embryo at various stages before birth. Each such lethal allele, in compound with T, gives rise to a balanced lethal system (Fig. 25.7), which maintains itself without artificial selection, since only heterozygotes, T/t^n, survive. The effects of some of these lethals are shown in Table 25.2. All these mutations appear to interfere with links in a chain of processes leading to and deriving from the chordamesoderm; the later links appear to connect the embryonic notochord, by means of its inductive effects, with the organization of nervous, skeletal, and muscular systems. The chain itself, that is, the system of inductive relationships leading to normal development, is thus shown to be controlled by genes.

In similar ways, specific genes may determine which of two alternative paths of development may be realized. Thus in mice with the mutant gene "flexed" (fl/fl) the cartilage between certain of the developing vertebrae of the tail differentiates not into the normal fibrous tissue of the intervertebral cushions or disks but into bone, so that neighboring vertebrae are fused, often at an angle to each other, forming crooked parts

or kinks. Whether bone or felted fibers arise depends, according to Kamenoff, on the speed of the preceding cell divisions.

PEDIGREE OF SYMPTOMS IN PLEIOTROPISM
Most of the mutations detected as morphological abnormalities in vertebrates are clear-

TABLE 25.2
Phenotypic and embryological effects of some lethal mutations at locus T in the house mouse

Times given are postcopulation, i.e., from fertilization.

Genotype	Effect
t^{12}/t^{12}	Development stops in morula stage (78–84 hours). Ribonucleic acid formation defective
T/t^{12}	Viable but tailless. Tail notochord fails to develop; tail structures resorbed before birth
$+/t^{12}$	Tail normal
t^0/t^0	Development stops on fifth day. No mesoderm or mesodermal structures formed; i.e., gastrulation fails
T/t^0	Tailless as above
$+/t^0$	Tail normal
t^4/t^4	Development stops on seventh or eighth day; defect in archenteron
T/t^4	Tailless as above
$+/t^4$	Tail normal
t^9/t^9	Development stops on ninth day; duplications of axial structures that escape from normal organization control
T/t^9	Tailless as above
$+/t^9$	Tail normal
T/T	Development stops on eleventh day; absence of notochord; mesodermal derivatives abnormal
T/t^n	Tailless as above
$+/T$	Tail short. Notochord missing from part of tail

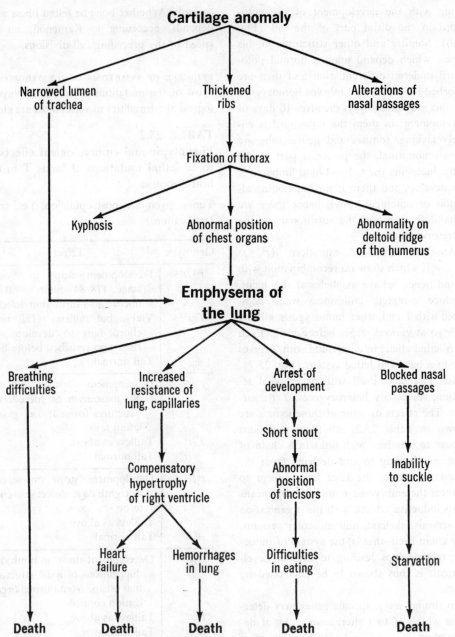

Cartilage anomaly

Narrowed lumen of trachea

Thickened ribs

Alterations of nasal passages

Fixation of thorax

Kyphosis

Abnormal position of chest organs

Abnormality on deltoid ridge of the humerus

Emphysema of the lung

Breathing difficulties

Increased resistance of lung, capillaries

Arrest of development

Blocked nasal passages

Short snout

Compensatory hypertrophy of right ventricle

Abnormal position of incisors

Inability to suckle

Heart failure

Hemorrhages in lung

Difficulties in eating

Starvation

Death   **Death**   **Death**   **Death**   **Death**

Fig. 25.8. A "pedigree of causes" of death due to a lethal gene in the rat. (*After Grüneberg*)

ly pleiotropic in their effects. The constellation of effects associated with some common cause is referred to in medical literature as a *syndrome*. Thus one syndrome in mice with members of the *T* series of alleles,

which we have already described, includes abnormalities such as taillessness, spina bifida, and absence of anus and urogenital openings. All these can be traced eventually to disturbed inductive relationships in the early stages of the development of the embryo.

Grüneberg has examined several such cases of developmental pleiotropism in rodents. In the rat, for example, a whole pedigree of symptoms is associated with a mutant that is lethal shortly after birth. This pedigree can be traced to a generalized defect of the cartilage, as shown in Figure 25.8.

In the case of another mutant gene, *Sd*, in the mouse, as studied by Gluecksohn-Schoenheimer, it was shown that one defect —absence of kidneys at birth in homozygous *Sd/Sd* animals—is due to the failure of induction between the developing ureteric bud and the kidney mesenchyme. In the absence of contact, the kidney fails to develop. Another effect—absence of tail in *Sd/Sd* and *Sd/+* embryos—traces to degenerative changes by which the tail bud with its normal neural tube, somites, and notochord are progressively destroyed. The two effects are apparently unrelated; yet a recently discovered temporary embryonic structure, the ventral tail ectoderm, may, in Grüneberg's opinion, have inductive relations to the development both of the tail and of the urogenital system. The pedigree of symptoms here may also trace to a single source.

The first or primary effect of the mutation in such cases remains and will remain unknown until the metabolic defect antecedent to the morphological abnormalities is identified. In the absence of such evidence, it is impossible to determine whether such mutants affect a single process or whether several are affected simultaneously. Pleiotropy in such cases is consequently a term describing associated effects far removed from the first effect of the mutation.

EFFECTS OF DEFICIENCIES ON DIFFERENTIATION

In Drosophila, a number of mutations are known to be due to deficiencies localized in well-mapped areas of the chromosomes. Poulson has studied the effects of a series of these mutations in the X chromosome on the differentiation of the embryo in the early stages of its development. Complete absence of the X chromosome (which occurs, for example, in some of the zygotes produced by attached-X females, cf. p. 158) leads to cessation of development in the earliest embryonic stage shortly after the egg is laid. In normal eggs at this time the egg nucleus divides rapidly and the cleavage nuclei move to the periphery of the egg, where they begin to form a blastoderm. In Nullo-X eggs the nuclei begin to divide but do not migrate to the periphery, so that this first stage of differentiation does not occur. If the zygote receives only approximately half of an X chromosome, some migration of cleavage nuclei occurs, but only an incomplete blastoderm is formed; or, if a blastoderm is formed, the germ layers fail to separate and differentiation is arrested after two to three hours of development. Apparently the genes in at least half of the X chromosome are necessary to initiate the first steps in differentiation. When smaller areas (fewer genes) of the X are missing, development proceeds for longer periods, but there is no close quantitative relationship between the number of genes lacking (as measured by numbers of bands absent in the salivary chromosome) and the extent of development (Table 25.3). This probably means that some loci exert a greater influence than others on early differentiation and organization. A special study was made of deficiencies at the left end of the X in the area of Notch (cf. p. 199) and the loci of white and facet alleles (Fig. 25.9). Here it was found that deficiencies of different lengths, provided they included the locus of facet, had early effects, the gut and muscles being incomplete or undifferentiated, whereas the neural tissues, derived from ectoderm, were greatly overdeveloped. Deficiencies including white locus permit longer development, the ectoderm being more or

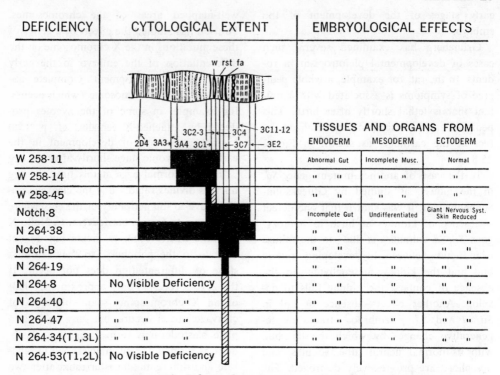

DEFICIENCY	CYTOLOGICAL EXTENT	EMBRYOLOGICAL EFFECTS		
		TISSUES AND ORGANS FROM		
		ENDODERM	MESODERM	ECTODERM
W 258-11		Abnormal Gut	Incomplete Musc.	Normal
W 258-14		" "	" "	"
W 258-45		" "	" "	"
Notch-8		Incomplete Gut	Undifferentiated	Giant Nervous Syst. Skin Reduced
N 264-38		" "	"	" "
Notch-B		" "	"	" "
N 264-19		" "	"	" "
N 264-8	No Visible Deficiency	" "	"	" "
N 264-40	" " "	" "	"	" "
N 264-47	" " "	" "	"	" "
N 264-34(T1,3L)	" " "	" "	"	" "
N 264-53(T1,2L)	No Visible Deficiency			

Fig. 25.9. Relation between extent of chromosomal deficiency and effect on embryonic development of 12 mutations near the Notch region of the X chromosome of *Drosophila melanogaster*. Black indicates visible deficiency in the salivary-gland chromosomes of the bands included in the salivary map at the top; crosshatched columns indicate genetic deficiency not visible in the chromosomes. Absence of facet locus produces the earliest effect on development; deficiency for white produces the later effect. (*After Poulson*)

less normal but with gut and muscles abnormal. In the region of facet, even deficiencies so short as to be undetectable in the salivary chromosome were lethal in early stages when homozygous, producing embryos without mesoderm and hypertrophied ectoderm. These results leave no doubt that particular gene loci control essential processes concerned with differentiation.

CELL-LETHALITY

The occurrence of a series of lethals, many of them deficiencies, at known locations in the X chromosome of *Drosophila melanogaster* provided Demerec with the opportunity of partially resolving the question

whether mutations lethal to the zygote when homozygous are also lethal to the cells in which they occur. He made use of the method of "twin spots" (cf. p. 175), which had been shown to arise from crossing over between linked loci in somatic cells very late in development, so that few descendant cells received the recombined chromosomes. Thus, some females carrying in one X chromosome the allele for yellow skin or hypoderm and in the other the nearby allele for singed bristles have, on adjacent areas of the thorax, the homozygous effect of yellow and its twin spot the homozygous effect of singed. The assumed origin of these spots is shown in Figure 25.10. If a lethal allele is

TABLE 25.3

Relation between extent of deficiencies in the X chromosome of *Drosophila melano-gaster* and their developmental effects in homozygous males. (*After Poulson*)

Deficiency	Extent	Embryo development arrested after:	Effects
Nullo-X	Whole chromosome — 1,000 bands	1 hour	Failure of migration of cleavage nuclei. No blastoderm
Df-XR	Right half of X; ± 500 bands	1–2 hours	Incomplete blastoderm
Df-XL	Left half of X; ± 500 bands	2–3 hours	Failure of separation of germ layers; differentiation arrested
Df-Notch (several; cf. Fig. 25.9)	1–45 bands	6 hours	Failure of mesoderm, hypertrophy of neural system; gut incomplete
Df-white (several; cf. Fig. 25.9)	1–16 bands	12 hours	Ectoderm nearly normal. Mesodermal and entodermal derivatives abnormal
Df-scute[8]	11–12 bands	20 hours	Full larval development except that muscle and trachea functions are defective

present very near one of these loci, one of the twin spots will frequently also be homozygous for the lethal. If it acts as a cell-lethal, one of the spots will be missing, that is, only one mosaic spot will appear. Of 15 X-chromosome deficiencies tested by this method, 13 were cell-lethal and only two were not. Of 24 other lethals whose loci were scattered at random in the X chromosome, 10 were cell-lethal and 14 were not. Loci at which cell-lethals occur are assumed to be indispensable for cell function and reproduction; those that do not have cell-lethal effects apparently alter developmental processes rather than cell viability in mature tissues. In this class are such lethals as Brachyury in the mouse, Creeper in the fowl, lethal giant larva in Drosophila, and others. Tissues taken from these lethals are viable when they are transplanted to normal hosts. The effects of such mutations are reparable; clearly these effects are not distinct and separable but are elements in an interacting system.

GENIC CONTROL OF HORMONAL COORDINATION

If we define hormones as those complex cellular products that in low concentrations produce effects on cells or tissues more or less remote from their points of origin, we may refer to these effects as hormonal coordination. There are many examples of genic control of such systems both in higher plants and in animals. One of the earliest of these was provided by the studies of Smith, MacDowell, and others on the dwarf mutant of the house mouse. Animals homozygous for this recessive allele are not easily distinguishable from their normal litter mates until about one to two weeks after birth, when their growth rate falls off. Thereafter they remain small, attain only about one-

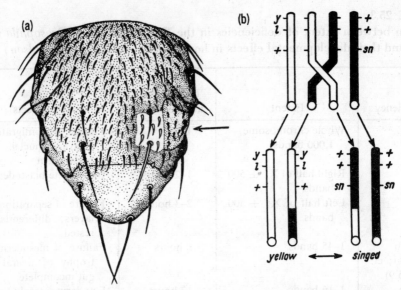

Fig. 25.10. Mosaic test for cell-lethality in *Drosophila melanogaster*. Left, thorax of a fly heterozygous for the mutations yellow body (*y*) and singed bristles (*sn*) with a pair of twin spots in which the effects of these recessives are visible—yellow hairs and a yellow bristle in the left spot, singed hairs and bristles in the right spot. Right, the assumed mechanism of somatic crossing over leading to the formation of the twin spots. In cases in which the lethal (*l*) in the yellow-carrying chromosome is cell-lethal, no yellow twin spot appears. (*After Hadorn, based on Sturtevant and Beadle and on Stern*)

third the normal weight, and never attain sexual maturity. The anterior lobe of the pituitary gland of the dwarfs is markedly reduced and two of its classes of secretory cells are absent. Probably as a consequence of this defect the thyroid and the adrenal cortex are deficient. The whole syndrome of characters associated with this mutation can be alleviated by implanting in the dwarfs active anterior pituitary tissue from normal mice or rats. Then growth is resumed and sexual maturity is attained; males so treated have produced young. Dwarf pituitaries implanted in immature normal females induce ovulation but are ineffective in promoting growth. It is thus clear that the mutation specifically affects the production of the growth hormone but not the gonadotrophic hormones, and all its effects trace to a deficiency in the differentiation of a particular type of secretory cell in the anterior pituitary.

Hadorn and others have studied the development of several mutants in Drosophila which, when homozygous, terminate development during larval or pupal stages. One of these mutants, which dies during the first larval instar, has a defective ring gland, the small group of cells in the brain which exercises hormonal control over moulting and metamorphosis. In another, known as *lethal giant larva* (*lgl*), the larva continues to grow beyond the time of normal pupation and becomes oversized but deficient in many structures, including the imaginal disks—the anlage of adult structures such as eyes, legs, and wings—which normally differentiate in late embryonic and larval stages. In this case it was shown that certain primordia, when transplanted from the mutant to the normal larvae, retain the capacity to grow and differentiate, while others have already lost this capacity. The effect of the lethal is not primarily to cause cell death but to disturb early development to the extent of creating in the mutant an unfavorable environment or one that is insufficient to meet the differing needs of the primordia for specific tissues, organs, and systems. A focus of this insufficiency in *lgl* homozygotes appears to lie in the disturbance of the endocrine function of the ring gland.

PLANT HORMONES

In several species of plants, hereditary dwarfism is associated with a deficient synthesis of *gibberellic* acids; when these are supplied exogenously the dwarfs are enabled to grow. The mutant form "lazy" in maize lies prostrate on the ground and fails to grow upward by negative geotropism as normal plants do. The mutant phenotype develops because the growth hormone that is effective in this case, one of the *auxins* (indolacetic acid) has a uniform distribution in the stem, whereas in a normal plant placed on its side, auxin accumulates on the lower side and stimulates growth there, causing the tip to turn upward.

PLUMAGE PATTERNS

Further understanding of the relation between genes and hormones has been obtained through the work of Danforth and others, who have studied the manner of determination of genetic variations in the plumage of birds. By exchanging transplants of skin between newly hatched chickens differing in sex, feather pattern, and color, it has been shown that, although the pattern of the feather is determined by the genes in the follicle, its form is influenced by the hormones of the host. Thus skin transplanted from a barred Plymouth Rock female to a Rhode Island male produces barred feathers of the male type. In the dove, on the other hand, sex differences in the plumage are regulated entirely by the genes without reference to the hormones, and it appears that the effects of hormones depend upon the

reactivity, or threshold, of the feather follicles. From this and other studies it appears that sex hormones in birds are essentially nonspecific substances to which tissues of different species or genotypes may or may not develop a capacity to respond. Genic effects are therefore mediated in two different ways with respect to hormones: (1) by controlling the chemical constitution of a substance or of the cells which produce it and (2) by conditioning the cytoplasm of the responding cells and thus determining to which hormones they will respond.

GENIC CONTROL OF GROWTH

Genetic differences in the final size of animals or plants are often mediated by differences in the rate of early growth. Castle and Gregory have indeed shown that as early as 40 hours after fertilization the embryos of a race of large rabbits are already larger than those of a race of smaller ones, probably owing to differences in the rate of very early cell division. These in turn are probably related, according to Gregory, to the larger amounts of glutathione in the embryos of races of rabbits and fowls which attain large size as adults. The implication is that genes that cause more rapid early growth may do so by way of the metabolic steps that are stimulated by the sulfhydryl ion of glutathione.

In races of cucurbits, genetic differences of the order of 500 times in the final volume of the fruit have already been determined when the early primordia of the fruits are formed. Large fruits usually contain more rather than larger cells; thus control is exercised through the rate of cell division. In other cases, a gene difference may determine the duration of growth. Bean plants with axillary flowers grow continuously in stature until checked by external conditions; those with terminal flowers produce the short, bushy type of plant. The control of this character difference is probably hormonal.

GENIC CONTROL OF FORM

Form differences, such as those between spherical and disk-shaped fruits in squash, normal and Creeper limbs in fowls, lobed and entire leaves in the morning glory, the many mutant differences in wings and eyes of Drosophila, and many other analyzed cases, can often be traced to unequal rates of growth of the various dimensions. Thus in the "Club" gourd, length constantly increases faster than width during most of its development, so that the shape changes from an almost isodiametric one in the smallest primordium to one in which the length is about fifteen times the width in the mature fruit. In other races, on the contrary, growth in width exceeds that in length by a constant amount. Where two dimensions grow at different rates and the ratio between the rates does not change, a constant and predictable change in form occurs during growth. This is the general phenomenon of allometry; to which attention has been particularly directed by Huxley, Teissier, and others. In the formula of simple allometry, $y = bx^{\alpha}$, where x and y are dimensions, b is the value of y when $x = 1$, and α is the growth ratio, a constant.

Experiment indicates that it is this growth ratio, rather than any particular ratio between dimensions as such, that is genically controlled. The duration of the period of unequal growth rates may be brief, establishing a shape for the young ovary which then persists through later development when growth is uniform in all dimensions; or it may con-tinue much longer. Such differences in dimensional growth rates occur primarily during the period of intense cell division and are related to constant differences in the plane in which the cells divide. The biochemical steps through which control is exercised are not yet known, but since correlations between growing parts are in evidence, it is apparently the whole growth system that is genically controlled in such cases.

SUMMARY

The examples given above show that growth and development of multicellular animals and plants are processes controlled by genes, usually acting in concert in accordance with the principle of genic balance. The control is exercised within the cells, through reactions between cells and tissues mediated by means of substances which have hormone-like effects or which affect inductive relations between parts, relative growth, or the relative viabilities of different cells and tissues. The presence of a complete or nearly complete complement of genes appears to be necessary for the initiation and continuance of such processes. The usual effect of a new mutation seems to be to reduce the quantity of some substance or reaction below the threshold level necessary for normal development. The effects must generally be detected at secondary levels, since primary, or first, effects of genes cannot be detected by the usual (observational) methods of studying development. These must now be supplemented by experimental methods.

26 CYTOPLASM IN HEREDITY AND DEVELOPMENT

UP TO THIS point we have focused our attention on the genes in the chromosomes and have discussed the roles they play in the transmission of heredity, in the origination and maintenance of the variety that makes evolution possible, and in the control of cell metabolism and development. It is time now to ask whether the control of these processes is vested only in the nuclear genes or whether there are systems, outside and independent of the nucleus, which are responsible in whole or in part for continuity and change in the characters of individuals, races, and species.

The evidence now available indicates that the primary mechanism of continuity is furnished by the self-reproduction of genes. It is this that is responsible for the repetition in the offspring of parental patterns of metabolism and development. If other systems of continuity exist, they must also be endowed with the capacity for self-reproduction and the ability to undergo alteration

and thus to permit evolutionary change. It has long been suspected that bodies with such properties occur in the cytoplasm of cells, and, indeed, at least one category of self-duplicating particles, *plastids,* has been clearly demonstrated in plant cells. Other cytoplasmic particles, such as mitochondria and microsomes, which have important functions in metabolism, have been revealed; but questions remain about their mode of reproduction and the degree of their independence of the nucleus. The central bodies that appear at the time of nuclear division in animal cells and some lower plants are also capable of division, but it is not known whether they can alter their properties by mutation. Their apparent absence in the dividing cells of higher plants indicates that they are not indispensable. The discovery of viruses that undergo regular replication and processes akin to mutation and recombination points to another possible category of transmissible bodies. Most of those investigated so far are parasites introduced into the cell by infection, but as we shall see, in several known cases bodies with some of the properties of viruses are passed on from parent to offspring and are responsible for hereditary traits. Finally, there may be in the cytoplasm, as Sonneborn has suggested, particular self-perpetuating molecular patterns, such as those responsible for antigenic properties.

CYTOPLASMIC INHERITANCE

Thus, a variety of organizations of microscopic and submicroscopic dimensions exist in the cytoplasm. The question is whether any of these have properties of stability, mutability, and ability to influence the phenotype which would provide a system of transmission different from the gene system

—a system which we should then refer to as *cytoplasmic inheritance*.

In looking for evidence of cytoplasmic inheritance we should turn first to cases in which reciprocal crosses give unlike results, since the nuclear heredity contributed by father and mother is usually equivalent, whereas the amount of cytoplasm contributed by the egg is always much greater than that in the sperm.

PREDETERMINATION

A clear case of maternal effect has been studied in the moth *Ephestia kühniella*. A mutant form lacking dark pigment in larval skin and eyes and other organs of both larvae and adults has a recessive gene *aa* in contrast to the normal dark form *AA* (cf. p. 343). Crosses of *aa* ♀ with *Aa* ♂ produce

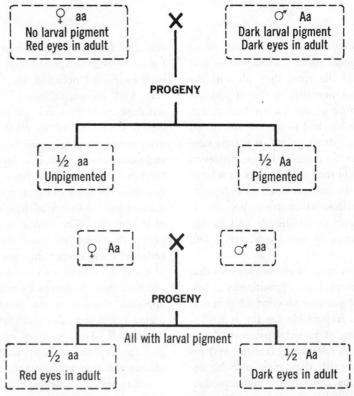

Fig. 26.1. Maternal effect of the gene A in reciprocal crosses in *Ephestia kühniella*.

larvae only *half* of which show the darkening effect of the *A* allele, whereas from crosses of *Aa* ♀ with *aa* ♂ *all* the larvae are dark because all eggs contain in the cytoplasm the pigment precursor, kynurenine, for which gene *A* is responsible (Fig. 26.1). This *maternal effect* wears off as the kynurenine in the egg is used up. As adults, the offspring of reciprocal crosses show only the effects of their own genotype. In a similar case in the silkworm, a mutant gene in the mother prevents diffusion of kynurenine into the egg, and thus the egg-coat color expresses the genotype of the mother. We are evidently dealing here with effects of maternal genes on the egg cytoplasm, and it is unnecessary to postulate hereditary elements in the cytoplasm to account for such cases.

A more striking case of predetermination by maternal genes has been worked out in the water snail Limnaea. Many species of snails are known in which the shell always coils to the right (dextral) and many others in which it coils to the left (sinistral). In a few species, both dextral and sinistral individuals occur. In one of these (*Limnaea peregra*), dextrality appears to behave as a simple dominant to sinistrality, as shown by

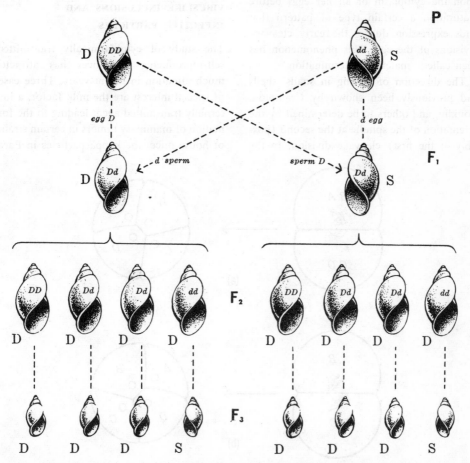

Fig. 26.2 The normal inheritance of dextral and sinistral coiling in *Limnaea peregra*. D, dextral phenotype; S, sinistral phenotype; *D*, gene for dextrality; *d*, gene for sinistrality. Note: This species is hermaphroditic and may reproduce either by crossing or by self fertilization. (*After H. E. Crampton*)

the breeding experiments of Boycott, Diver, and Garstang, as interpreted by Sturtevant. The character of the coiling is, however, determined not by the individual's own genes but by those of its mother. Some of these snails that are themselves phenotypic dextrals produce all sinistral offspring; and such individuals by appropriate genetic tests may be shown to be homozygous for the recessive sinistral gene. Their dextral character must have been determined by the presence of a dextral gene in their mothers (Fig. 26.2). This shows that it is not the "character" of the mother but her genes that impress upon the cytoplasm of all her eggs before maturation a certain type of pattern that finds expression during the early cleavage divisions of the egg. This phenomenon has been called "maternal determination."

The direction of coiling in snails' shells had previously been shown by Crampton, Conklin, and others to be determined by the orientation of the spindle at the second (possibly at the first) cleavage division. In the sinistral type the spindle is tipped toward the left of the median line; in the dextral type it is tipped toward the right (Fig. 26.3). This is in turn determined by some relationship of the egg to the mother before maturation. This gene thus acts on the eggs in the ovary, predetermining the direction of an early cell division and thus the type of asymmetry and the pattern of the future individual. A number of similar cases may be similarly explained by the action of nuclear genes. Maternal predetermination of these sorts does not constitute cytoplasmic inheritance.

VIRUSLIKE INCLUSIONS AND
INFECTIVE PARTICLES

The study of cytoplasmically transmitted, self-reproducing substances has attracted much attention in recent years. Three cases of special interest are the milk factor, a maternally transmitted agent leading to the formation of mammary tumors in certain strains of house mice; the kappa particles in Para-

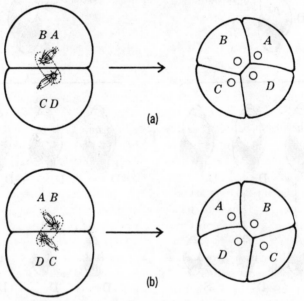

Fig. 26.3. Coiling pattern in a snail as determined by the orientation of the spindles for the second cleavage division. Cleavage leading to sinistral pattern is shown by *a* and that leading to dextral pattern by *b*. (*After Morgan*)

mecium; and the sigma factor for carbon-dioxide sensitivity in Drosophila.

THE MILK FACTOR

In outcrossing mice from a long-inbred strain in which nearly all females developed a particular type of mammary cancer, Bittner found that cancer susceptibility was maternally transmitted. Moreover, by using females from the high-cancer strain as foster mothers for new-born mice from noncancer strains and normal mothers as nurses for young from the high-cancer strain, it was shown that the substance that induces cancer-susceptibility is transmitted through the mother's milk, whence it has become known as the "milk factor." Recent evidence suggests that it is probably a virus, which, since it is found also in the seminal vesicles, may be transmitted like an infection by males of certain high-tumor strains. Whether it can reproduce itself indefinitely apart from a certain genetic constitution of the host is not yet known. It may be lost spontaneously from strains carrying it and thus is not necessarily a continuously transmitted entity.

THE KAPPA PARTICLES OF PARAMECIUM

Sonneborn and his associates have described the transmission of some cytoplasmic particles and their relation to nuclear genes in *Paramecium aurelia*. Certain strains of this species, known as "killer" strains, secrete into the water in which they live a substance, *paramecin*, which injures and kills individuals of "sensitive" strains of the same species. Killer strains contain large numbers of cytoplasmic particles of desoxyribonucleic acid which are known as kappa particles; sensitive strains contain no kappa particles. The maintenance of kappa particles and the production of paramecin depend upon the presence, in killer clones, of a dominant gene K, which is transmitted strictly as a nuclear gene; the kappa particles are transmitted through the cytoplasm.

The essential facts of genic and cytoplas-mic transmission in infusoria, which are necessary for understanding this case, are as follows. Infusoria may reproduce for many generations asexually, by direct fission, forming genetically uniform clones. In sexual reproduction, individuals of the same mating type (p. 321) unite or conjugate in pairs. Gene exchange occurs by migration in both directions of haploid nuclei over a cytoplasmic bridge between the conjugants (Fig. 23.4), followed by fusion of nuclei from different parents (p. 320). If the bridge persists beyond some minimum time necessary for gene exchange, an exchange of cytoplasm between the conjugants may also occur. After conjugation, the partners separate and reproduce by fission.

By appropriate procedures, individuals of killer clones may be crossed to sensitive ones. Observations on the descendants of such crosses have shown that killer clones carry a dominant allele K, whereas sensitives are usually kk.

When killers, KK, conjugate with sensitives, kk, the exconjugants are, of course, Kk, and should accordingly be killers. But if the conjugation is brief and little or no cytoplasm is exchanged, then a killer clone and a sensitive clone are produced (Fig. 26.4). A more prolonged conjugation results in exchange of cytoplasms, and then all descendant clones are killers and have kappa particles that can be shown by staining reaction to contain DNA. These particles are clearly vehicles of cytoplasmic transmission, but it has been shown that maintenance of the particles and the killer phenotype depends on the presence of the gene K in the nucleus. Thus a Kk individual may be either a killer or a sensitive depending on whether or not it has received kappa particles. However, kk individuals may inherit kappa particles in the cytoplasm but lose them after some fission generations. Certain killer clones, KK or Kk, can be converted to sensitives by making them undergo very rapid fissions during which the reproduction of the

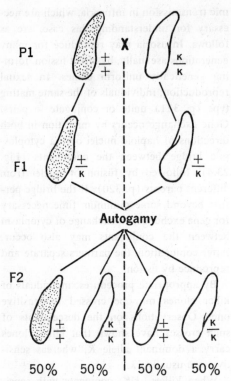

P1 $\frac{+}{+}$ X $\frac{K}{K}$

F1 $\frac{+}{K}$ $\frac{+}{K}$

Autogamy

F2 $\frac{+}{+}$ $\frac{K}{K}$ $\frac{+}{+}$ $\frac{K}{K}$

50% 50% 50% 50%

Fig. 26.4. Inheritance of the "killer" character in *Paramecium aurelia*, variety 4, when the killer gene *K* is transmitted but not the killer cytoplasm. (*After Sonneborn*)

kappa particles fails to keep pace with the cell divisions, with the result that the particles are finally lost entirely. Thereafter the gene *K* cannot initiate the production of the particles but can again maintain them if they are introduced during conjugation or by exposing the converted *KK* sensitives to a cell-free, concentrated suspension of ground killer animals. Such a sensitive clone then acquires and maintains a killer phenotype.

There is some evidence that kappa particles may exist in several varieties differing in the amount of paramecin produced and in the effects on sensitive animals. All are conditioned by the gene *K*.

Thus, in continuity and variety, kappa particles fulfill the requirements of true cytoplasmically transmitted elements. Although they originate from antecedent particles,

their continued reproduction depends on the genotype and on environmental conditions. Since they do not cause disease in the cells that harbor them, they resemble symbionts rather than parasites, if in fact they are not native, naturally occurring components of the Paramecium cytoplasmic system.

THE SIGMA SUBSTANCE IN DROSOPHILA

In *Drosophila melanogaster,* L'Heritier and Teissier found a true-breeding stock that differed sharply from others in its high sensitivity to carbon dioxide. Reciprocal crosses between this and normal strains gave different results, sensitive mothers having mostly sensitive offspring, of which the females again transmitted sensitivity during repeated outcrosses with nonsensitive males. Sensitive males may, however, transmit the peculiarity to a few of their offspring only, and of these some of the sensitive females may transmit it to some of their progeny. By replacing each of the chromosomes of the sensitive stock by homologues from a normal resistant stock, the sensitive character was shown to be transmitted outside the chromosomes and to be associated with a heat-labile substance, sigma, which is transmitted primarily through the egg cytoplasm but which can be separated from the animals and used to induce sensitivity in nonsensitive eggs by implantation of normal ovaries into sensitive females. Once sigma has entered the organism, it becomes included in the gametes and is subsequently transmitted.

The three cases just described are valid instances of extrachromosomal inheritance. It is to be noted that none of the cytoplasmic particles involved in these cases had been known as components of the cytoplasm; they were discovered in the course of investigating the extrachromosomal transmission of phenotypic traits.

PLASTID INHERITANCE

We come now to evidence of hereditary transmission of characters through self-reproducing bodies that are regular components of the cytoplasmic system. The clearest cases are in plants and concern inheritance of plastid characters. Correns and others studied the "albomaculatus" type of leaf variegation (Fig. 26.5), in which the normal green tissue is irregularly spotted with patches of paler green or white. These patches may be small or may include entire

Fig. 26.5. Albomaculatus variegation: a leaf of a variegated four o'clock, *Mirabilis jalapa.* (*After Correns*)

leaves or branches. This character occurs in a wide variety of plants, and its inheritance has been determined in more than 20 genera. Flowers on wholly green branches produce seeds that grow into normal plants; flowers on variegated branches yield offspring of three kinds—green, white, and variegated in variable proportions; flowers from branches wholly white give progeny without chlorophyll; but in every case the source of the pollen has no influence on the offspring. Inheritance is wholly maternal. Variegation seems clearly to be determined by agencies localized in the cytoplasm rather than in the chromosomes. The system of transmission by which the primordia of chloroplasts pass

through the cytoplasm of the egg and give rise to the plastids of the next generation has been referred to by Renner as a *plastome.* The existence of a plastome, as in "albomaculatus" leaf variegation and several similar cases, is good evidence of a stable system of self-perpetuating bodies, with clear effects on the phenotype, which are transmitted outside the nucleus.

In maize, Rhoades has made a study of the relation between a plastid abnormality and a regularly transmitted gene. He found that maize plants homozygous for a recessive allele, *ij* (iojap) in chromosome VII, may be variegated, with yellow or white "japonica" striping, or all white (in which case they die as seedlings), owing to the presence of defective colorless plastids. Reciprocal crosses of *ij/ij* striped plants with normal green (*Ij/Ij*) ones give different progenies, as shown in Figure 26.6. When normal green plants (*Ij/Ij*) are used as females and pollinated by pollen from *ij/ij* (striped) plants, the F_1 plants *Ij/ij* are wholly green (normal); but when *ij/ij* (striped) plants are pollinated by *Ij/Ij* pollen, the F_1 plants (*Ij/ij*) are of three different kinds: normal green, striped, and all-white (nonviable) seedlings. Whether or not the F_1 plants, all of which have the same genotype, *Ij/ij*, develop variegation obviously depends on the ovules from which they arose, that is, on the source of the egg cytoplasm.

When the striped F_1 plants (from cross 1, Fig. 26.6), *as females,* are test-crossed with normal green *Ij/Ij,* as males, they produce in some cases only normal green, in some cases striped, and in others only white seedlings. Some of the latter are *Ij/Ij,* but even when they lack the *ij* allele, they inherit the abnormal plastids. Rhoades has given additional evidence for the conclusion that under the influence of the *ij/ij* genotype, plastids may become permanently changed to the colorless state and that this change is perpetuated when the allele responsible for the change (*ij*) is replaced by its normal allele.

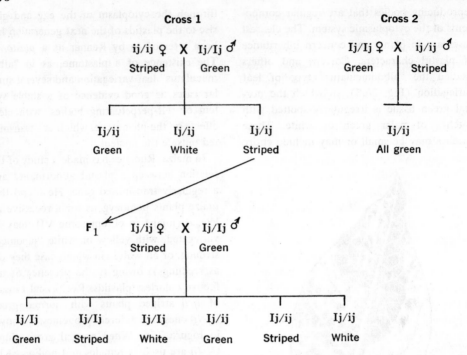

Fig. 26.6. Results of reciprocal crosses between striped (iojap) and normal corn plants and backcross of F$_1$ striped by normal green.

The abnormal plastids, or the cytoplasm which causes them to be abnormal, may then be passed on through some of the ovules. Whether an ear or a sector of an ear transmits only the abnormal condition (in which case all-white progenies are produced) or both normal and abnormal conditions (in which case striped progenies are produced) depends on the assortment of the two kinds of cytoplasmic inclusions in the cells that gave rise to the ear.

It is not known whether other races of variegated plants have arisen in this way— that is, by changed conditions induced in the cytoplasm by a mutated gene. They may have done so. It is possible also that plastid primordia may arise from mitochondria, which are centers of the same kind of enzyme activities that are associated with plastids.

The iojap mutant, according to Rhoades, has induced also a cytoplasmically trans-

mitted male sterility due to the degeneration of pollen cells, and this effect may be connected with failure of function of the mito-chondria. Once established, in any case, there seems little doubt that such characters of the cytoplasm may become continuous and influence the phenotype.

INDUCTION OF CYTOPLASMIC CHARACTERS IN MICROORGANISMS

Sonneborn and Beale have discovered in *Paramecium aurelia* a variety of homozygous stocks each of which is characterized by one type of antigen in the cilia. The antigenic type, or serotype, of the stock may maintain itself through many successive fissions and through conjugation also, provided temperature and nutritional conditions are kept constant and optimal. But environmental changes of several kinds—temperature, nutrition, exposure to ultraviolet—are capable of inducing specific transformations of serotype. Animals of seven different induced phenotypes were shown to have the same genotype. The serotype is thus transmitted cytoplasmically. A genetic analysis by Beale of four different stocks collected in different geographic areas revealed the existence of three genes, each responsible for a different antigen; but whether the phenotype made possible by a particular combination of these genes is expressed or not depends on environmental conditions. Thus one genotype will show a particular serotype at 25°, another at 29°. The genotype thus sets limits to the alterations in antigenic type which the cytoplasm may transmit, and the environment determines which of these possible forms the cytoplasm may express. This is an instructive instance of the way in which cytoplasmic and nuclear properties interact with one another and with the environment.

In yeast, the same phenotype (production of small, or "petite," colonies) may be produced by a gene mutation or by a normal genotype in which a cytoplasmically transmitted abnormality in the cytochrome oxidase system has arisen by "mutation." This vegetatively propagated character is lost when such cells fuse with those of normal genotype. It may be induced when normal cells produce buds in the presence of dilute solutions of a toxic dye, *euflavine,* and is thereafter inherited cytoplasmically. Ephrussi, to whom this analysis must be credited, believes that the euflavine has induced mutations in self-reproducing elements which he identifies with mitochondria. The dependence of the stability of the cytoplasmic system upon the genotype is shown by large differences between genotypes in the rate at which they produce spontaneous changes to the cytoplasmically transmitted abnormality. The similarity to the induction of plastid changes by the *ij* gene is apparent.

Ephrussi has also pointed out the similarity between this situation in yeast and that occurring during differentiation in metazoan cells:

"At the cell level the differentiation of the two lines of yeasts appears as a mutation; in terms of intracellular mechanism, however, if the ensemble of the population of intracellular units is taken into account it is to be regarded rather as a result of segregation. This segregation, accidental in the case of spontaneous mutation, can be directed by an environmental factor which causes an irreversible restriction of the potencies of newly formed cells without apparently affecting the totipotency of the generating cells."

OTHER CASES OF CYTOPLASMIC TRANSMISSION

Several cases have been studied in which maternal inheritance occurs in traits that are not concerned with plastids, and these provide a more difficult problem. Among these is a case of male sterility in maize described by Rhoades. This character, which consists in the abortion of much or all of the pollen (though not of the ovules) is transmitted solely through the mother and never by the pollen. Since gene markers are known for all the 10 chromosomes of maize, Rhoades was able to replace each of the chromosomes of the male-sterile race with one from normal stock. Male sterility was found not to belong to any of the 10 linkage groups thus tested and seems to be controlled by some agency in the cytoplasm.

A more complex situations occurs in the genus Epilobium, a member of the Onagraceae closely related to Oenothera, which has been studied intensively by Lehmann, Michaelis, Renner, and others. Reciprocal crosses between *Epilobium hirsutum* and the markedly different *E. roseum* are very dissimilar. Where *E. hirsutum* is the female parent, the offspring are nearly sterile and their anthers and petals are much reduced in size. Where *E. roseum* is the female parent, there is little sterility and the floral parts are well developed. There are also reciprocal differences in the size of the plant and of its vegetative organs. By repeated backcrossing of the F_1 (*roseum* ♀ × *hirsutum* ♂) with *hir-*

sutum males, Michaelis produced a type in which the cytoplasm was derived from *roseum* but the chromosomal complement was presumably now entirely from *hirsutum*. When this was crossed reciprocally with pure *hirsutum*, the differences observed were similar to those that occurred when pure *roseum* and pure *hirsutum* were crossed, indicating that these differences were due to the cytoplasm, since the genes were now presumably identical. Renner and Michaelis regard the evidence from Epilobium as strongly indicative of a hereditary vehicle in the cytoplasm. Lehmann and his students explain the differences in reciprocal crosses in this genus as due to the production of specific changes in the cytoplasm by particular gene combinations or to the various reactions of a given nucleus in different cytoplasms.

The extensive studies done by Wettstein on mosses of the family Funariaceae have led to similar conclusions. He observed no differences in reciprocal crosses between *varieties* of *Funaria hygrometrica,* the characters segregating in normal Mendelian fashion. When the two *species F. hygrometrica* and *F. mediterranea* were crossed, however, marked differences between the reciprocal crosses appeared. For most traits, the segregating gametophyte offspring tended to resemble the maternal parent, the paternal types often failing to appear. A few characters showed normal segregation. When the two *genera* Funaria and Physcomitrium were crossed, the offspring were all similar to or identical with the female parent. Many of the spores were sterile. Wettstein interprets these results as due to the failure of genomes similar to that of the male parent to survive and function in cytoplasm derived from a different source. This conclusion is supported by evidence from polyploid races produced by regeneration of gametophytes from sporophyte tissue. By this means it was possible to introduce as many as three sets of paternal chromosomes from one genus into the eggs of the other genus, but even with this preponderance of the male genomes, inheritance was still entirely maternal. These facts show convincingly that there are marked developmental incompatibilities between genes and cytoplasm and that, when the two are derived from different sources, the cytoplasm may prevent the genes from acting.

Goldschmidt, in fact, regards the cytoplasm as providing the specific substrate for gene action, one of its effects being to condition or set limits to what the genes can do. His opinion, derived from observations such as those we have described, is that "cytoplasmic differences of such an order that developmental processes would be changed qualitatively according to the cytoplasm present would be expected only in crosses between species and still higher categories."

MEROGONIC HYBRIDS

The relative roles of cytoplasm and nuclear heredity have also been studied by methods quite different from those hitherto considered. These involve the production of merogonic hybrids, having egg cytoplasm from one parent species and a sperm nucleus from another. The classic experiments in this field were performed by Theodor Boveri, who removed the nucleus from the eggs of a sea urchin of one species and artificially fertilized them by sperm of a species with markedly different characters. Although development did not persist beyond the pluteus stage, the merogonic hybrids seemed to resemble the species that furnished the sperm, indicating that the nucleus controlled development even when surrounded by cytoplasm from a very different source. Boveri's results were open to serious question, however, since there is evidence that the nuclear material was not entirely removed. In repeating these experiments, Hörstadius did indeed find differences between the reciprocal merogonic hybrids, indicating predetermination (cf. p. 360) of the egg cytoplasm by its own genes. The work of Hadorn, however, indicates that for certain traits the male nucleus may be without effect in some merogonic tissues. Two species of Triton (*T. palmatus* and *T. cristatus*) differ clearly in the character of the epidermis. Hadorn fertilized the egg of *palmatus* with the sperm of *cristatus* and succeeded in removing the *palmatus* nucleus before nuclear fusion. The embryo (thus haploid) develops only to the blastula stage; but a portion of the presumptive epidermis, if grafted to a normal larva of another species, *T. alpestris,* maintains its identity and develops to the adult state. Here it resembles the epidermis of the parent *palmatus,* which contributed the cytoplasm, rather than the parent *cristatus,* which contributed the nucleus. For this trait, at least, the cytoplasm rather than the nucleus seems to have the decisive effect, a result quite the opposite from Boveri's.

THE SPREAD OF PIGMENT IN THE SKIN

The problem of cytoplasmic transmission has been attacked in still a different way. For many years it has been known that when pieces of skin are transplanted from black to white areas of black-and-white spotted guinea pigs, the graft continues to produce black pigment in the skin (but not in the hairs) and, with time, black pigment spreads to the formerly colorless areas surrounding the graft. Billingham and Medawar showed that when areas altered in this way are transplanted to white areas, pigment production and spread to new white areas continue through several serial propagations. The effect resembles the spread and increase of an infective principle which passes from cell to cell after the nuclei of the original black cells are no longer present. Billingham and Medawar found in the white areas of guinea-pig skin dendritic cells like the melanocyte cells of the colored areas in which the pigment is formed. They assumed that cytoplasmic connections between the black and the white cells formed a bridge over which passed a principle capable of transforming colorless into colored cells and considered this property as an additional aspect of cellular heredity, important in development and differentiation. The hypothesis apparently does not explain the appearance of black hairs in grafts of white skin into black areas on rats and mice. This occurs by migration of melanoblasts. It is not yet apparent that an additional system of self-propagating elements has to be invoked to explain the spread of skin pigment in cases like those above.

27

THE ELEMENTS
OF THE GENETIC SYSTEM

THE PRINCIPLES of genetics have been set forth in this book in terms of genes, which are the elements by means of which the transmission mechanism of heredity, the genetic changes in populations, and the control of metabolism and development are being elucidated. Now, as we approach the end of this exposition, we should consider two sets of questions about the genetic system. The first concerns the resolution or analysis of the system: what is the nature of the elements that compose it, and what views may we reasonably hold about their three primary attributes—their abilities to duplicate themselves, to mutate, and to influence the phenotype? The second set of questions concerns the organization and integration of the elements into a system which functions in the individual and in evolution. The analytical questions are discussed in this chapter, the synthetic ones in Chapter 28.

Before we discuss these questions, which lie at the boundaries of our present knowl-

370

edge, it would be well to pause and reflect how we have learned what we know about the elements of heredity. The total genetic constitution, the genome, of all species which have been adequately studied can be resolved by breeding analysis into linkage groups, and each linkage group can be resolved into loci. Cytogenetical study enables us to identify each linkage group with a chromosome and each locus with a restricted small segment of the chromosome. Segments that resisted further analysis by crossing over were called genes. This might seem to imply that elements inferred from such evidence are the ultimate units of the system. However, there is no proof that this is so, nor can proof be given as long as the limit of the method used in analyzing the system is unknown. The method used is crossing over, and detection of crossing over depends on the ability to recover and to recognize the new combinations that arise from the exchanges. Where this event has a very low probability, very large numbers of observations will be required to reveal it. Our knowledge of the sensitivity of the method will depend upon the sizes of the populations with which we can deal.

CROSSING OVER WITHIN SERIES OF ALLELES
Recent work has shown that when very large populations are observed, derived from parents in which small segments of chromosomes bear suitable marker genes, crossing over can be proved to occur between what had been assumed to be alleles. The earlier diagnosis of allelism had been based on similarity of effect, noncomplementary interaction between mutants of independent origin (absence of reversion to wild type, cf. p. 113), and absence of recombination. In the white-eye series of alleles in Drosophila, for example, all mutants affect the depth of pigment in the eye; compounds of two alleles such as w^e/w produce a color intermediate between eosin and white, and no recombination was noted. The latter evidence is, of course, purely negative, and does not exclude crossing over as an event too rare to be expected in small samples.

In all such series that have been adequately analyzed, crossing over has been found to occur. A typical case is that of the lozenge alleles in *Drosophila melanogaster*. The first lozenge mutant was named for its effect on the shape of the eye; it behaved as a recessive at locus 27.7 in the X chromosome. Subsequently, many additional mutants at this locus were found, all recessive to normal and all sharing effects on eye shape, arrangement of eye facets, amount of eye pigment, and reduction of fertility in homozygous females. These appeared to form a series of multiple alleles, but when certain lozenge alleles were combined by Oliver in compound females (lz^g/lz^s), some of their characters were wild-type, indicating partial complementary interaction of the kind known to be associated with mutations at different loci. Rarely, compound females lz^g/lz^s mated to lz^g or lz^s males produced normal offspring that could

be proved to have a wild-type ($+$) allele at this locus, as though crossing over had occurred. A thorough analysis by Green and Green, using marker genes on either side of the lozenge locus, proved that crossing over between certain lozenge alleles actually does occur with low frequency. They were thus able to obtain the map of the lozenge gene, as shown in Figure 27.1.

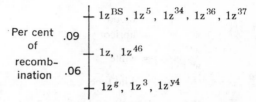

Fig. 27.1. A micromap of the lozenge gene, based on recombination of marked chromosomes. (*After Green and Green*)

Three groups of alleles were found in the gene. Members of different groups were shown to be nonidentical by the occurrence of crossing over between them. However, members of the same group are not proved to be identical by this test; it is only shown that, if nonidentical, the recombination fractions for different members of the same group are below those that can be revealed by the sizes of populations observed. There is, in fact, no absolute proof for identity. We may say, then, following Pontecorvo's nomenclature, that three *sites of mutation* have been identified within the lozenge *section*, or gene. This is the minimum number of sites; there may well be more.

A similar resolution of a gene into several sites of mutation separable by crossing over has been proved for several other allelic series in *Drosophila melanogaster*. Thus, at the first mutant locus identified in this species, white (locus 1.5 on the X chromosome), a series of alleles differing in depth of eye pigment was identified, including the mutants apricot, ivory, blood, etc. (cf. p. 114). The occurrence of recombination between white and some of these other alleles has been observed and at least three sites of mutation, separable from each other by crossing over, have been identified so far. An important point is that crossing over between two mutant alleles—for example, w^{bl} (blood) and w^{aE} (apricot E)—can give origin to two new alleles, namely, wild type and white. The phenotypes in this case are as follows:

$$
\begin{aligned}
w^{bl} \quad + \quad + &= \text{blood} \\
+ \quad w' \quad w'' &= \text{apricot} \\
\left. \begin{array}{ccc} w^{bl} & w' & w'' \\ + & w' & + \end{array} \right\} &= \text{white} \\
+ \quad + \quad + &= \text{wild type}
\end{aligned}
$$

The bithorax alleles have been resolved into five sites with recombination fractions between sites ranging down to 0.01 per cent (1 per 10,000). The number of allelic series in this species which can be analyzed into two or more sites of mutation has grown steadily as they have been more carefully studied: vermilion, star-asteroid, forked, stubble-stubbloid, and others. These loci had been placed on the linkage maps (Fig. 14.1) to express their recombination values with nearby marker loci. Their locations still serve the original purpose, but each of these genes may now be represented on a micromap similar to that for lozenge (Fig. 27.1), which expresses the arrangement and order of the sites of mutation within each gene.

RESOLUTION OF A GENE IN MAIZE

In maize, a series of alleles of the gene A_1 (locus 103, third linkage group of map, Fig. 14.2) has long been known to control varying amounts of anthocyanin pigment in the aleurone layer of the seed and in other plant tissues, resulting in mixtures of brown and purple pigments. One mutant of this series, A^b, has a dominant effect in compound with the recessive a. Heterozygotes A^b/a, in which the a chromosome was marked by other nearby mutants, were tested, and the results indicated that A^d, a new

dilute form of A, appears with a frequency of about 0.07 per cent (7 per 10,000), and nearly all of these represent recombination in or near A^b. Two different A^d alleles were identified, one producing spontaneous mutants with appreciable frequency, the other stable. These and other facts concerning these alleles are interpreted by Laughnan to mean that A^b consists of two duplicate elements separable both by ordinary crossing over and by oblique synapsis, so that if the components are called α and β, then the micromap arrangements of this locus would be as in Figure 27.2.

$$A^b \frac{\alpha \, \beta}{a} \longrightarrow \frac{}{\alpha} = A^d \text{ stable}$$

$$A^b \frac{\alpha \, \beta}{a} \longrightarrow \frac{\alpha \, a}{} = A^d \text{ "mutable"}$$

Fig. 27.2. Recombination within the A^b gene resulting in two new "alleles." (*After Laughnan*)

The fact that some alleles at this locus had been known to differ from others in mutability is thus ascribed to the presence of a duplication that may be resolved by crossing over into a stable (single) element and another element which will be subject to dissolution by rare crossovers and thus will appear to be unstable.

In the mold *Aspergillus nidulans* two sites have been identified in each of two allelic series, three sites in a third series, and five sites in a fourth. A similar resolution of the E series of multiple alleles into several sites has been accomplished in the silkworm. A review of the evidence on such sections of allelism has led Pontecorvo (1958) to conclude that "legitimate reciprocal crossing over between alleles of one gene does occur as a rule, not as an exception." If this is so, then the term *pseudoallelism*, used to designate groups of alleles which show recombination with each other, becomes unnecessary. The implication of the above is that successive mutations of the same gene will usually occur in different sites.

The multiplicity of sites within a gene has also been indicated in other organisms and by other methods. The maximum resolution has been reported in the bacteriophage T-4, in which Benzer has identified 33 sites within one section and 21 within another. In bacteria in which a sexual recombination system has not been found, the transfer of genetic material by transduction (p. 318) has shown that the loci controlling different steps in a synthesis, such as that of tryptophane or histidine in *Salmonella typhimurium* (p. 385), may consist of several sections, each consisting of several sites of mutation.

Complementary interaction between alleles may also reveal nonidentical alleles even when recombination between them has not been observed. This has been possible at locus T in the house mouse, within which at least a dozen nonidentical alleles have been revealed. Here, certain alleles that are lethal when homozygous (such as t^{12}, t^0, t^4, t^9 and T of Table 25.2) produce viable offspring when combined with other lethal alleles. The viability of t^{12}/t^0, for example, proves that the two alleles have complementary effects and are hence nonidentical. Occasionally, nonidentity of alleles may be proved both by complementarity and by recombination between the alleles, as in the case of two adenine-requiring mutants of Aspergillus, ad_1 and ad_3. These are linked with a recombination value of about 0.001, yet they are complementary, $ad_1 + / + ad_3$ being wild type.

Evidence such as this has led to the conclusion that many more elements exist within the genetic material in the chromosomes than were revealed by the linkage maps that specified the relative locations of the gene loci. Pontecorvo has estimated the numbers of sites to be of the order of millions in organisms like Drosophila and Aspergillus, and of tens of thousands in organisms like bac-

teriophage. We shall see later to what structural elements in the genetic material these "sites" may correspond.

THE GENE AS A UNIT OF FUNCTION

How does such a conclusion affect the concept of the gene? Obviously the gene cannot be conceived as the ultimate structural element of the genetic material, but it is nonetheless useful in helping us to get clear ideas about genetics. Atoms did not become less useful to the chemist when subatomic particles were discovered: on the contrary, this new knowledge led to better understanding of how the properties of particular atoms were related to their operation in chemical combinations and to the changes they undergo—to what one might call, borrowing a term from biology, their functions. The gene remains a fundamental unit of genetics because it is a unit of function. All the sites identified within the lozenge gene share a function expressed by the eye shape and color, by the spermathecae in the female, and doubtless elsewhere in the body; it exerts some influence on metabolism and development by which processes leading to its effects are controlled. The manner in which the gene exercises its control is probably related to its complex structure, in which many parts are nonidentical, as in a complex automatic machine in which the arrangement of the parts enables each to make its unique or essential contribution to a common product or process. In fact, instances are known in which the spatial order of gene loci, like those controlling successive steps in a synthesis (e.g., tryptophane in Salmonella, p. 385), corresponds to the order in which the successive steps in the synthesis occur. Individual sites of mutation within each section affect the step controlled by that section. The arrangement of the sections in order may have been brought about (in Salmonella) by natural selection, since presumably the order enables the synthesis to proceed more efficiently. In other organisms, e.g., Neurospora, no such correspondence between spatial order of gene loci and temporal order of steps in a synthesis has been found.

If the gene is a functional unit of a higher order than the sites of mutation of which it is composed, how are we to determine its limits? Obviously crossing over is no absolute criterion, since it occurs both within and between genes. Gene loci determining apparently different functions, like those for short ear and for dilute pigmentation in the mouse may be separated by "distances" even lower than those separating different sites of mutation within a gene. On the average, two sites belonging to two different units of function will be separated by longer distances than two sites belonging to one unit, but this is only an average distance, and variations from it must be expected. At present it may be said that recent work on recombination between alleles has raised again a question which the gross linkage maps of the gene loci seemed to have settled. The view based on those first maps was that the genetic material was discontinuous and made up of genes and nongenic segments, the genes having the arrangement of beads on a string. The question is now open whether the genetic material is structurally continuous, the genes being merely the successive segments of it. Attention has thus turned toward the elementary particles that make up the larger elements and particularly toward the structure of the genetic material at the molecular level.

THE PHYSICAL STRUCTURE
OF THE GENETIC MATERIAL

The chromosomes were identified a generation ago as the bearers of the genes, and since then a great deal of effort has been expended to discover the molecular organization responsible for the essential properties of hereditary elements: the abilities to replicate, to mutate, and to initiate chains of reactions. Several lines of evidence have pointed to essential constant connections between *nucleoproteins* and the hereditary material. These large compounds are found in all cells. They consist of two moieties, a nucleic acid and protein. As we have seen, two forms of nucleic acid have been identified: desoxyribonucleic acid (DNA) found in the nucleus, and ribonucleic acid (RNA) found mainly in the cytoplasm but also in the nucleus.

CYTOOPTICAL STUDIES OF DNA

The evidence concerning the physical structure of genetic material is derived from several sources. The reactivity of chromosomes with certain chemical groups, yielding colored substances, was the first property by which chromosomes (literally, colored bodies) were identified. One treatment, the Feulgen reaction, proved to be particularly fruitful, since the mild acid hydrolysis was found to split the purine bases and to liberate the aldehyde groups of the pentose sugars of DNA, after which the sulphurous acid fuchsin of the reagent reacts with the free aldehydes to produce a reddish-purple pigment that specifically indicates the presence of DNA. The intensity of the reaction, carried out on thin sections of nuclei, can be measured by the amount of light absorbed, which is proportional to the intensity. Photometric observations thus indicate the relative amounts of DNA present and its distribution. It is also possible to identify DNA by spectrophotometric observation without staining, since the maximum absorption of DNA is in the vicinity of the wave length 2,600 angstrom units. These may be called cytooptical methods.

CYTOCHEMICAL STUDIES

It has proved to be possible to check the identification of DNA by direct chemical methods, extracting it from nuclei by methods designed to separate it from its protein. Results from both methods show that DNA occurs generally only in the nucleus and is confined to the chromosomes. The amount of DNA is constant in the diploid nuclei of a species in which the haploid nuclei have half of this amount and the tetraploid nuclei, in the few cases measured, show twice the diploid content. There is thus a constant quantity of DNA for each set of chromosomes.

Studies of bacterial viruses show that their virus proteins contain DNA. By labeling the DNA of a virus with radioactive isotopes, Hershey has shown that DNA is transferred into a bacterium when infection with phage occurs, the coat or skin of the virus being left outside at the surface of the bacterium. The virus DNA is incorporated into the genetic system of the host cell when transduction occurs (p. 318).

Similarly, it is DNA that is transferred from one bacterial cell to another during the process of bacterial transformation (p. 319). The essential substance transferred is known as the *transforming principle*. The DNA particles thus introduced behave like genes that have been incorporated into the transformed cells, and Hotchkiss has succeeded in transferring particles of DNA, determining changes in two properties which behave as though they are linked and which can take part in a process like recombination. The DNA transferred must therefore have genic specificity and be able to replicate when the transformed cell reproduces.

Fraenkel-Conrat has shown that isolated RNA from tobacco mosaic virus can induce the formation of complete new virus when injected into the tobacco plant.

These observations suggest that chromosomes and genes have the ability to reproduce their own specific duplicates by virtue of the specific forms of DNA possessed by individual genes. It is for this reason that DNA is sometimes referred to as the bearer or determiner of the genetic "information." An understanding of the nature and method of replication of a substance so closely connected with heredity is clearly of great importance. Some progress in this direction has been made recently.

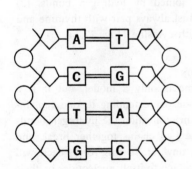

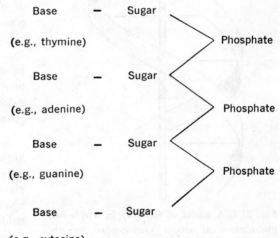

Fig. 27.3. Left: Parts of the two complementary chains of nucleotides of the model in Figure 27.4. Letters designate the bases; five-sided figures, the pentose sugars; circles, the phosphate groups; double lines, hydrogen bonds. Right: Diagram of the arrangement in A. (*After Watson and Crick*)

THE STRUCTURE OF DNA

DNA is found in the chromosomes in association with protein, from which it may be separated by chemical methods. It has a molecular weight of 5 to 10 million and is made up, according to Watson and Crick, of long chains of nucleotides. Each nucleotide consists of a nitrogen-containing base (a pyrimidine or a purine comparable in size to an amino acid), a pentose (five-carbon) sugar, and phosphoric acid. In DNA, the sugar is desoxyribose; the purines are of only two kinds (adenine and guanine); and the pyrimidines also are of only two kinds (thymine and cytosine). One of these bases is attached to a sugar group, and the latter are joined together by phosphate linkages as in Figure 27.3. There may be from three to four thousand such units in a DNA molecule. Watson and Crick have proposed a model of the way in which such chains may produce copies of themselves. The essential features are as follows: (1) The structural unit of DNA consists of two long chains of nucleotides coiled in a helix around a common axis (Fig. 27.4). (2) The two chains are complementary to each other in such a way that a purine on one is always paired with a pyrimidine on the other, the two being joined by hydrogen bonds. (3) Adenine must always pair with thymine and guanine with cytosine (Fig. 27.3).

REPLICATION

This scheme is only a model, but it is a plausible one. By extending it, one can imagine that in replication the hydrogen bonds holding the two chains together break and the chains unwind. In this form, each will be free to attach to itself nucleotides or their precursors from the environment within the cell, to replace each complementary base that was separated from it in the unwinding and bond breaking. Each chain can then serve as a mold or template on which its complement can be built up (Fig. 27.3).

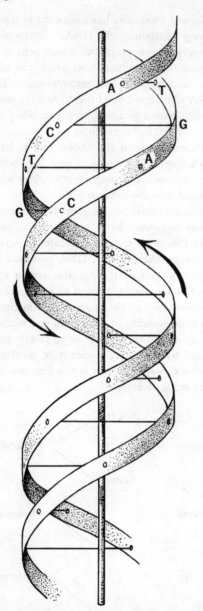

Fig. 27.4. A model of the way in which two phosphate-sugar chains (represented by ribbons) may be arranged in double helix form, held together by bases (attachment paths represented by bars) to form a unit of structure of DNA. (*After Watson and Crick*)

The result would be the production of a replicate of each of the complementary chains. The order of the bases on each would be preserved, since each specifies, because of the complementary pairing relations (adenine-thymine, guanine-cytosine), the order on the other.

MUTATION

If this is the usual method of replication, it can be imagined that occasionally a miscopying occurs—if, for example, adenine (which usually pairs with thymine) were to accept, perhaps because of a shift in the position of one of its hydrogen bonds, the alternative pyrimidine, namely, cytosine. Cytosine in the new position would subsequently pair with guanine, and the chain would reproduce itself in this new order. The changed sequence of bases would represent in molecular terms a mutation.

Crick has suggested that the sequence of bases, in which an enormous variety is possible, may be conceived as a kind of code by which the genetic information is transmitted to the cell and thus controls the cellular processes; but this mechanism is still unknown. It has been estimated that the length of DNA in one chromosome is of the order of four centimeters, perhaps enough for ten million turns in the helical structure, which must then be wound very tightly, the successive bases stacked compactly one upon another.

Correspondence between sites of mutation, recombination, and DNA. To illustrate the kind of thinking toward which these estimates lead, it is interesting to consider some speculations on the possible correspondence between DNA units and the units of mutation and recombination as detected in breeding experiments. By assuming that all DNA is in the chromosome, that crossing over involves reciprocal exchange of nucleotide linkages, with equal probability of occurring at any such linkage or small multiple of linkages, and that mutational sites are separated

from each other by one or a few linkages, Pontecorvo has estimated that in phage and Aspergillus the minimum recombination fractions observed would represent 13 and 8 nucleotide pairs, respectively. Benzer suggests that the ultimate unit of crossing over is a single nucleotide bond or some multiple of this, such as 10, which is the number estimated for one complete turn in the helix on the Watson-Crick model. A mutational site would be of similar extent and a section of gene might be from one to ten thousand nucleotide pairs. The assumptions on which all this is based are largely unverified and already known to be untenable in certain details. Nevertheless, they are useful in indicating the kinds of problems one has to face in attempts to translate units recognized by genetic analysis into units of known molecular size, such as the nucleotides of DNA. If, according to Pontecorvo, the resolving power of genetic analysis as attained so far is one 10 millionth of the linkage map, the map of DNA would be expressed in units of a limited number of nucleotides each.

We may say, then, that the linear order of genes on a chromosome as revealed by the linkage maps finds its analogue in the linear sequence in which the ultimate units are arranged in the most reasonable model that has yet been constructed from chemical data.

RNA IN HEREDITY

Attractive as it is to consider DNA as the carrier of the code by which genetic specificity or information is transmitted in heredity, it must be remembered that current views are colored strongly by studies of animal chromosomes and of bacterial viruses in which DNA protein is the chief constituent. Bacterial viruses are in fact far from typical of viruses in general. In the two viruses about which most is known—tobacco mosaic virus and human influenza virus—the nucleoprotein is RNA, the former containing about 6 per cent RNA and the latter about 1 per cent, with no appreciable DNA. The RNA contains purine bases (adenine and guanine) and pyrimidine bases (cytosine and urasil), but the ratios amongst these bases are not equal, as in DNA; thus the molecular structure of RNA differs from that of DNA, and the method of replication imagined for DNA cannot be applied to it. Yet it is probable, as Burnet and his colleagues have shown, that influenza virus has a genetic system comparable to that in organisms with DNA. It has been shown, for example, that mixed infections with two

strains of influenza virus may produce virus with qualities derived from both parent strains, as in recombination. This suggests, then, that RNA may serve as a determiner of genetic specificity. Since RNA probably bears the direct responsibility for protein synthesis, its replication is closely connected with protein production, which involves chains of polypeptides rather than polynucleotides. Some suggestions along this line have been given recently in a stimulating book by Burnet (see Bibliography), but detailed discussion is beyond the scope of this chapter.

28 ORGANIZATION OF THE GENETIC MATERIAL

THE IDEA that the mechanism of Mendelian heredity consisted of an assortment of discrete units, genes, which were shuffled and recombined at meiosis, met with a good deal of skepticism from general biologists when it was first elaborated by Morgan, Sturtevant, Muller, and Bridges in 1915. The first linkage maps portrayed a rather haphazard distribution of loci with no clear or general indication of relationship between spatial arrangement and function in metabolism and development. The system portrayed appeared to be a mosaic in which the discreteness of the parts received greater emphasis than the picture as a whole, which in living organisms must always be viewed functionally. The same might be said of the resolution into finer structure outlined in Chapter 27. This emphasis, of course, arose from the purpose to be served and the methods used, which were designed for analysis rather than synthesis.

The problem of the relationship between arrangement of elements and their functional activities remains one of the most challenging in genetics. But recently facts have been revealed and ideas have been formulated which indicate that the relationship of the elements is not haphazard, although principles can certainly not yet be framed to give order to the present scanty data. Thus it must be remembered that an important principle established by the analytical work was the linear order of loci in the chromosome. This was itself an indication of an order established by natural selection as a condition of successful functioning of the system of elements.

POSITION EFFECTS

The apparent lack of relation between the order of the loci and their effects on development was first brought seriously into question by Sturtevant's discovery of *position effects*. The first conclusively proved case was found during the analysis of exceptions to the usual rules of transmission of the Bar-eye mutation in *Drosophila melanogaster* (Fig. 28.1). This had long been known as a dominant located at 57.0 on the genetic map of the X chromosome. Its chief effect is to reduce the number of facets in the compound eye, leaving a more or less narrow band, or "bar," of ommatidia. Zeleny found that in cultures homozygous for Bar there occur "mutations" back to wild-type, or normal, eye and to a more extreme type with very narrow eyes called ultra-Bar. The frequency of these mutations is rather high, one reversion to normal appearing in about fifteen hundred offspring, and one ultra-Bar in about two thousand flies. The wild type obtained by reversion breeds true, but ultra-Bar reverts to Bar and to wild type with appreciable frequencies.

The nature of these peculiar mutations at the Bar "gene" was first clarified by Sturtevant and subsequently by Bridges and by Muller, Prokofieva-Belgovskaya, and Kossikov. The Bar chromosome proved to contain a duplication for a short section, con-

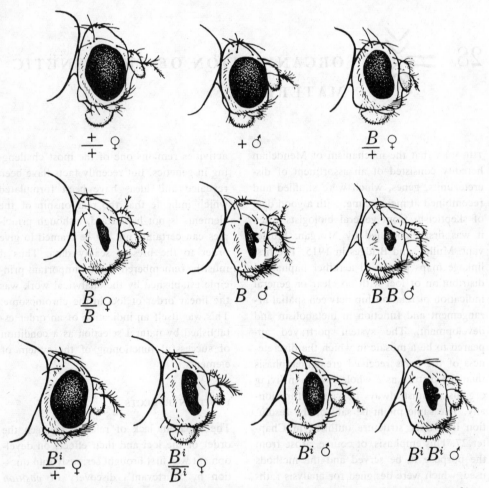

Fig. 28.1. Drawings of the head and right compound eye of members of the Bar series of phenotypes in *Drosophila melanogaster*. *B/B* indicates a Bar mutation in both X chromosomes, and *BB* indicates three Bar sections in the same chromosome (ultra-Bar). *B^i* is a less extreme allele of *B*, which also shows the position-effect phenomenon. (*After Morgan*)

sisting, as seen in salivary-gland cells, of about six disks (Fig. 28.2). The ultra-Bar chromosome contains this section in triplicate and the normal chromosome in single dose. If this region of the chromosome is symbolized by letters *ABCDEFGH,* then the normal chromosome is *ABCDEFGH,* Bar is *ABCDEFGBCDEFGH,* and ultra-Bar is *ABCDEFGBCDEFGBCDEFGH.* The original change that produced the mutation Bar from normal was, then, a duplication of a short section of the chromosome. The relatively frequent changes from Bar to ultra-Bar and back to normal and from ultra-Bar to Bar and to normal involve no alteration in the genes as such. They occur because the chromosomes containing duplications may undergo crossing over in several ways, as illustrated in Figure 28.3. As a result of this crossing over, chromosomes are formed which contain more or fewer Bar sections than the original chromosomes. For exam-

ple, crossing over between two Bar chromosomes, each containing the Bar section in duplicate, may give rise to chromosomes with a single Bar section (normal, or wild type) and with three Bar sections (ultra-Bar).

It follows from this analysis that a fly homozygous for Bar (that is, carrying two X chromosomes, each with the "mutant" Bar) must have four Bar sections, two in each chromosome. A fly heterozygous for normal and for ultra-Bar must also carry four Bar sections, one in the normal and three in the ultra-Bar chromosome. Since these flies carry the same sets of genes, they are expected to be alike in phenotype. But, as discovered by Sturtevant, the flies homozygous for Bar (*B/B*) have larger eyes (68.1 ± 1.1 ommatidia) than the flies heterozygous for normal and ultra-Bar (*BB/+*) (45.4 ± 0.2 ommatidia). This difference being quite significant statistically, it can be

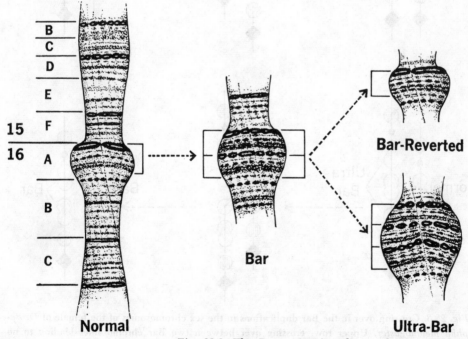

Fig. 28.2. The Bar region in salivary chromosome I, showing duplication of bands in Bar (*B/B*) and ultra-Bar (*BB/BB*). (*From Bridges*)

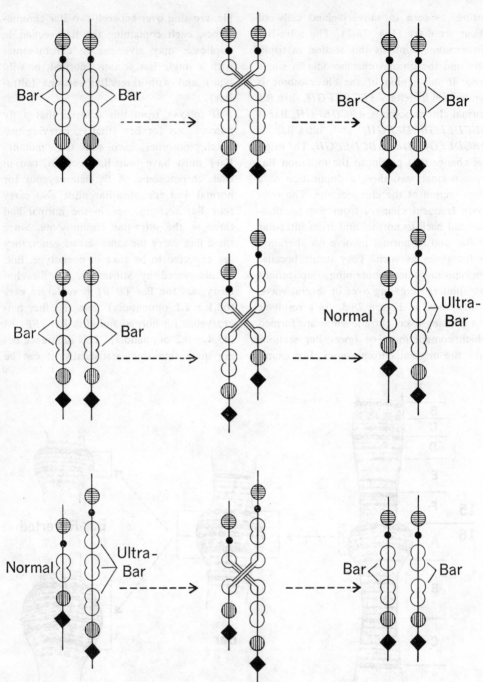

Fig. 28.3. Crossing over in the Bar duplications in the sex chromosomes of the female of *Drosophila melanogaster*. Upper row, crossing over between two Bar chromosomes leading to no changes in the Bar region; middle row, crossing over between two Bar chromosomes giving rise to a normal (non-Bar) and an ultra-Bar chromosome; lower row, crossing over between a normal and an ultra-Bar chromosome, giving rise to two Bar chromosomes.

concluded that juxtaposition of Bar sections in the same chromosome produces a stronger effect on the developing eye than the same sections would produce if placed in different chromosomes. In fact, it is probable that the difference between normal and Bar is also due to position effect; in other words, the original mutation giving rise to Bar from normal probably involved no change in the genes themselves but only change in their functioning due to alteration in their position. Indeed, in the normal chromosome, *ABCDEFGH*, the genes *B* and *G* have, respectively, the genes *A* and *H* as neighbors; it is *ABCDEFG · BCDEFG · H* in a Bar chromosome, the genes *B* and *G* being neighbors; in an ultra-Bar chromosome there are two *BG* associations. The whole Bar story is explained very simply if one supposes that the association of the genes *B* and *G* causes a reduction of the number of facets in the compound eyes.

Since the discovery of position effect in Bar, other cases have been found in Drosophila by Dubinin and others, and Catcheside found at least one case in a plant, Oenothera. In Drosophila, translocations and inversions obtained by mutation are very often lethal in homozygous condition. Since translocation and inversion homozygotes (Fig. 15.1) have the same genes as normal flies but differently arranged in the chromosomes, the lethality or other phenotypic effects produced by homozygosis for translocations and inversions may be due to position effects. An alternative hypothesis, namely, that the lethality is caused by destruction or injury of the genes which coincides with the chromosome breakage, is, however, difficult to exclude, and consequently the position-effect hypothesis cannot be regarded as proved in these cases. Such a proof has, however, been given by Dubinin for other changes associated with chromosomal aberrations. If a fourth chromosome of *Drosophila melanogaster* containing a normal dominant allele of the gene cubitus interruptus,

or if a third chromosome containing the normal dominant allele of the gene hairy is broken close to the loci of these genes, the normal alleles lose their dominance. Suppose, then, that we have a translocation in which the third chromosome is broken near hairy and the fourth near cubitus interruptus, and suppose that, by means of appropriate crosses, we make individuals heterozygous for such a translocation, heterozygous also for the recessive genes hairy and cubitus interruptus, the recessives lying in the normal, unbroken chromosomes. Such heterozygotes show the effects of hairy and of cubitus interruptus in their phenotype, as if the normal alleles of these genes contained in the translocated chromosomes had undergone a "mutation" that deprived them of their normal dominance. Dubinin showed that these normal alleles regain their original dominance if, by crossing over, they are removed from the translocated chromosomes and replaced in chromosomes with the normal gene order. This evidence of reversibility of the changes in the alleles of hairy shows that the loss of dominance in translocations was not caused by mutations but by changes in the associations between genes.

POSITION ALLELES

Relations resembling position effects between different components of a series of alleles were discovered by E. B. Lewis. In a number of cases in Drosophila, it was found that the effects of such alleles on the phenotype depended on the way in which they were arranged in the heterozygotes or compounds. Thus in the case of two recessive alleles separable by crossing over, such as m^1 and m^2, $\dfrac{m^1 +}{+ m^2}$ shows the mutant phenotype and $\dfrac{m^1 m^2}{+ +}$ is wild type. The first of these is called the *trans* arrangement, the second the *cis* arrangement. Nonidentical alleles whose expressions differ according to whether they are in trans or cis arrangement have been called *position pseudoalleles*. The effects in combination of some of the lozenge alleles (cf. Fig. 27.1) are shown in Figure 28.4. The essential feature here is that when each position on one chromosome is occupied by a normal allele, the usual rules of dominance apply; when any two positions on *opposite* chromosomes are occupied by mutant alleles, the mutant effect obtains. This rule has been made the basis of an explanation by Lewis of the functional relations of po-

$$\frac{1z^{BS} \quad + \quad +}{+ \quad 1z^{46} \quad +}$$

$$\frac{1z^{BS} \quad + \quad +}{+ \quad + \quad 1z^{g}}$$

$$\frac{1z^{BS} \quad 1z^{46} \quad +}{+ \quad + \quad +}$$

$$\frac{1z^{BS} \quad + \quad 1z^{g}}{+ \quad + \quad +}$$

$$\frac{+ \quad 1z^{46} \quad +}{+ \quad + \quad 1z^{g}}$$

$$\frac{+ \quad 1z^{46} \quad 1z^{g}}{+ \quad + \quad +}$$

Transarrangements, lozenge phenotypes

Cisarrangements, wild phenotypes

Fig. 28.4. The alleles of the lozenge gene in *Drosophila melanogaster* used in the analysis of this gene, showing genotypes of the possible (and observed) combinations. (*After Green and Green*)

sition pseudoalleles. If each site is concerned with one step in a synthesis required to produce the normal characters, such as A→B→C, this may proceed along one chromosome if all sites are occupied by normal alleles; but occupation of any site by a mutant allele blocks the synthesis along that chromosome. If not carried out by either chromosome, the synthesis fails and the mutant character results. However, this explanation would not apply to those cases of pseudoallelism in which position effects are not found, that is, in which the trans arrangement is wild-type, $\frac{m^1 +}{+ m^2}$, showing complementary interaction of the two recessives.

The occurrence of position effects, even in the limited numbers of cases in which they have been studied, shows that the effects on development of at least some genes depend not only on the intrinsic properties of

the gene but also upon its relations with adjacent elements—that is, upon a pattern of arrangement.

BLOCKS OF GENES WITH RELATED EFFECTS

In bacteria, the ease of identifying mutants with changed biochemical requirements has led to the analysis of relations between spatial location and function. Two cases are especially instructive, although they may not be typical of relations in higher organisms.

In *Salmonella typhimurium,* the mousetyphoid bacillus, Demerec has shown that the mutants in one series, each of which blocks the synthesis of tryptophane, are closely adjacent genetically. Evidence for this was obtained, not by recombination experiments, as in the case of organisms with a sexual recombination system, but by the use of transduction (p. 318). For example, when bacteriophage grown on wild-type Salmonella was used to infect a double mutant strain of Salmonella requiring both tryptophane and cystine, some of the bacteria isolated were prototrophs; that is, they could grow on a minimal medium lacking both tryptophane and cystine. From previous experiments it was known that the effective transport (transduction) of a normal allele by phage from a wild type to a strain with a single nutritional requirement occurs with a frequency of about one per 5 million (5×10^{-6}) infecting particles. If the two nutritional mutants were independent, transductions for both should occur with a frequency of $(5 \times 10^{-6})^2$. But simultaneous transductions of try$^+$ and cys$^+$ occurred with so much higher frequency in this case that it was assumed that this tryptophane locus (known as try) and the cystine locus (cys B) were so close together genetically that both would usually be transported together by transduction, so that transduction might be used as a substitute for recombination. This implies that something comparable to a transforming principle (DNA, p. 319) is carried by phage and enters the recipient genetic system by crossing over with it. By using this assumption and the transduction method, marker alleles being near try, Demerec was able to construct a micromap showing the order of arrangement of the tryptophane mutants (Fig. 28.5). Four groups of tryptophane mutants were identified: A, B, C, and D. Within one group the mutants of independent origin are probably nonidentical in the sense that try D–7/try D–9 show "recombination" by the transduction method. Mutants in different sections are farther apart (in "recombination" values) than mutants in the same

section and show complementarity with each other. The "distance" between try A and the nearest marker cys B is greater than that between sections. That each tryptophane section controls a part of a related function was shown by the biochemical work of Brenner. A mutant in section A (try 8) is unable to synthesize anthranillic acid out of an unknown precursor but can grow if supplied with anthranillic acid, indole, or tryptophane; mutants in section B are unable to transform anthranillic acid (which they accumulate) into an unidentified compound B; a mutant in section C (try 3) cannot transform compound B (which it accumulates) but can grow if supplied with either indole or tryptophane, which it cannot make for itself; the six mutants in section D cannot transform indole into tryptophane and can grow only if supplied with tryptophane itself. Group-D mutants can provide what is needed for growth of mutants of A, B, and C; group-B mutants can "feed" group A. The basis for the complementary relations between members of different groups can now be understood, and the similarity between the reasoning involved here and in the case of the synthesis of brown eye pigment in Drosophila (p. 346) is apparent.

It is most striking that the spatial order of the groups of tryptophane mutants on the "genetic" map corresponds to the temporal order or sequence of the steps they control

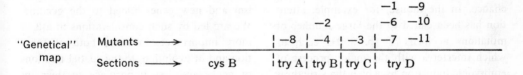

Fig. 28.5. Micromap of the tryptophane mutants in *Salmonella typhimurium*, showing their order on the "genetical" map above and the sequence of steps in the synthesis interrupted by specific mutants. (*After M. Demerec*)

in the synthesis of tryptophane. The whole region is clearly concerned with this main function, since a mutation in any part of it can interrupt the whole synthesis. The parts that correspond to different genes or sections (A, B, C, D) appear to be immediately adjacent, so that B has first call, so to speak, on a product elaborated by A, and so on, and the sections are arranged as though, in Demerec's words, they were parts of an assembly line for the construction of tryptophane, a compound essential for the metabolism and survival of the cell.

A complexity which is greater in terms of the numbers of mutational sites identified but which conforms to the same type of order has been shown by P. E. Hartman among the mutants affecting the synthesis of histidine in Salmonella. By methods like those described above, 34 nonidentical histidine-requiring mutants have been identified, in four functional groups, A, B, C, and D, linearly arranged in the order of the four steps in the synthesis.

It is assumed that the metabolic system in Salmonella is such as to give an evolutionary advantage to juxtaposition of elements controlling sequential steps in an essential synthesis. There is as yet no evidence that this plays an important role in the evolution of functionally related units in higher organisms, although there are more instances of close linkage between genes with related effects than would be expected to occur by chance. In the mouse, for example, attention has been called to the large number of mutations at locus T (p. 350), each of which interferes with the major process of embryonic induction by which the structures of the axial system of notochord, medullary tube, spinal cord, and brain are formed, with related effects on the *mesenchyme* and somites. It was assumed, in that case, that mutations in different sites, detected by complementary interaction rather than by recombination, interfere with different partial processes contributing to the central function of induction. In the absence of evidence of recombination among these, the complexity of the gene was assumed to have arisen by internal differentiation, functionally related elements being held together by the advantage, in evolution, of close juxtaposition of those whose effects interact in assuring an essential step in normal development.

More frequently it is assumed that linearly arranged clusters of genes have arisen by duplication, such as seems to have occurred in the case of Bar.

THE ORIGIN OF NEW GENES THROUGH DUPLICATION

The occurrence of immediately adjacent elements with similar functions led Bridges in 1918 to suggest that "the main interest in duplications lay in their offering a method for evolutionary increase in lengths of chromosomes with identical genes which could subsequently mutate separately and diversify their effects." This was supported by his later discovery (1935) of "repeats" (p. 202) in the salivary chromosomes of Drosophila and was again emphasized by the proof that the Bar-eye effects are due to adjacent duplications. If pseudoalleles were to arise by adjacent duplication, then the duplicated alleles would acquire new properties because they differ in position and spatial relations from the parent allele. In this way, new functions might be acquired by the organism and new genes added to the genome. We are led by such considerations to attach more importance, in terms both of function and of evolution, to the spatial relations of genes and less importance to their intrinsic properties.

In summary, it is now possible to regard the genetic system as consisting of elements differing in their levels of organization: sites of mutation as parts of genes, genes as parts of regions related to larger functions, and chromosomes consisting of organized aggregations of these with indications of unity not merely at the structural but also at the functional level, the whole forming an integrated genome adapted to the conditions of life of the population of which the individual organism is a part.

THE IMPORTANCE OF PATTERN

As we have seen, it is not yet possible to construct a theory relating the functional effects of genes with their order in the genetic maps. This is in part because, as yet, only a few sections of the maps in a few organisms have been carefully studied from this point of view, and in part because it is not yet known how the maps usually based on the meiotic chromosomes (or on analogues of these based on transduction experiments) correspond with the juxtaposition of genes at the height of their metabolic and synthetic activities, which probably comes during the interphases of mitosis.

Nevertheless, it is already possible to see that the pattern in which the elements are arranged plays a role in determining the effects produced. This is evident not only in the occurrence of position effects, which arise when the same genes are in different arrangements relative to each other, but in the fact that many different kinds of rearrangements of chromosomal materials, duplications, transpositions, etc., may have phenotypic effects like those ascribed to mutated genes. Goldschmidt, in fact, has long maintained that what has been called "the normal allele" is merely the effect of the normal pattern in which the elements of varying levels of organization are arranged in the chromosome; and that the "mutant allele" is the expression of a change in this pattern. He conceives the chromosome not as an assemblage of corpuscular genes but as a hierarchy of fields, of patterns within the larger unit.

"The facts have forced us to turn from an independent homogeneous corpuscle to an indefinitely limited part of a whole having a typical serial pattern which alone allows for normal function. The logical consequence is that the section, acting as a small field, is itself only part of a larger field or different fields, also overlapping ones. In terms of the model of function, this would mean that the 'master reaction' controlled by the small field, the segment, is related to the still more primary effects of the larger field, as the pattern change within the segment is related to the whole segmental action. This means that a pattern change—mutation—within any segment would not disturb the action of the next higher member of the hierarchy of fields, but an accumulation of such pattern changes would impair the higher field functions."

We have already encountered such ideas in the suggestion that the specificity of DNA is given by a particular sequence of bases; mutation was conceived as an alteration of this sequence—a change in pattern. Schmitt has recently suggested that, on the basis of biophysical evidence derived from the behavior of biologically active fibrous proteins such as collagen and myosin, their biological activity is determined by units of supramolecular size with a specific arrangement of molecules. He suggests that specific juxtaposition of macromolecules could produce integrated aggregations with the properties attributed to genes. Again, it is the pattern of arrangement to which specific activity is attributed.

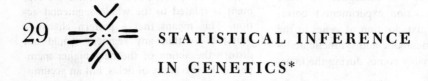

29 STATISTICAL INFERENCE IN GENETICS*

1. INTRODUCTION

Statistical inference is that branch of scientific methodology that concerns the drawing of conclusions from data that are subject to chance variation. Since chance is directly involved in the act of Mendelian segregation, statistical methods are needed to a greater or lesser extent in all genetic reasoning from actual experimental data. Furthermore, we shall see that a proper understanding of quantitative inheritance, mediated by multiple factors, involves statistical ideas. The purpose of this chapter is to present a few of the many statistical notions and techniques that have been used in genetics. Our attention will be confined to the simplest and most generally useful methods and to the basic principles of statistical reasoning.

---

* By Howard Levene, Associate Professor of Mathematical Statistics and Biometrics, Columbia University.

STATISTICS OF SEGREGATION RATIOS

2. A SIMPLE PROBLEM

One of the most common problems in experimental genetics is to decide whether the outcome of a breeding experiment is in accordance with that predicted by theory. For example, suppose that mice from an albino strain are crossed with unrelated, wild, agouti mice and the resulting agouti hybrids are backcrossed to the albino parents. Then, according to the theory that albino is a simple Mendelian recessive, we expect half the backcross offspring to be white and half to be agouti. Suppose that in an actual experiment 14 mice are white and 6 are agouti, or $14/20 = 70$ per cent are white. Does this disprove the theory that 50 per cent should be white? It is clear that according to the theory we could find, by chance, any number of white from 0 to 20, although the extreme values are very unlikely. In order to answer our question, then, it will first be necessary to examine more closely what may be expected under these conditions.

To simplify the problem, let us consider penny tossing, with heads and tails replacing white and agouti mice. One hundred of the writer's students were asked to toss a penny 100 times each and record the number of heads in each successive group of 10 tosses. Some of the results are given in Table 29.1. More extensive figures showed that the first 100 groups of 10 tosses reported gave from 0 per cent to 90 per cent heads, the first 100 groups of 20 tosses gave from 25 per cent to 80 per cent heads, the 100 groups of 100 tosses gave from 36 per cent to 61 per cent heads, whereas the 10 successive groups of 1000 tosses gave from 46.4 per cent to 52.1 per cent heads, and the entire 10,000 tosses gave 49.66 per cent heads. Obviously, the larger the group of tosses, the less variable the percentage of heads from one group to the next. The exact extent of this reduction in variability will be discussed in later sections.

groups of twenty tosses we never observed less than 25 per cent or more than 80 per cent heads. Accordingly, we may agree that if less than 25 per cent or more than 80 per cent of some outcome is observed in 20 trials, we will say that this outcome does not have a 50 per cent chance of happening. (In mathematical language we say that the probability of this outcome is not $\frac{1}{2}$.) Now, we observed 70 per cent of albino mice, so under this rule we would not reject the possibility that the probability of an albino mouse coming from this cross is really $\frac{1}{2}$. However, some obvious objections can be raised to this rule. One is that the use of 100 groups of 20 was somewhat arbitrary. If more than 100 groups were used, the range would probably be wider; and, in fact, with enough groups we might have observed every number of heads from 0 to 20, or 0 per cent to 100 per cent. A more serious objection is that our criterion of 25 per cent to 80 per cent was based on one particular series of 100 groups, and other series would give dif-

TABLE 29.1
Percentage of heads in successive groups of tosses of a penny

Group No.	Percentage of heads 10 tosses	Percentage of heads 20 tosses	Percentage of heads 100 tosses	Percentage of heads 1000 tosses
1	40	40	47	49.6
2	40	50	47	46.5
3	40	40	60	50.4
4	60	45	47	48.8
5	50	60	53	52.0
6	30	35	57	52.1
7	60	35	53	49.9
8	30	50	52	50.0
9	80	50	44	46.4
10	40	65	36	50.9
Average	47	47	49.6	49.66

3. A DECISION RULE
Now, returning to the original genetic problem, we can reason as follows. In tossing a penny, it is known that in the long run heads will appear 50 per cent of the time. In 100

ferent results and hence different rules. In fact, the second set of 100 groups of 20 tosses by these students gave from 15 per cent to 75 per cent. A more satisfactory procedure might be to make many thousands of groups of 20 tosses and then tabulate the proportion of the time that 0, 1, 2, etc., up to 20 heads were observed. We would then reject the hypothesis that albino has a 50 per cent chance of occurring, whenever the observed number of albinos was one that had occurred only rarely in the penny tossing. Even with such a rule, the question would arise whether enough thousands of penny tosses had been observed, and all the work would have to be largely redone to get a rule for a breeding experiment with 19 or 21 animals. Fortunately, mathematical theory comes to the rescue.

4. PROBABILITY: BINOMIAL TRIALS

Let us consider an indefinitely long series of identical experiments, each with two possible outcomes that we will call *success* and *failure.* If the result of a single experiment, or *trial,* is unpredictable, if the chance of success is the same for all trials, and if the outcome of one trial has no effect on the outcome of any other trial, we say that we have a sequence of *independent binomial* trials. Let a number, N, of such trials be made; let X be the number of successes observed; and let $f = X/N$ be the proportion of successes. Then, just as we found for our penny tossing, it is found that as N gets larger and larger f becomes less and less variable and tends to some number characteristic of the conditions of the experiment. If we imagine that N becomes larger and larger without bound, f will tend to a limiting value, denoted by p, called the *probability* of a success. For example, it is known that for penny tossing, if we call a head a success, we have independent binomial trials with p approaching very close to ½.

If the event labeled "success" is essentially impossible (e.g., that our mouse backcross should give an offspring that is a cat), then it will never happen; at every stage, $f = 0/N = 0$ and $p = 0$. Similarly, an event that is certain to happen has probability equal to one. Let us suppose a success can happen in

two different ways, A and B, each of which excludes the other. For example, success could be the occurrence of a heterozygote *Cc*, with A the event "*C* from mother, *c* from father" and B the event "*c* from mother, *C* from father." Then if the symbol X( ) denotes the number of times the event within the parentheses occurs in N trials, f( ) denotes the proportion of times the event occurs in N trials, and P( ) denotes the probability of the event, we have

$$X(A \text{ or } B) = X(A) + X(B) \tag{1}$$

since the number of times A or B happens is simply the number of A's plus the number of B's, and

$$\begin{aligned} f(A \text{ or } B) &= \frac{X(A) + X(B)}{N} \\ &= \frac{X(A)}{N} + \frac{X(B)}{N} \\ &= f(A) + f(B) \end{aligned} \tag{2}$$

and thus

$$P(A \text{ or } B) = P(A) + P(B) \tag{3}$$

That is, the probability of a success is the sum of the probabilities of the mutually exclusive ways in which it can occur. In particular, since it is certain that either a success or a failure will occur, and either of these excludes the other,

$$\begin{aligned} P(\text{success}) + P(\text{failure}) &= P(\text{success} \\ \text{or failure}) &= 1 \end{aligned} \tag{4}$$

so that

$$P(\text{failure}) = 1 - P(\text{success}) \tag{5}$$

From now on we will follow a customary practice and let $q = 1 - p$ stand for the probability of a failure. Now, it is proved in most textbooks on college algebra and in many statistics texts, including Hoel, Walker and Lev, and Wilks, that if we have N independent binomial trials, with p the probability of success in each trial, then the probability that there will be exactly X successes is equal to the term in p^X in the binomial expansion of $(p + q)^N$, or

$$P(X) = \frac{N!}{X!(N - X)!} p^X q^{N-X} \qquad (6)$$

where p^X means the number p raised to the Xth power and the symbol N! (read N factorial) stands for the product of all the integers up to and including N:

$$N! = N(N - 1)(N - 2) \cdots 4 \cdot 3 \cdot 2 \cdot 1 \quad (7)$$

[By convention, and in order to avoid exceptions to formula (6) when $X = 0$ or N, mathematicians define 0! as 1.] For example, if $N = 4$, $p = \frac{1}{3}$, $X = 2$, we have

$$P(2) = \frac{4!}{2!(4 - 2)!} \left(\frac{1}{3}\right)^2 \left(\frac{2}{3}\right)^2$$

$$= \frac{24}{(2)(2)} \left(\frac{1}{9}\right) \left(\frac{4}{9}\right) \qquad (8)$$

$$= 6 \left(\frac{1}{9}\right) \left(\frac{4}{9}\right) = \frac{24}{81} = 0.296$$

It may also be noted that for $X = 0$ or N, the formula (6) simplifies, so that

$$P(0) = (1 - p)^N \qquad (9)$$
$$P(N) = p^N$$

or, for the example in (8), $P(0) = (\frac{2}{3})^4 = \frac{16}{81}$, and $P(4) = (\frac{1}{3})^4 = \frac{1}{81}$.

Probabilities calculated from (6) are called *binomial probabilities* because of the connection with the binomial theorem. There are a number of extensive tables giving these probabilities, the most useful being those of the Bureau of Standards, those of the Army Ordnance Corps, and the Harvard tables (see References, p. 417). Since different tables are arranged differently, the reader is referred to the introduction to each table for directions for its use.

5. TESTING A STATISTICAL HYPOTHESIS

Returning to our original genetic example, if all the animals are from the same original inbred stocks and all backcross animals are raised under the same conditions, and if we call albino a success, we have a series of independent binomial trials with an unknown

p. The hypothesis that albino acts as a simple Mendelian character with normal viability can be translated into a *statistical hypothesis* (usually denoted by the symbol H_o) that $p = \frac{1}{2}$. A statistical hypothesis is *tested* by formulating a *statistical decision rule*. Such a rule lists *all* the possible outcomes of the experiment and for *each* outcome, states whether the hypothesis is *accepted* or *rejected*. If the hypothesis is accepted, we act as if it were true unless and until further evidence appears to the contrary. If the hypothesis is rejected, we act as if it were false unless and until further evidence suggests some other decision. If we reject H_o, genetic theory may suggest some alternative hypothesis that may in its turn be translated into a statistical hypothesis and tested.

It has already been suggested that for the backcross problem, a reasonable rule would be to reject the hypothesis H_o that $p = \frac{1}{2}$, if unusually few or unusually many albinos appear among our 20 animals, so that all we must do is decide what "unusual" means in this connection. To do this we introduce the idea of *level of significance*, α (the Greek letter alpha). Then if H_o is really true (i.e., $p = \frac{1}{2}$), α is the probability that we nevertheless reject H_o. It is customary to require that α be no greater than some more or less arbitrary small number, such as 0.05, 0.01, or 0.001. The more serious the consequences of wrongly rejecting H_o, the smaller α should be made. Let us require that α be no greater than 0.05. Consulting Table 29.2 for $p = \frac{1}{2}$, and using the addition formula (3) repeatedly, we discover that the probability that X is 5 or less, or 15 or more, is $.001 + .005 + .015 + .015 + .005 + .001 +$ (negligible quantities) $= .042$. Accordingly, if we use the rule *Reject H_o whenever the number of albinos, X, is 5 or less or 15 or more* and H_o is really true, the probability of rejecting H_o, or level of significance, is $\alpha = 0.042$. Furthermore, if we were also to reject H_o for $X = 6$, or for $X = 14$, α would be greater than 0.05, so that the rule above seems to be the proper one.

TABLE 29.2

Probability of exactly X successes in 20 independent binomial trials for various probabilities, p, of success in a single trial

X \ p	.45	.46	½	¾
0			.000001	
1			.00002	
2	.001	.001	.0002	
3	.004	.003	.001	
4	.014	.011	.005	
5	.036	.031	.015	
6	.075	.066	.037	
7	.122	.112	.074	.0001
8	.162	.155	.120	.001
9	.177	.176	.160	.003
10	.159	.165	.176	.010
11	.119	.128	.160	.027
12	.073	.082	.120	.061
13	.037	.043	.074	.112
14	.015	.018	.037	.169
15	.005	.006	.015	.202
16	.001	.002	.005	.190
17			.001	.134
18			.0002	.067
19			.00002	.021
20			.000001	.003
Total	1.000	.999	1.000	1.000

6. THE POWER CURVE

Now, of course, we hope that if H_o is really false and p is not ½, there will be a greater chance of rejecting H_o. This probability of rejecting H_o, when, in fact, p has some value other than ½, is called the *power* of the test for the alternative p and is denoted by $1 - \beta_p$ (β is the Greek letter beta). Clearly this power will depend on the rule chosen and on the particular alternative value of p. For example, looking at Table 29.2 for p = ¾, the power is the probability of 5 or less or 15 or more successes, or $1 - \beta_{3/4} = .202 + .190 + .134 + .067 + .021 + .003 +$ (negligible terms) $= .617$. Thus, although it would still be possible to accept $H_o : p = $ ½ when p was actually ¾, under these conditions more than half of all samples of 20 animals would lead to the rejection of H_o. By precisely the same

method, we can calculate $1 - \beta_p$ for our rule and for any desired value of p and finally draw a graph, called the *power curve* of the rule in question, on which the supposed true values of p are given on the horizontal axis and the corresponding probabilities of rejecting H_o, $1 - \beta_p$, are given on the vertical axis. Figure 29.1 shows the power curve for our rule. It will be noted that the further the true p is from ½ (i.e., the "more wrong" H_o is), the greater the chance of detecting it.

If we had chosen a larger α, we would have obtained a rule whose power curve was everywhere higher, whereas a smaller α would give a rule with a lower curve. Thus, the smaller we set α, the probability of rejecting H_o when it is true, the smaller becomes $1 - \beta_p$, the probability of rejecting H_o when it is false and the probability that a mouse will be albino is really not ½ but p. For this reason, it is undesirable to set α smaller than is absolutely necessary. If we are dissatisfied with the discriminating ability of our rule, as shown by the power curve, the only alternative is to make N larger. The power curve will then rise more sharply on either side of p = ½, as shown in Figure 29.1 for N = 100, where the rule *Reject* H_o *if* X ≤ 39 *or* X ≥ 61 gives $\alpha = .035$. (Note: X ≤ 39 is read "X is less than or equal to 39" or "X is no greater than 39," and X ≥ 61 is read "X is greater than or equal to 61" or "X is no less than 61.")

It should be particularly noted that this analysis should be made *before* any mice are raised; that is, thinking should take place before experimenting. First, the rule for coming to a decision must not be influenced by the particular outcome observed. Second, the power curve should be studied to see if there is adequate discrimination against the alternatives likely to be encountered. If not, it may be necessary to change the originally desired α or increase N; if this is impracticable, it may be decided that the experiment is not worth doing. Having performed this preliminary analysis, we can now do our backcross and examine the result. Since, in the original example, X = 14, our rule tells

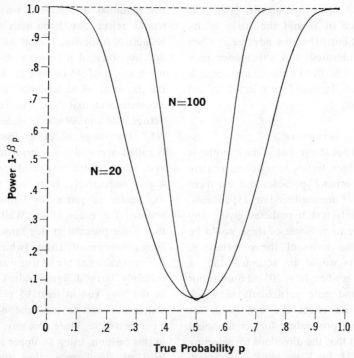

Fig. 29.1. Power curves for testing the hypothesis that the probability of a success is 1/2, on the basis of the result of N trials. If the true probability of a success is p, the corresponding probability of rejecting the hypotheis is $1 - \beta_p$.

us to accept H₀. (It is then sometimes said that the result of the backcross was *not significant* at the 4.2 per cent level of significance, whereas if X had been 15 the hypothesis would have been rejected or the experiment would have been *significant* at the 4.2 per cent level. The use of the word "significant" in this connection is confusing unless it is understood that it refers not to H₀ itself but to the *discrepancy* of the observations from what is expected under H₀, but it is so widely used that the student must become familiar with it.) Accordingly, we will act as if the probability of an albino were really ½ and our result due to chance.

7. ANOTHER APPROACH TO TESTS OF HYPOTHESES

The discussion above of statistical decision rules, or *tests*, as they are often called, is the best one for showing their logical basis. However, in order that the reader may follow the genetic literature, another frequently encountered approach must be explained. Again, it is decided that extreme values lead to rejecting H₀. Then, from Table 29.2 it is observed that under H₀ the probability of the observed number, 14, or more successes is .058. Hence if we used the rule *Reject* H₀ *for* X ≥ 14, we would have α = .058. Since we would presumably also wish to reject H₀ if too few successes were observed, we double this value and say P = .116 (use of capital P here being almost universal), perhaps adding that the result is not significant at the 5 per cent level. In the light of our previous discussion, the statement "P = .116" means that if we had chosen a test with α = .116, the observed X would have led to rejection of H₀, that the same would have been true if any α > .116 had been chosen, and that if any α < .116 had been used in constructing the test, H₀ would have been accepted on the basis of our sample. This approach is less satisfactory to the experimenter than an advance choice of α and the study of its consequences, but it has the advantage when results are published that the reader may decide on the α he thinks proper and see at a glance whether H_o would be rejected by the test with this α.

8. CONFIDENCE INTERVALS

It was pointed out above that, if the hypothesis that we have been testing is rejected, we may then consider other hypotheses and test them in turn. In our mouse-breeding experiment, we could clearly test hypotheses giving any arbitrary value to p. Some of these would be rejected on the basis of the observed X, whereas others would be accepted. Let us do this for all p when N = 20 and α must not exceed .05, and note particularly in which cases we would reject the hypothesis for X = 14. Before proceeding further it should be pointed out that the directions for selecting a rule, *Reject H_o for X too large or too small, choosing the cut-off points for X so that $\alpha \leq .05$* often lead to ambiguity. To avoid complications, we will therefore modify these directions so that we *Reject H_o when X is so small that the probability of this or a smaller value does not exceed .05/2, or when X is so large that the probability of this or a larger value does not exceed .05/2.* This insures that $\alpha \leq .05/2 + .05/2 = .05$ and gives a unique rule if we make the probability at each end or *tail* as big as possible but less than .05/2.

For N = 20, we find from Table 29.2 that for p = .45 the probability that $X \geq 14$ is .021, whereas for p = .46 this probability is .026. Now it is clear intuitively, and can be proved from formula (6), that the larger p is, the larger is the probability that X will exceed any given value and the smaller the probability that it will not. Consequently, when X = 14 is observed we would reject any hypothetical p of .45 or less at the .05 level because X is too large and accept any p of .46 or more. Similarly, from tables of

the binomial distribution, we find that we would reject any hypothesis with $p \geq .89$ because X is too small. Thus we would accept any hypothetical p between .46 and .88 and reject any p of .45 or less, or .89 or more, at the .05 level of significance. We now make the statement that "the true value of p lies between .45 and .89 with confidence coefficient .95." The range of values from .45 to .89 is called a *confidence interval* for p, and .45 and .89 are called *lower* and *upper confidence limits*, respectively. It is not too hard for the reader to prove for himself, and it is proved, for example, in Walker and Lev, that if we proceed in this same fashion in a large number of cases (which *may* have different values of N and true p and will almost certainly have different values of X), then in the long run at least 95 per cent of the statements will be true and no more than 5 per cent false. More precisely, if we proceed in this fashion, using an upper limit α on our level of significance, then the probability of obtaining an X leading to a true statement is at least $1 - \alpha$. Strictly speaking, our procedure should have involved interpolation between p = .45 and p = .46 in the binomial table. Since we did not do this, we chose .45, which makes the confidence interval too long and the confidence coefficient too large, in order to be on the safe side.

If we choose a larger confidence coefficient, $1 - \alpha$, the confidence interval becomes larger, and *vice versa*. We can make a very precise statement about the value of p, with low confidence in its correctness, or have high confidence in a very imprecise statement. Pushed to extremes, we can say p = .7, with confidence coefficient zero, or say p lies between 0 and 1 with confidence coefficient 1. Nevertheless, if we do not want an *interval estimate*, but the best possible guess, or *estimate*, of the value of p, we will use f, which in the present case is .7. Finally, we can obtain a shorter confidence interval with the same confidence coefficient by taking more observations. Thus if we observed the same f = .7 in a sample of 100 observations, the confidence limits with confidence coefficient .95 would be .60 and .79.

There is one special case where a confidence limit can be obtained with particular ease. If we have found no successes and wish an upper confidence limit for the true p, with confidence coefficient $1 - \alpha$, we have merely to solve the equation

$$\alpha/2 = (1 - p)^N \qquad (10)$$

$$\text{or} \quad p = 1 - \sqrt[N]{\alpha/2} \qquad (11)$$

The Nth root may be found by the use of logarithms. If, *before* we learned that X = 0, we had decided that we were only interested

in an upper confidence limit and not a lower one, we would have replaced $\alpha/2$ by α in formulas (10) and (11).

Clopper and Pearson calculated a large number of confidence intervals in this manner and from them constructed the graph shown in Figure 29.2. Suppose we observe X = 20 successes in a sample of N = 50 observations. To obtain a confidence interval with 95 per cent confidence coefficient $(1 - \alpha = .95)$, we would find X/N = .40 on the bottom scale and then follow the vertical line at .40 upward till it crossed the curve labeled 50, to correspond to the N for this sample, and then move to the left from this intersection

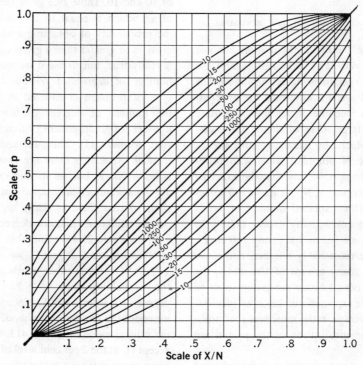

Fig. 29.2. Confidence belts, with 95 per cent confidence coefficient, for an unknown probability, p, on the basis of an observed proportion, X/N. A vertical line through the observed X/N crosses the two curves numbered to correspond to the sample size, N, at heights representing the upper and lower confidence limits for p. (*Reproduced with the permission of Professor E. S. Pearson from C. J. Clopper and E. S. Pearson, The use of confidence or fiducial limits illustrated in the case of the binomial, Biometrika, 26 (1934), p. 404.*)

to find p = .27 on the left-hand scale. This is the lower confidence limit. Continuing upward on the line X/N = .40 we again intersect the N = 50 curve at p = .55, which is the upper confidence limit. Confidence limits for sample sizes not shown may be obtained by interpolation between curves. This graph can also be used for testing hypotheses with α = .05 by reading to the right from the hypothetical p and then down to the lower and upper critical values of X/N. Similar graphs for $1 - \alpha$ = .80, .90, and .99 may be found in Dixon and Massey.

THE CHI-SQUARE METHOD

9. AN APPROXIMATION TO THE BINOMIAL TEST

Tables of the binomial distribution are not available for very large values of N, and use of formula (6) becomes increasingly laborious as N grows large. Luckily there are approximations that become increasingly accurate as N grows large. One of these is the *chi-square test*, which also has many other uses.

If we have N binomial trials with probability of success p, we say that the *expected number* of successes is Np; e.g., in 100 tosses of a penny, the expected number of heads is 50. We do not actually expect exactly 50 heads each time we toss a penny 100 times, but 50 is the most likely number, and if we have a great many groups of 100 tosses, the average number of heads per group tends to 50, so that the expected number is an idealization of the average in the same way that probability was an idealization of the proportion of successes.

The chi-square test applies to experiments in which each trial can have a definite number, k, of outcomes and we count the number of times each outcome occurs. These *observed numbers* are then compared with the expected number under the hypothesis to be tested. The formula is

$$\chi^2 = \sum \left[\frac{(X_{OBS} - X_{EXP})^2}{X_{EXP}} \right] \tag{12}$$

where χ is the Greek letter chi from which the chi-square test gets its name, X_{OBS} is the observed number of trials with a particular outcome, X_{EXP} is the expected number of trials with this outcome, and the symbol Σ, which is the Greek capital letter sigma but in the present context is called a *summation sign*, directs us to calculate the expression following it for each class of outcome and then to add all these expressions.

Let us again consider the hypothesis p = $\frac{1}{2}$, with N = 20 and the observed X = 15. There are two classes of outcome, success and failure, with X_{OBS} equal to 15 and 5 respectively and X_{EXP} equal to Np and Nq, or 10 and 10. Table 29.3 gives the calculation of χ^2, which is equal to 5. Table 29.4 gives the probability of obtaining a value of χ^2 as great as or greater than a given value when H_0 is really true, but to use it we must know the number of *degrees of freedom*, n. For the type of problem considered in this chapter the number of degrees of freedom is the number of independent differences in the sum (formula 12). Thus, for testing a hypothetical value of p there are two differences, $X_{OBS} - X_{EXP}$; but, as in our example, they are always numerically equal but of opposite sign, so that there is really only one independent difference and one degree of freedom.

From Table 29.4 we find that for 1 degree of freedom and α = .05, we reject H_0 if $\chi^2 \geq 3.841$; or, in other words, if H_0 is true, the probability that $\chi^2 \geq 3.841$ with one degree of freedom is .05. Since our χ^2 = 5, we reject H_0. On the other hand, for α = .02, the critical value of χ^2 is 5.412, so we would accept H_0 at the 2 per cent level of significance. From more extensive tables of χ^2, such as the Biometrika tables, the probability that $\chi^2 \geq 5$ is .0254.

Now the χ^2 method is only an approximate method, good for large N, and N = 20 is not very large, so let us see how good the approximation is. It is easy to see that, for N = 20 and H_0:p = $\frac{1}{2}$, $\chi^2 \geq 5$ whenever X $\geq$ 15 or X $\leq$ 5. But we have already found that

TABLE 29.3

Calculation of χ^2, with and without Yates' correction, for the mouse backcross

	Albino	Agouti	Total
OBSERVED NUMBER	15	5	20
EXPECTED NUMBER	10	10	20
OBS-EXP	5	−5	0
(OBS-EXP)^2	25	25	
(OBS-EXP)^2/EXP	2.5	2.5	5 = χ^2
With Yates' correction:			
OBS-EXP	4.5	−4.5	0
(OBS-EXP)^2	20.25	20.25	
(OBS-EXP)^2/EXP	2.025	2.025	4.05 = χ^2 corrected

the probability that $X \geq 15$ or $X \leq 5$ is .042. Thus the χ^2 approximation, .025, is not very close, but is at least of the correct order of magnitude. The approximation can be considerably improved whenever we have one degree of freedom and hence essentially only one difference, by using *Yates' correction for continuity*. This consists in making the difference $X_{OBS} - X_{EXP}$ one-half unit closer to zero and then calculating χ^2 as before. This is done in the last three lines of Table 29.3, giving a corrected $\chi^2 = 4.05$. From the Biometrika table of χ^2 we find the probability that $\chi^2 \geq 4.05$ is .044, in excellent

agreement with the exact binomial probability of .042.

There is another way of obtaining an approximate binomial test, which in addition leads to approximate confidence intervals. This method uses the normal distribution and is discussed in Section 29 of this chapter.

10. THE MORE GENERAL CASE OF THE CHI-SQUARE TEST

The chi-square test has many other applications, for most of which no simple, exact test such as the binomial one is available. For example, it may be used to test agreement

TABLE 29.4

Probabilities, P (top line), for various degrees of freedom, n (left column), that χ^2 is greater than the value, $\chi^2(n)$, in the body of the table. (*From R. A. Fisher, "Statistical Methods for Research Workers," by permission of the author and publishers, Oliver & Boyd, Ltd.*)

n \ P	.99	.98	.95	.90	.80	.70	.50	.30	.20	.10	.05	.02	.01
1	.00016	.00063	.0039	.016	.064	.148	.455	1.074	1.642	2.706	3.841	5.412	6.635
2	.0201	.0404	.103	.211	.446	.713	1.386	2.408	3.219	4.605	5.991	7.824	9.210
3	.115	.185	.352	.584	1.005	1.424	2.366	3.665	4.642	6.251	7.815	9.837	11.341
4	.297	.429	.711	1.064	1.649	2.195	3.357	4.878	5.989	7.779	9.488	11.668	13.277
5	.554	.752	1.145	1.610	2.343	3.000	4.351	6.064	7.289	9.236	11.070	13.388	15.086
6	.872	1.134	1.635	2.204	3.070	3.828	5.348	7.231	8.558	10.645	12.592	15.033	16.812
7	1.239	1.564	2.167	2.833	3.822	4.671	6.346	8.383	9.803	12.017	14.067	16.622	18.475
8	1.646	2.032	2.733	3.490	4.594	5.527	7.344	9.524	11.030	13.362	15.507	18.168	20.090
9	2.088	2.532	3.325	4.168	5.380	6.393	8.343	10.656	12.242	14.684	16.919	19.679	21.666
10	2.558	3.059	3.940	4.865	6.179	7.267	9.342	11.781	13.442	15.987	18.307	21.161	23.209

of an observed Mendelian segregation with a theoretical one when there are more than two classes. Again, formula (12) is used, but the number of degrees of freedom is different. As a concrete example, suppose we have two factors, A and B, each apparently showing dominance, and we want to test the hypothesis that an F_2 gives a $9:3:3:1$ segregation. Suppose an F_2 of 408 animals gives 247 AB, 81 Ab, 53 aB, and 27 ab. Table 29.5 shows the calculation of χ^2, which turns out to be

11. THE CHI-SQUARE TEST FOR LINKAGE

We now rewrite the observed values of the preceding section in the form of a *fourfold table* in Table 29.6 (I). Now, by adding across and down, we get *marginal totals* giving the number of A's and a's and the number of B's and b's, respectively. Dividing these by the total number of individuals, 408, we get the marginal totals of the "estimated probabilities" table, 29.6 (II). Looking at these, it seems that A is not following a $3:1$ segrega-

TABLE 29.5
Calculation of χ^2 for agreement of a two-factor segregation with a $9:3:3:1$ ratio

Phenotype	AB	Ab	aB	ab	Total
Observed value	247	81	53	27	408
Expected value	$408(9/16)$	$408(3/16)$	$408(3/16)$	$408(1/16)$	$408(16/16)$
Expected value	229.5	76.5	76.5	25.5	408
Obs-exp	17.5	4.5	−23.5	1.5	0
$(Obs-exp)^2$	306.25	20.25	552.25	2.25	
$(Obs-exp)^2/exp$	1.334	.265	7.219	.088	$8.906 = \chi^2$

equal to 8.906. Now, for all cases like this one, where the probability of each class is completely specified by the hypothesis being tested, there are $n = k - 1$ degrees of freedom, where k is the number of classes. This is because $k - 1$ of the observed values may vary arbitrarily, but the kth value is fixed by the requirement of the total number of cases adding up to the observed total, N. Thus we have $n = 3$ degrees of freedom in this example. From Table 29.4 we see that the probability that $\chi^2 \geq 7.815$ is .05 for 3 degrees of freedom; so, using $\alpha = .05$, we would reject the hypothesis of a $9:3:3:1$ ratio because our χ^2 was $8.906 > 7.815$. Now one obvious possibility for disturbing this ratio is linkage. However, from the present test we are not justified in claiming linkage but can only say there is some disturbance. We will now describe another χ^2 test specifically designed to test for linkage, or, more precisely, to test H_o that A segregates independently of B.

tion, since $f = .196$ for a, instead of the theoretical .25. We can, in fact, perform a chi-square test for this one-factor segregation as explained above, and on doing so we find $\chi^2 = 6.043$. From Table 29.4 we find P lies between .02 and .01, so we would reject the hypothesis of a $3:1$ ratio for A if we had chosen $\alpha = .02$ or larger. The discrepancy might be due to poor viability of aa individuals, but only a different sort of experiment could prove this.

It is now possible that the departure from a $9:3:3:1$ ratio was due simply to the aberrant segregation of A; however, we had better continue with our test for linkage before deciding. We will again use a chi-square test, but the expected values will not now be in a $9:3:3:1$ ratio. Instead we proceed as follows: From the marginal totals of Table 29.6 (II), we see that .196 of all individuals are a and that .265 of all individuals are b. Now if A and B are segregating independently, we would expect a fraction .265 of all the .196

TABLE 29.6
Calculation of expected values under hypothesis of independent assortment for a two-factor segregation

I. Observed Numbers

	B	b	Total
A	247	81	328
a	53	27	80
Total	300	108	408

II. Estimated Probabilities for Independent Assortment

	B	b	Total
A	.591	.213	.804
a	.144	.052	.196
Total	.735	.265	1.000

III. Expected Numbers

	B	b	Total
A	241.1	86.9	328
a	58.9	21.1	80
Total	300.0	108.0	408

a individuals to be also *b*, or, in other words, expect (.196)(.265) = .052 of all individuals to be *ab*. Similarly, (.196)(.735) = .144 will be *aB*, (.804)(.265) = .213 *Ab*, and (.804)(.735) = .591 *AB*. In other words, we have calculated these four estimated probabilities in such a way that the proportion of *a*'s is the same among the *b*'s, the *B*'s, and so on; this is precisely what is meant by independent assortment. The results of these calculations are shown in Table 29.6. Now, the expected values are obtained simply by multiplying these estimated probabilities by the number of individuals, 408. The remaining calculations for χ^2 go on in the usual way, as shown in Table 29.7, giving $\chi^2 = 2.24$. We now remark that the "expected values" were calculated from *all* the marginal totals, and hence we are really only comparing our observed table with all other possible tables having the *same* marginal totals. Now if we insert some arbitrary number of *AB*'s into the table, the marginal totals at once dictate the remaining 3 entries. Thus there is only *one* degree of freedom, and this is always true for a fourfold table. We verify this by the fact that there is only one numerical value for the difference of observed and expected in Table 29.7, and therefore we again use Yates' correction in calculating χ^2. Finally, the observed $\chi^2 = 2.24$ gives P between .20 and .10, and so we accept the hypothesis of independence and decide there is no evidence of linkage. Consequently, we decide that the departure from a 9:3:3:1 ratio is entirely due to the segregation of *A*. It should be noted that the test for linkage by a fourfold table would be used in exactly the same way if instead of an F_2 we had a single or double backcross, the change in individual segregation ratios being taken care of automatically by the marginal totals.

12. CONTINGENCY TABLES

The fourfold table is a special case of a more general table called a *contingency table*. Such a table may have any number, r, of rows and any number, c, of columns. Mechanically, marginal totals are calculated; from them marginal probabilities are estimated; the body of the estimated probability table is obtained as before, the entry in the ith row and the jth column being the product of the marginal probabilities of the ith row and jth column; and the expected values are obtained by multiplying the estimated probabilities by the grand total. The number of degrees of freedom is easily shown to be $(r - 1)(c - 1)$. Such contingency tables may be used for a number of different problems. First, a single sample of individuals may be classified into r classes according to one criterion and c classes according to another, and we test H_o, that the two criteria are independent. The linkage test was of this type.

TABLE 29.7
Calculation of χ^2 for the example of Table 29.6

Phenotype	AB	Ab	aB	ab	Total
Obs	247	81	53	27	408
Exp	241.1	86.9	58.9	21.1	408
Diff	5.9	−5.9	−5.9	5.9	0
Diff corr	5.4	−5.4	−5.4	5.4	0
(Diff corr)^2	29.16	29.16	29.16	29.16	
(Diff corr)^2/exp	.12	.34	.49	1.38	2.33 = χ^2 corrected

On the other hand, we may have a sample from each of r different sets of conditions and have c possible classes in each sample. The hypothesis to be tested is that the probability of falling into the various classes is the same in each sample or set of conditions. Although this situation is conceptually very different and not all the "marginal probabilities" make sense, the arithmetic is exactly the same and χ^2 again has $(r-1)(c-1)$ degrees of freedom. An example of this sort would be three samples of people, classified in blood groups O, A, B, and AB, taken in London, Tokyo, and Calcutta, and H_o that the frequency of the four phenotypes is the same in all three cities. Another application might be to compare the proportions of yellow and green seeds in the seven different pea experiments in Table 3.2 and to test H_o that the probability, p, of green was the same throughout. Such a test, where the experiments are supposedly all alike but we want to make sure, is often called a *test of homogeneity*. Here the number of degrees of freedom would be $(7-1)(2-1) = 6$, or one less than the number of experiments.

As we saw earlier, the chi-square method is only approximate and is valid for large samples. There is no hard-and-fast rule for when it is valid, but a rule that is usually safe is to require that no class have an *expected* frequency less than 2 and that most of the expected frequencies be at least 5. Notice that it does not matter if one of the classes has a zero observed frequency as long as the expected frequency is at least 2.

QUANTITATIVE VARIATION

13. THE NATURE OF QUANTITATIVE VARIATION

The methods so far discussed have been appropriate for the study of qualitative variation. Each individual studied has been classified as falling into one of a number of distinct descriptive classes, e.g., agouti versus albino, or yellow round, yellow wrinkled, green round, and green wrinkled. Numbers, and hence statistics, entered only when we counted how many individuals fell into each class. On the other hand, in quantitative variation, as it was discussed in Chapter 8, each individual is represented by a numerical value, and even to grasp a set of numbers from a large sample of individuals, let alone test a genetic theory about them, requires a new kind of statistical analysis. The essential difference is the numerical "label" on each individual. For example, suppose we are studying the number of vertebrae of some species of fish. There may be only a limited number of possible values, so we could count how many fish fall into each class and use the chi-square method. However, this would ignore the information in the numbers attached to the classes; 29 and 30 are considered to be as different as 29 and 43. An even worse error is to treat the number of vertebrae as though it were a binomial variable, as if there were N places where there could be a vertebra and the occurrence of a vertebra at one place were independent of the occurrence of one at another place.

A distinction is sometimes made between *discrete* variables—such as number of vertebrae, number of eggs laid, etc., which can only take on certain distinct values—and *continuous* variables, such as height, weight, and number of years lived, where in theory all values, including fractional ones, are possible. In practice, however, weight can only be measured to the nearest pound, or milligram, or thousandth of a milligram, depending on the apparatus used, and is therefore operationally discrete. Thus the same methods are used on both discrete data and continuously variable data, as long as more than a very few different values are possible. On the other hand, all kinds of data can be adapted to the use of binomial methods by dividing into, say, "under 21" and "21 and over." This, of course, involves the loss of some of the information in the original data.

14. HUMAN HEIGHT

As an example we will take the height of a random sample of 100 adult men. In Table 29.8, these heights are given to the nearest tenth of an inch. To make the table easier to follow, the heights are arranged in order of increasing magnitude. On examining the table, certain features are evident. The range of values is from 60.2 to 76.5 inches. There are comparatively few persons with extreme values, 80 per cent of the total having heights between 64.4 and 72.0 inches, and there is a piling up in the upper sixties. There are as many with height under 67.85 inches as above; therefore 67.85 is the *median* of the distribution of heights.

15. THE FREQUENCY DISTRIBUTION

The general picture becomes clearer if we round off the heights to the nearest inch and then count how many times each value appears. The number of occurrences is called the *absolute frequency* of that value, whereas the number of occurrences divided by the sample size is called the *relative frequency* or simply the *frequency* of the value. The fre-

TABLE 29.8

Heights in inches of a random sample of 100 adult men, arranged in order of magnitude

60.2	65.5	67.3	68.6	70.6
62.5	65.6	67.3	68.7	70.7
62.5	65.6	67.5	68.7	70.9
62.8	65.6	67.5	68.8	70.9
63.3	65.8	67.5	68.9	71.0
63.5	65.8	67.6	69.0	71.1
63.9	65.9	67.6	69.1	71.2
64.0	66.1	67.6	69.2	71.2
64.1	66.2	67.8	69.3	71.7
64.2	66.2	67.8	69.4	72.0
64.4	66.3	67.9	69.4	72.1
64.4	66.4	67.9	69.5	72.3
64.5	66.5	67.9	69.6	72.4
64.5	66.5	67.9	69.8	72.4
64.7	66.7	68.0	70.0	72.6
64.8	66.9	68.1	70.3	73.7
64.8	67.0	68.1	70.4	74.0
65.0	67.1	68.4	70.5	74.0
65.3	67.1	68.5	70.5	74.8
65.3	67.2	68.5	70.6	76.5

quency distribution of heights is given in Table 29.9. Before looking at this table, a word about rounding numbers is in order. The rule is that numbers with a fractional part less than ½ are rounded to the nearest lower integer, and those with a fractional part greater than ½ are rounded to the nearest higher integer. Thus "68" means all numbers from 67.5+ to 68.5−. If the recorded value was exactly 67.5, the rule would break down. For ordinary use in computation, we would then arbitrarily round to the nearest *even* integer; however, this would be bad for forming a frequency distribution, since there would be too many men with even heights and too few with odd heights. Accordingly, in forming Table 29.9, numbers such as 67.5 were rounded by tossing a penny and rounding up for heads and down for tails. Similar methods would be used to round to the nearest two inches or five inches, and so on.

Although the frequency distribution is

TABLE 29.9
Frequency distribution of heights from Table 29.8 rounded to nearest inch

Height	Number of cases	Relative frequency	Frequency of heights no greater than X
X	F_X	f_X	
60	1	.01	.01
61	0	.00	.01
62	1	.01	.02
63	4	.04	.06
64	6	.06	.12
65	9	.09	.21
66	11	.11	.32
67	12	.12	.44
68	15	.15	.59
69	13	.13	.72
70	6	.06	.78
71	10	.10	.88
72	6	.06	.94
73	1	.01	.95
74	3	.03	.98
75	1	.01	.99
76	0	.00	.99
77	1	.01	1.00
Total	100	1.00	

easier to grasp than the original data (particularly if the original data has not been rearranged, as in Table 29.8, in order of increasing magnitude), a graphic representation of the frequency distribution is still easier to follow.

16. HISTOGRAMS
Such a graphic representation is the histogram. To form a histogram from the frequency distribution of heights, the various heights are marked off on the horizontal axis and rectangles are erected to represent the various classes. The base of the rectangle covers the range of values included in the class—for example, 67.5 to 68.5 for the 68-inch class—and the area of the rectangle represents the frequency of the class—for example, 15/100 in the 68-inch class. Since

the area of a rectangle equals the base times the altitude, and in this example the base is 1, the area here equals the altitude.

Looking now at the histogram for the distribution of heights in Figure 29.3, we see that the most numerous class is 68 inches. This is the *mode,* or most "fashionable" value. Going away from the mode in either direction, the frequency declines steadily and more or less symmetrically, except for certain irregularities that could be due to chance. Thus most individuals have a height fairly near a typical central value with relatively few at the extremes. The same sort of picture appears again and again in dealing with measurements. Evidently, in such cases the most salient aspects of the distribution can be described by specifying the central value and amount of variability—the spread of the distribution. The median and the mode have already been given as measures of the center, and the range from largest to smallest is a measure of the spread. However, for various mathematical reasons, the measures that are almost universally used are the mean and the standard deviation.

17. THE MEAN AND STANDARD DEVIATION
The *arithmetic mean,* or simply the *mean,* of a sample is the sum of the measurements divided by the *sample size,* or the number of individuals in the sample. If X stands for the measurement in question, then the sample mean is always denoted by $\overline{X}$ (read X bar), and if N stands for the sample size and we recall that the symbol Σ directs us to add up all terms of the kind following it, we have the formula

$$\overline{X} = \frac{1}{N} \Sigma X \tag{13}$$

The standard deviation of the sample is denoted by the symbol s, defined by

$$s = \sqrt{\frac{1}{N-1} \Sigma (X - \overline{X})^2} \tag{14}$$

In words, we first subtract the mean from each individual value, forming *deviations*

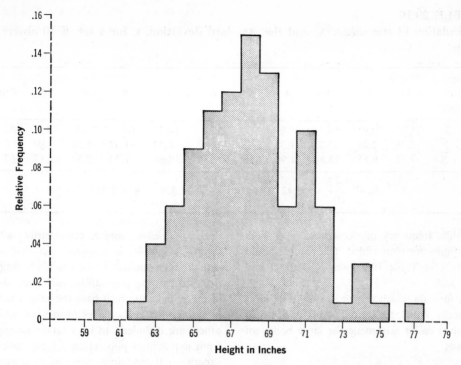

Fig. 29.3. Histogram of height distribution of 100 men. The area of each rectangle (its height times width) is equal to the fraction of the men whose height is included within the base of the rectangle.

from the mean, then square these deviations and add them, then obtain the *mean square deviation*, s^2, dividing by $N - 1$ instead of N for reasons to be discussed later, and finally take the square root. By squaring the deviations, we prevent positive and negative deviations from canceling each other out, since a squared number is always positive; however, this leaves our answer in square inches, if the data were in inches, and we must take the square root to return to the original units. The reader can undoubtedly think of an easier way of preventing the deviations from canceling; suffice it to say that for theoretical reasons beyond the scope of this book, the standard deviation is the most satisfactory measure of spread. It may also be noted in passing that s^2, the square of the standard deviation, though in the wrong units to measure spread, is nevertheless of such theoretical importance in the study of variability that it has its own name, the *variance*.

Table 29.10 gives a numerical example for the heights of the first 10 men measured. For the whole set of 100 the reader should verify that the mean $\overline{X} = 67.98$, the variance $s^2 = 9.066$, and the standard deviation $s = 3.01$.

The mean and variance may also be calculated from the rounded values in the frequency table, with some loss of accuracy but a saving in work. In calculating the mean by this method, each value of X, such as 68, must be added as many times as it occurs; or, more simply, the value of X is multiplied by the number of times, F_X, it occurred (for example, in Table 29.9, 68 would be multiplied by 15), and these values are then added. Similarly, for the variance, each squared deviation from the mean is multiplied by its

TABLE 29.10

Calculation of the mean, $\overline{X}$, and the standard deviation, s, for a set of 10 observations

Observation number	1	2	3	4	5	6	7	8	9	10	Total
X	71.2	70.9	64.7	69.8	71.1	65.8	64.1	67.1	70.0	69.5	684.2
$X - \overline{X}$	2.78	2.48	−3.72	1.38	2.68	−2.62	−4.32	−1.32	1.58	1.08	0
$(X - \overline{X})^2$	7.73	6.15	13.84	1.90	7.18	6.86	18.66	1.74	2.50	1.17	67.73

$$X = \frac{684.2}{10} = 68.42 \qquad s^2 = \frac{67.73}{9} = 7.526 \qquad s = 2.74$$

absolute frequency of occurrence, and these quantities are then added. The reader should verify that Table 19.9 gives $\overline{X} = 67.99$ and s = 3.05.

A formula which can be shown to be algebraically equal to formula (14) and which involves easier arithmetic for large bodies of data is

$$s = \sqrt{\frac{1}{N - 1}(\Sigma X^2 - N\overline{X}^2)} \qquad (15)$$

However, for occasional use, formula (14) is simpler to remember and use. If extensive computing of means and variances is to be done, other devices can be found in textbooks in which statistics are presented in more detail.

18. SAMPLE AND POPULATION

One of the most important distinctions in statistics is that between a sample and a population. A *population* consists of *all* the individuals or measurements having certain specified characteristics. A population may actually exist—for example, all the people living in New York City, all American college students, all the freshmen at Columbia College in 1955, or all grizzly bears—or the population may exist only potentially—as, for example, all freshmen who may go to Columbia as long as there is no change in college policy, all mice that could be produced from a given inbred strain, or all measurements made under some set of specified conditions. A *random sample*, customarily called simply a sample, is a smaller set that has actually been studied. To be a random sample from an existing population, each individual in the population must have the same chance of being included, independently of which others are included; to be a random sample from a potential population, or experiment, experimental conditions must remain constant except for random, chance fluctuations, and the result of one experimental trial must not affect the next.

The basic problem of biological statistics is to make inferences about characteristics of the population on the basis of observations on a sample. Numbers calculated from a sample, such as X and f from a binomial sample and $\overline{X}$ and s from measurement data, are called *statistics*, and the corresponding quantities for the population are called *parameters*. We are already familiar with the parameters Np and p corresponding to X and f for binomial trials, and it is clear what is meant by population values of $\overline{X}$ and s in an existing population. It is not so obvious what are the parameters corresponding to $\overline{X}$ and s in a potential population. Since, no matter how many observations are taken, still more can always be made, we cannot define the population mean as the average of all the members of the population. Nevertheless, it is true that as more and more observations are taken and the sample size, N, tends to infinity, the sample mean, $\overline{X}$, tends to a limiting value. This value is denoted by m and is called the population mean, or true mean, of the measurement X. Similarly, s tends to a population or true standard deviation denoted by σ (the Greek letter sigma). An alternative way of viewing m and σ is to consider them to be the mean and variance of a theoretical distribution, which has the same relationship to an observed distribution as a parameter has to a statistic.

19. THEORETICAL DISTRIBUTIONS

The areas of the different rectangles in the histogram, defined above, were made equal to the *relative* frequencies in order that samples of different sizes could be compared directly. Now, if we let the sample size become very large, then the relative frequency of some occurrence, such as 68 inches, will tend toward the probability of that occurrence and consequently the area of the rectangle at 68 inches, for example, will tend to the probability that an individual has a height between 67.5 inches and 68.5 inches. The limiting form of the histogram as N becomes infinite is called the *population histogram*. Now for large N, it is possible to make a histogram for heights measured to the nearest tenth of an inch, and this histogram will be somewhat smoother than the one where heights are measured only to the nearest inch. Of course, the relative frequency of a height between 67.95 and 68.05 inches will be only about one tenth as large as the frequency of a height between 67.5 and 68.5 inches, but because we made relative frequency equal to the area rather than the height of a rectangle, the general shape and size of the histogram will not be affected by the finer subdivision. If we now imagine that we were to take finer and finer measurements, we would ultimately get a histogram that would be a smooth curve. This curve is called the *population frequency curve,* and on it the probability of observing a height between any two given values will be equal to the area under the curve between those two given values.

20. THE NORMAL CURVE

Many quantitative characters, including height, have population frequency curves that are very similar to a certain mathematical curve called the *normal curve*.

The normal curve may take many different shapes, but there is really only one basic shape. If we report all measurements in terms of distance to the right or to the left of the population mean, and if these distances are in terms of standard deviation units, then we say that these measurements are in standard units. We will use the letter Z to denote measurements in standard units. In mathematical terms

$$Z = \frac{X - m}{\sigma} \qquad (16)$$

or $\quad X = m + Z\sigma \qquad (17)$

Any character expressed in Z units has a true mean equal to zero and true standard deviation equal to one. When expressed in standard units, all normal curves have the shape shown in Figure 29.4. We see that the curve is symmetrical and that, consequently, the probability that a measurement will be larger than the true mean is one half. For the normal curve, the probability that a measurement lies within one standard deviation unit of the mean is about two-thirds, and the probability that a measurement lies beyond two Z units from the mean is approximately .05. There is very little probability of an observation further away from the true mean than three standard deviation units. Table 29.11 is a short table of the normal probability distribution. It gives selected values of P and corresponding values of Z. The probability that Z will be numerically larger (in either direction) than the tabled value is P. In this way, for example, the probability of a deviation from the mean in standard deviation units which is numerically greater than .67 is ½, and consequently the probability

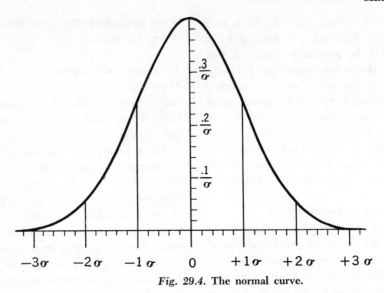

.3/σ

.2/σ

.1/σ

−3σ   −2σ   −1σ   0   +1σ   +2σ   +3σ

Fig. 29.4. The normal curve.

of a Z greater than +.67 is ¼ and the probability of a Z less than −.67 is also ¼. The probability of a deviation numerically less than 1.96 is .95. By subtraction, we find that the probability of Z falling between −.84 and −.39 is .15.

21. THEORETICAL BASIS OF THE NORMAL CURVE

There are several mechanisms that will lead to approximately normal distributions. First, the normal curve is an approximation to the binomial distribution. The larger the sample size, the more the binomial distribution will resemble a normal distribution. The entries in Table 8.1, which are proportional to binomial probabilities for sample sizes 2, 4, 6, and 12 and p = ½, illustrate this. It is further shown in Figure 29.5, which has been calculated from Table 29.2 and shows the theoretical histogram for a binomial distribu-

tion with N = 20 and p = ½. Superimposed upon it is a normal curve with the same mean and standard deviation. Exactly such a theoretical histogram would be obtained for a quantitative character in an F_2 involving 20 genes, none of which showed dominance and each of which contributed the same differential effect to the character in question. If, further, there were a small amount of environmental variability, the result would be to smooth the sharp corners of the histogram and to make it look a good deal more like a normal curve. A still more general theoretical explanation of the normal curve is given by the so-called *central-limit theorem* of probability. This states that if a character is the result of the addition of a large number of *independent effects,* all of which are of the same general order of magnitude, then the resulting character will be approximately normally distributed. Since

TABLE 29.11
Probabilities, P (first line), that a normally distributed variable differs from zero by as much as the value, Z_P (second line)

P	.9	.8	.7	.6	.5	.4	.3	.2	.1	.05	.02	.01	.002	.001	.0001
Z_P	.13	.25	.39	.52	.67	.84	1.04	1.28	1.64	1.96	2.33	2.58	3.09	3.29	3.89

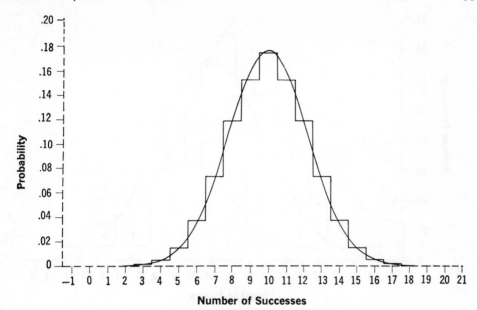

Fig. 29.5. Histogram giving the probabilities of various numbers of successes for a binomial distribution with $N = 20$ and $p = 1/2$. The normal curve with the same mean and standard deviation is superimposed.

these independent effects can be environmental or genetic, the mere fact that some characteristic is normally distributed does not tell us anything about whether it is due to genetic or environmental influence. In view of all this, it may seem strange that in fact we often find characters whose distribution is not extremely close to the normal distribution. The most usual types of discrepancies are a lack of symmetry, with the curve extending further in one direction than in the other, or exceptionally long "tails" so that there is a larger probability of extreme deviations than is given by the normal distribution. Such effects may arise because of the *interaction* of various causes affecting the character or because the causes, instead of producing independent *absolute* additions to the character, produce *percentage* additions. Another reason for departure from the normal distribution is the presence of one cause which has a very much larger effect than any of the others. For example,

we might be considering height in a sample composed of both men and women. Here sex would be the one cause that produced a larger effect. When carried to the extreme, this might cause the production of a *bimodal* curve with two peaks. Nevertheless, in spite of all these disturbances, many characters met with in practice show distributions that are close enough to the normal curve for it to be used for drawing various conclusions.

Figure 29.6 shows the same histogram of the heights of 100 men as Figure 29.3, but a normal curve with the same mean and variance is superimposed to show the degree of agreement.

22. DISTRIBUTION OF THE SAMPLE MEAN
Just as we talked about the distribution of X, so we can talk about the distribution of $\overline{X}$. We now suppose that our particular sample mean based on N observations is one of a possible M different sample means that could have been obtained. We can then consider

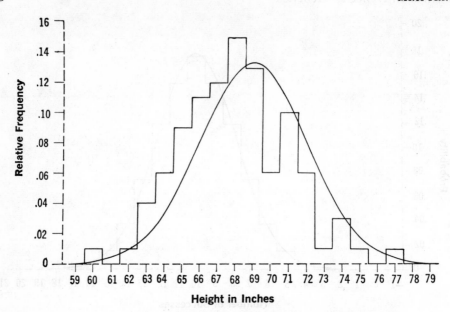

Fig. 29.6. Histogram for the heights of 100 men. The same as Figure 29.3 but with the normal curve of the same mean and standard deviation superimposed.

the probability that $\overline{X}$ lies between any two given values. The population mean of $\overline{X}$ is the same as the population mean of X, since the sample mean of M values of $\overline{X}$ is the same as the sample mean of MN values of X, and as M becomes large so does MN. Furthermore, it can be shown that the population variance of $\overline{X}$ is given by

$$\sigma_{\overline{X}}^2 = \frac{\sigma^2}{N} \tag{18}$$

The standard deviation of the sample mean is of course the square root of the expression (18).

Since X is a constant multiple of the sum of N independent and identically distributed variables, X, the central-limit theorem applies exactly and $\overline{X}$ will be much more nearly normally distributed than will X. In fact, for N as big as 10, $\overline{X}$ will be very nearly normally distributed provided the original distribution of X did not depart too widely from the normal distribution. In practice, it is usually safe to assume that $\overline{X}$ is normally distributed to a close enough approximation

to use the tables of the normal distribution. It is thus seen that the complete distribution of $\overline{X}$ is known as soon as we know the population mean and population standard deviation of X.

23. TESTING HYPOTHESES ABOUT THE MEAN
We frequently want to test the hypothesis that the population mean m has some specific value, m_o. We will first consider the special case when the population standard deviation, σ, is known. For example, in the case of our sample of heights, we might know $\sigma = 3$ and wish to test H_o that $m = 67$. For $N = 100$, $\sigma_{\overline{X}}^2 = \sigma^2/N = \frac{9}{100} = .09$, and $\sigma_{\overline{X}} = \sqrt{.09} = .3$. Alternatively, $\sigma_{\overline{X}} = \sigma/\sqrt{N} = 3/\sqrt{100} = \frac{3}{10}$ as before. Now for $\alpha = .05$, we reject H_o if $\overline{X}$ differs from m_o by more than $1.96\sigma_{\overline{X}} = .588$, so that we reject H_o if $\overline{X} \leq 66.412$ or $\overline{X} \geq 67.588$. Since we observed $\overline{X} = 67.98$, we reject the hypothesis that the true mean is 67 at the 5 per cent level of significance.

Before the sample was taken, we might

have wanted to know the power of the test when the true m was, say, 67.5. This is the probability that $\overline{X}$ lies outside the above limits when m is really 67.5. To obtain it we calculate $Z = (\overline{X} - 67.5)/.3$ for these two values of $\overline{X}$, getting $Z_1 = (66.412 - 67.5)/.3 = -1.088/.3 = -3.63$ and $Z_2 = (67.588 - 67.5)/.3 = +.088/.3 = +.29$. From Table 29.11, the probability that $Z \leq -3.63$ is less than .0005, whereas the probability that $Z \geq +.29$ is between .35 and .40. Hence the power, the probability of rejecting H_o that m = 67 if, in fact, m = 67.5, is between .35 and .40.

Often, when $H_o:m = m_o$ is being tested at level of significance α, there is some other value m_1, such that if m really equals m_1 this is such an important departure from H_o that the power of the test should have some large value $1 - \beta$. Some simple algebra shows that this result can be attained if the sample size is at least as large as

$$N = \frac{\sigma^2(Z_\alpha + Z_{2\beta})^2}{(m_o - m_1)^2} \qquad (19)$$

where the symbol Z with a subscript is simply the Z_p from Table 29.11 corresponding to the "two-tailed" probability given by the subscript. In the example above, suppose we want $1 - \beta = .9$ for m = 67.5. From Table 29.11, $Z_\alpha = 1.96$, and $Z_{2\beta} = 1.28$. Thus

$$N = \frac{(3)^2(1.96 + 1.28)^2}{(67 - 67.5)^2} = \frac{9(10.5)}{.25} = 378.0 \quad (20)$$

so it would be becessary to take a sample of at least 378 men to have this sensitive a test.

24. STUDENT'S DISTRIBUTION

We have just seen that we can test a hypothesis about a mean by calculating Z given by the formula

$$Z = \frac{\overline{X} - m_o}{\sigma/\sqrt{N}} \qquad (21)$$

and then rejecting the hypothesis if Z is larger than the critical value given by Table 29.11. However, in many cases σ is unknown,

and therefore formula (21) cannot be used. In such cases it seems reasonable to modify the formula by replacing σ by s. We will denote this new quantity by t as given in

$$t = \frac{\overline{X} - m_o}{s/\sqrt{N}} \qquad (22)$$

and will reject the hypothesis if t is too large. Unfortunately, in deciding whether t is too large, we cannot use Table 29.11 because t is not in general normally distributed. The distribution of t was first found by W. S. Gosset, writing under the pseudonym of "Student," and is known as *Student's distribution*, or the t distribution. Table 29.12 is a short table of Student's distribution arranged in the same manner as Table 29.11. The shape of Student's distribution and hence the critical values of t depend on the number of degrees of freedom, n, used in estimating σ. When σ is estimated from a single sample, the number of degrees of freedom is equal to N − 1, which was the number we used in dividing to get s. As n becomes large, the shape of Student's distribution approximates more and more closely to the shape of the normal distribution, and it will be noted in Table 29.12 that by the time n is as big as 30 the agreement of the critical values with those for the normal distribution is quite good.

If we were to repeat the test in the last section using Student's t instead of Z, there would be almost no change in the results, since we found s was 3.01 and n was 99. Accordingly, for an illustrative example we will test the hypothesis $H_o:m = 67$, using the data in Table 29.10. The calculation of t is as follows:

$$t = \frac{68.42 - 67}{2.74/\sqrt{10}} = \frac{1.42}{2.74/3.16} = \frac{1.42}{.867} = 1.64 \quad (23)$$

Looking in Table 29.12, with n = 9 degrees of freedom, we find that t = 1.64 corresponds to a value of P between .20 and .10, so that we would reject the hypothesis that m = 67 if we were using $\alpha = .20$ but would accept the hypothesis if we were using $\alpha = .10$.

The calculation of the power for Student's

TABLE 29.12

Probabilities, P (top line), for various degrees of freedom, n (left column), that Student's t differs from zero in either direction by as much as the value, $t_P(n)$, in the body of the table (*From R. A. Fisher and F. J. Yates, "Statistical Tables for Biological, Agricultural and Medical Research," by permission of the authors and publishers, Oliver & Boyd, Ltd.*)

P n	.9	.5	.2	.1	.05	.02	.01	.001
1	.158	1.000	3.078	6.314	12.706	31.821	63.657	636.619
2	.142	.816	1.886	2.920	4.303	6.965	9.925	31.598
3	.137	.765	1.638	2.353	3.182	4.541	5.841	12.941
4	.134	.741	1.533	2.132	2.776	3.747	4.604	8.610
5	.132	.727	1.476	2.015	2.571	3.365	4.032	6.859
6	.131	.718	1.440	1.943	2.447	3.143	3.707	5.959
7	.130	.711	1.415	1.895	2.365	2.998	3.499	5.405
8	.130	.706	1.397	1.860	2.306	2.896	3.355	5.041
9	.129	.703	1.383	1.833	2.262	2.821	3.250	4.781
10	.129	.700	1.372	1.812	2.228	2.764	3.169	4.587
12	.128	.695	1.356	1.782	2.179	2.681	3.055	4.318
15	.128	.691	1.341	1.753	2.131	2.602	2.947	4.073
20	.127	.687	1.325	1.725	2.086	2.528	2.845	3.850
30	.127	.683	1.310	1.697	2.042	2.457	2.750	3.646
60	.126	.679	1.296	1.671	2.000	2.390	2.660	3.460
∞	.126	.674	1.282	1.645	1.960	2.326	2.576	3.291

distribution is difficult for two reasons. First, in order to calculate the power it is necessary to assume some value for the population standard deviation, which is not known in advance. Second the power requires the use of a table called a *table of noncentral t,* which is not as readily available as the other tables we have been using. However, for sample sizes larger than 30, if we can assume some reasonable value for the population standard deviation, we can use the tables of the normal curve in the same manner as in the previous section.

25. CONFIDENCE INTERVALS FOR THE TRUE MEAN

It is quite easy to obtain confidence intervals for the true mean using either t or Z. Let us again take the data of Table 29.10 and suppose that we are testing the hypothesis that m = m_o with α = .05. From Table 29.12 we find that

the critical value of t for the 5 per cent level of significance with 9 degrees of freedom is 2.262. Accordingly we will reject the hypothesis if $\overline{X}$ differs from m_o by more than 2.262 times $s_{\overline{X}}$; or, in other words, if m_o differs from the observed value of $\overline{X}$, 68.42, by more than

$$2.262 \frac{s}{\sqrt{N}} = 2.262(.867) = 1.96 \qquad (24)$$

Accordingly, the set of all hypothetical m which will not be rejected when we observe $\overline{X}$ = 68.42 is simply those values of m that differ from 68.42 by, at most, 1.96, so that our confidence interval for m is simply the interval from 66.46 to 70.38, and we can say that the true mean lies in that interval with confidence coefficient .95. If σ had been known, then we would have used it instead of s and would have looked up the critical value in the table of the normal distribution; but there would have been no other change in finding the confidence interval.

26. THE DISTRIBUTION OF SUMS AND DIFFERENCES

Let us suppose that we have two different populations, and let us denote measurements on the first population by X and measurements on the second population by Y. The population mean and variance of X will be m_X and σ_X^2, and the population mean and variance of Y will be m_Y and σ_Y^2. Then $X + Y$ will have mean $m_X + m_Y$ and $X - Y$ will have mean $m_X - m_Y$. If, in addition, X and Y are independent, then the variance of $X + Y$ will be equal to $\sigma_X^2 + \sigma_Y^2$ and the variance of $X - Y$ will also be $\sigma_X^2 + \sigma_Y^2$. At first glance it might seem that $X - Y$ should have variance $\sigma_X^2 - \sigma_Y^2$; however, this is not so. The variance comes from the random deviations in positive and negative directions; and when we subtract Y, all we do is interchange the positive deviations and the negative deviations with no real change in the amount of variability. If, in addition, X and Y are normally distributed, $X + Y$ and $X - Y$ will also be normally distributed.

If $\overline{X}$ is the mean of N_X values of X, $\overline{Y}$ is the mean of N_Y values of Y, and X is independent of Y, then in the same way $\overline{X} - \overline{Y}$ will be approximately normally distributed with mean $m_X - m_Y$ and variance

$$\sigma_{\overline{X}-\overline{Y}}^2 = \frac{\sigma_X^2}{N_X} + \frac{\sigma_Y^2}{N_Y} \tag{25}$$

If it happens that the two populations have the same variance, that is, $\sigma_X^2 = \sigma_Y^2 = \sigma^2$, say, then the formula for the variance of the difference of the means reduces to

$$\sigma_{\overline{X}-\overline{Y}}^2 = \sigma^2 \left(\frac{1}{N_X} + \frac{1}{N_Y} \right) \tag{26}$$

27. INFERENCES ABOUT THE DIFFERENCE OF TWO MEANS

A very frequently occurring type of problem is to test whether two different populations (or, what amounts to the same thing, two different experimental groups), have the same mean. For example, we may want to know whether two strains differ genetically with respect to some size characteristic or whether some treatment has affected the characteristic, and so on. In all these cases, if we denote the true mean of the first population by m_X and the true mean of the second population by m_Y, we are interested in testing the hypothesis $H_o: m_X = m_Y$, which can also be stated as $H_o: m_X - m_Y = 0$. From the result of the previous section it follows that

$$Z = \frac{\overline{X} - \overline{Y}}{\sqrt{\dfrac{\sigma_X^2}{N_X} + \dfrac{\sigma_Y^2}{N_Y}}} = \frac{\overline{X} - \overline{Y}}{\sigma_{\overline{X}-\overline{Y}}} \tag{27}$$

will be normally distributed with mean zero and variance one if H_o is true, and accordingly we can test the hypothesis by seeing whether Z exceeds the critical value obtained from the table of the normal distribution. Just as in the one sample case, we can find the power of the test for any assumed value of $m_X - m_Y$. Furthermore, we can find a confidence interval for $m_X - m_Y$ in the form

$$(\overline{X} - \overline{Y}) - Z_\alpha \sigma_{\overline{X}-\overline{Y}} \leq m_X - m_Y \leq$$
$$(\overline{X} - \overline{Y}) + Z_\alpha \sigma_{\overline{X}-\overline{Y}} \tag{28}$$

where Z_α is the critical value of Z for a two-tailed test at level of significance α and is found from Table 29.11, and $\sigma_{\overline{X}-\overline{Y}}$ is the same as in formula (25).

When the population variance is unknown, it is again possible in this case to use Student's distribution. However, in order to do so it is necessary that the two populations have the *same* variance; that is, we must have $\sigma_X^2 = \sigma_Y^2 = \sigma^2$, say. Under these conditions we use a pooled estimate of σ^2,

$$s^2 = (n_X s_X^2 + n_Y s_Y^2)/(n_X + n_Y) \tag{29}$$

where $n_X = N_X - 1$ and $n_Y = N_Y - 1$ are the number of degrees of freedom in the first and second samples, respectively. In other words, s^2 is equal to the sum of squared deviations in the second sample divided by the total number of degrees of freedom in the two samples together,

$$s^2 = \frac{\Sigma(X - \overline{X})^2 + \Sigma(Y - \overline{Y})^2}{n} \tag{30}$$

where $n = N_X + N_Y - 2$. Then t, defined by

$$t = \frac{\overline{X} - \overline{Y}}{s\sqrt{\frac{1}{N_X} + \frac{1}{N_Y}}} \quad (31)$$

has Student's distribution with n degrees of freedom.

As an example, suppose we have a sample of ten men from population 1, their heights measured as shown in Table 29.10, and a sample of nine men from another population, 2, their heights measured as shown in Table 29.13. Suppose that we wish to test the hypothesis that the population mean height is the same in the two populations. Here $\overline{X} = 68.42$, $\Sigma(X - \overline{X})^2 = 67.73$, $N_X = 10$, $n_X = 9$, $\overline{Y} = 70.36$, $\Sigma(Y - \overline{Y})^2 = 69.56$, $N_Y = 9$, $n_Y = 8$, and

$$s^2 = \frac{67.73 + 69.56}{9 + 8} = 8.076 \quad (32)$$

$$s = 2.842 \quad (33)$$

$$s_{\overline{X} - \overline{Y}} = 2.842 \sqrt{\tfrac{1}{10} + \tfrac{1}{9}} = 1.31 \quad (34)$$

and

$$t = \frac{68.42 - 70.36}{1.31} = -1.48 \quad (35)$$

with 17 degrees of freedom. From Table 29.12 it follows that P is between .2 and .1, and hence we accept H_o, that the means do not differ, at any usual level of significance.

TABLE 29.13
Nine observations on adult male height, Y

Observation number	Y
1	73.7
2	72.9
3	66.7
4	71.8
5	73.1
6	67.8
7	66.1
8	69.1
9	72.0

Again we can find a confidence interval for $m_X - m_Y$. For example, for confidence coefficient $1 - \alpha = .99$, or $\alpha = .01$, the critical value of t with 17 degrees of freedom for a two-tailed test is approximately 2.90 and the confidence limits with 99 per cent confidence coefficient are

$$\overline{X} - \overline{Y} \pm t_\alpha s_{\overline{X} - \overline{Y}} \quad (36)$$

or

$$-1.94 \pm 2.90(1.31) \quad (37)$$

so that

$$-5.74 \leq m_X - m_Y \leq +1.94 \quad (38)$$

That is, the mean of population 1 may be as much as 5.74 inches smaller or as much as 1.94 inches larger than the mean of population 2, at this confidence level.

As we have seen, the methods just described are strictly correct only if population 1 and population 2 have the same variance. However, in practice it is impossible to know whether the populations actually do have the same variance, although we may have some idea as to the relative magnitude of the two variances. If $N_X = N_Y$, then the method just described will be fairly accurate even for individual sample sizes as small as 10 and even if one of the population variances is as much as 3 or 4 times as big as the other. However, if the sample sizes are unequal with, let us say, N_X twice as big as N_Y, then the method just described will be too inaccurate to be useful unless the larger of the two variances is not more than twice as big as the other and unless the smaller of the two sample sizes is at least 10. If the smaller sample size is less than 10, or if the two sample sizes are even more discrepant, then the difference between the two population variances must be less in order to have a satisfactory approximation. If the smaller of the two sample sizes is at least 30, then we may substitute s_X^2 for σ_X^2 and s_Y^2 for σ_Y^2 in the general formula (25) for the variance of the difference of two means and use the table of the normal distribution, regardless of how widely the two population variances differ.

28. THE METHOD OF PAIRED COMPARISONS

Data sometimes appear in a form in which there are pairs of measurements—for example, measurements on the same individual before and after some treatment—and we wish to test whether the true mean is affected by the treatment. Under these conditions, if we subtract the value before from the value after treatment we obtain a new variable which we may call U and which will have mean 0 if, in fact, the treatment had no effect. We can then use the single sample Student's statistic to test the hypothesis that U has mean equal to 0. Table 29.14 shows a set of five observations on a variable X and five on Y, where X is the value after treatment and Y before treatment, and shows the value of U. We find that t = −4.472 with four degrees of freedom, so that .01 < P < .02. We would reject the hypothesis if we had been working at the 5 per cent or 2 per cent level but accept it if we had been working at the 1 per cent level.

TABLE 29.14
Values, X, of a measurement after, and, Y, before treatment, for 5 individuals

Individual number	X	Y	U = X − Y
1	0	1	− 1
2	1	4	− 3
3	2	3	− 1
4	2	5	− 3
5	3	5	− 2

As far as the mechanical work of doing the arithmetic is concerned, Table 29.14 could be analyzed either by the method of paired comparisons or by the two-sample t method discussed in the preceding section. However, given actual data, only one of these methods will be correct in any given situation. The two-sample t method requires that we have two completely independent samples, so that there is no relationship between any observation in the first sample and any observation in the second sample; the method of paired comparisons requires that there be a natural pairing, with each value of X associated with a particular value of Y. Accordingly, a little thought will always determine which of the two methods should be used. Finally, it should be noted that, although the two-sample t method requires that both population variances be equal in order for the t distribution to be strictly applicable, this is not the case in the method of paired comparisons, since here we obtain an estimate of the standard deviation of U directly from the observed values of U.

It is often necessary to compare the means of three or more populations. The technique for doing this is called, strangely enough, the *analysis of variance* and includes methods corresponding to both the two-sample t and the method of paired comparisons. Most statistical texts discuss the analysis of variance at length.

29. THE NORMAL APPROXIMATION TO THE BINOMIAL DISTRIBUTION

If we are dealing with a binomial distribution, where X is the number of successes in N trials and the probability of a success on an individual trial is p, then as we have seen X is approximately normally distributed when N is large. Furthermore, the true mean and variance of X depend in a simple manner on p, with $m_X = Np$ and $\sigma_X^2 = Np(1 - p) = Npq$. Similarly, f will be approximately normally distributed with mean $m_f = p$ and variance $\sigma_f^2 = pq/N$. Accordingly, we can test the hypothesis $H_o : p = p_o$ by simply calculating

$$Z = \frac{X - Np_o}{\sqrt{Np_o(1 - p_o)}} = \frac{f - p_o}{\sqrt{\dfrac{p_o(1 - p_o)}{N}}} \quad (39)$$

and rejecting the hypothesis if Z exceeds the critical value in Table 29.11. The reader should verify that the quantity Z^2 will be precisely equal to the quantity χ^2 for testing the same hypothesis if χ^2 is calculated without Yates' correction. A correction equivalent to Yates' correction can also be applied to Z, but we shall not discuss it here. If Npq is less than 5, the approximate test (39) should be used with caution, and it may be safer to use the exact binomial test.

If N is sufficiently large and p is not too close to 0 or 1—for example, if Npq is greater than 25—then we can get an approximate confidence interval for the value of p by simply calculating

$$f \pm Z_\alpha \sqrt{\frac{f(1-f)}{N}} \tag{40}$$

For greater accuracy, the quantity f under the square root in formula (40) should be replaced by the value of p at the upper confidence limit when we use the plus sign and the value of p at the lower confidence limit when we use the minus sign. However, this would involve a great deal of additional labor, and for N as large as was suggested above it would make very little difference. It is for this reason that we suggest a larger value of N for using this approximation for a confidence interval than for making the simple test of the hypothesis. When Npq is small, confidence intervals for p may be obtained by the exact methods described earlier, or formula (40) may be modified by the use of Table VIII 1 in Fisher and Yates (see References, p. 417).

30. THE STANDARD ERROR

The standard deviation of a statistic such as $\overline{X}$ or f is often referred to as the *standard error* of $\overline{X}$ (or whatever the statistic is) to distinguish it from the standard deviation of a single observation, X. The idea is that the standard deviation is a measure of the *variability* of some character, whereas standard error is a measure of the *reliability* of an estimate of a parameter. Often in scientific papers the standard error is appended to a statistic in the form $\overline{X} \pm s_{\overline{X}}$ or $\overline{X} \pm \sigma_{\overline{X}}$. Thus, for the heights, the mean height in

Table 29.8 might be reported as $67.98 \pm .301$. If this is taken literally it gives a confidence interval with confidence coefficient .68 (corresponding to Z = 1); however, it is customary to multiply mentally by the desired Z_α, for example $Z_{.05} = 2$ approximately.

Some caution must, however, be used in reading such formulas. In some of the older literature, the *probable error*, .6745 times the standard error, corresponding to a confidence interval with confidence coefficient $\frac{1}{2}$, was used in place of the standard error, and in many of these texts there is nothing to indicate which was used. More rarely, especially in purely zoological work, the standard deviation is used, thus 67.98 ± 3.01, in order to show the variability of the population. Other usages also occur.

Finally, it should be noted that to report the mean in Table 29.10 as $68.42 \pm .87$ would be misleading, since it suggests reference to the normal curve, when in fact t with 9 degrees of freedom should be used. A standard error should never be added unless the table of the normal curve is appropriate.

31. THE STUDY OF VARIABILITY

Usually when we are comparing two groups we are interested in how their means differ. However, sometimes we are also interested in the comparison of their variability. As long as we are making comparisons within a single species, we can use the standard deviation. But when we are comparing two species as different as, say, mouse and man, it clearly makes little sense to compare the standard deviations directly. Obviously a man will vary in weight during the course of a single day by more than the total weight of a mouse. One way to circumvent the difference and obtain a reasonable measure of variability which is comparable between widely different forms is to use the *coefficient of variation* (C.V.). The coefficient of variation, v, is simply the standard deviation expressed as a percentage of the mean, or, in symbols,

$$v = 100 \frac{\sigma}{m} \qquad (41)$$

In these terms it makes sense to consider whether mice are more variable or less variable than man.

When the number of observations on which a sample standard deviation, s, is based is 30 or more, s is approximately normally distributed with expected value σ and standard error $\sigma/\sqrt{2N}$. The difference between two sample standard deviations may then be tested for significance by using the results of Section 29.26. For smaller samples, a more exact test in which the ratio of the two sample variances is compared with a critical value from a table of the F distribution must be used. Most statistical texts have such a table.

When N is 30 or more, the coefficient of variation, v, is approximately normally distributed about its true value with standard error

$$\sigma_v = \frac{v}{\sqrt{2N}} \sqrt{1 + 2\left(\frac{v}{100}\right)^2} \qquad (42)$$

provided also that this standard error is no bigger than $\frac{2}{3}$. Other methods for testing the coefficient of variation are beyond the scope of this chapter.

32. TWO TAILS OR ONE?

Up to now we have in every case tacitly assumed that a two-sided, or two-tailed, test was appropriate. Such a test should, in fact, be used whenever the true state of affairs could deviate in either direction from the hypothetical one. To make our ideas more definite, suppose we are testing $H_0: p = p_0$ against the alternative that p may have any value whatever. Then either large or small values of the sample proportion, f, should lead to rejection H_0. Note that the chi-square test, though rejecting only for large χ^2, is actually two-sided in this sense.

Often a scientist expects a departure from p_0 in only one direction say p larger, and is tempted to use a one-sided test, which would have greater power against this alternative. Nevertheless, he might observe a very small f and would then be tempted to change his preconceived ideas, reject H_0 with a statement that p was less than p_0, and invent some explanation for this. Hence, in reality we are almost always using a two-sided test, and this should be taken into account in the formal description of the test.

The author can think of only one exception in genetics. In testing H_0 that a crossover frequency is .5 (independent assortment), a one-sided test may be used on the ground that p > .5 is impossible. Yet even here M. E. Wright has found an f "significantly" greater than .5, and Fisher, Lyon, and Owen then developed a theory for more than 50 per cent crossovers. Although this theory is not generally accepted, the occurrence of p > .5 in this case shows the fallacy of using one-sided tests.

PROBLEMS

Other problems requiring the use of statistical methods are included at the ends of the appropriate chapters.

29.1 In the F_2 of a cross between agouti, AA, and albino, aa, mice there were 11 agouti and 9 albino mice, or 45 per cent albino. Is this in agreement with a 3 : 1 ratio? What would be your answer if there had been 10 of each?

29.2 From a certain cross there were 15 agouti and 5 albino offspring. Calculate an exact upper bound to the probability of an albino with confidence coefficient .97, using Table 29.2. If tables of the binomial distribution are available, give a lower bound also.

29.3 Repeat Problem 29.2, with confidence coefficient .95, using the graph in Figure 29.2.

NOTE: Problems 29.4, 29.5, and 29.6 refer to a cross between certain plants with white and colored flowers, in which an F_2 ratio of 3 colored to 1 white is expected. We wish to test the hypothesis of a 3 : 1 ratio at the 5 per cent level of significance.

29.4 Calculate how many plants would have to be grown before it was *possible* to reject the hypothesis because there were *too many* white plants.

29.5 How many plants would have to be grown before it was *possible* to reject the hypothesis because there were *too few* white plants?

29.6 If tables of the binomial distribution are available, find how many plants would have to be grown to have probability ½ of rejecting the hypothesis if the true ratio were 1 : 1. How many would have to be grown to have a .90 probability of rejection?

29.7 Toss a coin 30 times and count the number of heads. Find confidence intervals with confidence coefficients .80, .95, .99 for the probability of heads. Compare your results with those of other students.

29.8 Use the chi-square method to determine whether there is a real difference in the rate of criminality in co-twins of criminal twins between identical and fraternal twins (data of Table 11.4). Use the total values and also the largest single series (Rosanoff et al.).

29.9 Use the data of Table 11.5 to test whether differences in education affect the differences in IQ between members of pairs of identical twins reared apart. Use the chi-square method for contingency tables (with Yates' correction) by counting the number of pairs falling into each of the empty cells in the table:

Difference in IQ	Difference in education	
	11 or less	12 or more
8 or less		
9 or more		

(*Note:* The method of correlation discussed in statistics texts is more sensitive, when valid, but the method described above is often very useful.)

29.10 An anthropologist studied the ABO blood groups in three primitive tribes. The number of individuals of the different types was:

	O	A	B	AB
Tribe 1	26	40	22	12
Tribe 2	40	90	50	20
Tribe 3	45	50	40	20

Test whether the tribes are significantly different in ABO phenotype frequency.

29.11 Suppose a certain quantitative character is normally distributed in a population, with mean 100 and standard deviation 10. What proportion of individuals will have a value greater than 126; a value less than 85; a value less than 108; a value between 120 and 123? If a more detailed table of the normal distribution is available, compare the results calculated from it with those calculated from Table 29.11.

29.12 The error in a certain chemical analysis is known to be normally distributed with standard deviation 3. The value obtained for this substance in a certain animal is 73. Test the hypothesis that the true value for this animal is 80. Give a confidence interval with confidence coefficient .99 for the true value.

NOTE: Holt, in the Annals of Eugenics, *18,* pp. 211–231, counted the number of fingerprint ridges on the right hands of 254 men and boys and 240 women and girls. The frequency distributions are shown on page 417. (The heading 7 stands for all ridge numbers from 0 to 14, 22 for 15 to 29, etc.)

29.13 Test the hypothesis that the true mean for males is 62. Within what limits can we be 99 per cent sure that the true mean lies for males; for females?

29.14 Is there a real difference between females and males? What is P? Give a confidence interval with 95 per cent confidence

				Number of ridges					
	7	22	37	52	67	82	97	112	127
Males	7	6	30	36	33	65	49	24	2
Females	10	23	26	37	50	50	33	9	2

coefficient for the difference males-minus-females.

29.15 Take 100 cardboard disks and write on them the heights of the 100 men in Table 29.8. Put them in a box or hat, mix them up, and draw one out. Write down the number on the disk, put it back, mix the disks and draw another one. Proceed in this way until you have a sample of 10. This is a random sample of 10 from an infinitely large population with frequencies given by Table 29.8. Test the hypothesis that the true mean in that population is 71, using the Student t test. Give a confidence interval with confidence coefficient .90 for the true mean. Note whether this confidence interval includes the true value of 67.98 (10 per cent of the time it would not).

29.16 Take a second sample of 10 as in Problem 29.15 and test the hypothesis that the two samples come from populations with the same mean (assume the variances are the same). Give a confidence interval for the difference, with confidence coefficient .95. Compare your results in Problems 29.15 and 29.16 with those arrived at by other students.

29.17 Give a confidence interval with confidence coefficient .95 for the true standard deviation in the population of men, based on the sample of 100 in Table 29.8.

29.18 Calculate the coefficient of variation for the 100 male heights in Table 29.8 and give a confidence interval with confidence coefficient .95 for the true value.

REFERENCES

Clopper, C. J., and E. S. Pearson. 1934. The use of confidence or fiducial limits illustrated in the case of the binomial. Biometrika, 26: 404–413.

Dixon, W. J., and F. J. Massey, Jr. 1957. Introduction to Statistical Analysis, 2d ed. McGraw-Hill Book Company, Inc., New York.

Fisher, R. A. Many eds. Statistical Methods for Research Workers. Oliver & Boyd, Ltd., London.

Fisher, R. A., M. F. Lyon, and A. R. G. Owen. 1947. The sex chromosome in the house mouse. Heredity, 1 : 355–365.

——— and F. Yates. Statistical Tables for Biological, Agricultural, and Medical Research, many eds. Oliver & Boyd, Ltd., London.

Hoel, P. G. 1954. Introduction to Mathematical Statistics, 2d ed. John Wiley & Sons, Inc., New York.

Pearson, E. A., and H. O. Hartley. 1954. Biometrika Tables for Statisticians. Cambridge University Press, Cambridge, England.

1955. Tables of the cumulative binomial probability distribution. The Annals of the Computation Laboratory of Harvard University, XXXV, Cambridge, Mass.

United States Army Ordnance Corps. 1952. Tables of the Cumulative Binomial Probabilities. Ordnance Corps Pamphlet ORDP 20–1. Distributed by Department of Commerce, Office of Technical Services, Washington.

United States Department of Commerce. 1950. Tables of the Binomial Probability Distribution. National Bureau of Standards, Appl. Math. Series 6.

Walker, H. M., and J. Lev. 1953. Statistical Inference. Henry Holt and Company, Inc., New York.

Warwick, B. E. 1932. Probability Tables for Mendelian Ratios with Small Numbers. Texas Agricultural Experiment Station Bulletin 463.

Wilks, S. S. 1948. Elementary Statistical Analysis. Princeton University Press, Princeton, N.J.

Wright, M. E., 1947. Two sex linkages in the house mouse, with unusual recombination values. Heredity 1:349–354.

APPENDIX

Experiments in Plant Hybridization [1]

BY GREGOR MENDEL

(*Read at the Meetings of the 8th February and 8th March, 1865.*)

INTRODUCTORY REMARKS

EXPERIENCE of artificial fertilization, such as is effected with ornamental plants in order to obtain new variations in color, has led to the experiments which will here be discussed. The striking regularity with which the same hybrid forms always reappeared whenever fertilization took place between the same species induced further experiments to be undertaken, the object of which was to follow up the developments of the hybrids in their progeny.

To this object numerous careful observers,

[1] This translation was made by the Royal Horticultural Society of London, and is reprinted, by permission of the Council of the Society, with footnotes added and minor changes suggested by Professor W. Bateson, enclosed within [ ]. The original paper was published in the *Verhandlungen naturforschender Verein in Brünn, Abhandlungen*, iv. 1865, which appeared in 1866.

such as Kölreuter, Gärtner, Herbert, Lecoq, Wichura, and others, have devoted a part of their lives with inexhaustible perseverance. Gärtner especially, in his work "Die Bastarderzeugung im Pflanzenreiche" (The Production of Hybrids in the Vegetable Kingdom), has recorded very valuable observations; and quite recently Wichura published the results of some profound investigations into the hybrids of the willow. That, so far, no generally applicable law governing the formation and development of hybrids has been successfully formulated can hardly be wondered at by anyone who is acquainted with the extent of the task and can appreciate the difficulties with which experiments of this class have to contend. A final decision can only be arrived at when we shall have before us the results of detailed experiments made on plants belonging to the most diverse orders.

Those who survey the work done in this

department will arrive at the conviction that among all the numerous experiments made, not one has been carried out to such an extent and in such a way as to make it possible to determine the number of different forms under which the offspring of hybrids appear, or to arrange these forms with certainty according to their separate generations, or definitely to ascertain their statistical relations.[1]

It requires indeed some courage to undertake a labor of such far-reaching extent; this appears, however, to be the only right way by which we can finally reach the solution of a question the importance of which cannot be overestimated in connection with the history of the evolution of organic forms.

The paper now presented records the results of such a detailed experiment. This experiment was practically confined to a small plant group and is now, after eight years' pursuit, concluded in all essentials. Whether the plan upon which separate experiments were conducted and carried out was the best suited to attain the desired end is left to the friendly decision of the reader.

SELECTION OF THE EXPERIMENTAL PLANTS

The value and utility of any experiment are determined by the fitness of the material to the purpose for which it is used, and thus in the case before us it cannot be immaterial what plants are subjected to experiment and in what manner such experiments are conducted.

The selection of the plant group which shall serve for experiments of this kind must be made with all possible care if it be desired to avoid from the outset every risk of questionable results.

The experimental plants must necessarily—

1. Possess constant differentiating characters.

2. The hybrids of such plants must, during the flowering period, be protected from

[1] [It is to the clear conception of these three primary necessities that the whole success of Mendel's work is due. So far as I know this conception was absolutely new in his day.]

the influence of all foreign pollen or be easily capable of such protection.

The hybrids and their offspring should suffer no marked disturbance in their fertility in the successive generations.

Accidental impregnation by foreign pollen, if it occurred during the experiments and were not recognized, would lead to entirely erroneous conclusions. Reduced fertility or entire sterility of certain forms, such as occurs in the offspring of many hybrids, would render the experiments very difficult or entirely frustrate them. In order to discover the relations in which the hybrid forms stand towards each other and also towards their progenitors it appears to be necessary that all members of the series developed in each successive generation should be, *without exception,* subjected to observation.

At the very outset special attention was devoted to the Leguminosae on account of their peculiar floral structure. Experiments which were made with several members of this family led to the result that the genus Pisum was found to possess the necessary qualifications.

Some thoroughly distinct forms of this genus possess characters which are constant, and easily and certainly recognizable, and when their hybrids are mutually crossed they yield perfectly fertile progeny. Furthermore, a disturbance through foreign pollen cannot easily occur, since the fertilizing organs are closely packed inside the keel and the anther bursts within the bud, so that the stigma becomes covered with pollen even before the flower opens. This circumstance is of especial importance. As additional advantages worth mentioning, there may be cited the easy culture of these plants in the open ground and in pots, and also their relatively short period of growth. Artificial fertilization is certainly a somewhat elaborate process but nearly always succeeds. For this purpose the bud is opened before it is perfectly developed, the keel is removed, and each stamen carefully extracted by means of forceps, after which the stigma can at once be dusted over with the foreign pollen.

In all, 34 more or less distinct varieties of peas were obtained from several seedsmen and subjected to a two years' trial. In the case of one variety there were noticed, among a larger number of plants all alike, a few forms which were markedly different. These, however, did not vary in the following year and agreed entirely with another variety obtained from the same seedsman; the seeds were therefore doubtless merely accidentally mixed. All the other varieties yielded perfectly constant and similar offspring; at any rate, no essential difference was observed during two trial years. For fertilization, 22 of these were selected and cultivated during the whole period of the experiments. They remained constant without any exception.

Their systematic classification is difficult and uncertain. If we adopt the strictest definition of a species, according to which only those individuals belong to a species which under precisely the same circumstances display precisely similar characters, no two of these varieties could be referred to one species. According to the opinion of experts, however, the majority belong to the species *Pisum sativum,* while the rest are regarded and classed, some as subspecies of *P. sativum* and some as independent species, such as *P. quadratum, P. saccharatum,* and *P. umbellatum.* The positions, however, which may be assigned to them in a classificatory system are quite immaterial for the purposes of the experiments in question. It has so far been found to be just as impossible to draw a sharp line between the hybrids of species and varieties as between species and varieties themselves.

DIVISION AND ARRANGEMENT OF THE EXPERIMENTS

If two plants which differ constantly in one or several characters be crossed, numerous experiments have demonstrated that the common characters are transmitted unchanged to the hybrids and their progeny; but each pair of differentiating characters, on the other hand, unite in the hybrid to form a new character, which in the progeny of the hybrid is usually variable. The object of the experiment was to observe these variations in the case of each pair of differentiat-

ing characters and to deduce the law according to which they appear in the successive generations. The experiment resolves itself therefore into just as many separate experiments as there are constantly differentiating characters presented in the experimental plants.

The various forms of peas selected for crossing showed differences in the length and color of the stem; in the size and form of the leaves; in the position, color, and size of the flowers; in the length of the flower stalk; in the color, form, and size of the pods; in the form and size of the seeds; and in the color of the seed coats and of the albumen [cotyledons]. Some of the characters noted do not permit of a sharp and certain separation, since the difference is of a "more or less" nature, which is often difficult to define. Such characters could not be utilized for the separate experiments; these could only be applied to characters which stand out clearly and definitely in the plants. Lastly, the result must show whether they, in their entirety, observe a regular behavior in their hybrid unions and whether from these facts any conclusion can be come to regarding those characters which possess a subordinate significance in the type.

The characters which were selected for experiment relate:

1. To the *difference in the form of the ripe seeds.* These are either round or roundish, the depressions, if any, occurring on the surface, being always only shallow; or they are irregularly angular and deeply wrinkled (*P. quadratum*).

2. To the *difference in the color of the seed albumen* (endosperm).[1] The albumen of the ripe seeds is either pale-yellow, bright yellow-and-orange colored, or . . . [of] a more or less intense green tint. This difference of color is easily seen in the seeds as [= if] their coats are transparent.

3. To the *difference in the color of the seed coat.* This is either white, with which character white flowers are constantly corre-

---

[1] [Mendel uses the terms "albumen" and "endosperm" somewhat loosely to denote the cotyledons, containing food material, within the seed.]

lated; or it is gray, gray-brown, leather-brown, with or without violet spotting, in which case the color of the standards is violet, that of the wings purple, and the stem in the axils of the leaves is of a reddish tint. The gray seed coats become dark brown in boiling water.

4. To the *difference in the form of the ripe pods*. These are either simply inflated, not contracted in places; or they are deeply constricted between the seeds and more or less wrinkled (*P. saccharatum*).

5. To the *difference in the color of the unripe pods*. They are either light to dark green, or vividly yellow, in which coloring the stalks, leaf veins, and calyx participate.[1]

6. To the *difference in the position of the flowers*. They are either axial, that is, distributed along the main stem; or they are terminal, that is, bunched at the top of the stem and arranged almost in a false umbel; in this case the upper part of the stem is more or less widened in section (*P. umbellatum*).[2]

7. To the *difference in the length of the stem*. The length of the stem [3] is very various in some forms; it is, however, a constant character for each, in so far that healthy plants, grown in the same soil, are only subject to unimportant variations in this character.

In experiments with this character, in order to be able to discriminate with certainty, the long axis of 6 to 7 ft. was always crossed with the short one of ¾ ft. to 1½ ft.

Each two of the differentiating characters

[1] One species possesses a beautifully brownish-red colored pod, which when ripening turns to violet and blue. Trials with this character were only begun last year. [Of these further experiments it seems no account was published. Correns has since worked with such a variety.]

[2] [This is often called the mummy pea. It shows slight fasciation. The form I know has white standard and salmon-red wings.]

[3] [In my account of these experiments (*R.H.S. Journal*, vol. xxv, p. 54) I misunderstood this paragraph and took "axis" to mean the *floral* axis, instead of the main axis of the plant. The unit of measurement, being indicated in the original by a dash (′), I carelessly took to have been an *inch*, but the translation here given is evidently correct.]

enumerated above were united by cross fertilization. There were made for the

1st trial	60 fertilizations on	15 plants
2nd trial	58 fertilizations on	10 plants
3rd trial	35 fertilizations on	10 plants
4th trial	40 fertilizations on	10 plants
5th trial	23 fertilizations on	5 plants
6th trial	34 fertilizations on	10 plants
7th trial	37 fertilizations on	10 plants

From a larger number of plants of the same variety only the most vigorous were chosen for fertilization. Weakly plants always afford uncertain results, because even in the first generation of hybrids, and still more so in the subsequent ones, many of the offspring either entirely fail to flower or only form a few and inferior seeds.

Furthermore, in all the experiments reciprocal crossings were effected in such a way that each of the two varieties which in one set of fertilization served as seed bearer in the other set was used as the pollen plant.

The plants were grown in garden beds, a few also in pots, and were maintained in their naturally upright position by means of sticks, branches of trees, and strings stretched between. For each experiment a number of pot plants were placed during the blooming period in a greenhouse, to serve as control plants for the main experiment in the open as regards possible disturbance by insects. Among the insects [4] which visit peas the beetle *Bruchus pisi* might be detrimental to the experiments should it appear in numbers. The female of this species is known to lay the eggs in the flower, and in so doing opens the keel; upon the tarsi of one specimen, which was caught in a flower, some pollen grains could clearly be seen under a lens. Mention must also be made of a circumstance which possibly might lead to the introduction of foreign pollen. It occurs, for instance, in some rare cases that certain parts of an otherwise quite normally developed flower wither, resulting in a partial exposure of the fertilizing organs. A defective develop-

[4] [It is somewhat surprising that no mention is made of thrips, which swarm in pea flowers. I had come to the conclusion that this is a real source of error and I see Laxton held the same opinion.]

ment of the keel has also been observed, owing to which the stigma and anthers remained partially uncovered.[1] It also sometimes happens that the pollen does not reach full perfection. In this event there occurs a gradual lengthening of the pistil during the blooming period, until the stigmatic tip protrudes at the point of the keel. This remarkable appearance has also been observed in hybrids of Phaseolus and Lathyrus.

The risk of false impregnation by foreign pollen is, however, a very slight one with Pisum, and is quite incapable of disturbing the general result. Among more than 10,000 plants which were carefully examined there were only a very few cases where an indubitable false impregnation had occurred. Since in the greenhouse such a case was never remarked, it may well be supposed that *Bruchus pisi,* and possibly also the described abnormalities in the floral structure, were to blame.

[F₁] TH FORMS OF THE HYBRIDS [2]
Experiments which in previous years were made with ornamental plants have already afforded evidence that the hybrids, as a rule, are not exactly intermediate between the parental species. With some of the more striking characters, those, for instance, which relate to the form and size of the leaves, the pubescence of the several parts, etc., the intermediate, indeed, is nearly always to be seen; in other cases, however, one of the two parental characters is so preponderant that it is difficult, or quite impossible, to detect the other in the hybrid.

This is precisely the case with the pea hybrids. In the case of each of the seven crosses the hybrid character resembles [3] that of one of the parental forms so closely that the other either escapes observation completely or cannot be detected with certainty. This circumstance is of great importance in the determination and classification of the forms under which the offspring of the hybrids appear. Henceforth in this paper those characters which are transmitted entire, or almost unchanged in the hybridization, and therefore in themselves constitute the characters of the hybrid, are termed the *dominant,* and those which become latent in the process *recessive.* The expression "recessive" has been chosen because the characters thereby designated withdraw or entirely disappear in the hybrids, but nevertheless reappear unchanged in their progeny, as will be demonstrated later on.

It was furthermore shown by the whole of the experiments that it is perfectly immaterial whether the dominant character belongs to the seed bearer or to the pollen parent; the form of the hybrid remains identical in both cases. This interesting fact was also emphasized by Gärtner, with the remark that even the most practiced expert is not in a position to determine in a hybrid which of the two parental species was the seed or the pollen plant.[4]

Of the differentiating characters which were used in the experiments the following are dominant:

1. The round or roundish form of the seed with or without shallow depressions.

2. The yellow coloring of the seed albumen [cotyledons].

3. The gray, gray-brown, or leather-brown color of the seed coat, in association with violet-red blossoms and reddish spots in the leaf axils.

4. The simply inflated form of the pod.

5 The green coloring of the unripe pod in association with the same color in the stems, the leaf veins, and the calyx.

6. The distribution of the flowers along the stem.

7. The greater length of stem.

With regard to this last character it must be stated that the longer of the two parental stems is usually exceeded by the hybrid, a fact which is possibly only attributable to the greater luxuriance which appears in all parts of plants when stems of very different length

[1] [This also happens in sweet peas.]

[2] [Mendel throughout speaks of his crossbred peas as "hybrids," a term which many restrict to the offspring of two distinct *species.* He, as he explains, held this to be only a question of degree.]

[3] [Note that Mendel, with true penetration, avoids speaking of the hybrid character as "transmitted" by either parent, thus escaping the error pervading the older views of heredity.]

[4] [Gärtner, p. 223.]

are crossed. Thus, for instance, in repeated experiments, stems of 1 ft. and 6 ft. in length yielded without exception hybrids which varied in length between 6 ft. and 7½ ft.

The hybrid seeds in the experiments with seed coat are often more spotted and the spots sometimes coalesce into small bluish-violet patches, The spotting also frequently appears even when it is absent as a parental character.[1]

The hybrid forms of the seed shape and of the albumen [color] are developed immediately after the artificial fertilization by the mere influence of the foreign pollen. They can, therefore, be observed even in the first year of experiment, whilst all the other characters naturally only appear in the following year in such plants as have been raised from the crossed seed.

[F₂] THE GENERATION [BRED] FROM THE HYBRIDS

In this generation there reappear, together with the dominant characters, also the recessive ones with their peculiarities fully developed, and this occurs in the definitely expressed average proportion of three to one, so that among each four plants of this generation three display the dominant character and one the recessive. This relates without exception to all the characters which were investigated in the experiments. The angular wrinkled form of the seed, the green color of the albumen, the white color of the seed coats and the flowers, the constrictions of the pods, the yellow color of the unripe pod, of the stalk, of the calyx, and of the leaf venation, the umbel-like form of the inflorescence, and the dwarfed stem, all reappear in the numerical proportion given, without any essential alteration. *Transitional forms were not observed in any experiment.*

Since the hybrids resulting from reciprocal crosses are formed alike and present no appreciable difference in their subsequent development, consequently the results [of the reciprocal crosses] can be reckoned together in each experiment. The relative numbers

[1] [This refers to the coats of the seeds borne by *F₁* plants.]

which were obtained for each pair of differentiating characters are as follows:

Expt. 1. Form of seed.—From 253 hybrids 7,324 seeds were obtained in the second trial year. Among them were 5,474 round or roundish ones and 1,850 angular wrinkled ones. Therefrom the ratio 2.96 to 1 is deduced.

Expt. 2. Color of albumen.—258 plants yielded 8,023 seeds, 6,022 yellow, and 2,001 green; their ratio, therefore, is as 3.01 to 1.

In these two experiments each pod yielded usually both kinds of seeds. In well-developed pods which contained on the average six to nine seeds, it often happened that all the seeds were round (Expt. 1) or all yellow (Expt. 2); on the other hand there were never observed more than five wrinkled or five green ones in one pod. It appears to make no difference whether the pods are developed early or later in the hybrid or whether they spring from the main axis or from a lateral one. In some few plants only a few seeds developed in the first formed pods, and these possessed exclusively one of the two characters, but in the subsequently developed pods the normal proportions were maintained nevertheless.

As in separate pods, so did the distribution of the characters vary in separate plants. By way of illustration the first 10 individuals from both series of experiments may serve.

As extremes in the distribution of the two seed characters in one plant, there were ob-

EXPERIMENT 1

	Form of seed	
Plants	Round	Angular
1	45	12
2	27	8
3	24	7
4	19	10
5	32	11
6	26	6
7	88	24
8	22	10
9	28	6
10	25	7

EXPERIMENT 2

Color of albumen	
Yellow	Green
25	11
32	7
14	5
70	27
24	13
20	6
32	13
44	9
50	14
44	18

served in Expt. 1 an instance of 43 round and only 2 angular, and another of 14 round and 15 angular seeds. In Expt. 2 there was a case of 32 yellow and only 1 green seed, but also one of 20 yellow and 19 green.

These two experiments are important for the determination of the average ratios, because with a smaller number of experimental plants they show that very considerable fluctuations may occur. In counting the seeds, also, especially in Expt. 2, some care is requisite, since in some of the seeds of many plants the green color of the albumen is less developed, and at first may be easily overlooked. The cause of this partial disappearance of the green coloring has no connection with the hybrid character of the plants, as it likewise occurs in the parental variety. This peculiarity [bleaching] is also confined to the individual and is not inherited by the offspring. In luxuriant plants this appearance was frequently noted. Seeds which are damaged by insects during their development often vary in color and form, but, with a little practice in sorting, errors are easily avoided. It is almost superfluous to mention that the pods must remain on the plants until they are thoroughly ripened and have become dried, since it is only then that the shape and color of the seed are fully developed.

Expt. 3. Color of the seed coats.—Among 929 plants 705 bore violet-red flowers and gray-brown seed coats; 224 had white flowers and white seed coats, giving the proportion 3.15 to 1.

Expt. 4. Form of pods.—Of 1,181 plants 882 had them simply inflated, and in 299 they were constricted. Resulting ratio, 2.95 to 1.

Expt. 5. Color of the unripe pods.—The number of trial plants was 580, of which 428 had green pods and 152 yellow ones. Consequently these stand in the ratio 2.82 to 1.

Expt. 6. Position of flowers.—Among 858 cases 651 had inflorescences axial and 207 terminal. Ratio, 3.14 to 1.

Expt. 7. Length of stem.—Out of 1,064 plants, in 787 cases the stem was long, and in 277 short. Hence a mutual ratio of 2.84 to 1. In this experiment the dwarfed plants were carefully lifted and transferred to a special bed. This precaution was necessary, as otherwise they would have perished through being overgrown by their tall relatives. Even in their quite young state they can be easily picked out by their compact growth and thick dark-green foliage.[1]

If now the results of the whole of the experiments be brought together, there is found, as between the number of forms with the dominant and recessive characters, an average ratio of 2.98 to 1, or 3 to 1.

The dominant character can have here a *double signification*—viz. that of a parental character, or a hybrid character.[2] In which of the two significations it appears in each separate case can only be determined by the following generation. As a parental character it must pass over unchanged to the whole of the offspring; as a hybrid character, on the other hand, it must maintain the same behavior as in the first generation [F_2].

[F_3] THE SECOND GENERATION [BRED] FROM THE HYBRIDS

Those forms which in the first generation [F_2] exhibit the recessive character do not

---

[1] [This is true also of the dwarf or "Cupid" sweet peas.]

[2] [This paragraph presents the view of the hybrid character as something incidental to the hybrid and not "transmitted" to it—a true and fundamental conception here expressed probably for the first time.]

further vary in the second generation [F_3] as regards this character; they remain constant in their offspring.

It is otherwise with those which possess the dominant character in the first generation [bred from the hybrids]. Of these, *two*-thirds yield offspring which display the dominant and recessive characters in the proportion of 3 to 1 and thereby show exactly the same ratio as the hybrid forms, while only *one*-third remains with the dominant character constant.

The separate experiments yielded the following results:

Expt. 1. Among 565 plants which were raised from round seeds of the first generation, 193 yielded round seeds only and remained therefore constant in this character; 372, however, gave both round and wrinkled seeds, in the proportion of 3 to 1. The number of the hybrids, therefore, as compared with the constants, is 1.93 to 1.

Expt. 2. Of 519 plants which were raised from seeds whose albumen was of yellow color in the first generation, 166 yielded exclusively yellow, while 353 yielded yellow and green seeds in the proportion of 3 to 1. There resulted, therefore, a division into hybrid and constant forms in the proportion of 2.13 to 1.

For each separate trial in the following experiments 100 plants were selected which displayed the dominant character in the first generation, and in order to ascertain the significance of this, ten seeds of each were cultivated.

Expt. 3. The offspring of 36 plants yielded exclusively gray-brown seed coats, while of the offspring of 64 plants, some had gray-brown and some had white.

Expt. 4. The offspring of 29 plants had only simply inflated pods; of the offspring of 71, on the other hand, some had inflated and some constricted.

Expt. 5. The offspring of 40 plants had only green pods; of the offspring of 60 plants some had green, some yellow ones.

Expt. 6. The offspring of 33 plants had only axial flowers; of the offspring of 67, on the other hand, some had axial and some terminal flowers.

Expt. 7. The offspring of 28 plants inherited the long axis, and those of 72 plants some the long and some the short axis.

In each of these experiments a certain number of the plants came constant with the dominant character. For the determination of the proportion in which the separation of the forms with the constantly persistent character results, the two first experiments are of especial importance, since in these a larger number of plants can be compared. The ratios 1.93 to 1 and 2.13 to 1 gave together almost exactly the average ratio of 2 to 1. The sixth experiment gave a quite concordant result; in the others the ratio varies more or less, as was only to be expected in view of the smaller number of 100 trial plants. Experiment 5, which shows the greatest departure, was repeated, and then, in lieu of the ratio of 60 and 40, that of 65 and 35 resulted. *The average ratio of 2 to 1 appears, therefore, as fixed with certainty.* It is therefore demonstrated that, of those forms which possess the dominant character in the first generation, two-thirds have the hybrid character, while one-third remains constant with the dominant character.

The ratio of 3 to 1, in accordance with which the distribution of the dominant and recessive characters results in the first generation, resolves itself therefore in all experiments into the ratio of 2 : 1 : 1 if the dominant character be differentiated according to its significance as a hybrid character or as a parental one. Since the members of the first generation [F_2] spring directly from the seed of the hybrids [F_1], *it is now clear that the hybrids form seeds having one or other of the two differentiating characters,*[1] *and of these one-half develop again the hybrid form, while the other half yield plants which remain constant and receive the dominant or the recessive characters* [*respectively*] *in equal numbers.*

THE SUBSEQUENT GENERATIONS [BRED] FROM THE HYBRIDS

The proportions in which the descendants of the hybrids develop and split up in the

[1] This is the Principle of Segregation (cf. Chap. 3).

first and second generations presumably hold good for all subsequent progeny. Experiments 1 and 2 have already been carried through six generations, 3 and 7 through five, and 4, 5, and 6 through four, these experiments being continued from the third generation with a small number of plants, and no departure from the rule has been perceptible. The offspring of the hybrids separated in each generation in the ratio of 2 : 1 : 1 into hybrids and constant forms.

If *A* be taken as denoting one of the two constant characters, for instance the dominant, *a*, the recessive, and *Aa* the hybrid form in which both are conjoined, the expression

$$A + 2Aa + a$$

shows the terms in the series for the progeny of the hybrids of two differentiating characters.

The observation made by Gärtner, Kölreuter, and others, that hybrids are inclined to revert to the parental forms, is also confirmed by the experiments described. It is seen that the number of the hybrids which arise from one fertilization, as compared with the number of forms which become constant, and their progeny from generation to generation, is continually diminishing, but that nevertheless they could not entirely disappear. If an average equality of fertility in all plants in all generations be assumed, and if, furthermore, each hybrid forms seed of which one-half yields hybrids again, while the other half is constant to both characters in equal proportions, the ratio of numbers for the offspring in each generation is seen by the following summary, in which *A* and *a* denote again the two parental characters, and *Aa* the hybrid forms. For brevity's sake it may be assumed that each plant in each generation furnishes only 4 seeds.

In the tenth generation, for instance, $2^n - 1 = 1,023$. There result, therefore, in each 2,048 plants which arise in this generation 1,023 with the constant dominant character, 1,023 with the recessive character, and only two hybrids.

				Ratios
Generation	*A*	*Aa*	*a*	*A* : *Aa* : *a*
1	1	2	1	1 : 2 : 1
2	6	4	6	3 : 2 : 3
3	28	8	28	7 : 2 : 7
4	120	16	120	15 : 2 : 15
5	496	32	496	31 : 2 : 31
n				$2^n - 1$: 2 : $2^n - 1$

THE OFFSPRING OF HYBRIDS IN WHICH SEVERAL DIFFERENTIATING CHARACTERS ARE ASSOCIATED

In the experiments described above plants were used which differed only in one essential character.[1] The next task consisted in ascertaining whether the law of development discovered in these applied to each pair of differentiating characters when several diverse characters are united in the hybrid by crossing. As regards the form of the hybrids in these cases, the experiments showed throughout that this invariably more nearly approaches to that one of the two parental plants which possesses the greater number of dominant characters. If, for instance, the seed plant has a short stem, terminal white flowers, and simply inflated pods; the pollen plant, on the other hand, a long stem, violet-red flowers distributed along the stem, and constricted pods; the hybrid resembles the seed parent only in the form of the pod; in the other characters it agrees with the pollen parent. Should one of the two parental types possess only dominant characters, then the hybrid is scarcely or not at all distinguishable from it.

Two experiments were made with a considerable number of plants. In the first experiment the parental plants differed in the

[1] [This statement of Mendel's in the light of present knowledge is open to some misconception. Though his work makes it evident that such varieties may exist, it is very unlikely that Mendel could have had seven pairs of varieties such that the members of each pair differed from each other in *only* one considerable character (*wesentliches Merkmal*). The point is probably of little theoretical or practical consequence, but a rather heavy stress is thrown on *"wesentlich."*]

form of the seed and in the color of the albumen; in the second in the form of the seed, in the color of the albumen, and in the color of the seed coats. Experiments with seed characters give the result in the simplest and most certain way.

In order to facilitate study of the data in these experiments, the different characters of the seed plant will be indicated by *A, B, C,* those of the pollen plant by *a, b, c,* and the hybrid forms of the characters by *Aa, Bb,* and *Cc.*

EXPERIMENT 1

AB, seed parents;	*ab,* pollen parents;
A, form round;	*a,* form wrinkled;
B, albumen yellow.	*b,* albumen green.

The fertilized seeds appeared round and yellow like those of the seed parents. The plants raised therefrom yielded seeds of four sorts, which frequently presented themselves in one pod. In all, 556 seeds were yielded by 15 plants, and of these there were:

315 round and yellow,
101 wrinkled and yellow,
108 round and green,
32 wrinkled and green.

All were sown the following year. Eleven of the round yellow seeds did not yield plants, and three plants did not form seeds. Among the rest:

38 had round yellow seeds	*AB*
65 round yellow and green seeds	*ABb*
60 round yellow and wrinkled yellow seeds	*AaB*
138 round yellow and green, wrinkled yellow and green seeds	*AaBb*

From the wrinkled yellow seeds 96 resulting plants bore seed, of which:

28 had only wrinkled yellow seeds	*aB*
68 wrinkled yellow and green seeds	*aBb*

From 108 round green seeds 102 resulting plants fruited, of which:

35 had only round green seeds	*Ab*
67 round and wrinkled green seeds	*Aab*

The wrinkled green seeds yielded 30 plants which bore seeds all of like character; they remained constant *ab.*

The offspring of the hybrids appeared therefore under nine different forms, some of them in very unequal numbers. When these are collected and coordinated we find:

38 plants with the sign *AB*
35 plants with the sign *Ab*
28 plants with the sign *aB*
30 plants with the sign *ab*
65 plants with the sign *ABb*
68 plants with the sign *aBb*
60 plants with the sign *AaB*
67 plants with the sign *Aab*
138 plants with the sign *AaBb*

The whole of the forms may be classed into three essentially different groups. The first includes those with the signs *AB, Ab, aB,* and *ab:* they possess only constant characters and do not vary again in the next generation. Each of these forms is represented on the average 33 times. The second group includes the signs *ABb, aBb, AaB, Aab:* these are constant in one character and hybrid in another and vary in the next generation only as regards the hybrid character. Each of these appears on an average 65 times. The form *AaBb* occurs 138 times: it is hybrid in both characters, and behaves exactly as do the hybrids from which it is derived.

If the numbers in which the forms belonging to these classes appear be compared, the ratios of 1, 2, 4 are unmistakably evident. The numbers 38, 65, 138 present very fair approximations to the ratio numbers of 33, 66, 132.

The developmental series consists, therefore, of nine classes, of which four appear therein always once and are constant in both characters; the forms *AB, ab,* resemble the parental forms, the two other present combinations between the conjoined characters *A, a, B, b,* which combinations are likewise possibly constant. Four classes appear always twice and are constant in one character and hybrid in the other. One class appears four times and is hybrid in both characters. Consequently the offspring of the hybrids, if two kinds of differentiating characters are combined therein, are represented by the expression

$$AB + Ab + aB + ab + 2ABb + 2aBb$$
$$+ 2Aab + 2Aab + 4AaBb$$

This expression is indisputably a combination series in which the two expressions for the characters A and a, B and b are combined. We arrive at the full number of the classes of the series by the combination of the expressions:

$$A + 2Aa + a$$
$$B + 2Bb + b$$

EXPERIMENT 2

ABC, seed parents; abc, pollen parents;
   A, form round; a, form wrinkled;
   B, albumen yellow; b, albumen green;
   C, seed-coat gray- c, seed-coat white.
      brown.

This experiment was made in precisely the same way as the previous one. Among all the experiments it demanded the most time and trouble. From 24 hybrids 687 seeds were obtained in all: these were all either spotted, gray-brown or gray-green, round or wrinkled.[1] From these in the following year 639 plants fruited, and, as further investigation showed, there were among them:

8 plants ABC	22 plants $ABCc$
14 plants ABc	17 plants $AbCc$
9 plants AbC	25 plants $aBCc$
11 plants Abc	20 plants $abCc$
8 plants aBC	15 plants $ABbC$
10 plants aBc	18 plants $ABbc$
10 plants abC	19 plants $aBbC$
7 plants abc	24 plants $aBbc$
	14 plants $AaBC$
	18 plants $AaBc$
45 plants $ABbCc$	20 plants $AabC$
36 plants $aBbCc$	16 plants $Aabc$
38 plants $AaBCc$	
40 plants $AabCc$	
49 plants $AaBbC$	78 plants $AaBbCc$
48 plants $AaBbc$	

[1] [Note that Mendel does not state the cotyledon color of the first crosses in this case; for as the coats were thick, it could not have been seen without opening or peeling the seeds.]

The whole expression contains 27 terms. Of these 8 are constant in all characters, and each appears on the average 10 times; 12 are constant in two characters and hybrid in the third; each appears on the average 19 times; 6 are constant in one character and hybrid in the other two; each appears on the average 43 times. One form appears 78 times and is hybrid in all of the characters. The ratios 10, 19, 43, 78 agree so closely with the ratios 10, 20, 40, 80, or 1, 2, 4, 8, that this last undoubtedly represents the true value.

The development of the hybrids when the original parents differ in three characters results therefore according to the following expression:

$$ABC + ABc + AbC + Abc + aBC$$
$$+ aBc + abC + abc$$
$$+ 2ABCc + 2AbCc + 2aBCc + 2abCc$$
$$+ 2ABbC$$
$$+ 2ABbc + 2aBbC + 2aBbc + 2AaBC$$
$$+ 2AaBc$$
$$+ 2AabC + 2Aabc + 4ABbCc$$
$$+ 4aBbCc + 4AaBCc$$
$$+ 4AabCc + 4AaBbC + 4AaBbc$$
$$+ 8ABabCc.$$

Here also is involved a combination series in which the expressions for the characters A and a, B and b, C and c, are united. The expressions

$$A + 2Aa + a$$
$$B + 2Bb + b$$
$$C + 2Cc + c$$

give all the classes of the series. The constant combinations which occur therein agree with all combinations which are possible between the characters A, B, C, a, b, c; two thereof, ABC and abc, resemble the two original parental stocks.

In addition, further experiments were made with a smaller number of experimental plants in which the remaining characters by twos and threes were united as hybrids: all yielded approximately the same results. There is therefore no doubt that for the whole of the characters involved in the experiments the principle applies that *the off-*

spring of the hybrids in which several essentially different characters are combined exhibit the terms of a series of combinations, in which the developmental series for each pair of differentiating characters are united. It is demonstrated at the same time that *the relation of each pair of different characters in hybrid union is independent of the other differences in the two original parental stocks.*[1]

If n represents the number of the differentiating characters in the two original stocks, 3^n gives the number of terms of the combination series, 4^n the number of individuals which belong to the series, and 2^n the number of unions which remain constant. The series therefore contains, if the original stocks differ in four characters, $3^4 = 81$ classes, $4^4 = 256$ individuals, and $2^4 = 16$ constant forms; or which is the same, among each 256 offspring of the hybrids there are 81 different combinations, 16 of which are constant.

All constant combinations which in peas are possible by the combination of the said seven differentiating characters were actually obtained by repeated crossing. Their number is given by $2^7 = 128$. Thereby is simultaneously given the practical proof *that the constant characters which appear in the several varieties of a group of plants may be obtained in all the associations which are possible according to the [mathematical] laws of combination, by means of repeated artificial fertilization.*

As regards the flowering time of the hybrids, the experiments are not yet concluded. It can, however, already be stated that the time stands almost exactly between those of the seed and pollen parents and that the constitution of the hybrids with respect to this character probably follows the rule ascertained in the case of the other characters. The forms which are selected for experiments of this class must have a difference of at least 20 days from the middle flowering period of one to that of the other; furthermore, the seeds when sown must all be placed at the same depth in the earth, so that they may germinate simultaneously. Also,

[1] This is the Principle of Independent Assortment (cf. Chap. 6).

during the whole flowering period, the more important variations in temperature must be taken into account, and the partial hastening or delaying of the flowering which may result therefrom. It is clear that this experiment presents many difficulties to be overcome and necessitates great attention.

If we endeavor to collate in a brief form the results arrived at, we find that those differentiating characters, which admit of easy and certain recognition in the experimental plants, all behave exactly alike in their hybrid associations. The offspring of the hybrids of each pair of differentiating characters are, one-half, hybrid again, while the other half are constant in equal proportions having the characters of the seed and pollen parents, respectively. If several differentiating characters are combined by cross-fertilization in a hybrid, the resulting offspring form the terms of a combination series in which the combination series for each pair of differentiating characters are united.

The uniformity of behavior shown by the whole of the characters submitted to experiment permits, and fully justifies, the acceptance of the principle that a similar relation exists in the other characters which appear less sharply defined in plants and therefore could not be included in the separate experiments. An experiment with peduncles of different lengths gave on the whole a fairly satisfactory result, although the differentiation and serial arrangement of the forms could not be effected with that certainty which is indispensable for correct experiment.

THE REPRODUCTIVE CELLS OF THE HYBRIDS

The results of the previously described experiments led to further experiments, the results of which appear fitted to afford some conclusions as regards the composition of the egg and pollen cells of hybrids. An important clue is afforded in Pisum by the circumstance that among the progeny of the hybrids constant forms appear, and that this occurs, too, in respect of all combinations of the associated characters. So far as experience goes, we find it in every case confirmed that constant progeny can only be formed when the egg cells and the fertilizing pollen are of like character, so that both are provided with the material for creating quite similar individuals, as is the case with the normal fertilization of pure species. We must therefore regard it as certain that exactly similar factors must be at work also in the production of the constant forms in the hybrid plants. Since the various constant forms are produced in *one* plant, or even in *one* flower of a plant, the conclusion appears logical that in the ovaries of the hybrids there are formed as many sorts of egg cells, and in the anthers as many sorts of pollen cells, as there are possible constant combination forms, and that these egg and pollen cells agree in their internal composition with those of the separate forms.

In point of fact, it is possible to demonstrate theoretically that this hypothesis would fully suffice to account for the development of the hybrids in the separate generations, if we might at the same time assume that the various kinds of egg and pollen cells were formed in the hybrids on the average in equal numbers.[1]

In order to bring these assumptions to an experimental proof, the following experiments were designed. Two forms which were constantly different in the form of the seed and the color of the albumen were united by fertilization.

If the differentiating characters are again indicated as *A, B, a, b,* we have:

AB, seed parent;   *ab*, pollen parent;
A, form round;   *a*, form wrinkled;
B, albumen yellow.   *b*, albumen green.

The artificially fertilized seeds were sown together with several seeds of both original stocks, and the most vigorous examples were chosen for the reciprocal crossing. There were fertilized:

1. The hybrids with the pollen of *AB*.
2. The hybrids with the pollen of *ab*.
3. *AB* with the pollen of the hybrids.
4. *ab* with the pollen of the hybrids.

[1] [This and the preceding paragraph contain the essence of the Mendelian principles of heredity.]

For each of these four experiments the whole of the flowers on three plants were fertilized. If the above theory be correct, there must be developed on the hybrids egg and pollen cells of the forms *AB, Ab, aB, ab,* and there would be combined:

1. The egg cells *AB, Ab, aB, ab* with the pollen cells *AB*.
2. The egg cells *AB, Ab, aB, ab* with the pollen cells *ab*.
3. The egg cells *AB* with the pollen cells *AB, Ab, aB, ab*.
4. The egg cells *ab* with the pollen cells *AB, Ab, aB, ab*.

From each of these experiments there could then result only the following forms:

1. *AB, ABb, AaB, AaBb.*
2. *AaBb, Aab, aBb, ab.*
3. *AB, ABb, AaB, AaBb.*
4. *AaBb, Aab, aBb, ab.*

If, furthermore, the several forms of the egg and pollen cells of the hybrids were produced on an average in equal numbers, then in each experiment the said four combinations should stand in the same ratio to each other. A perfect agreement in the numerical relations was, however, not to be expected, since in each fertilization, even in normal cases, some egg cells remain undeveloped or subsequently die, and many even of the well-formed seeds fail to germinate when sown. The above assumption is also limited in so far that, while it demands the formation of an equal number of the various sorts of egg and pollen cells, it does not require that this should apply to each separate hybrid with mathematical exactness.

The first and second experiments had primarily the object of proving the composition of the hybrid egg cells, while the third and fourth experiments were to decide that of the pollen cells.[2] As is shown by the above demonstration, the first and third experiments and the second and fourth experiments should produce precisely the same combinations, and even in the second year the result

[2] [To prove, namely, that both were similarly differentiated, and not one or other only.]

should be partially visible in the form and color of the artificially fertilized seed. In the first and third experiments, the dominant characters of form and color, *A* and *B*, appear in each union and are also partly constant and partly in hybrid union with the recessive characters *a* and *b*, for which reason they must impress their peculiarity upon the whole of the seeds. All seeds should therefore appear round and yellow, if the theory be justified. In the second and fourth experiments, on the other hand, one union is hybrid in form and in color, and consequently the seeds are round and yellow; another is hybrid in form but constant in the recessive character of color, whence the seeds are round and green; the third is constant in the recessive character of form but hybrid in color, consequently the seeds are wrinkled and yellow; the fourth is constant in both recessive characters, so that the seeds are wrinkled and green. In both these experiments there were consequently four sorts of seed to be expected—viz., round and yellow, round and green, wrinkled and yellow, wrinkled and green.

The crop fulfilled these expectations perfectly. There were obtained in the

First experiment, 98 exclusively round yellow seeds.

Third experiment, 94 exclusively round yellow seeds.

In the second experiment, 31 round and yellow, 26 round and green, 27 wrinkled and yellow, 26 wrinkled and green seeds.

In the fourth experiment, 24 round and yellow, 25 round and green, 22 wrinkled and yellow, 26 wrinkled and green seeds.

There could scarcely be now any doubt of the success of the experiment; the next generation must afford the final proof. From the seed sown there resulted for the first experiment 90 plants, and for the third 87 plants which fruited: these yielded for the

First Exp.	Third Exp.		
20	25	round yellow seeds	*AB*
23	19	round yellow and green seeds	*ABb*
25	22	round and wrinkled yellow seeds	*AaB*
22	21	round and wrinkled green and yellow seeds	*AaBb*

In the second and fourth experiments the round and yellow seeds yielded plants with round and wrinkled yellow and green seeds, *AaBb*.

From the round green seeds, plants resulted with round and wrinkled green seeds, *Aab*.

The wrinkled yellow seeds gave plants with wrinkled yellow and green seeds, *aBb*.

From the wrinkled green seeds plants were raised which yielded again only wrinkled and green seeds, *ab*.

Although in these two experiments likewise some seeds did not germinate, the figures arrived at already in the previous year were not affected thereby, since each kind of seed gave plants which, as regards their seed, were like each other and different from the others. There resulted therefore from the

2nd Exp.	4th Exp.	
31	24	plants of the form *AaBb*
26	25	plants of the form *Aab*
27	22	plants of the form *aBb*
26	27	plants of the form *ab*

In all the experiments, therefore, there appeared all the forms which the proposed theory demands, and they came in nearly equal numbers.

In a further experiment the characters of flower color and length of stem were experimented upon, and selection was so made that in the third year of the experiment each character ought to appear in half of all the plants if the above theory were correct. *A, B, a, b* serve again as indicating the various characters.

A, violet-red flowers   *a*, white flowers
B, axis long   *b*, axis short

The form *Ab* was fertilized with *ab*, which produced the hybrid *Aab*. Furthermore, *aB* was also fertilized with *ab*, whence the hybrid *aBb*. In the second year, for further fertilization, the hybrid *Aab* was used as seed parent and the hybrid *aBb* as pollen parent.

Seed parent, *Aab*   Pollen parent, *aBb*
Possible egg cells, *Ab, ab*   Pollen cells, *aB, ab*

From the fertilization between the possible egg and pollen cells four combinations should result, viz.,

   AaBb + aBb + Aab + ab

. From this it is perceived that, according to the above theory, in the third year of the experiment out of all the plants,

Half should have violet-red flowers (*Aa*)	Classes 1, 3
Half should have white flowers (*a*)	Classes 2, 4
Half should have a long axis (*Bb*)	Classes 1, 2
Half should have a short axis (*b*)	Classes 3, 4

From 45 fertilizations of the second year, 187 seeds resulted, of which only 166 reached the flowering stage in the third year. Among these the separate classes appeared in the numbers following:

Class	Color of flower	Stem	
1	violet-red	long	47 times
2	white	long	40 times
3	violet-red	short	38 times
4	white	short	41 times

There subsequently appeared

The violet-red flower-color (*Aa*) in 85 plants

The white flower-color   (*a*) in 81 plants

The long stem   (*Bb*) in 87 plants

The short stem   (*b*) in 79 plants

The theory adduced is therefore satisfactorily confirmed in this experiment also.

For the characters of form of pod, color of pod, and position of flowers, experiments were also made on a small scale and results obtained in perfect agreement. All combinations which were possible through the union of the differentiating characters duly appeared and in nearly equal numbers.

Experimentally, therefore, the theory is confirmed that *the pea hybrids form egg and pollen cells which, in their constitution, represent in equal numbers all constant forms* which result from the combination of the characters united in fertilization.

The difference of the forms among the progeny of the hybrids, as well as the respective ratios of the numbers in which they are observed, find a sufficient explanation in the principle above deduced. The simplest case is afforded by the developmental series of each pair of differentiating characters. This series is represented by the expression $A + 2Aa + a$, in which A and a signify the forms with constant differentiating characters, and Aa the hybrid form' of both. It includes in three different classes four individuals. In the formation of these, pollen and egg cells of the form A and a take part on the average equally in the fertilization; hence each form [occurs] twice, since four individuals are formed. There participate consequently in the fertilization

   The pollen cells $A + A + a + a$
   The egg cells $A + A + a + a$

It remains, therefore, purely a matter of chance which of the two sorts of pollen will become united with each separate egg cell. According, however, to the law of probability, it will always happen, on the average of many cases, that each pollen form, A and a, will unite equally often with each egg cell form, A and a, consequently one of the two pollen cells A in the fertilization will meet with the egg cell A and the other with an egg cell a, and so likewise one pollen cell a will unite with an egg cell A, and the other with egg cell a.

  Pollen cells A A a a

  Egg cells A A a a

The result of the fertilization may be made clear by putting the signs for the conjoined egg and pollen cells in the form of fractions, those for the pollen cells above and those for the egg cells below the line. We have then

$$\frac{A}{A} + \frac{A}{a} + \frac{a}{A} + \frac{a}{a}$$

In the first and fourth term the egg and pollen cells are of like kind, consequently the product of their union must be constant, viz., A and a; in the second and third, on the other hand, there again results a union of the two differentiating characters of the stocks, consequently the forms resulting from these fertilizations are identical with those of the hybrid from which they sprang. *There occurs accordingly a repeated hybridization.* This explains the striking fact that the hybrids are able to produce, besides the two parental forms, offspring which are like themselves; $\frac{A}{a}$ and $\frac{a}{A}$ both give the same union Aa, since, as already remarked above, it makes no difference in the result of fertilization to which of the two characters the pollen or egg cells belong. We may write then

$$\frac{A}{A} + \frac{A}{a} + \frac{a}{A} + \frac{a}{a} = A + 2Aa + a$$

This represents the average result of the self-fertilization of the hybrids when two differentiating characters are united in them. In individual flowers and in individual plants, however, the ratios in which the forms of the series are produced may suffer not inconsiderable fluctuations.[1] Apart from the fact that the numbers in which both sorts of egg cells occur in the seed vessels can only be regarded as equal on the average, it remains purely a matter of chance which of the two sorts of pollen may fertilize each separate egg cell. For this reason the separate values must necessarily be subject to fluctuations, and there are even extreme cases possible, as were described earlier in connection with the experiments on the form of the seed and the color of the albumen. The true ratios of the numbers can only be ascertained by an average deduced from the sum of as many single values as possible; the greater the num-

[1] [Whether segregation by such units is more than purely fortuitous may perhaps be determined by seriation.]

ber, the more are merely chance effects eliminated

The developmental series for hybrids in which two kinds of differentiating characters are united contains, among sixteen individuals, nine different forms, viz.,

$$AB + Ab + aB + ab + 2ABb + 2aBb$$
$$+ 2AaB + 2Aab + 4AaBb$$

Between the differentiating characters of the original stocks, Aa and Bb, four constant combinations are possible, and consequently the hybrids produce the corresponding four forms of egg and pollen cells AB, Ab, aB, ab, and each of these will on the average figure four times in the fertilization, since 16 individuals are included in the series. Therefore the participators in the fertilization are

Pollen cells $AB + AB + AB + AB + Ab$
$+ Ab + Ab + Ab + aB + aB$
$+ aB + aB + ab + ab + ab$
$+ ab.$

Egg cells $AB + AB + AB + AB + Ab$
$+ Ab + Ab + Ab + aB + aB$
$+ aB + aB + ab + ab + ab$
$+ ab.$

In the process of fertilization, each pollen form unites on an average equally often with each egg-cell form, so that each of the four pollen cells AB unites once with one of the forms of egg cell AB, Ab, aB, ab. In precisely the same way the rest of the pollen cells of the forms, Ab, aB, ab, unite with all the other egg cells. We obtain, therefore

$$\frac{AB}{AB} + \frac{AB}{Ab} + \frac{AB}{aB} + \frac{AB}{ab} + \frac{Ab}{AB} + \frac{Ab}{Ab} + \frac{Ab}{aB}$$

$$+ \frac{Ab}{ab} + \frac{aB}{AB} + \frac{aB}{Ab} + \frac{aB}{aB} + \frac{aB}{ab} + \frac{ab}{AB}$$

$$+ \frac{ab}{Ab} + \frac{ab}{aB} + \frac{ab}{ab}$$

or

$$AB + ABb + AaB + AaBb + ABb + Ab$$
$$+ AaBb + Aab + AaB + AaBb + aB$$
$$+ aBb + AaBb + Aab + aBb + ab$$
$$= AB + Ab + aB + ab + 2ABb$$
$$+ 2aBb + 2AaB + 2Aab + 4AaBb\ [2]$$

[2] [In the original the sign of equality (=) is here represented by +, evidently a misprint.]

In precisely similar fashion is the developmental series of hybrids exhibited when three kinds of differentiating characters are conjoined in them. The hybrids form eight various kinds of egg and pollen cells—*ABC, ABc, AbC, Abc, aBC, aBc, abC, abc*—and each pollen form unites itself again on the average once with each form of egg cell.

constricted when ripe. The ratios of the numbers in which the different forms appeared in the separate generations were the same as with Pisum. Also, the development of the constant combinations resulted according to the law of simple combination of characters, exactly as in the case of Pisum. There were obtained

Constant combinations	Axis	Color of the unripe pods	Form of the ripe pods
1	Long	Green	Inflated
2			Constricted
3		Yellow	Inflated
4			Constricted
5	Short	Green	Inflated
6			Constricted
7		Yellow	Inflated
8			Constricted

The law of combination of different characters, which governs the development of the hybrids, finds therefore its foundation and explanation in the principle enunciated, that the hybrids produce egg cells and pollen cells which in equal numbers represent all constant forms which result from the combination of the characters brought together in fertilization.

EXPERIMENTS WITH HYBRIDS OF OTHER SPECIES OF PLANTS

It must be the object of further experiments to ascertain whether the law of development discovered for Pisum applies also to the hybrids of other plants. To this end several experiments were recently commenced. Two minor experiments with species of Phaseolus have been completed, and may be here mentioned.

An experiment with *Phaseolus vulgaris* and *Phaseolus nanus* gave results in perfect agreement. *Ph. nanus* had, together with the dwarf axis, simply inflated, green pods. *Ph. vulgaris* had, on the other hand, an axis 10 feet to 12 feet high and yellow-colored pods,

The green color of the pod, the inflated forms, and the long axis were, as in Pisum, dominant characters.

Another experiment with two very different species of Phaseolus had only a partial result. *Phaseolus nanus*, L., served as seed parent, a perfectly constant species, with white flowers in short racemes and small white seeds in straight, inflated, smooth pods; as pollen parent was used *Ph. multiflorus*, W., with tall winding stem, purple-red flowers in very long racemes, rough, sickle-shaped crooked pods, and large seeds which bore black flecks and splashes on a peach-blood-red ground.

The hybrids had the greatest similarity to the pollen parent, but the flowers appeared less intensely colored. Their fertility was very limited; from 17 plants, which together developed many hundreds of flowers, only 49 seeds in all were obtained. These were of medium size and were flecked and splashed similarly to those of *Ph. multiflorus*, while the ground color was not materially different. The next year 44 plants were raised from these seeds, of which only 31 reached the flowering stage. The characters of *Ph. nanus,* which had been altogether latent in the hybrids, reappeared in various combinations; their ratio, however, with relation to the dominant plants was necessarily very fluctuating owing to the small number of trial plants. With certain characters, as in those of the axis and the form of pod it was, however, as in the case of Pisum, almost exactly 1 : 3.

Insignificant as the results of this experiment may be as regards the determination of the relative numbers in which the various forms appeared, it presents, on the other hand, the phenomenon of a remarkable change of color in the flowers and seed of the hybrids. In Pisum it is known that the characters of the flower and seed color present themselves unchanged in the first and further generations, and that the offspring of the hybrids display exclusively the one or the other of the characters of the original stocks. It is otherwise in the experiment we are considering. The white flowers and the seed color of *Ph. nanus* appeared, it is true, at once in the first generation [*from* the hybrids] in one fairly fertile example, but the remaining 30 plants developed flower colors which were of various grades of purple-red to pale violet. The coloring of the seed coat was no less varied than that of the flowers. No plant could rank as fully fertile; many produced no fruit at all; others only yielded fruits from the flowers last produced, which did not ripen. From 15 plants only were well-developed seeds obtained. The greatest disposition to infertility was seen in the forms with preponderantly red flowers, since out of 16 of these only 4 yielded ripe seeds. Three of these had a similar seed pattern to *Ph. multiflorus,* but with a more or less pale ground color; the fourth plant yielded only one seed of plain brown tint. The forms with preponderantly violet-colored flowers had dark brown, black-brown, and quite black seeds.

The experiment was continued through two more generations under similar unfavorable circumstances, since even among the offspring of fairly fertile plants there came again some which were less fertile or even quite sterile. Other flower and seed colors than those cited did not subsequently present themselves. The forms which in the first generation [bred from the hybrids] contained one or more of the recessive characters remained, as regards these, constant without exception. Also of those plants which possessed violet flowers and brown or black seed, some did not vary again in these respects in the next generation; the majority, however, yielded, together with offspring exactly like themselves, some which displayed white flowers and white seed coats. The red flowering plants remained so slightly fertile that nothing can be said with certainty as regards their further development.

Despite the many disturbing factors with which the observations had to contend, it is nevertheless seen by this experiment that the development of the hybrids, with regard to those characters which concern the form of the plants, follows the same laws as in Pisum. With regard to the color characters, it certainly appears difficult to perceive a substantial agreement. Apart from the fact that from the union of a white and a purple-red coloring a whole series of colors results [in F_2], from purple to pale violet and white, the circumstance is a striking one that among 31 flowering plants only one received the recessive character of the white color, while in Pisum this occurs on the average in every fourth plant.

Even these enigmatical results, however, might probably be explained by the law governing Pisum if we might assume that the color of the flowers and seeds of *Ph. multiflorus* is a combination of two or more entirely independent colors, which individually act like any other constant character in the plant. If the flower color A were a combination of the individual characters $A_1 + A_2 + \ldots$ which produce the total impression of a purple coloration, then by fertilization with the differentiating character, white color, a, there would be produced the hybrid unions $A_1a + A_2a + \ldots$ and so would it be with the corresponding coloring of the seed coats.[1] According to the above

[1] [As it fails to take account of factors introduced by the albino, this representation is im-

assumption, each of these hybrid color unions would be independent and would consequently develop quite independently from the others. It is then easily seen that from the combination of the separate developmental series a complete color series must result. If, for instance, $A = A_1 + A_2$, then the hybrids A_1a and A_2a form the developmental series—

$$A_1 + 2A_1a + a \qquad A_2 + 2A_1a + a$$

The members of this series can enter into nine different combinations, and each of these denotes another color—

1 A_1A_2	2 A_1aA_2	1 A_2a
2 A_1A_2a	4 A_1aA_2a	2 A_2aa
1 A_1a	2 A_1aa	1 aa.

The figures prescribed for the separate combinations also indicate how many plants with the corresponding coloring belong to the series. Since the total is 16, the whole of the colors are on the average distributed over each 16 plants, but, as the series itself indicates, in unequal proportions.

Should the color development really happen in this way, we could offer an explanation of the case above described, viz., that the white flowers and seed-coat color only appeared once among 31 plants of the first generation. This coloring appears only once in the series and could therefore also only be developed once in the average in each 16, and with three color characters only once even in 64 plants.

It must, nevertheless, not be forgotten that the explanation here attempted is based on a mere hypothesis, only supported by the very imperfect result of the experiment just described. It would, however, be well worth while to follow up the development of color in hybrids by similar experiments, since it is probable that in this way we might learn the significance of the extraordinary variety in the coloring of our ornamental flowers.

So far, little at present is known with cer-

tainty beyond the fact that the color of the flowers in most ornamental plants is an extremely variable character. The opinion has often been expressed that the stability of the species is greatly disturbed or entirely upset by cultivation, and consequently there is an inclination to regard the development of cultivated forms as a matter of chance devoid of rules; the coloring of ornamental plants is indeed usually cited as an example of great instability. It is, however, not clear why the simple transference into garden soil should result in such a thorough and persistent revolution in the plant organism. No one will seriously maintain that in the open country the development of plants is ruled by other laws than in the garden bed. Here, as there, changes of type must take place if the conditions of life be altered, and the species possesses the capacity of fitting itself to its new environment. It is willingly granted that by cultivation the origination of new varieties is favored, and that by man's labor many varieties are acquired which, under natural conditions, would be lost; but nothing justifies the assumption that the tendency to the formation of varieties is so extraordinarily increased that the species speedily lose all stability, and their offspring diverge into an endless series of extremely variable forms. Were the change in the conditions the sole cause of variability we might expect that those cultivated plants which are grown for centuries under almost identical conditions would again attain constancy. That, as is well known, is not the case, since it is precisely under such circumstances that not only the most varied but also the most variable forms are found. It is only the Leguminosae, like Pisum, Phaseolus,[1] Lens, whose organs of fertilization are protected by the keel, which constitute a noteworthy exception. Even here there have arisen numerous varieties during a cultural period of more than 1,000 years under most various conditions; these maintain, however, under unchanging environments a stability as great as that of species growing wild.

It is more than probable that as regards the variability of cultivated plants there ex-

---

perfect. It is, however, interesting to know that Mendel realized the fact of the existence of compound characters, and that the rarity of the white recessives was a consequence of this resolution.]

[1] [Phaseolus nevertheless is insect-fertilized.]

ists a factor which so far has received little attention. Various experiments force us to the conclusion that our cultivated plants, with few exceptions, are *members of various hybrid series,* whose further development in conformity with law is varied and interrupted by frequent crossings *inter se.* The circumstance must not be overlooked that cultivated plants are mostly grown in great numbers and close together, affording the most favorable conditions for reciprocal fertilization between the varieties present and the species itself. The probability of this is supported by the fact that among the great array of variable forms solitary examples are always found, which in one character or another remain constant, if only foreign influence be carefully excluded. These forms behave precisely as do those which are known to be members of the compound hybrid series. Also with the most susceptible of all characters, that of color, it cannot escape the careful observer that in the separate forms the inclination to vary is displayed in very different degrees. Among plants which arise from *one* spontaneous fertilization there are often some whose offspring vary widely in the constitution and arrangement of the colors, while that of others shows little deviation, and among a greater number solitary examples occur which transmit the color of the flowers unchanged to their offspring. The cultivated species of Dianthus afford an instructive example of this. A white-flowered example of *Dianthus caryophyllus,* which itself was derived from a white-flowered variety, was shut up during its blooming period in a greenhouse; the numerous seeds obtained therefrom yielded plants entirely white-flowered like itself. A similar result was obtained from a subspecies, with red flowers somewhat flushed with violet, and one with flowers white, striped with red. Many others, on the other hand, which were similarly protected, yielded progeny which were more or less variously colored and marked.

Whoever studies the coloration which results, in ornamental plants, from similar fertilization, can hardly escape the conviction that here also the development follows a definite law, which possibly finds its expression *in the combination of several independent color characters.*

CONCLUDING REMARKS

It can hardly fail to be of interest to compare the observations made regarding Pisum with the results arrived at by the two authorities in this branch of knowledge, Kölreuter and Gärtner, in their investigations. According to the opinion of both, the hybrids in outward appearance present either a form intermediate between the original species, or they closely resemble either the one or the other type, and sometimes can hardly be discriminated from it. From their seeds usually arise, if the fertilization was effected by their own pollen, various forms which differ from the normal type. As a rule, the majority of individuals obtained by one fertilization maintain the hybrid form, while some few others come more like the seed parent, and one or other individual approaches the pollen parent. This, however, is not the case with all hybrids without exception. Sometimes the offspring have more nearly approached, some the one and some the other of the two original stocks, or they all incline more to one or the other side; while in other cases *they remain perfectly like the hybrid* and continue constant in their offspring. The hybrids of varieties behave like hybrids of species, but they possess greater variability of form and a more pronounced tendency to revert to the original types.

With regard to the form of the hybrids and their development, as a rule an agreement with the observations made in Pisum is unmistakable. It is otherwise with the exceptional cases cited. Gärtner confesses even that the exact determination whether a form bears a greater resemblance to one or to the other of the two original species often involved great difficulty, so much depending upon the subjective point of view of the observer. Another circumstance could, however, contribute to render the results fluctuating and uncertain, despite the most careful observation and differentiation. For the experiments, plants were mostly used which rank as good species and are differentiated by a large number of characters. In addition to the sharply defined characters, where it is a question of greater or less similarity, those characters must also be taken into account which are often difficult to define in words, but yet suffice, as every plant specialist knows, to give the forms a peculiar appearance. If it be accepted that the development of hybrids follows the law which is valid for Pisum, the series in each separate experiment must contain very many forms, since the number of the terms, as is known, increases, with the number of the differentiating characters, as the powers of three. With a relatively small number of experimental plants the result therefore could only be approximately right, and in single cases might fluctuate considerably. If, for instance, the two original stocks differ in seven characters, and 100 or 200 plants were raised from the seeds of their hybrids to determine the grade of relationship of the offspring, we can easily see how uncertain the decision must become, since for seven differentiating characters the combination series contain 16,384 individuals under 2,187 various forms; now one and then another relationship could assert its predominance, just according as chance presented this or that form to the observer in a majority of cases.

If, furthermore, there appear among the differentiating characters at the same time *dominant* characters, which are transmitted entire or nearly unchanged to the hybrids, then in the terms of the developmental series that one of the two original parents which possesses the majority of dominant characters must always be predominant. In the experiment described relative to Pisum, in which three kinds of differentiating characters were concerned, all the dominant characters belonged to the seed parent. Although the terms of the series in their internal composition approach both original parents equally, yet in this experiment the type of the seed parent obtained so great a preponderance that out of each 64 plants of the first generation 54 exactly resembled it, or only differed in one character. It is seen how rash it must be under such circumstances to draw from the external resemblances of hybrids conclusions as to their internal nature.

Gärtner mentions that in those cases where the development was regular, among the offspring of the hybrids, the two original species were not reproduced, but only a few individuals which approached them. With very extended developmental series it could not in fact be otherwise. For seven differentiating characters, for instance, among more than 16,000 individuals—offspring of the hybrids—each of the two original species would occur only once. It is therefore hardly possible that these should appear at all among a small number of experimental plants; with some probability, however, we might reckon upon the appearance in the series of a few forms which approach them.

We meet with an *essential difference* in those hybrids which remain constant in their progeny and propagate themselves as truly as the pure species. According to Gärtner, to this class belong the *remarkably fertile hybrids, Aquilegia atropurpurea canadensis, Lavatera pseudolbia thuringiaca, Geum urbano-rivale,* and some Dianthus hybrids; and, according to Wichura, the hybrids of the willow family. For the history of the evolution of plants this circumstance is of special importance, since constant hybrids acquire the status of new species. The correctness of the facts is guaranteed by eminent observers, and cannot be doubted. Gärtner had an opportunity of following up *Dianthus Ameria deltoides* to the tenth generation, since it regularly propagated itself in the garden.

With Pisum it was shown by experiment that the hybrids form egg and pollen cells of *different* kinds, and that herein lies the reason of the variability of their offspring. In other hybrids, likewise, whose offspring behave similarly, we may assume a like cause; for those, on the other hand, which remain constant, the assumption appears justifiable that their reproductive cells are all alike and agree with the foundation cell [fertilized ovum] of the hybrid. In the opinion of renowned physiologists, for the purpose of propagation one pollen cell and one egg cell unite in Phanerogams [1] into a single cell, which is capable by assimilation and formation of new cells to become an independent organism. This development follows a constant law, which is founded on the material composition and arrangement of the elements which meet in the cell in a vivifying union. If the reproductive cells be of the same kind and agree with the foundation cell [fertilized ovum] of the mother plant, then the development of the new individual will follow the same law which rules the mother plant. If it chance that an egg cell unites with a *dissimilar* pollen cell, we must then assume that between those elements of both cells, which determine opposite characters, some sort of compromise is effected. The resulting compound cell becomes the foundation of the hybrid organism, the development of which necessarily follows a different scheme from that obtaining in each of the two original species. If the compromise be taken to be a complete one, in the sense, namely, that the hybrid embryo is formed from two similar cells, in which the differences are *entirely and permanently accommodated* together, the further result follows that the hybrids, like any other stable plant species, reproduce themselves truly in their offspring. The reproductive cells which are formed in their seed vessels and anthers are of one kind and agree with the fundamental compound cell [fertilized ovum].

[1] In Pisum it is placed beyond doubt that for the formation of the new embryo a perfect union of the elements of both reproductive cells must take place. How could we otherwise explain that among the offspring of the hybrids both original types reappear in equal numbers and with all their peculiarities? If the influence of the egg cell upon the pollen cell were only external, if it fulfilled the *role* of a nurse only, then the result of each artificial fertilization could be no other than that the developed hybrid should exactly resemble the pollen parent, or at any rate do so very closely. This the experiments so far have in no wise confirmed. An evident proof of the complete union of the contents of both cells is afforded by the experience gained on all sides that it is immaterial, as regards the form of the hybrid, which of the original species is the seed parent or which the pollen parent.

With regard to those hybrids whose progeny is *variable* we may perhaps assume that between the differentiating elements of the egg and pollen cells there also occurs a compromise, in so far that the formation of a cell as foundation of the hybrid becomes possible; but, nevertheless, the arrangement between the conflicting elements is only temporary and does not endure throughout the life of the hybrid plant. Since, in the habit of the plant, no changes are perceptible during the whole period of vegetation, we must further assume that it is only possible for the differentiating elements to liberate themselves from the enforced union when the fertilizing cells are developed. In the formation of these cells all existing elements partipate, in an entirely free and equal arrangement, by which it is only the differentiating ones which mutually separate themselves. In this way the production would be rendered possible of as many sorts of egg and pollen cells as there are combinations possible of the formative elements.

The attribution attempted here of the essential difference in the development of hybrids to *a permanent or temporary union* of the differing cell elements can, of course, only claim the value of an hypothesis for which the lack of definite data offers a wide scope. Some justification of the opinion expressed lies in the evidence afforded by Pisum that the behavior of each pair of differentiating characters in hybrid union is independent of the other differences between the two original plants, and, further, that the hybrid produces just so many kinds of eggs and pollen cells as there are possible constant combination forms. The differentiating characters of two plants can finally, however, only depend upon differences in the composition and grouping of the elements which exist in the foundation cells [fertilized ova] of the same in vital interaction.[2]

Even the validity of the law formulated for Pisum requires still to be confirmed, and a repetition of the more important experiments is consequently much to be desired, that, for instance, relating to the composi-

[2] *"Welche in den Grundzellen derselben in lebendiger Wechselwirkung stehen."*

tion of the hybrid fertilizing cells. A differential [element] may easily escape the single observer,[1] which although at the outset may appear to be unimportant, may yet accumulate to such an extent that it must not be ignored in the total result. Whether the variable hybrids of other plant species observe an entire agreement must also be first decided experimentally. In the meantime we may assume that in material points an essential difference can scarcely occur, since the unity in the developmental plan of organic life is beyond question.

In conclusion, the experiments carried out by Kölreuter, Gärtner, and others with respect to *the transformation of one species into another by artificial fertilization* merit special mention. Particular importance has been attached to those experiments and Gärtner reckons them among "the most difficult of all in hybridization."

If a species *A* is to be transformed into a species *B*, both must be united by fertilization and the resulting hybrids then be fertilized with the pollen of *B*; then, out of the various offspring resulting, that form would be selected which stood in nearest relation to *B* and once more be fertilized with *B* pollen, and so continuously until finally a form is arrived at which is like *B* and constant in its progeny. By this process the species *A* would change into the species *B*. Gärtner alone has effected thirty such experiments with plants of genera Aquilegia, Dianthus, Geum, Lavatera, Lychnis, Malva, Nicotiana, and Oenothera. The period of transformation was not alike for all species. While with some a triple fertilization sufficed, with others this had to be repeated five or six times, and even in the same species fluctuations were observed in various experiments. Gärtner ascribes this difference to the circumstance that "the specific [*typische*] power by which a species, during reproduction, effects the change and transformation of the maternal type varies considerably in different plants, and that, consequently, the periods within which the one species is changed into the other must also vary, as also the number of

[1] "*Dem einzelnen Beobachter kann leicht ein Differenziale entgehen.*"

generations, so that the transformation in some species is perfected in more, and in others in fewer generations." Further, the same observer remarks "that in these transformation experiments a good deal depends upon which type and which individual be chosen for further transformation."

If it may be assumed that in these experiments the constitution of the forms resulted in a similar way to that of Pisum, the entire process of transformation would find a fairly simple explanation. The hybrid forms as many kinds of egg cells as there are constant combinations possible of the characters conjoined therein, and one of these is always of the same kind as that of the fertilizing pollen cells. Consequently there always exists the possibility with all such experiments that even from the second fertilization there may result a constant form identical with that of the pollen parent. Whether this really be obtained depends in each separate case upon the number of the experimental plants, as well as upon the number of differentiating characters which are united by the fertilization. Let us, for instance, assume that the plants selected for experiment differed in three characters and the species *ABC* is to be transformed into the other species *abc* by repeated fertilization with the pollen of the latter; the hybrids resulting from the first cross form eight different kinds of egg cells, viz.,

$$ABC, ABc, AbC, aBC, Abc, aBc, abC, abc$$

These in the second year of experiment are united again with the pollen cells *abc*, and we obtain the series

$$AaBbCc + AaBbc + AabCc + aBbCc$$
$$+ Aabc + aBbc + abCc + abc$$

Since the form *abc* occurs once in the series of eight terms, it is consequently little likely that it would be missing among the experimental plants, even were these raised in a smaller number, and the transformation would be perfected already by a second fertilization. If by chance it did not appear, then the fertilization must be repeated with one of those forms nearest akin, *Aabc, aBbc, abCc*. It is perceived that such an experiment must extend the farther *the smaller the number of experimental plants and the larger the number of differentiating characters* in the two original species; and that, furthermore, in the same species there can easily occur a delay of one or even of two generations such as Gärtner observed. The transformation of widely divergent species could generally only be completed in five or six years of experiment, since the number of different egg cells which are formed in the hybrid increases, as the powers of two, with the number of differentiating characters.

Gärtner found by repeated experiments that the respective period of transformation varies in many species, so that frequently a species *A* can be transformed into a species *B* a generation sooner than can species *B* into species *A*. He deduces therefrom that Kölreuter's opinion can hardly be maintained that "the two natures in hybrids are perfectly in equilibrium." It appears, however, that Kölreuter does not merit this criticism but that Gärtner rather has overlooked a material point, to which he himself elsewhere draws attention, viz., that "it depends which individual is chosen for further transformation." Experiments which in this connection were carried out with two species of Pisum demonstrated that as regards the choice of the fittest individuals for the purpose of further fertilization it may make a great difference which of two species is transformed into the other. The two experimental plants differed in five characters, while at the same time those of species *A* were all dominant and those of species *B* all recessive. For mutual transformation *A* was fertilized with pollen of *B,* and *B* with pollen of *A,* and this was repeated with both hybrids the following year. With the first experiment *B/A* there were 87 plants available in the third year of experiment for selection of the individuals for further crossing, and these were of the possible 32 forms; with the second experiment *A/B* 73 plants resulted, which *agreed throughout perfectly in habit with the pollen parent;* in their internal composition, however, they must have been just as varied as the forms in the other experiment. A defi-

nite selection was consequently only possible with the first experiment; with the second the selection had to be made at random, merely. Of the latter only a portion of the flowers were crossed with the *A* pollen, the others were left to fertilize themselves. Among each five plants which were selected in both experiments for fertilization there agreed, as the following year's culture showed, with the pollen parent:

First Experiment	Second Experiment	
2 plants	—	in all characters
3 plants	—	in 4 characters
—	2 plants	in 3 characters
—	2 plants	in 2 characters
—	1 plant	in 1 character

In the first experiment, therefore, the transformation was completed; in the second, which was not continued further, two or more fertilizations would probably have been required.

Although the case may not frequently occur in which the dominant characters belong exclusively to one or the other of the original parent plants, it will always make a difference which of the two possesses the majority of dominants. If the pollen parent has the majority, then the selection of forms for further crossing will afford a less degree of certainty than in the reverse case, which must imply a delay in the period of transformation, provided that the experiment is only considered as completed when a form is arrived at which not only exactly resembles the pollen plant in form, but also remains as constant in its progeny.

Gärtner, by the results of these transformation experiments, was led to oppose the opinion of those naturalists who dispute the stability of plant species and believe in a continuous evolution of vegetation. He perceives[1] in the complete transformation of one species into another an indubitable proof that species are fixed within limits beyond which they cannot change. Although this opinion cannot be unconditionally accepted,

[1] ["Es sieht" in the original is clearly a misprint for "Er sieht."]

we find on the other hand in Gärtner's experiments a noteworthy confirmation of that supposition regarding variability of cultivated plants which has already been expressed.

Among the experimental species there were cultivated plants, such as *Aquilegia atropurpurea* and *canadensis*, *Dianthus caryophyllus*, *chinensis*, and *japonicus*, *Nicotiana rustica* and *paniculata*, and hybrids between these species lost none of their stability after four or five generations.

BIBLIOGRAPHY

The following bibliography has as its principal purpose to suggest material for further reading to the student who may wish to acquire more information about a given aspect of genetics than he can find in the present book. This bibliography is obviously highly selective and incomplete. The literature on genetics is today so enormous that a book considerably larger than this volume would be needed merely to list the titles of the books and journal articles dealing with genetics. No such extended bibliography has been published.

A. HISTORY OF GENETICS

Genetics as a science is still rather young, and its history has never been written. An account of the pre-Mendelian period can be found in:

Roberts, H. F. 1929. "Plant Hybridization before Mendel." Princeton.

Zirkle, C. 1946. The early history of the idea of the inheritance of acquired characters and of pangenesis. Trans. Amer. Philosoph. Soc., 35.

An English translation of Mendel's classical paper is reprinted in the present volume
444

(the original has been published, of course, in German). For Mendel's biography see:
Iltis, H. 1932. "Life of Mendel." New York (translation of part of the original German edition).

The state of genetics in the pioneer years following the rediscovery of Mendel's laws can be judged from:

Bateson, W. 1902. "Mendel's Principles of Heredity." London.
————. 1908. "The Methods and Scope of Genetics." London.

The great seminal discoveries of Morgan and his school are summarized in:

Morgan, T. H. 1919. "The Physical Basis of Heredity." Philadelphia.

A cross section of genetics as it was when the first half-centennial of the rediscovery of Mendel's laws was celebrated in 1950 can be found in:

Dunn, L. C. (ed.). 1951. "Genetics in the Twentieth Century." New York.

In this book, written by 27 authors, see particularly the very interesting article by

C. Zirkle, "The knowledge of heredity before 1900," and the historical sketches by W. E. Castle, H. J. Muller, and A. H. Sturtevant, which nicely complement each other to present a fair picture of the early years of genetics.

B. THE HEREDITY-ENVIRONMENT PROBLEM AND THE CONCEPTS OF GENOTYPE AND PHENOTYPE

The classic work in this field is that of:

Johannsen, W. 1909. *"Elemente der exakten Erblichkeitslehre."* Jena.

Experiments in the interactions of heredity and environment in the formation of the phenotype in certain plant species are described in:

Clausen, J., D. D. Keck, and W. M. Hiesey. 1940. Experimental studies on the nature of species, I. Carnegie Inst. Washington Publ. 520.
————. 1948. Experimental studies on the nature of species, III. Carnegie Inst. Washington Publ. 581.

Concerning the nature-nurture problem in man, and particularly the observations of human twins, reviews of the known facts and of the often-incompatible interpretations can be found in:

Newman, H. H., F. N. Freeman, and K. J. Holzinger. 1937. "Twins: A Study of Heredity and Environment." Chicago.
Penrose, L. S. 1949. "The Biology of Mental Defect." London.
Osborn, F. 1951. "Preface to Eugenics." New York.
Kallmann, F. J. 1953. "Heredity in Health and Mental Disorder." New York.
Darlington, C. D. 1953. "The Facts of Life." New York.
Dobzhansky, T. 1956. "The Biological Basis of Human Freedom." New York.

The general literature on human genetics must, of course, be consulted in connection with the nature-nurture problem (see below).

C. GENETICS OF MAN AND MEDICAL GENETICS

A most readable account of human genetics above the elementary level is that of:

Stern, C. 1949. "Principles of Human Genetics." San Francisco.

Also to be consulted are the following three sources, of which the first is an extensive compilation of the otherwise extremely scattered literature on the inheritance of various traits:

Gates, R. R. 1946. "Human Genetics." New York.
Sorsby, A. (ed.). 1953. "Clinical Genetics." London.
Neel, J. V., and W. J. Schull. 1954. "Human Heredity." Chicago.

Literature references bearing on the problems of human populations and races are listed under Sec. I below.

The literature dealing with the serological genetics of man (the "blood-group genes"), now very voluminous, has been ably summarized in:

Wiener, A. S. 1943. "Blood Groups and Transfusion." Springfield.
Race, R. R., and R. Sanger. 1950. "Blood Groups in Man." London.
Mourant, A. R. 1954. "The Distribution of the Human Blood Groups." Springfield.

D. GENETICS OF MICROORGANISMS

This has been probably the most active field of research in genetics in recent years. The following are excellent summaries, which will, however, become antiquated within a few years:

Catcheside, D. G. 1951. "The Genetics of Microorganisms." New York.
Braun, W. 1953. "Bacterial Genetics." Philadelphia.
Luria, S. E. 1953. "General Virology." New York.
Viruses. 1953. Cold Spring Harbor Symposia Quant. Biol., 18.
Beale, G. H. 1954. "The Genetics of *Paramecium aurelia.*" Cambridge.
Sonneborn, T. M. 1957. Breeding systems, reproductive methods, and species prob-

lems in Protozoa. In E. Mayr (ed.), "The Species Problem." Washington.

E. GENETICS OF FORMS OTHER THAN MAN AND MICROORGANISMS

The pertinent literature is extremely scattered. Some of it is summarized from time to time in the following publications:

Bibliographia Genetica. A total of 17 volumes was published by 1957.

Advances in Genetics. A total of eight volumes have been published.

The number of publications dealing with the genetics of Drosophila is particularly great. Bibliographic references to this vast literature can be found in:

Muller, H. J. 1939. "Bibliography on the Genetics of Drosophila," I. Edinburgh.

Herskowitz, I. H. 1952. "Bibliography on the Genetics of Drosophila," II. Farnham Royal, Bucks.

The evolutionary and population genetics of Drosophila has been summarized in:

Patterson, J. T., and W. S. Stone. 1952. "Evolution in the Genus Drosophila." New York.

The mutants of *Drosophila melanogaster* have been reviewed in:

Bridges, C. B., and K. S. Brehme. 1944. The mutants of *Drosophila melanogaster*. Carnegie Inst. Washington Publ. 552. (A new edition of this work is expected shortly.)

The following publication, though it deals with the morphology and ecology of Drosophila, is indispensable also to those working on the genetics of these flies:

Demerec, M. (ed.). 1950. "Biology of Drosophila." New York.

F. CYTOGENETICS

A masterly summary of classical cytology is that of:

Wilson, E. B. 1925. "The Cell in Development and Heredity." New York.

A brilliant attempt to give a synthesis of the significant facts of cytology and genetics has been made by:

Darlington, C. D. 1937. "Recent Advances in Cytology." Philadelphia.

This attempt has led to much fruitful research but also to a great deal of polemics. A critical but not unconstructive attitude is represented by:

Swanson, C. P. 1957. "Cytology and Cytogenetics." Englewood Cliffs, N.J.

The evolutionary aspects of cytogenetics have been magnificently summarized and analyzed in:

White, M. J. D. 1954. "Animal Cytology and Evolution." London.

There is no botanical work corresponding to that of White for cytogenetics of animals. The nearest approach is the book of Stebbins (see under Sec. I, below).

The most recent reviews summarizing the data on the numbers of chromosomes in animals and plants, respectively, are:

Makino, S. 1951. "An Atlas of the Chromosome Numbers in Animals." Ames, Iowa.

Darlington, C. D., and A. P. Wylie. 1955. "Chromosome Atlas of Flowering Plants." London.

G. GENES AND CHROMOSOMES

This is an aspect of general cytogenetics (Sec. F, above), hence the books cited under Sec. F may profitably be consulted. The parallelism between the behavior of genes and of chromosomes has been pointed out by:

Sutton, W. S. 1903. The chromosomes in heredity. Biol. Bulletin, 4. Reprinted in Gabriel, M. L., and S. Fogel (eds.). 1955. "Great Experiments in Biology." Englewood Cliffs, N.J.

Boveri, T. 1904. *"Ergebnisse über die Konstitution der chromatischen Substanz des Zellkerns."* Jena.

A crucial experimental proof that the chromosomes are gene carriers has been provided by:

Bridges, C. B. 1916. Nondisjunction as proof of the chromosome theory of heredity. Genetics, 1.

The theory of linear arrangement of genes in chromosomes and the construction of genetic maps of chromosomes is due to the pioneering work of:

Morgan, T. H. 1911. An attempt to analyze the constitution of the chromosomes on the basis of sex-limited inheritance in Drosophila. Jour. Exper. Zoology, 11.

Sturtevant, A. H. 1913. The linear arrangement of six sex-linked factors in Drosophila, as shown by their mode of association. Jour. Exper. Zoology, 14.

Muller, H. J. 1916. The mechanism of crossing over. Amer. Naturalist, 50.

For genetic maps of Drosophila chromosomes, consult the summary of Bridges and Brehme, cited under Sec. E, above.

H. MUTATION, SPONTANEOUS AND INDUCED

The theory of mutation was propounded originally by De Vries. An English translation of his chief work is:

De Vries, H. 1910. "The Mutation Theory." Chicago.

The discovery of the induction of mutations by X rays was announced in:

Muller, H. J. 1927. Artificial transmutation of genes. Science, 66. Reprinted in Gabriel and Fogel (see Sec. G).

Reviews of the modern state of the field of mutation studies can be found in:

Hollaender, A. (ed.). 1954–1956. "Radiation Biology." 3 vols., New York.

Consult especially the two extensive reviews by H. J. Muller of the general problem of mutation, those by B. P. Kaufmann on induced chromosome aberrations in animals, by N. H. Giles on induced chromosome aberration in the plant Tradescantia, by J. G. Carlson on the immediate effects of radiation on chromosomes, and by W. L. Russell on the genetic effects of radiation in mammals. Much important work on mutation has also been reviewed in two of the Cold Spring Harbor Symposia on Quantitative Biology, vols. 16 (1951) and 21 (1956). For studies on mutation in microorganisms and in Drosophila, see Secs. D and E.

I. GENETICS OF POPULATIONS, RACES, AND SPECIES; EVOLUTION

A very able exposition of the mathematical theory of population genetics, the greater part of it accessible even to those without much mathematical training, is that of:

Li, C. C. 1955. "Population Genetics." Chicago.

Those with a better foundation in mathematics may read also:

Mather, K. 1949. "Biometrical Genetics." New York.

Lerner, I. M. 1950. "Population Genetics and Animal Improvement." London.

Kempthorne, O. 1957. "An Introduction to Genetic Statistics." New York.

The great seminal works on evolutionary genetics are:

Hardy, G. H. 1908. Mendelian proportions in a mixed population. Science, 28. Reprinted in Gabriel and Fogel (see Sec. G).

Weinberg, W. 1908. *Über den Nachweis der Vererbung beim Menschen.* Jahreshefte Verein. Naturkunde Württemberg, 64.

Fisher, R. A. 1930. "Genetical Theory of Natural Selection." Oxford.

Wright, S. 1931. Evolution in Mendelian populations. Genetics, 16.

Haldane, J. B. S. 1932. "The Causes of Evolution." London.

Outlines of the modern "synthetic" or "biological" theory of evolution may be found in:

Mayr, E. 1942. "Systematics and the Origin of Species." New York.

Schmalhausen, I. I. 1949. "Factors of Evolution." Philadelphia.

Simpson, G. G. 1949. "The Meaning of Evolution." New Haven.

———. 1953. "The Major Features of Evolution." New York.

Stebbins, G. L. 1950. "Variation and Evolution in Plants." New York.

Clausen, J. 1951. "Stages in the Evolution of Plant Species." Ithaca.

Dobzhansky, T. 1951. "Genetics and the Origin of Species," New York.

Rensch, B. 1954. *"Neuere Probleme der Abstammungslehre."* Stuttgart.

White, M. J. D. 1954. "Animal Cytology and Evolution." Cambridge, England.

Apart from discussions in the more general treatises mentioned above, the genetic theory of race is discussed in:

Human evolution. 1951. Cold Spring Harbor Symposia Quant. Biol., 15.

Dobzhansky, T., and C. Epling. 1944. Contributions to the genetics, taxonomy, and ecology of *Drosophila pseudoobscura* and its relatives. Carnegie Inst. Washington Publ. 554.

Boyd, W. C. 1950. "Genetics and the Races of Man." Boston.

Coon, C. S., S. M. Garn, and J. B. Birdsell. 1950. "Races." Springfield.

The problem of heterosis has been discussed in some of the articles in the following two symposia:

Gowen, J. W. 1952. "Heterosis." Ames, Iowa.

Population genetics. 1955. Cold Spring Harbor Symposia Quant. Biol., 20.

A novel and interesting treatment of the problems of heterosis and its bearing on evolution can be found in:

Lerner, I. M. 1954. "Genetic Homeostasis." New York.

J. PHYSIOLOGICAL, BIOCHEMICAL, AND DEVELOPMENTAL GENETICS

The first comprehensive attempt to formulate a general physiological theory of inheritance was:

Goldschmidt, R. B. 1927. *"Physiologische Theorie der Vererbung."* Berlin.

This book was expanded in:

Goldschmidt, R. B. 1938. "Physiological Genetics." New York.

A recent attempt to synthesize a picture of the biochemical basis of inheritance is in:

Wagner, R. P., and H. K. Mitchell. 1955. "Genetics and Metabolism." New York.

The present state of the field of the biochemical basis of inheritance was assayed by a number of different authors in:

McElroy, W. D., and Bentley Glass (eds.). 1957. "A Symposium on the Chemical Basis of Heredity." Baltimore.

The effects of genes on embryological processes is discussed in:

Hadorn, Ernst. 1955. *"Letalfaktoren in ihrer Bedeutung für Erbpathologie und Genphysiologie der Entwicklung."* Stuttgart.

An extensive synthetic essay on the whole range of genetic theory is:

Goldschmidt, R. B. 1955. "Theoretical Genetics." Berkeley and Los Angeles.

Reports of recent work on finer analysis of the genetic material and on its structure will be found in the following:

Benzer, S. 1955. Fine structure of a genetic region in bacteriophage. Proc. Nat. Acad. Sci., 41:344–354.

Burnet, F. M. 1956. Enzyme, antigen, and virus. London.

Crick, F. H. C. 1954. The structure of the hereditary material. Scientific Amer., 191, October, p. 91.

Hotchkiss, R. D. 1955. Bacterial transformation. Jour. Cell. Comp. Neurol. Suppl., 2:1–22.

Pauling, L. 1954. The duplication of molecules. In D. Rudnick (ed.), Aspects of Synthesis and Order in Growth. 13th Growth Symposium. Princeton.

Pontecorvo, G. 1958. Trends in genetic analysis. New York.

Stanley, W. M., and M. A. Laufer. 1952. In T. M. Rivers (ed.), Viral and Rickettsial Diseases of Man, 2d ed. Philadelphia.

Watson, J. D., and F. H. C. Crick. 1953. The structure of DNA. Cold Spring Harbor Symposium Quant. Biol., 18:123–131.

INDEX